PHYSICAL
CHEMISTRY

PHYSICAL
CHEMISTRY

FARRINGTON DANIELS
Professor of Chemistry
University of Wisconsin

ROBERT A. ALBERTY
Associate Professor of Chemistry
University of Wisconsin

NEW YORK · JOHN WILEY & SONS, INC.

LONDON · CHAPMAN & HALL, LIMITED

Library of Congress Catalog Card Number: 55-5480

PRINTED IN THE UNITED STATES OF AMERICA

Preface

Physical Chemistry seeks to provide material for a first course in physical chemistry. We have endeavored to make it clear and interesting, with emphasis on practical examples, but without sacrificing the fundamental mathematical developments on which it is based. In this effort we owe much to contact with many student classes, to the advice of several colleagues through the years at the University of Wisconsin, and to a wealth of helpful suggestions which have come for decades from teachers all over the world. We greatly appreciate these suggestions and welcome continuing comments designed to improve the book in possible future editions.

Outlines of Theoretical Chemistry, as it was then entitled, was first written in 1913 by Dr. Frederick H. Getman, who carried it through 1927 in four revisions. Dr. Getman did excellent work in bringing together for elementary students the early developments of physical chemistry. We are grateful for his pioneer work.

In 1930 the senior author accepted the responsibility for writing the book, and in each of the five editions since that time he has endeavored to raise the level of presentation, to incorporate the new advances in physical chemistry, and to point out significant applications. After this quarter century, he is glad to welcome a younger associate to help with the judgments and the burdens of further revision. The junior author, connected for a decade with the physical chemistry staff of the University of Wisconsin, brings to the book added experience in teaching, and research contact with colloid chemistry and electrolytes. He has rewritten the chapters on crystals, ionic equilibria, and colloids and has helped with the revision throughout the book.

In the present book some of the more elementary material has been eliminated because the student meets it now in earlier courses. In order to make room for new material, sections have been eliminated or condensed, for the book can be no longer. To save space the appendix has been greatly shortened; some of the derivations formerly given there have been omitted and others have been replaced by *exercises*, distributed throughout the book to provide challenges for the more thorough students.

Many new problems have been substituted for old ones. Different types are offered in each chapter to meet the needs of students with different educational backgrounds and with different professional fields in mind. A few typical problems are worked out in each chapter, as *examples*. The answers are given for the first set of *problems* at the end of each chapter, and then the student is "on his own."

There are many different ways in which physical chemistry may be presented. The sequence of material given here, based on long experience, is designed to approach the abstract subjects after contact with simpler and more familiar material while still introducing the mathematical formulas early enough for use in the later parts of the book.

We have tried to bring out fundamental principles and to give glimpses of the frontiers of physical chemistry. We have endeavored to keep the book on the elementary level, describing and explaining phenomena in words as well as correlating them through mathematical formulas. It is important to keep a proper balance, making adequate use of mathematical abstractions but without losing contact with laboratory realities.

Previous editions have been improved by careful criticisms and help from Professors Paul Bender, Paul C. Cross, George W. Murphy, Darrell W. Osborne, Thomas F. Young, and many others. In the preparation of the present edition, helpful criticisms and suggestions have been given by many friends and associates, including Professors Sturges Bailey, Paul Bender, James A. Campbell, C. Daniel Cornwell, Charles F. Curtiss, John D. Ferry, Louis J. Gosting, Clyde A. Hutchison, Edward L. King, John L. Margrave, John E. Willard, John W. Williams, and others. Valuable help in checking some of the calculations and problems has been given by Dr. Lung Yuan and Mr. Rex Smith. Special acknowledgment is made to Mrs. John L. Margrave for her careful typing of the manuscript, to Mr. Harry A. Schopler for the new figures, and to Mr. Arthur K. Nelson and Bernard Schlessinger for proofreading.

FARRINGTON DANIELS
ROBERT A. ALBERTY

Madison, Wisconsin
March, 1955

W.S. Moore - Physical Chemistry-
Rossini - Thermal Chemistry
Gladstone.

Contents

Table of Important Constants

The following approximate values will be used for problems. Most of them are sufficiently important to memorize during the course of the work.

Acceleration of gravity	980.7	cm sec^{-2}
Molar volume (0°, 1 atm)	22.41	l mole^{-1}
Ice point (0°)	273.1°	K
One calorie (defined)	4.184	joules
R	8.314	joules deg^{-1} mole^{-1}
	1.987	cal deg^{-1} mole^{-1}
	0.08205	l-atm deg^{-1} mole^{-1}
Faraday	96,500	coulombs equiv^{-1}
	23,060	cal volt^{-1} equiv^{-1}
Avogadro number	6.02×10^{23}	mole^{-1}
Planck's constant	6.62×10^{-27}	erg sec
Velocity of light	3×10^{10}	cm sec^{-1}
Conversion $\log_{10}$ to $\log_e$	2.303	

These and other constants are given with the highest precision now warranted on page 655.

Introduction

Survey of Physical Chemistry. The purpose of the study of physical chemistry is to understand the laws of chemistry and physics and to predict and control chemical phenomena.

Physical chemistry emerged as a separate branch of science in the latter part of the last century. It has continually broadened its scope with new discoveries and has become more exact with improvements in experimental measurements and with greater use of mathematics. The boundaries of physical chemistry are not sharp; they overlap physics on the one side and all branches of chemistry on the other. Physical chemistry draws its facts from all these fields of knowledge and correlates them by means of word descriptions, graphical representations, and mathematical equations. Of these the mathematical equations are the most powerful.

Physical chemistry comprises many different aspects of chemistry which superficially appear unrelated. However, as the student progresses in physical chemistry he will find that certain ideas and equations are used again and again. One fundamental field which underlies much of physical chemistry is thermodynamics. Thermodynamics deals with the interconversion of various forms of energy and makes it possible to answer the question "How far will this particular reaction go before equilibrium is reached?" A second fundamental field is kinetics, which involves the time factor and deals with the problem of the rates of chemical reactions. A third fundamental field is the study of the structure of molecules. Information concerning structure comes from many sources, such as X-ray diffraction, electron diffraction, microwave absorption, infrared absorption, etc., and this information is useful in considerations of thermodynamics and kinetics. The studies of molecular structure lead to the prediction of physical chemical behavior on the basis of the properties of individual molecules, whereas the studies of thermodynamics and kinetics lead to predictions based on the statistical behavior of large numbers of molecules.

A characteristic feature of physical chemistry is the use of mathematical methods. Thus experimental results are expressed by equations whenever possible. The fundamental principles of physical chemistry may be stated as equations, and many useful relations may be obtained from them by straightforward mathematical operations. A number of more commonly used relations are summarized in the Appendix, and special books are available for the parts of calculus and other branches of mathematics that are needed.

Physical chemistry is in a process of continual change and development. Ideas held at present may fade in importance as this development continues, but the methods will continue to be useful. Thus in studying physical chemistry the methods should be studied as well as the results.

Fundamental Units. The phenomena of chemistry and physics are concerned with matter at rest or in motion, with electricity, and with radiation. Marked progress has been made in understanding these phenomena by visualizing the primary units involved—the atom and the molecule of matter, the electron of electricity, and the photon of radiation. It has been found experimentally that there are 6.02×10^{23} molecules in a gram molecule or mole, and this number has become an important constant of physical chemistry known as the Avogadro constant. For example, the quantity of electricity called the faraday, which will electrolyze a gram equivalent of ions, is obtained by multiplying the charge of the electron by the Avogadro constant. This number, 6.02×10^{23}, is so large that it is difficult to visualize. Very few practical operations can be carried out in chemistry which involve less than a millionth of a mole, but even a millionth of a mole contains almost a billion billion molecules.

As far as possible in scientific work, measurements are expressed in terms of centimeters, grams, and seconds, and their derived units; that is, the measurements are expressed in the *cgs* system. The erg, the fundamental unit of energy, is based on the centimeter, the gram, and the second. The centimeter is defined in terms of a standard meter bar, and the gram in terms of a standard kilogram weight; both bar and weight are very exact standards kept in government laboratories for reference. The unit of time, the second, is defined by means of astronomical observations.

In making calculations it is necessary that the units of the quantities in an equation be consistent or that conversion factors be introduced. In order to avoid errors that result from inadequate attention to units, it is convenient to indicate the units of the quantities in an equation and to check the equation to see that these units cancel in such a way as to give the proper units in the final result. The values and units of important constants which are used in physical chemistry are given on page viii and in more complete form on page 655.

Scientific Research. Chemistry and all other sciences are based on experimentally established facts. When a number of facts have been collected and classified, we may draw inferences as to the probable behavior of systems under conditions that have not been investigated. When a number of phenomena have been observed and studied with exact measurements, we can often develop a *law* that will predict the behavior of similar systems under different conditions. The law is not necessarily an expression of infallible truth but is rather a condensed statement of facts that have been discovered by experiment. It enables us to obtain needed facts without continued recourse to experiment.

Natural laws may be discovered either by the correlation of experimentally determined facts, as we have just shown, or by means of a speculation as to the probable cause of the phenomenon in question. Such a speculation regarding the cause of a phenomenon is called an *hypothesis*. After an hypothesis has been subjected to the test of experiment and has been shown to apply to a large number of phenomena it is termed a *theory*.

Usually science progresses through four stages: first, observation and measurement; second, inductive reasoning from these facts; third, deductive reasoning based on hypotheses and theories; and fourth, experimental testing to prove or disprove the theoretical deductions.

Many hypotheses are destined to be discarded when new facts and more precise data are obtained, but they fulfill a very necessary function in the development of science. A successful hypothesis is not necessarily a permanent hypothesis, but it is one that stimulates additional research, opens up new fields, or explains and coordinates previously unrelated facts. The scientist needs imagination in creating new hypotheses, but he needs also ingenuity and skill in devising experiments to test them and critical judgment in evaluating the results. Physical chemistry has many unsolved problems and opportunities for pioneering in frontier fields.

Science is based on truth, and the scientist cannot allow himself to be influenced by any prejudice. Science has become such a potent factor in our national and international affairs that the scientist now faces a social responsibility that extends beyond the laboratory.

REFERENCES

E. Bright Wilson, *Introduction to Scientific Research*, McGraw-Hill Book Co., New York, 1952.

Daniels, "History of Physical Chemistry," *Ind. Eng. Chem.*, 43, 278–288 (1951).

2

Gases

The Behavior of Ideal Gases. The gaseous state is characterized by the fact that the molecules are so far apart that they exhibit only slight attraction for each other, thus permitting the material to expand and fill completely a containing vessel of any size or shape. As a first approximation, the physical behavior of a gas is not affected by the chemical nature of its molecules, and, thus, all gases respond in nearly the same way to the variables pressure, volume, and temperature.

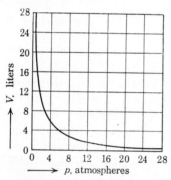

Fig. 2-1. Volume of 1 mole of an ideal gas plotted against pressure at a constant temperature of 0°C.

In an ideal gas there is no interaction whatever between the molecules, and the energy of the gaseous material remains unchanged if the gas is expanded into a larger volume.

The measurements of the volume of a gas at different pressures go back to the classical work of Robert Boyle in 1662. Boyle found that at constant temperature the volume of a gas decreases when pressure is applied and that it is inversely proportional to the applied pressure, a fact that can be expressed mathematically by the formula

$$v = k_1/p \quad \text{(temperature constant)} \quad (1)$$

where k_1 is a constant. This important relation between the pressure and volume of a gas is shown graphically in *Fig. 2-1*. The curve plotted here is a special case of a hyperbola.

In 1802 Gay-Lussac reported his discovery that the volume v of a given quantity of gas kept at a constant pressure increases with increasing temperature. In unpublished earlier work, Charles had found that certain gases expand to the same extent when the temperature is increased.

These investigators found that if the pressure is kept constant the volume v of a given quantity of gas at any temperature t is equal to the volume v_0 at some reference temperature, plus an increase in volume which is proportional to the difference between temperature t and the reference temperature. Thus

$$v = v_0(1 + \alpha t) \tag{2}$$

This is the equation for a straight line obtained when v is plotted against t. The value of α varies slightly from one gas to another, but the same value is approached by all gases at very low pressures. It is convenient then to introduce the concept of the *ideal* gas in which there is no attraction between the molecules of the gas and α always has the same value. This condition is approached as the pressure is reduced and the molecules become so far apart that they can exert no attractive force on each other. Experimental measurements of volume and temperature at lower and lower pressures permit an extrapolation to zero pressure, and it is found for all gases that α is $1/273.16$ when the temperature t is taken on the centigrade scale. Zero on the centigrade scale is taken as the freezing temperature of water, and $100°$ on the scale is taken as the boiling point of water, at the standard atmospheric pressure (a mercury barometer reading of 760 mm).

Thus when temperature is expressed in degrees centigrade

$$v = v_0 + \frac{1}{273.16} v_0 t \quad \text{(pressure constant)} \tag{3}$$

where v_0 is the volume at $0°C$. According to this equation, v_t would be zero at $-273.16°C$. In reality the volume of the gas will not become zero at $-273.16°C$ because it will liquefy first and equation 3 will not be valid.

A temperature scale of great importance called the scale of absolute temperature or the Kelvin scale is used, in which the zero is taken as $273.16°$ below zero on the centigrade scale. Then

$$T°K = t°C + 273.16°C \text{ *} \tag{4}$$

where K indicates the absolute or Kelvin scale and C the centigrade scale. The symbol T is used for the Kelvin scale and the symbol t for the centigrade scale.

* In this book and in much of the literature $T°$ is taken as $273.1° + t°$. The exact value is not known with precision, and if $273.2°$ were taken as the conversion value a large amount of data would need recalculation. If the temperature scale is not specified it is generally assumed that the centigrade scale is meant.

The Gay-Lussac-Charles law can be expressed simply by introducing equation 4 into equation 3 to obtain

$$v = k_2 T \quad \text{(pressure constant)} \qquad (5)$$

where k_2 is a constant composed of several constants in equations 3 and 4. Thus, an immediate advantage of the absolute scale is that the volume of a given quantity of an ideal gas is directly proportional to the abso-

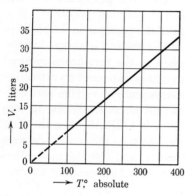

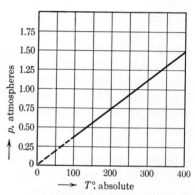

FIG. 2-2. Volume of 1 mole of an ideal gas plotted against absolute temperature at constant pressure. (p = 1 atmosphere.)

FIG. 2-3. Pressure of 1 mole of an ideal gas plotted against absolute temperature at constant volume. (V = 22.4 liters.)

lute temperature, if the pressure is kept constant. The relationship between v and T is illustrated in *Fig. 2-2*, in which the dotted line indicates that many gases will liquefy at the lower temperatures and that the relationship applies only to material that remains as an ideal gas.

If the volume is kept constant, it follows that the pressure of the gas is directly proportional to its absolute temperature as shown by the formula

$$p = k_3 T \quad \text{(volume constant)}$$

and by the straight line in *Fig. 2-3*.

The combination of Boyle's law and the law of Gay-Lussac and Charles * leads, as shown in the following exercise, to the expression

$$pv = \text{(constant)} T \qquad (6)$$

* The discovery of these laws and their combination are described by Roseman and Katzoff, *J. Chem. Education*, **11**, 350 (1934).

Exercise I. The application of the fundamental equation of partial differentiation *
to the volume of a gas which is a function of temperature and pressure, $v = f(p, T)$,
leads to

$$dv = \left(\frac{\partial v}{\partial p}\right)_T dp + \left(\frac{\partial v}{\partial T}\right)_p dT$$

Substitute $\left(\frac{\partial v}{\partial p}\right)_T$ from Boyle's law and $\left(\frac{\partial v}{\partial T}\right)_p$ from the law of Gay-Lussac and
Charles into this expression, and integrate to obtain

$$\ln v + \ln p = \ln T + \ln \text{(constant)}$$

or
$$pv = \text{(constant)}T$$

The Gas Constant. In physical chemistry the gram-molecular
weight or the mole is commonly used because the properties under investigation depend on the number of molecules present and a mole of
any substance contains the same number of molecules.

The chemical atomic weight † of oxygen is arbitrarily taken as 16.0000.
Thus a mole of oxygen, O_2, weighs 32.000 grams, and it is found that the
volume of this weight of oxygen at 0°C and 1 atmosphere pressure (760
mm of mercury at 0°C) is 22.414 liters if correction is made for nonideality.

When 1 mole of an ideal gas is taken the constant of equation 6 has
a special significance and is known as the molar gas constant, R. The
capital V is used for the volume occupied by a mole of gas, whereas v
signifies the volume of any specified quantity of gas.

Then equation 6 becomes

$$pV = RT \tag{7}$$

It has been found by many careful experiments, in which corrections
are made for slight interactions between the molecules, that 1 mole of
an ideal gas occupies 22.414 liters at 0°C or 273.16°K. Then,

$$R = \frac{pV}{T} = \frac{(1 \text{ atm})(22.414 \text{ l mole}^{-1})}{(273.16 \text{ deg})}$$

$$= 0.08205 \text{ l-atm deg}^{-1} \text{ mole}^{-1} \tag{8}$$

It should be noted that the molar gas constant has the dimensions of
energy per mole divided by temperature. The term pV is a form of
energy because it involves a force acting through a distance.

* Appendix, page 653.
† It will be necessary later (page 613) to distinguish between two scales of atomic
weights, the traditional chemical scale, used generally in physical chemistry, in
which 16.0000 is assigned to ordinary oxygen; and the physical scale, in which
16.0000 is assigned to the most abundant isotope of oxygen.

The pressure may be changed to dynes per square centimeter by multiplying the barometer height, 76 cm of mercury, by the density of mercury, 13.595 at 0°, and the acceleration of gravity, 980.7 cm per second per second. The pressure in dynes per square centimeter multiplied by the volume in cubic centimeters gives the work in ergs. Ergs in turn are converted into joules by dividing by 10^7. Then,

$$R = \frac{pV}{T} = \frac{\left\{ \begin{array}{c} (76.00 \text{ cm})(13.595 \text{ g cm}^{-3}) \\ \times (980.7 \text{ cm sec}^{-2})(22{,}414 \text{ cm}^3 \text{ mole}^{-1}) \end{array} \right\}}{(273.16 \text{ deg})(10^7 \text{ erg joule}^{-1})}$$

$$= 8.314 \text{ joules deg}^{-1} \text{ mole}^{-1} \qquad (9)$$

Joules may be changed into calories by dividing by the conversion factor 4.184 joules per calorie.

$$R = \frac{8.314 \text{ joules deg}^{-1} \text{ mole}^{-1}}{4.184 \text{ joules cal}^{-1}} = 1.987 \text{ cal deg}^{-1} \text{ mole}^{-1} \qquad (10)$$

In calculations involving the gas laws it is usually convenient to express R in liter-atmospheres; in electrochemical problems involving volts and coulombs R is best expressed in joules; and in thermochemical and thermodynamical problems R is usually given in calories. It is necessary to be thoroughly familiar with the different constants and to know which units to use in a specified problem and how to convert one into another.

Usually it is not convenient to have exactly 1 mole of a gas, and so equation 7 is made more general by introducing a factor n which represents the number of moles taken. Thus the more generally useful form of the gas law is

$$pv = nRT \qquad (11)$$

The Avogadro Law. According to Avogadro's law, proposed in 1811, equal volumes of gases at the same temperature and pressure contain the same number of molecules. This law provided a sure foundation for the determination of molecular weights, and it has played an important part in the development of physical chemistry. The simple gas law, $pV = RT$, follows naturally from this law, because, if 1 mole of any gaseous substance contains the same number of molecules, and these, in turn, exert no specific influence on each other, the relations involving volume, pressure, and temperature should be the same for all ideal gases and approximately the same for real gases.

The actual number of molecules in a gram molecule or mole has been determined accurately in many different ways which are entirely independent of each other, and the agreement is excellent. This number,

6.02×10^{23} molecules per mole, is called the *Avogadro constant*, and it is a fundamental constant of physical chemistry, with many important applications. The experiments on which the value of this constant is based are described in later chapters.

Perrin determined the constant from observation of the random motion of small particles; Rutherford, from a determination of the charge on the alpha particle from radium; Boltwood and Curie, by direct counting of alpha particles and by measurement of the volume of helium resulting from them; Planck, from an experimental determination of the constants of radiation; and Millikan, from the charge of an electron as determined by the oil-drop experiment and the value of the faraday constant of electrolysis.

The best value * at present, which is 6.023×10^{23}, has been obtained by averaging values from a number of different types of accurate measurements.

The weight of a single atom or molecule is obtained by dividing the respective atomic or molecular weight by the Avogadro constant. For example, the weight of an atom of hydrogen is $1.008/6.02 \times 10^{23} = 1.67 \times 10^{-24}$ gram; and the weight of a molecule of carbon dioxide is $44.01/6.02 \times 10^{23} = 7.30 \times 10^{-23}$ gram.

Gas Density and Molecular Weight. The density of a gas is defined in physical chemistry as the weight in grams of 1 liter. The densities are useful in calculating molecular weights. According to Avogadro's law, it should be possible to determine the molecular weight of a gaseous substance by weighing a given volume at a known pressure and temperature and comparing it with the weight of the same volume of another gas of known molecular weight. To determine the molecular weight of a gas it is only necessary then to find the weight of 22.414 liters of the gas at 0° and 760 mm of pressure and to make minor corrections for the departure of the gas from the behavior of an ideal gas. A mole of gas is too large to weigh accurately, but a measurement may be made on a smaller quantity at any pressure and temperature, and then converted to the weight of a mole under standard conditions, using the simple gas law.

For example, if g grams of a gas is taken instead of M grams (M being the molecular weight in grams), then g/M is the number of moles taken, which is represented by n. Then,

$$pv = nRT = \frac{g}{M} RT = \frac{g}{M} 0.08205T \tag{12}$$

* This value, together with the best values of other fundamental constants, is given on page 655.

In using this equation, since R is given in liter-atmospheres, it is necessary to convert the pressure p into atmospheres and the volume v into
liters.* If the pressure is expressed in millimeters of mercury, the value
must be divided by 760. With this formula, any one of the quantities
pressure, volume, and temperature can be readily calculated when all
the others are known.

Example 1. Calculate the volume occupied by 20 grams of carbon dioxide at
740 mm pressure and 30° assuming that the ideal gas law holds.

$$v = \frac{gRT}{pM} = \frac{(20 \text{ g})(0.08205 \text{ l-atm deg}^{-1} \text{ mole}^{-1})(303.1 \text{ deg})}{(\frac{740}{760} \text{ atm})(44.01 \text{ g mole}^{-1})}$$

$$= 11.60 \text{ liters}$$

In the *Regnault method* for determining the molecular weight of a gas,
a glass bulb is weighed when completely evacuated and again when
filled with the gas. The volume is obtained by weighing it when filled
with water. A second bulb of the same size is used as a counterpoise to
minimize troublesome corrections for air buoyancy (about 0.0012 gram
per ml) and moisture adhering to the surface. Exact weighing of large
bulbs is difficult.

The work of Baxter and Starkweather † is a classic example of the
use of this method. These authors weighed five samples of gas in two
different 2-liter globes with an average reproducibility of 3×10^{-5} of
the weight of the gas content.

The *Victor Meyer method* is convenient for the approximate determination of molecular weights of substances that can be weighed in the
liquid state, thus avoiding the weighing of large vessels. A weighed
quantity of liquid in a glass bulblet is evaporated in an air-filled tube
heated to a constant temperature. An equivalent volume of air is driven
out and measured with a gas buret at known pressure and temperature.

Example 2. In a Victor Meyer apparatus the evaporation of 0.110 gram of a
pure hydrocarbon $H(CH_2)_nH$ displaced 27.0 ml of air as measured in a mercury
buret at 26.1° and 743 mm. What is the molecular weight of the hydrocarbon and
the value of the whole number n?

$$M = \frac{gRT}{pv} = \frac{(0.110 \text{ g})(0.08205 \text{ l-atm deg}^{-1} \text{ mole}^{-1})(299.2 \text{ deg})}{(\frac{743}{760} \text{ atm})(0.0270 \text{ l})}$$

$$= 102 \text{ g mole}^{-1}$$

Since $M = 14n + 2$, n must be 7.

---

* In physical-chemical calculations it is always necessary to be sure that the
quantities entering a formula are expressed in the correct units.

† Baxter and Starkweather, *Proc. Natl. Acad. Sci. U. S.*, *12*, 703 (1926).

The molecular weights calculated with equation 12 are usually too high (often by 1 or 2 per cent) because most gases show deviations from the simple gas law. More exact calculations can be made, as is shown presently; but an approximate value of the molecular weight is sufficient to enable one to choose between the formula weight, obtained by chemical analysis, and some simple multiple of it. For example, even a rough determination is sufficient to distinguish between C_2H_6O and $C_4H_{12}O_2$.

Behavior of Real Gases. Whereas the behavior of ideal or perfect gases is given exactly by the simple relation, $pV = RT$, the behavior of most real gases, especially at high pressures or low temperatures, can be described only with more complicated equations. When simple laws which apply to idealized systems have to be complicated by the addition of further terms in order to represent actual systems it is frequently possible to find the causes of these deviations.

Pressure-volume data for two common gases at 0° are shown in Table I, where the pressure p is given in atmospheres, and the volume

Table I.   Pressure-Volume Relations of Gases at 0°

p atm	Hydrogen V liters mole^{-1}	pV	$\dfrac{pV}{RT}$	Carbon Dioxide V liters mole^{-1}	pV	$\dfrac{pV}{RT}$
0.1	224.14	22.41	1.000	224.1	22.41	1.000
1	22.428	22.43	1.001	22.262	22.26	0.9933
50	0.4634	23.17	1.034	0.04675	2.338	0.1043
100	0.2386	23.86	1.065	0.04497	4.497	0.2007
200	0.12712	25.42	1.134	0.04285	8.570	0.3824
300	0.09004	27.01	1.205	0.04152	12.46	0.5560
400	0.07163	28.65	1.278	0.04051	16.20	0.7229
600	0.05318	31.91	1.424	0.03894	23.36	1.042
800	0.04392	35.14	1.568	0.03779	30.23	1.349
1000	0.03837	38.37	1.712	0.03687	36.87	1.645

V in liters occupied by 1 mole. If the gases were ideal and the simple gas law applicable, the product of pressure and volume should be equal to 22.414 liters at all pressures. The table shows that this product (pV) is far from being constant and that it varies differently with pressure for different gases. Even at 1 atm there is a slight departure from the behavior of a perfect gas.

For an ideal gas the value of the ratio pV/RT is 1.000, and the value of this ratio, known as the *compressibility factor*, for a real gas provides one of the best ways of recording deviations from ideal behavior. The compressibility factors for H_2, O_2, and CO_2 at 0°C are plotted versus pressure in *Fig. 2-4*. The behavior of an ideal gas is represented by the horizontal dashed line. In the limit of zero pressure the compressibility factor of any gas is unity.

A low value of the compressibility factor indicates that the gas is more compressible than an ideal gas. All gases show a minimum in the

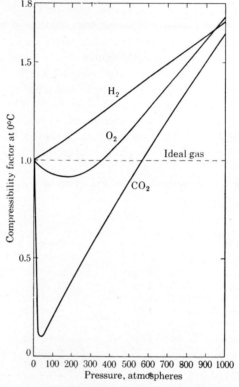

FIG. 2-4. Influence of high pressures on the compressibility factor, pV/RT, for typical gases.

plot of compressibility factor versus pressure if the temperature is low enough. Hydrogen and helium, which have very low boiling points, exhibit this minimum only at temperatures much below 0°C.

The effect of temperature on the change of compressibility factor of nitrogen with pressure is shown in *Fig. 2-5*. The influence of temperature as well as pressure on the departure from ideal behavior is thus obvious. The values of pressure, volume, and temperature are determined experimentally. Nitrogen is more compressible at 0° than an ideal gas at low pressures and less compressible at high pressures; and the

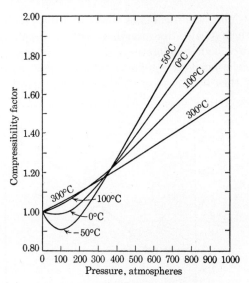

FIG. 2-5. Influence of high pressures on the compressibility factor, pV/RT, for nitrogen.

departure from ideal behavior becomes less at high temperatures and at low pressures, where the molecules are farther apart.

Exact Molecular Weights. When values of the molecular weights more exact than those obtainable by the simple gas-law calculation are necessary, determinations may be made at lower and lower pressures, usually by the Regnault method. The deviations from the simple gas law become less at the lower pressures and approach zero; but serious experimental difficulties are involved in weighing a large volume of gas at a low pressure. Precise measurements of densities at several low pressures can be used to determine the atomic weights of the elements that make up the molecule, with an accuracy as great as that obtainable by chemical analysis. This method is called the method of limiting densities.

As the pressure decreases, the volume increases and the weight per liter decreases. The density d defined by g/v decreases; but the ratio of density to pressure d/p or g/vp should remain constant if the gas is perfect, since pv is constant and the total weight g remains unchanged. For ordinary gases, however, the ratio of density to pressure is not constant but decreases as the pressure decreases, as shown in *Fig. 2-6.*

For permanent gases it has been found that practically a straight line is produced when d/p is plotted against p at pressures below 1 atm. The straight line is extrapolated beyond the region of experimental measure ments until it intersects the Y axis where $p = 0$. The intercept can be obtained mathematically from the data without graphing. Gases that liquefy at fairly high temperatures show greater deviations, and the straight-line relation does not hold. More complicated mathematical formulas may then be necessary for the extrapolation.*

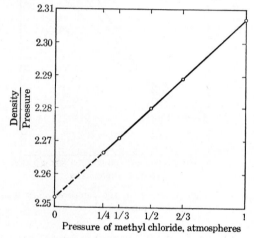

Fig. 2-6. Determination of $(d/p)_0$ for methyl chloride.

Since the deviations from the ideal-gas law approach zero as the pressure is reduced, the exact molecular weight M is given by a modification of equation 12,

$$M = (d/p)_0 RT \qquad (13)$$

where $(d/p)_0$ is the ratio of density to pressure extrapolated to zero pressure.

Example 3. Calculate the molecular weight of methyl chloride and the atomic weight of chlorine from the following data, having given the atomic weights of car-

Pressure, atm	1	$\frac{2}{3}$	$\frac{1}{2}$	$\frac{1}{3}$	$\frac{1}{4}$
Density at 0°, g/l	2.3074	1.5263	1.1401	0.75713	0.56660

bon and hydrogen as tabulated. The extrapolated ratio of density to pressure at 0° is 2.2528 as shown in Fig. 2-6. Then

$$M = (2.2528 \text{ atm}^{-1} \text{ g } \text{l}^{-1})(0.08205 \text{ l-atm deg}^{-1} \text{ mole}^{-1})(273.16 \text{ deg})$$

$$= 50.495 \text{ g mole}^{-1}$$

If we subtract from 50.495 the atomic weight of carbon, 12.010, and three times the atomic weight of hydrogen, 3.024, a value of 35.461 is obtained for the atomic weight of chlorine. The accepted value is 35.457.

* Birge and Jenkins, *J. Chem. Phys.*, *2*, 167 (1934).

Abnormal Densities. The molecular weights of a great many substances have been determined by measurements of the density of the gas. Generally, they agree with the molecular weights obtained from the sum of the atomic weights. Difficulty, however, was encountered with a few substances whose molecular weights seemed abnormal. The experimental results were in error, Avogadro's hypothesis was not universally applicable, or some new phenomenon was entering in. This situation arises frequently in the development of science. Exceptions to a general law are found, and for a time the fate of the whole law is uncertain. More exact experiments or slight corrections (such as will be shown for the gas law) may save the law, or perhaps it may have to be discarded or modified. In these cases the difficulty was traced to the fact that some of the gases dissociated or broke down into smaller units or that they associated into multiples of the molecular weight. Iodine has a molecular weight corresponding to I_2 from 200 to 600°; but at 1400°, and above, it has half the density and consists of monatomic molecules. At intermediate temperatures the densities range between these two values.

The molecular weight of ammonium chloride should be 53.5 according to the sum of the atomic weights, but gas density measurements gave a value about half of this. It was suspected that the low molecular weight was occasioned by the reaction

$$NH_4Cl = NH_3 + HCl$$

the ammonia and hydrochloric acid at the high temperature occupying twice the volume of ammonium chloride vapor and giving half the density when dissociation was complete. This interpretation was proved to be correct when it was shown that the heated vapor contained an alkaline gas NH_3 and an acid gas HCl which could be separated by fractional diffusion through a porous plug of solid ammonium chloride. The gas diffusing through the plug turned litmus paper blue. It is shown on page 30 that gases of low molecular weight diffuse more rapidly than those of high molecular weight.

Use is made of these experimentally measured densities in calculating quantitatively the extent of the dissociation of the heavier molecules into lighter ones, as shown on page 241.

The Critical Constants. At sufficiently low temperatures a gas may be made to liquefy by applying pressure, thus reducing the volume and bringing the molecules close enough together so that the attractive force between them will be effective. All gases have been liquefied in this way. However, there is a temperature above which it is impossible to liquefy a gas no matter how great a pressure is applied. This tem-

perature is called the *critical temperature*; and the minimum pressure
necessary to bring about liquefaction at the critical temperature is called
the *critical pressure*.   The volume occupied by a mole of gas or liquid at
the critical temperature and pressure is called the *critical volume*.

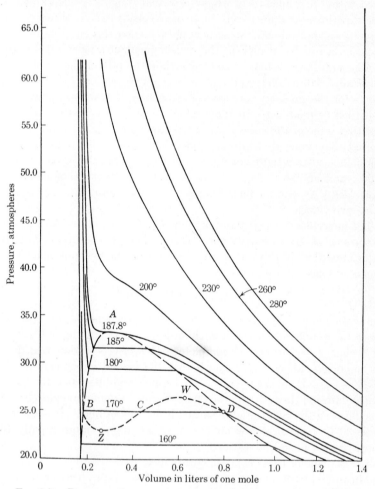

FIG. 2-7.   Pressure-volume curve for isopentane showing critical region.

The significance of the critical temperature is shown in *Fig. 2-7*, in
which pressure is plotted against volume for 1 mole of isopentane at the
several temperatures indicated on the graph.

Lines on a graph which refer to a specified constant temperature are
called *isothermals*.   At 280° the pressure-volume curve is a hyperbolic

curve similar to that shown in Fig. 2-1 for an ideal gas. At 200° there is a nick in the curve showing that in the neighborhood of a pressure of 39 atm the gas is deviating considerably from the behavior of an ideal gas and the molecules are close enough to exhibit some attraction for each other, thus making the over-all volume of the gas smaller than that of an ideal gas, in which no such attraction exists.

At all temperatures below 187.8° the curves exhibit theoretically horizontal sections as shown by isothermals below 185°. These horizontal lines indicate that an infinitesimal increase in pressure causes a very large decrease in volume, owing to the fact that the gas is liquefying. At the right of the diagram gas alone is present, and the curves follow the simple gas law approximately; at the extreme left liquid alone is present, and, since the liquid is much less compressible than the gas, the curve is steeper than that for the gas. Along the straight horizontal part of the curve both gas and liquid exist together. This region in which gas and liquid are coexistent is enclosed by the dashed line, the maximum point A of which gives the critical temperature, critical pressure, and critical volume. The wavy line $DWCZB$ is discussed on page 20.

All gases give curves similar to those shown in Fig. 2-7 and exhibit critical temperatures below which it is possible to produce liquefaction by application of sufficient pressure.

The critical constants for several types of molecules are given in Table II. The significance of the compressibility at the critical point (p_cV_c/RT_c) will be discussed later.

Equation of van der Waals. Van der Waals in 1879 made an early attempt to introduce additional terms into the simple gas equation and thus give an expression which describes more exactly the behavior of real gases. An examination of Figs. 2-4 and 2-5 reveals that at low pressures real gases may be more compressible than an ideal gas and that at high pressures they may be less compressible. The tendency to be more compressible is due to the fact that the molecules have some attraction for each other and tend to draw together. The tendency to be less compressible is due to the fact that the molecules of the gas are less compressible than the gas, and the volume of the molecules themselves becomes an appreciable part of the total volume when the pressure becomes high and the total gas volume small.

Van der Waals put these ideas into a general equation as follows:

$$\left(p + \frac{a}{V^2}\right)(V - b) = RT \tag{14}$$

where the constant a expresses the fact that an attraction exists between

Table II. Critical Constants and Boiling Points

Gas	T_{BP}, °K	T_c, °K	$\dfrac{T_{BP}[1]}{T_c}$	p_c, atm	V_c, l mole^{-1}	T_{MP},[1] °K	$\dfrac{p_c V_c}{RT_c}$
Simple Nonpolar Molecules [2]							
He	4.2	5.3	0.79	2.26	0.0578	0.9	0.300
H_2	20.4	33.3	0.68	12.8	0.0650	14.0	0.304
Ne	27.2	44.5	0.61	25.9	0.0417	24.5	0.296
A	87.4	151	0.58	48	0.0752	83.9	0.291
Xe	164.1	289.81	0.57	57.89	0.1202	133	0.293
N_2	77.3	126.1	0.61	33.5	0.0901	63.2	0.292
O_2	90.1	154.4	0.58	49.7	0.0744	54.7	0.292
CH_4	111.7	190.7	0.59	45.8	0.0990	89.1	0.290
CO_2	194.6	304.2	0.64	72.8	0.0942	—	0.274
Hydrocarbons							
Ethane, C_2H_6	184.6	305.5	0.60	48.2	0.139	89.98	0.267
Propane, C_3H_8	231.1	370.0	0.62	42.1	0.195	185.5	0.270
Isobutane, C_4H_{10}	261.5	407	0.64	37	0.250	113.6	0.276
n-Butane, C_4H_{10}	272.7	426	0.64	36	0.250	134.9	0.257
n-Hexane, C_6H_{14}	342.1	507.9	0.67	29.6	0.367	178.8	0.260
n-Octane, C_8H_{18}	397.7	570	0.70	24.7	0.490	216.6	0.259
Benzene, C_6H_6	352.7	561.6	0.63	47.9	0.256	278.6	0.265
Cyclohexane, C_6H_{12}	353.9	554	0.64	40.57	0.312	279.7	0.280
Ethylene, C_2H_4	169.3	282.8	0.60	50.5	0.126	103.7	0.274
Acetylene, C_2H_2	189.5	308.6	0.61	61.6	0.113	191.3	0.275
Polar Molecules [2]							
H_2O	373.1	647.3	0.58	217.7	0.0566	273.1	0.232
NH_3	239.7	405.5	0.59	112.2	0.0720	195.4	0.243
CH_3OH	337.9	513.2	0.66	78.67	0.118	175.4	0.220
CH_3Cl	249.7	416.3	0.60	65.8	0.148	175.5	0.285
C_2H_5Cl	285.9	460.4	0.62	52	0.196	134.2	0.269

[1] These quantities are discussed in a later chapter.
[2] Polar and nonpolar molecules are defined on page 78.

two molecules of the gas. The total forces exerted between two small neighboring regions of gas will depend on the number of molecules in the regions. The larger the volume holding 1 mole of gas, the fewer are the molecules in a given region and the less the attraction. The attraction from one region then varies inversely as the volume, and in the other region it also varies inversely as the volume. The total attraction between two small regions then is inversely proportional to the product of the two, that is, to V^2.

Since the force of this attraction a/V^2 augments the pressure in tending to make the volume small, it is added to the term p.

The term b is connected with the volume of the molecules themselves, and, since the molecules are much less compressible than the gas, b is subtracted from the total volume V to give an effective compressible volume. The volume b appears to have a value about 4 times the volume occupied by the molecules themselves if they are considered to be simple spheres.

When V is large both b and a/V^2 become negligible; and the van der Waals equation reduces to the simple gas equation, $pV = RT$. In general, all gases tend to become ideal at low pressures and approach the behavior given by the simple gas law.

Van der Waals' constants for a few gases are listed in Table III.*

Table III. Van der Waals' Constants

Gas	a liter^2 atm mole^{-2}	b liters mole^{-1}	Gas	a liter^2 atm mole^{-2}	b liters mole^{-1}
H_2	0.2444	0.02661	CH_4	2.253	0.04278
He	0.03412	0.02370	C_2H_6	5.489	0.06380
N_2	1.390	0.03913	C_3H_8	8.664	0.08445
O_2	1.360	0.03183	$C_4H_{10}(n)$	14.47	0.1226
Cl_2	6.493	0.05622	$C_4H_{10}(iso)$	12.87	0.1142
NO	1.340	0.02789	$C_5H_{12}(n)$	19.01	0.1460
NO_2	5.284	0.04424	CO	1.485	0.03985
H_2O	5.464	0.03049	CO_2	3.592	0.04267

They can be calculated from experimental measurements of p, v, and T or from the three critical constants as shown later on page 21.

Exercise II. Equation 14 applies to 1 mole of gas. Show that van der Waals' general equation for n moles of gas is

$$\left(p + \frac{n^2 a}{v^2}\right)(v - nb) = nRT \tag{15}$$

* Lange, *Handbook of Chemistry*, Handbook Publishers, Sandusky, Ohio, 1954.

Example 4. Calculate the pressure exerted by 1 mole of water vapor in 10 liters at 150°, using (a) the ideal gas law and (b) van der Waals' equation.

(a) $$p = \frac{RT}{V} = \frac{(0.08205 \text{ l-atm deg}^{-1} \text{ mole}^{-1})(423.1 \text{ deg})}{(10.00 \text{ l mole}^{-1})} = 3.47 \text{ atm}$$

(b) $$p = \frac{RT}{V - b} - \frac{a}{V^2} = \frac{(0.08205 \text{ l-atm deg}^{-1} \text{ mole}^{-1})(423.1 \text{ deg})}{(10.00 - 0.03049) \text{ l mole}^{-1}}$$

$$- \frac{5.464 \text{ l}^2\text{-atm mole}^{-2}}{100 \text{ l}^2 \text{ mole}^{-2}}$$

$$= 3.43 \text{ atm}$$

The attractive force between molecules which gives rise to the term a/V^2 in van der Waals' equation is responsible not only for the deviations from the gas laws at ordinary pressures but also for the condensation of gases to liquids, for certain types of solubility, and for many physical and chemical phenomena. It is electrical in nature, for, although the molecules are uncharged, they contain within them positive and negative parts which can induce electric charges in a neighboring molecule, and these charged parts of molecules then attract oppositely charged units in their vicinity and tend to bring the molecules closer together.

Van der Waals' equation has been very successful in expressing the behavior of gases at atmospheric pressure and up to a few atmospheres, but it is inadequate for calculating the properties of gases under high pressures. It has been useful in the theoretical studies of the behavior of gases.

There is an interesting relationship between the van der Waals constants, a and b, and the critical constants T_c, p_c, and V_c. Multiplying out the terms in van der Waals' equation 14 and rearranging in descending powers of V, we have

$$V^3 - V^2 \left(b + \frac{RT}{p} \right) + V \frac{a}{p} - \frac{ab}{p} = 0 \qquad (16)$$

This cubic equation has three possible solutions, each value of p giving three corresponding roots of V. The terms a, b, R, and T are constants. This equation is shown graphically by the dashed line $DWCZB$ on the 170.0° isothermal in Fig. 2-7, where the three values are evident as three intersections B, C, and D on the horizontal line corresponding to a fixed value of the pressure. This dashed calculated line then appears to give a continuous transition from the gaseous phase to the liquid phase, but in reality the transition is abrupt and discontinuous, both liquid and vapor existing as indicated along the straight horizontal lines. This theoretical dashed line $DWCZB$ does not correspond to normal physical conditions; for example the slope of the curve at C is positive, a fact which would lead to the unnatural condition that an increase in pressure produces an increase in volume. However, it is possible to supersaturate the vapor and have pressures of gas in an unstable condition represented by the beginning of the dashed line DW, before the vapor has a chance to liquefy and bring the pressure down to that of the horizontal line. At the critical temperature (187.8° for isopentane) and pressure there is only one real root, the critical volume V_c.

Exercise III. At the critical temperature the three roots, V, of the van der Waals equation become equal to the critical volume V_c. That is, B, C and D in Fig. 2-7 unite at a point and

$$V^3 - V^2 \left(b + \frac{RT_c}{p_c} \right) + V \frac{a}{p_c} - \frac{ab}{p_c} = 0$$

Expanding $(V - V_c)^3$ by the binomial theorem and equating like coefficients of V in the two equations show that

$$a = 3p_c V_c^2 \qquad b = V_c/3 \qquad \text{and} \qquad R = \tfrac{8}{3} p_c V_c / T_c$$

The Principle of Corresponding States.* The critical constants may be used to define a set of reduced variables.

$$p_r = p/p_c \qquad V_r = V/V_c \qquad T_r = T/T_c$$

The properties of a gas may be stated in terms of these reduced variables rather than p, V, and T. When this is done it is found that all substances obey very nearly the same equation of state. According to the principle of corresponding states the compressibility factor, pV/RT, of all gases would be the same when expressed in terms of reduced pressure and reduced temperature. This principle is the basis of the Hougen and Watson † generalized compressibility charts. Such a chart is shown in *Fig. 2-8*, in which the compressibility factor is plotted against the reduced pressure p/p_c for several different reduced temperatures T/T_c. Large charts accurately drawn with more values of the reduced temperature are available. Such charts are especially useful at high pressures when other data are not available.

* Hirschfelder, Curtiss, and Bird, *The Molecular Theory of Gases and Liquids*, John Wiley & Sons, New York, 1954.

† Hougen and Watson, *Chemical Process Principles*, John Wiley & Sons, New York, 1947, Part II, Chapter XII.

GASES

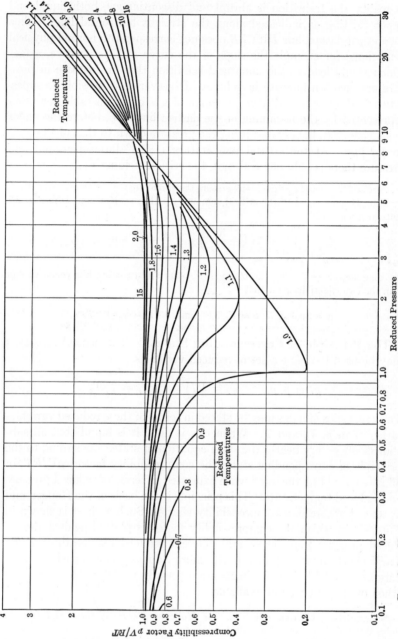

FIG. 2-8. Hougen and Watson chart for calculating pressure, volume, and temperature relations at high pressure.

Example 5. With the Hougen and Watson chart, estimate the volume occupied by a mole of oxygen at $-88°C$ and 44.7 atm. The critical temperature and pressure are found in Table II.

$$\frac{T}{T_c} = \frac{273.1 - 88.0}{154.4} = 1.20 \qquad \frac{p}{p_c} = \frac{44.7}{49.7} = 0.90$$

From the chart, $pV/RT = 0.80$,

$$V = \frac{0.80RT}{p} = \frac{(0.80)\,(0.08205)\,(185.1)}{44.7} = 0.272 \text{ liter mole}^{-1}$$

According to the principle of corresponding states the compressibility factor at the critical point should be a universal constant. The compressibility factors at the critical point are given for a number of substances in Table II. It may be seen that for simple nonpolar molecules this ratio has a value near 0.29. The fact that the average value for hydrocarbons is somewhat lower, approximately 0.27, indicates that they would follow a plot such as Fig. 2-8 which differs from that for the simpler molecules. As shown by the last group of substances, polar molecules give a still greater deviation.

Exercise IV. Show that van der Waals' equation can be written in terms of the reduced temperature T_r, reduced pressure p_r, and reduced volume V_r as

$$\left(p_r + \frac{3}{V_r^2}\right)(3V_r - 1) = 8T_r \qquad (17)$$

if a, b, and R are also expressed in terms of the critical constants.

It may be noted that all constants connected with the individual nature of the gases have vanished.

Equations of State. An equation, like the ideal gas law or van der Waals' equation, which gives the relation between pressure, volume, and temperature for a substance is called an equation of state. Equation 17 is referred to as a reduced equation of state. Various equations * have been designed for particular applications, and for accurate work over a wide range of conditions a large number of constants are required. For example, the Beattie-Bridgeman equation † uses five constants in addition to R.

Exact molecular weights can be obtained with the help of Berthelot's equation given in example 6, or other suitable equations of state, and they are sufficiently accurate to be used for the calculation of atomic weights over limited ranges.

---

* Woolsey, *J. Chem. Education,* *16*, 60 (1939).

† Beattie and Bridgeman, *J. Am. Chem. Soc.,* *49*, 1665 (1927); *50*, 3133 (1928).

Example 6. Calculate the atomic weight of nitrogen from the fact that the density of nitric oxide NO at 0° and 760 mm is 1.3402 grams per liter. The critical constants are 177.1°K and 64 atm.

Calculating the molecular weight M by Berthelot's equation gives

$$M = \frac{gRT}{pv}\left[1 + \frac{9}{128}\frac{p}{p_c}\frac{T_c}{T}\left(1 - 6\frac{T_c^2}{T^2}\right)\right]$$

$$= \frac{(1.3402)(0.082054)(273.16)}{(1)(1)}\left[1 + \frac{(9)(1)(177.1)}{(128)(64)(273.16)}\left(1 - 6\frac{177.1^2}{273.16^2}\right)\right]$$

$$= 30.039[1 - 1.08 \times 10^{-3}] = 30.005$$

The atomic weight of nitrogen = $30.005 - 16.000 = 14.005$. The accepted atomic weight of nitrogen is 14.008. In calculations of this type, when the correction term in brackets is small, it is sufficient to calculate the correction term approximately with a slide rule.

Another type of equation of state is the virial equation

$$\frac{pV}{RT} = 1 + \frac{B(T)}{V} + \frac{C(T)}{V^2} + \cdots \tag{18}$$

where the coefficients $B(T)$, $C(T)$ $\cdots$ which are functions of the absolute temperature T are called the second, third $\cdots$ virial coefficients. The range of usefulness of the virial equation is limited by the convergence of the series, so that it is useful in the study of gases at low and moderate densities. An advantage of the virial equation is that the coefficients may be expressed in terms of intermolecular attractions by means of statistical mechanics. Thus it is possible to make a quantitative interpretation of the deviations from the ideal gas law in terms of the forces between molecules.

The different equations of state are compared in Table IV.

Table IV. pV/RT for Nitrogen at 1000 Atmospheres

Temperature	Observed	Ideal	Van der Waals	Berthelot	Hougen and Watson Chart
0°C	2.0632	1.0000	2.426	0.731	2.10
50°C	1.9285	1.0000	2.182	1.071	1.95

The decision as to which equation of state should be used depends on the amount of data available and the purpose of the study. For pressures of about 1 atm and an accuracy of about 1 per cent the simple gas law equation is usually adequate for gases that are far above their critical temperatures. For greater accuracy or for pressures up to a few atmospheres the van der Waals equation is satisfactory. The Hougen and Watson chart gives good results even up to pressures of hundreds of atmospheres when the critical temperatures and critical pressures are known. If one desires to fit the data with great accuracy over large pressure ranges the virial equation is recommended because of its flexibility. Such an equation is really a condensed summary of the data. It requires a different set of constants for each temperature, and it becomes very cumbersome for practical application.

Mixtures of Gases. If 1 liter of oxygen is added to another liter of oxygen at constant temperature and pressure the volume of the gas will obviously be 2 liters. If two ideal gases are mixed the volumes will be additive also, provided that there is no chemical interaction (as there is with NH_3 and HCl) and no intermolecular attraction. Real gases at atmospheric pressure show only slight departure from this additive relation.

Edwards and Roseveare * measured the following volume changes at $25°$ and 1 atm when 3174 ml of the first gas was mixed with 3421 ml of the second gas at 1 atm and the pressure was readjusted after mixing to 1 atm: Nitrogen + hydrogen increased 1.23 ml; carbon dioxide + hydrogen increased 2.14 ml; and ethylene + hydrogen increased 2.94 ml. At high pressures and with more complex molecules in which attractive forces are stronger the departures will be greater.

In a mixture of gases at constant volume instead of constant pressure it is clear that when two or more gases are introduced into a given volume the total number of moles will be equal to the sum of the number of moles of the different gases, thus

$$n_{\text{total}} = n_A + n_B + n_C + \cdots \tag{19}$$

where n is the number of moles and A, B, and C are different gases. The pressure of a gas is determined by the number of molecular collisions per square centimeter, and so the number of moles n of *any* gas in a given volume v determines the pressure p of the gas, according to the relation $p = nRT/v$. Multiplying each term in equation 19 by RT/v

$$n_{\text{total}} \frac{RT}{v} = n_A \frac{RT}{v} + n_B \frac{RT}{v} + n_C \frac{RT}{v} + \cdots \tag{20}$$

and

$$p_{\text{total}} = p_A + p_B + p_C + \cdots \tag{21}$$

The terms p_A, p_B, and p_C are the *partial pressures* of the gases, i.e., the pressure which each gas would have if it were alone in the given volume.

* Edwards and Roseveare, *J. Am. Chem. Soc.*, *64*, 2816 (1942).

According to *Dalton's law*, discovered long ago in the laboratory, the total pressure is the sum of the partial pressures of the several gases.

Exercise V. Suggest an experiment which will show that in a specified mixture of gases the total pressure is equal to the sum of the partial pressures.

Most mixtures of simple gases follow Dalton's law at atmospheric pressure but many show marked departures at high pressures, just as the pure gases show deviations from the ideal gas law at high pressures.

The Kinetic Theory. According to the kinetic theory, the molecules and atoms of any substance are in a constant state of motion at all temperatures above absolute zero. When heat is supplied to any material, for example, by contact with a warmer body, by a chemical reaction, or by absorption of radiation, the molecules move faster, and the temperature rises, unless prevented by some other heat-absorbing process. In solids and, to a lesser extent, in liquids, the molecules are restricted in their movement by attractive forces which hold them near a fixed position so that the motion corresponds to a molecular oscillation rather than to a flow of matter. As the temperature increases, the oscillations in the solid or liquid become more vigorous until finally the kinetic energy of the fastest-moving molecules is sufficient to cause the molecules to break away from the other molecules and enter the gaseous state—that is, the substance vaporizes.

The molecules in the gas do not oscillate in the neighborhood of a point as they did before, but they are completely separated from each other and move in straight lines with an average velocity which increases as the temperature of the gas increases. The volume occupied by the molecules of the gas themselves is much smaller than the volume of the containing vessel which they fill, and, accordingly, a molecule moves for considerable distances before it collides with one of its neighbors. The average distance through which the molecules move between collisions is called the *mean free path*.

The combined effect of the impacts of the molecules on the walls of the containing vessel accounts for the pressure exerted by the gas. When these walls are moved outward by a gas and the gas expands against an external pressure, the gas does work at the expense of the kinetic energy of its molecules. If the gas is insulated, this loss of kinetic energy will slow down the motion of the molecules and produce a cooling effect, but, if it is in good thermal contact with its surroundings, heat will flow in and offset the loss of kinetic energy so that the temperature remains constant.

The molecules of a gas undergo an enormous number of collisions with other molecules, and their direction and velocity are constantly changing in a random manner. The distribution of velocities in a group of molecules has been determined mathematically by Maxwell and Boltzmann and used in a number of different calculations, as discussed later on pages 344 and 646. In the present chapter the kinetic theory is used with simplifying assumptions to develop a simple equation which is important in describing the quantitative behavior of gases.

Referring to *Fig. 2-9*, it is imagined that in this cube, which has edges l centimeters in length, there are n molecules each having the mass m. The temperature of the gas is fixed. It is assumed that the molecules are very small compared with the distances between them, that there are no forces of attraction between the molecules, and that the collisions of the molecules with each other and with the sides of the box are perfectly elastic (that is, that no energy is used up inside a molecule by re-arrangements of its parts).

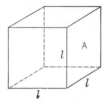

Fig. 2-9. Imaginary cube used in the derivation of the kinetic equation, $pv = \frac{1}{3}mnu^2$.

Each of the n molecules is moving with its own velocity u_i, which is determined by the history of its previous collisions. The average velocity of the molecules is not important; the average of the squares of the velocities is involved in calculating the pressure. This quantity u, known as the root-mean-square velocity, is defined by the expression

$$u = \sqrt{\frac{\sum\limits_{i=1}^{n} u_i^{2}}{n}}$$

where the sign Σ indicates the summation of the squares of all the individual velocities, $u_1, u_2, u_3 \cdots u_n$.

As a result of their collisions with each other inside the box, the molecules will be moving sometimes in one direction, sometimes in another; since these directions may be resolved along three different axes at right angles to each other, it may be supposed that one-third of the molecules or $n/3$ molecules are moving always in the direction perpendicular to the wall A.

Considering the collisions of molecules with A, one molecule will strike A every $2l$ centimeters as it moves back and forth across the box. If its velocity is u centimeters per second, it will collide $u/2l$ times per second with A. Since the collisions are perfectly elastic, an individual molecule will rebound with velocity $-u$, having suffered no loss in kinetic energy. Since momentum is defined as the product of mass and velocity, the momentum before collision is mu and after collision is $-mu$, so that the change in momentum per collision per molecule is $2mu$. Since there are $u/2l$ collisions per second, the change in momentum for each molecule per second is then

$$2mu \; u/2l = mu^2/l$$

The total change in momentum of the $n/3$ molecules hitting the wall A per second is the force exerted on the wall by the enclosed gas. Since the wall A has an area of l^2 square centimeters the force per square centimeter or the pressure p is given by the expression

$$p = \frac{\text{Force}}{\text{Area}} = \frac{n}{3} \frac{mu^2}{l} \frac{1}{l^2} \tag{22}$$

But the volume v of the box is l^3, and we have

$$p = \frac{n}{3} \frac{mu^2}{v} \tag{23}$$

or

$$pv = \tfrac{1}{3}nmu^2 \tag{24}$$

This is the fundamental equation of the kinetic theory of gases, which finds frequent application in physical chemistry. It is not restricted to gases in a cubical vessel, because any vessel may be considered to be made up of a large number of small cubes for each of which this derivation applies. It must be remembered, however, that the equation applies strictly only to ideal gases, in which there is no attraction between the molecules and no internal loss of energy on collision. It can be applied, however, with fair accuracy to most real gases.

Equation 24 may be rewritten in the form

$$pv = (\tfrac{2}{3})\tfrac{1}{2}nmu^2 = \tfrac{2}{3} \text{ total kinetic energy} \tag{25}$$

since the kinetic energy of a moving body is $\tfrac{1}{2}mu^2$. Inasmuch as the kinetic energy of the molecules depends on the temperature, it will remain constant at constant temperature. According to equation 25 then pv is constant at constant temperature—and we have thus derived Boyle's law.

An expression may be deduced also from the fundamental kinetic equation which is equivalent to Avogadro's law.

For one gas,

$$pv = \tfrac{1}{3}n_1 m_1 u_1{}^2$$

and for another gas of different molecular weight,

$$pv = \tfrac{1}{3}n_2 m_2 u_2{}^2$$

so

$$\tfrac{1}{3}n_1 m_1 u_1{}^2 = \tfrac{1}{3}n_2 m_2 u_2{}^2 \qquad (26)$$

At the same temperature the kinetic energies are assumed to be equal:

$$\tfrac{1}{2}m_1 u_1{}^2 = \tfrac{1}{2}m_2 u_2{}^2 \qquad (27)$$

If equation 26 is divided by equation 27, several quantities cancel out, and we have

$$n_1 = n_2 \qquad (28)$$

This equation shows that, at equal temperatures, pressures, and volumes, the number of molecules in each gas is the same—provided that the gases are ideal and that the conditions assumed in the derivation of equation 24 apply.

Velocity of Molecules. If the fundamental kinetic equation is solved for u, and mn is taken equal to the molar weight M for 1 mole, we have

$$u = \sqrt{3pV/mn} = \sqrt{3RT/M} \qquad (29)$$

Example 7. What is the root-mean-square velocity of a molecule of hydrogen at $0°$?

$$u = \sqrt{\frac{3RT}{M}} = \sqrt{\frac{(3)(8.314 \times 10^7 \text{ ergs deg}^{-1} \text{ mole}^{-1})(273.1 \text{ deg})}{2.016 \text{ g mole}^{-1}}}$$

$$= 1.84 \times 10^5 \text{ cm sec}^{-1}$$

In this calculation R is taken in ergs per degree per mole in order to have consistent units in the cgs (centimeter-gram-second) system.

It is seen that on the average a hydrogen molecule at $0°$ travels at a rate faster than a mile per second, but at ordinary pressures it travels only an exceedingly short distance before colliding with another molecule and starting off in a different direction.

This derivation, like all those depending on the relation $pV = RT$, is exact only for perfect gases. Even if the expression $\sqrt{3pV/mn}$ is used, the answer still may be erroneous (perhaps to about 1 per cent) because in the derivation an ideal gas was assumed with no attraction between the molecules.

Relative rates of diffusion and molecular weights may be estimated from the fundamental kinetic equation. Since the density d of a gas is equal to the mass divided by the volume, $d = mn/V$;

$$u = \sqrt{3pV/mn} = \sqrt{3p/d} \tag{30}$$

If the pressure and temperature of two different gases are the same, the ratio of the root-mean-square velocities u_1 and u_2 may be calculated from the two densities, d_1 and d_2, or from the molecular weights, M_1 and M_2, as shown by equation 31:

$$u_1/u_2 = \sqrt{d_2/d_1} = \sqrt{M_2/M_1} \tag{31}$$

Under certain conditions the times required for two gases to flow through a small aperture are inversely proportional to the velocities of the molecules and, hence, directly proportional to the square root of the molecular weights. The proportionality is exact if the cross section of the aperture is small compared with the average distance through which a molecule travels before colliding with another molecule. At ordinary pressures this distance is so small that the conditions are no longer satisfied and a correction term is required.

REFERENCES

Glasstone, *Textbook of Physical Chemistry*, D. Van Nostrand Co., New York, 1946, Chapter IV.

Herzfeld and Smallwood, "Kinetic Theory of Ideal Gases" in *Treatise on Physical Chemistry*, ed. by Taylor and Glasstone, Vol. 2, D. Van Nostrand Co., 1951.

Roseman and Katzoff, "The Equation of State of a Perfect Gas," *J. Chem. Education, 11*, 350–54, 1934.

Hirschfelder, Curtiss, and Bird, *The Molecular Theory of Gases and Liquids*, John Wiley & Sons, New York, 1954.

Newitt, *The Design of High Pressure Plant and the Properties of Fluids at High Pressures*, Oxford University Press, Oxford, 1940.

PROBLEMS

1. How much does a liter of octane gas C_8H_{18} weigh at 150° and 1 atm pressure?
Ans.   3.29 g.

2. A 1-liter flask containing an organic vapor at 25° is evacuated to 0.0001 mm (of mercury). How many molecules remain in the flask?   *Ans.* 3.24×10^{15}.

3. It is stated that the buoyancy of air is about 0.0012 gram per ml at room temperature. Assuming that air behaves as an ideal gas, calculate exactly the weight of 1 ml of air at 25° and 1 atm if the relative humidity of the air is 70 per cent and the vapor pressure of water at 25° is 23.7 mm. The composition of dry air is 80 per cent nitrogen and 20 per cent oxygen by volume.   *Ans.* 11.69×10^{-4} g ml^{-1}.

4. Using van der Waals' equation, calculate the pressure exerted by 1 mole of CO_2 at 0° which has a volume of (a) 1.00 liter, (b) 0.05 liter. (c) Repeat the calculations at 100° and 0.05 liter.   *Ans.*   (a) 19.82, (b) 1621, (c) 2739 atm.

5. The density of ammonia in grams per liter was determined at various pressures by weighing the gas in large glass bulbs. The values of d/p (d = density in grams per liter, p = pressure in atmospheres) at 0° were as follows: 0.77169 at 1 atm, 0.76773 at ⅔ atm, 0.76585 at ½ atm, 0.76383 at ⅓ atm. What is the limiting value of d/p at zero pressure, as determined graphically, and what is the molecular weight of ammonia? If the atomic weight of hydrogen is taken as 1.008, what is the atomic weight of nitrogen?   *Ans.* 14.006.

6. (a) Calculate the volume occupied by a kilogram of carbon dioxide at 100° and 50 atm using the ideal gas equation. (b) Calculate the volume using the Hougen-Watson chart.   *Ans.* (a) 13.9, (b) 12.2 liters.

7. Calculate the temperature at which the root-mean-square velocity of a nitrogen molecule is the same as that of a helium molecule at 27°.   *Ans.* 2100°K.

8. Estimate the number of tons of carbon dioxide over a square mile of the earth's surface if the atmospheric pressure is 760 mm and the air contains 0.03 per cent of carbon dioxide by volume.   *Ans.* 8850 tons.

---

9. A certain hydrocarbon is found to have a vapor density of 2.550 grams per liter at 100° and 760 mm. Chemical analysis shows that the substance contains 1 atom of carbon to 1 atom of hydrogen. What is its molecular formula?

10. In a Victor Meyer experiment, 0.2350 gram of a liquid is vaporized, and the volume of displaced air measured over water in a gas buret is 40.2 ml at 23.0° and 730 mm. Since the air in the buret has become saturated with water, it is necessary to subtract the vapor pressure of the water, which is 21.0 mm, from the total pressure. What is the molecular weight of the vaporized material?

11. If the atmospheric pressure is 740 mm, how many kilograms of oxygen are there over a square foot of land? The per cent by volume of oxygen in air and hence the per cent of the total pressure is 20.0 per cent. One foot is equivalent to 30.48 cm.

12. Baxter and Starkweather measured the density of nitrogen at 0° as follows:

Pressure, mm	253.3	506.7	760.0
Density, g/l	0.41667	0.83348	1.25036

Calculate the atomic weight of nitrogen.

13. Calculate the pressure exerted by 35 grams of carbon dioxide in a 1-liter vessel at 24° using (a) the ideal gas law and (b) van der Waals' equation.

14. Flasks A and B are filled with oxygen and nitrogen, respectively, at 25° and connected by a stopcock.

		Volume	Pressure
A	O_2	500 ml	1 atm
B	N_2	1500 ml	½ atm

Calculate (a) the total pressure and (b) the partial pressure of each gas after the stopcock is opened and the gases are mixed at constant temperature, assuming ideality.

15. A 6-to-1 mixture by volume of neon and argon is allowed to diffuse through a small orifice into an evacuated space. What is the composition of the mixture that first passes through?

16. Calculate the volume of 100 grams of methane at 0° and 100 atm using (a) the ideal gas law, (b) van der Waals' equation, and (c) Hougen-Watson chart.

17. (a) What is the root-mean-square velocity of molecules of CH_4 at 27°? (b) At what temperature do C_2H_6 molecules have the same velocity as those of CH_4 at 27°?

---

18. Four hundred milliliters of an organic vapor weighed 0.5220 gram at 27° and 750 mm. Chemical analysis gave carbon 37.52 per cent, hydrogen 12.56 per cent, and oxygen 49.90 per cent by weight. What is the formula of the organic substance?

19. A mixture of 0.1 gram of hydrogen and 0.2 gram of nitrogen is to be stored at 760 mm pressure and 26°. What must the volume of the container be, if it is assumed that there is no interaction between nitrogen and hydrogen?

20. The ratio of the weight of 1 liter of ethyl chloride to the pressure in atmospheres at three different pressures at 0° is as follows: 2.9002 g atm^{-1} at 760 mm, 2.8919 at 475 mm, 2.8863 at 285 mm. Calculate the molecular weight of ethyl chloride and the atomic weight of chlorine by the method of limiting densities, taking the atomic weights of carbon and hydrogen as known.

21. The melting point of ice is 0.000°C or 32.000°F; the boiling point of water at 760 mm pressure is 100.000°C or 212.000°F. (a) Devise a formula for converting °F to °C. (b) At what temperature do the centigrade and Fahrenheit scales give the same reading?

22. What pressure will be generated if 100 grams of methanol, CH_3OH, is evaporated at 100° in an evacuated vessel having a volume of 2 liters?

23. A certain liquid is weighed out in a Victor Meyer apparatus and vaporized. The weight of liquid is 0.110 gram, the pressure 737 mm, and the temperature 25.0°. If the volume of displaced air, collected over mercury, is 22.5 ml, what is the molecular weight of the substance?

24. (a) How many grams of air are there in the atmosphere surrounding the earth, if it is assumed that the earth is a sphere with a diameter of 12 million meters and that the atmospheric pressure is 760 mm everywhere on the surface? (b) How many moles of air are there in the total atmosphere, if it is assumed that the average molecular weight of air is 28.8? (c) How many molecules of oxygen are there in the earth's atmosphere, if one-fifth of the air by volume is oxygen?

25. Fractional diffusion of gases may be used in separating isotopes. Although this method is more efficient for isotopes of low small mass, it has been used in separating U^{238} and U^{235}. Calculate the ratio of the rates with which $U^{238}F_6$ and $U^{235}F_6$ will diffuse through a porous barrier.

26. Calculate the root-mean-square velocity of (a) carbon tetrachloride molecules at 100°; (b) ammonia molecules at 100°. (c) How many times longer will it take for a millimole of carbon tetrachloride vapor to diffuse out of a small opening than a millimole of ammonia? (d) How many times longer will it take for a milligram of ammonia to diffuse out of a small opening than a milligram of carbon tetrachloride vapor?

---

27. One liter of a gas is contained in a balloon at 25° and 1 atm pressure. If the gas is heated to 45°, what must be the applied pressure in order that the volume remain constant?

28. How many molecules of sulfur dioxide are contained in a liter: (a) at 1 atm pressure and 25°? (b) at 1 atm pressure and 1000°? (c) at 1 mm pressure and 25°? (d) at 1 mm pressure and 1000°?

29. The weight of a certain evacuated vessel is found to increase 0.2500, 0.5535, and 0.5268 gram when oxygen, chlorine, and a compound of oxygen and chlorine,

respectively, are separately admitted into the vessel under the same conditions of temperature and pressure. Calculate from these data alone the molecular weights of chlorine and the oxide of chlorine. What can you say from these data regarding the number of atoms in the chlorine molecule?

30. Calculate the number of grams of hydrogen in a vessel of 500-ml capacity when hydrogen is forced in at 100 atm at 200° using (a) simple gas laws, (b) van der Waals' equation, (c) Hougen-Watson chart.

31. At what temperature will the velocity of carbon dioxide molecules equal the velocity of oxygen molecules at 0°? What is this velocity?

32. It takes 30 minutes for the pressure of a certain evacuated vessel of 1-liter capacity to rise from 0.001 mm to 0.003 mm by leakage of air through a pinhole in the glass. How long will it take for chlorine at the same temperature and external pressure to leak in and raise the pressure from 0.001 mm to 0.003 mm? The average molecular weight of air is 28.8.

33. Exactly 1.100 grams of carbon dioxide was introduced into a 1-liter flask which contained some pure oxygen before being subjected to partial evacuation. The flask was warmed to 100° and the pressure found to be 608 mm Hg. Considering oxygen and carbon dioxide to be the only gases present, calculate the weight of oxygen in the flask.

34. (a) Using the Hougen-Watson chart, estimate the volume of a vessel necessary to hold 1000 grams of n-octane, C_8H_{18}, at 354°C under a pressure of 50 atm. (b) How is this chart to be interpreted if 1000 grams of octane is placed in this vessel under 50 atm pressure at 183°C?

35. A glass bulb fitted with a stopcock was evacuated and found to weigh 46.8542 grams without correcting for the buoyancy of the air. When the stopcock was opened and dry air was allowed to fill the bulb, the weight increased to 47.0465 grams. The barometric pressure was 745 mm, and the temperature was 27°. (a) Calculate the total volume of the bulb from the known average molecular weight of air, 28.8. (b) Calculate the weight if the bulb were filled with dry hydrogen at this temperature and pressure.

36. A temperature scale using an ideal gas thermometer is defined by taking the melting point of mercury as zero and its normal boiling point as 100°. Calculate the normal boiling point of water and the absolute zero on this scale. Mercury boils at 356.9°C and freezes at −38.87°C.

37. Using the data of Problem 12, determine the limiting value of d/p at zero pressure and the atomic weight of nitrogen, not by graphing, but by calculation, using the method of least squares.

38. Ordinary carbon contains 98.9 per cent of carbon with a mass of 12.00 and 1.1 per cent of an isotope of carbon with a mass of 13.00. By a certain physical-chemical operation (page 614) the concentration of this isotope is increased from 1.1 to approximately 2.0 per cent. It is planned to determine the exact percentage of this heavier isotope by measuring the density of carbon dioxide with a gas density balance. If this concentration of 2 per cent must be known to 1 part in 500 for the experiment planned, how accurately in parts per million must the gas density of the CO_2 be measured? To what fraction of a degree must the temperature be known at about 25° and to what fraction of a millimeter must the pressure be known at about 740 mm in order to achieve this accuracy?

3

The Crystalline State

Properties of Solids. In solids strong forces hold the atoms and molecules together, thereby giving the solids fixed shape, rigidity, and mechanical strength. These forces are of different types, and they produce differences in the physical properties of the solids. *Crystalline* solids are those in which the atoms are arranged in some definite order constantly repeated. The binding force here may be due to an electric attraction between positive and negative ions in the crystal, as in sodium chloride; to the existence of chemical bonds in which the atoms are held together by valence bonds in continuing structures, as in the diamond; or to attraction between molecules arranged in definite order, as in solid carbon dioxide. *Amorphous* solids such as pitch or glass may be regarded as supercooled liquids in which the force of attraction holding the molecules together is so great that the material is rigid but there is no regularity of structure.

The crystalline and the amorphous solids differ in several respects. A pure crystalline material usually has a sharp melting point. When an amorphous solid is heated, it gradually softens and becomes mobile over a wide range of temperature without undergoing a sharp change from solid to liquid. The surfaces of an amorphous substance do not, in general, exhibit definite recurring faces at definite angles, such as are often displayed by crystalline solids.

The properties of a crystalline medium such as tensile strength, elasticity, heat conductance, electric conductance, refractive index, and rate of solution may be different along different directions; and such a medium is called *anisotropic*. If a given property has the same value in all directions, the crystal is said to be *isotropic* with respect to that property. The characteristic color patterns of anisotropic crystals with polarized light (discussed on page 63) are used for identification, particularly in the microscopic examination of chemicals and minerals.

The size and perfection of crystals depend to a large extent on the rate at which they are formed. The slower the rate of crystallization, the more perfect is the crystal, because the atoms or molecules have more time to find their proper positions in the crystal lattice. In order

34

to grow large crystals the purified salt is melted in a large pot which is then allowed to cool very slowly at an automatically controlled rate. In this way sodium chloride, silver chloride, potassium bromide, lithium fluoride, and other salts have been prepared in large transparent pieces, several inches in diameter, which are valuable for optical work.

Crystal Forms. Chemical compounds exist in a great many different crystal forms, depending on the type of binding force, the kind of

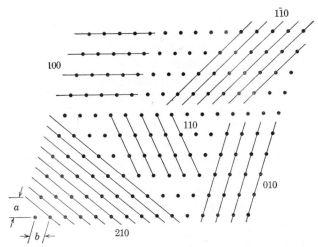

FIG. 3-1. Planes through lattice points as seen along the *c* axis of a crystal.

atomic grouping, the relative size of the different ions or atoms, and many other factors. Many thousand different crystals are known, distinguishable one from another by shapes, angles between faces, and X-ray diffraction patterns (as will be described presently). In spite of the great variety of crystal forms, a given chemical compound or mineral always exhibits the same angle between two given faces at a given temperature. This law was discovered first by Steno in 1669. It provides an excellent means for the identification of materials by the determination of the crystalline properties. Large crystals may be studied directly; small crystals may be examined with a microscope; and all crystals may be studied by means of the diffraction of X rays when passed through crystals or reflected from them.

A crystal consists of a repetition in three dimensions of a basic group of atoms. This repeating pattern is similar to that of a wallpaper pattern except that it is in three dimensions. For some purposes it is convenient to represent the *crystal lattice* by a *space lattice* which is a distribution of points produced by moving a single point by fixed increments along the three axes of the crystal. The increments are determined by translational symmetry, i.e., the total environment of every one of these points is identical with that of all of the other points.

The *unit cell* is a convenient (often the smallest) volume of the crystal bounded by three pairs of parallel sides by whose movement along the three axes a, b, c the whole crystal may be reproduced. The unit cell must be selected so that it has the same symmetry as that of the whole crystal.

The lattice points in one plane of a crystal are illustrated in *Fig. 3-1*, which may be taken as an end view of the crystal along the c axis which is perpendicular to the plane of the a and b axes. A number of different planes may be drawn through the lattice points as illustrated in Fig. 3-1, in which the planes are seen edgewise. Each type of plane is a possible crystal face, but the faces of simple crystals are those planes which have a high density of lattice points and wide interplanar spacings.

Designation of Crystal Planes. It is convenient to designate a given type of plane with three numbers as illustrated in Fig. 3-1. These three numbers are referred to as the *Miller indices*. The indices of a set of planes are obtained by counting the number of planes crossed between one lattice point and the next going in the directions of the a, b, and c axes, respectively. For the set of planes in the lower left-hand corner, two planes are crossed in going one lattice distance in the direction of the a axis and one plane is crossed in going one lattice distance horizontally while no plane would be crossed in going one lattice distance into the paper since the planes are parallel to the c axis. Thus, this set of planes is designated by the numbers 210.* The indices of the planes in the upper right-hand corner are 1$\bar{1}$0. The negative sign indicates that, if a plane is intercepted by going in the positive direction along a, it is necessary to go in the negative direction along b in order to intercept the same plane.

Since the planes we have been discussing are possible crystal faces, three index numbers may be used to designate each of the various faces of a crystal. Planes of high atomic density have low indices, as may be seen in Fig. 3-1, and are more likely to appear as faces. This is the basis of the law of rational indices according to which the faces on a crystal may be described by three small whole numbers. The faces are indexed in *Fig. 3-2* for several types of crystals belonging to the cubic system. Intercepts in the negative direction are represented by a minus sign over the index number.

* The Miller indices may also be defined as the reciprocals of the intercepts of a plane on the axes in terms of the unit distances between lattice points. The plane in the lower left corner of Fig. 3-1 intercepts the a, b, and c axes at ½, 1, and ∞, so that the indices are 210.

It is possible to deduce the shape of the unit cell from the crystal shape by finding the angles and relative dimensions which make it possible to describe all the faces of the crystal by the smallest whole numbers. This process is not as simple in the more complicated types of crystals as in the cubic crystals. The relative dimensions of the crystal are not a direct indication of the dimensions of the unit cell, and it is commonly found that when a given type of crystal is grown under different conditions the growth of various faces may be quite different.

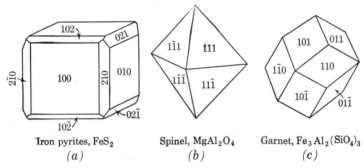

Iron pyrites, FeS_2 Spinel, $MgAl_2O_4$ Garnet, $Fe_3Al_2(SiO_4)_3$
(a) (b) (c)

Fig. 3-2. Crystals belonging to the cubic system.

All crystals may be divided into six or seven systems which have characteristic unit cells. Before discussing these crystal systems it is important to discuss the subject of symmetry, since it is the symmetry of atomic arrangement that determines the angles of the unit cell and the number of its edges which are equal in length.

Symmetry. The symmetry of a crystal is discussed in terms of the various ways the crystal may be rotated, reflected in a plane, or inverted through a point without changing its appearance. Thus, if a perpendicular axis is passed through the center of a face of a cube, the cube may be rotated so as to bring four different faces into the same position, giving the same appearance. Such an axis is referred to as an axis of fourfold symmetry, and a cube has three such axes.

If a cube is rotated about an axis passing through two diagonally opposite corners the same appearance is presented three times during a revolution, and there are four such threefold axes of symmetry. An axis passing through the midpoints of two opposite edges is a twofold axis of symmetry. It is interesting that axes of fivefold or greater than sixfold symmetry do not occur in crystals, and would not be expected since it is not possible to devise patterns with these symmetries to fill space.

A cube has another type of symmetry, since we may imagine planes that divide the crystal into halves which are mirror images of each other. There are two types of such planes: those perpendicular to edges of the cube and those bisecting the angles of the upper and lower faces. Finally, for each face, edge, or corner of a cube there is an exactly similar face, edge, or corner diametrically opposite and at exactly the same distance

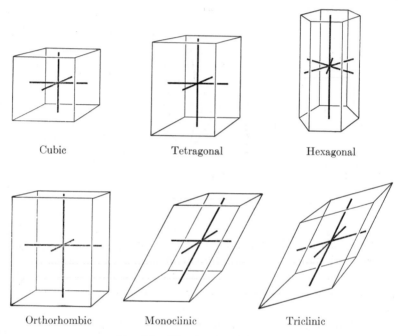

Cubic   Tetragonal   Hexagonal

Orthorhombic   Monoclinic   Triclinic

Fig. 3-3.   The six crystal systems.

from the center. Thus the center of a cube is a typical case of a center of symmetry or a center of inversion.

The crystals illustrated in Fig. 3-2 have all the kinds of symmetry described for a cube and so they belong to the cubic system. It may not be so easy to recognize the symmetry of a crystal if it has grown so that crystallographic equivalent faces are very unequal in size, but the interfacial angles are constant and reveal the symmetries of the internal atomic arrangement.

Typical unit cells for the six crystal systems are illustrated in *Fig. 3-3*, and the essential symmetries are summarized in Table I. α, β, and γ are the angles between the three axes of the crystal, and a, b, c are lengths.

Table I. Six Crystal Systems

System		Angles	Axes	Essential Symmetry
Cubic		$\alpha = \beta = \gamma = 90°$	$a = b = c$	Four threefold axes
Tetragonal		$\alpha = \beta = \gamma = 90°$	$a = b \neq c$	One fourfold axis
Hexagonal or	(1)	$\alpha = \beta = 90°$; $\gamma = 120°$	$a = b \neq c$	One sixfold axis or one threefold
trigonal	(2)	$\alpha = \beta = \gamma \neq 90°$	$a = b = c$	axis
Orthorhombic		$\alpha = \beta = \gamma = 90°$	$a \neq b \neq c$	Three mutually perpendicular twofold axes, or two planes intersecting in a twofold axis
Monoclinic		$\alpha = \gamma = 90°$; $\beta \neq 90°$	$a \neq b \neq c$	One twofold axis, or one plane of symmetry
Triclinic		$\alpha \neq \beta \neq \gamma \neq 90°$	$a \neq b \neq c$	No planes, no axes of symmetry

In the *cubic* system there are four threefold axes so that there are three mutually perpendicular directions all equivalent to each other. Thus the properties of a cubic crystal are identical along these three directions.

In the *tetragonal* system the three axes intersect at right angles and two of the axes are of equal length while the third is either longer or shorter.

In the *trigonal* or *hexagonal* system there is one threefold axis or one sixfold axis. In hexagonal crystals there are three equivalent directions which are at 120° to each other in a plane normal to the principal axis.

In the *orthorhombic* system the three axes of unequal length all intersect each other at right angles.

In the *monoclinic* system there are three axes of unequal length, two of which intersect at right angles, while the third axis is perpendicular to one and not to the other.

In *triclinic* crystals there are no planes or axes of symmetry, although there may be a center of symmetry.

The property which determines to which system a crystal belongs is symmetry. Crystals may be divided on the basis of their external symmetry into 32 symmetry classes or point groups. The internal symmetry of crystals is more complicated, and it may be shown that all unit cells may be classified according to 230 space groups. There are 230, and only 230, ways of repeating a particular pattern, as, for example, a molecule, in space to give a crystalline material.

Diffraction of X Rays by Crystals. X rays are electromagnetic waves of very short wavelength which are produced when rapidly moving electrons collide with atoms. As a result of collision, electrons in inner orbits are displaced, and the energy liberated when electrons make the transition from a higher energy level to the vacancy in the inner orbit is given out in the form of X rays.

The interference of light waves striking a grating has been utilized in physics for many years. In 1912 Laue predicted that the spacing of atoms in crystals is such that the lattice could act as a three-dimensional

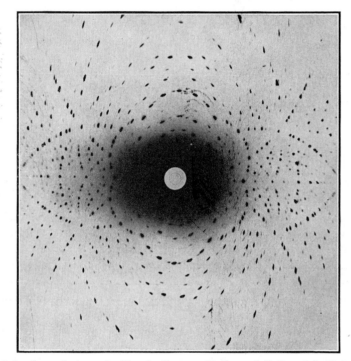

FIG. 3-4. Laue photograph of beryl. Courtesy Professor S. Bailey of the University of Wisconsin.

diffraction grating for X rays, which have wavelengths very much shorter than those of visible light. Friedrich and Knipping passed a beam of X rays through a crystal and observed a diffraction pattern which proved that Laue's prediction was correct. In the Laue method, polychromatic or "white" X rays are passed through a carefully oriented crystal which is mounted a few centimeters in front of a photographic film. A Laue photograph of beryl is shown in *Fig. 3-4*. Such photographs indicate much about the symmetry of a crystal. However, since the interpretation of these patterns is more difficult than for those obtained by use of monochromatic X rays this method will not be discussed further.

Although X rays are actually diffracted by the crystal lattice just as visible light is diffracted by a grating, Bragg pointed out that it is convenient to consider that the X rays are "reflected" from planes in the crystal. In contrast to ordinary reflection, X rays are reflected only at certain angles which are determined by the wavelength of the X rays and the interplanar spacing in the crystal. The intensity of reflection of X rays at various angles can be determined by the blackening of photographic film or by means of a Geiger-Müller counter, described on page 604.

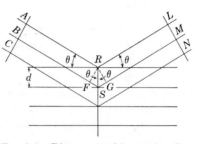

A simple relation exists between the wavelength of the X rays, the distance between planes in the crystal, and the angle of reflection. This equation, which is generally called the Bragg equation, may be derived by reference to *Fig. 3-5*, in which the horizontal lines represent layers in the crystal separated

FIG. 3-5. Diagram used in proving that $n\lambda = 2d \sin \theta$.

by the distance d. The plane ABC is drawn perpendicular to the incident beam of parallel monochromatic X rays, and the plane LMN is drawn perpendicular to the reflected ray. As the angle of incidence θ is changed the incident ray will be reflected only when the waves are in phase at plane LMN, that is, when the difference in distance between planes ABC and LMN, measured along rays reflected from different planes, is a whole-number multiple of the wavelength.

It can be shown that the angle of reflection is equal to the angle of incidence. The lines RF and RG are drawn perpendicular to the beams, and it can be seen that the ray BSM travels farther than the ray ARL by an amount equal to $FS + SG$. This extra distance is equal to a whole number n of wavelengths if the angle θ is such that the light at LM is in phase with the light at AB. Then,

$$FS + SG = n\lambda \qquad (1)$$

Furthermore, since

$$\sin \theta = FS/d = SG/d$$

$$FS = SG = d \sin \theta$$

and

$$n\lambda = 2d \sin \theta \qquad (2)$$

This is an important equation which gives the relationship of the distance between planes in a crystal and the angle at which the reflected radiation has a maximum intensity; i.e., all the X rays are in phase with no interference.

The reflection corresponding to $n = 1$ is called the first-order reflection; the reflection corresponding to $n = 2$ is the second-order reflection; and so on. Each successive order exhibits a wider angle. In discussing X-ray reflections it is customary to set $n = 1$ in equation 2 and consider that the second-order reflection is from planes separated by half the lattice distance, etc. Equation 2 may be written

$$\lambda = 2(d/n) \sin \theta$$

$$= 2d_{hkl} \sin \theta \tag{3}$$

where d_{hkl} is the distance between planes having the Miller indices hkl. Thus, the second-order reflection from the 100 planes is labeled 200, the second-order reflection from the 110 planes is labeled 220, and the second-order reflection from the 111 planes is labeled 222.

If the X rays are incident on the face of a crystal for which d is known, the value of λ for the radiation used may be determined by measuring the angles at which the reflections of maximum intensity occur. On the other hand, if the wavelength of the incident radiation is known, it becomes possible to determine the spacing of the atomic planes of atoms or ions within the crystal. The angles at which X rays are reflected are determined by the unit cell distances. The relative intensities of the reflections are determined by the arrangement of atoms in the unit cell. Consequently, the study of the intensities is of great importance in determining the detailed lattice structure.

Cubic Lattices. Since the cubic system is the simplest it is explored in some detail here. There are only three lattices which have cubic symmetry: primitive, body centered, and face centered. These are illustrated in *Fig. 3-6*.

In the *primitive, or simple, cubic lattice* in Fig. 3-6a the lattice points shown as black dots at the corners of a cube may represent atoms, ions, or molecules. Three types of reflecting planes are illustrated, 100, 110, and 111. The reflections from these planes occur at the smallest angles of all the possible planes that can be imagined in a cubic crystal since other types of planes are closer together and θ will be larger according to equation 2. The distance between planes in a cubic crystal is $a/\sqrt{h^2 + k^2 + l^2}$, where a is the length of a side of a unit cell and h, k, and l are the Miller indices of the planes under consideration.

Exercise I. Show that, in a primitive cubic lattice where a is the distance between lattice points, the perpendicular distance between sets of parallel planes is

Note in ① simple cubic each atom is associated with 8 unit cells, ∴ ⅛atom per unit cell.
in ② face centered cubic 8/8 =1 + 6/2 =3 = 4 atoms per unit [face] centered cube

$d_{hkl} = a/\sqrt{h^2 + k^2 + l^2}$, where h, k, and l are the Miller indices of the planes. This relation may be readily tested for planes with Miller indices 100, 110, and 111.

The spacings between the planes in a simple cubic crystal are a, $a/\sqrt{2}$, $a/\sqrt{3}$, $a/\sqrt{4}$, $a/\sqrt{5}$, $a/\sqrt{6}$, $a/\sqrt{8}$, etc., where $a/\sqrt{7}$ is miss-

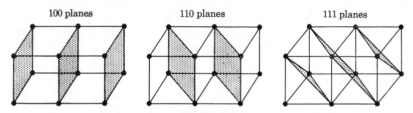

(a) Two unit cells of simple cubic lattice

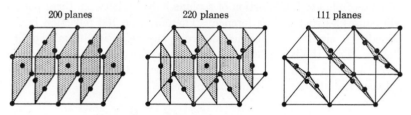

(b) Two unit cells of face-centered cubic lattice

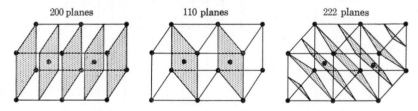

(c) Two unit cells of body-centered cubic lattice

Fig. 3-6. Planes through cubic lattices.

ing because 7 cannot be obtained from $h^2 + k^2 + l^2$ where h, k, and l have values of $0, 1, 2, 3 \cdots$.

In the *face-centered cubic lattice* illustrated in Fig. 3-6 there are additional lattice points in the center of each face of the unit cell. These extra lattice points lie in the planes for which the Miller indices are either all even or all odd (that is, 111, 200, 220, 311, etc.), and so reflections are obtained from these planes. However, since the face-centered lattice points lie halfway between the planes for which the Miller indices are not all even or all odd, the reflections from these planes are destroyed by interference. The spacings which will appear are $a/\sqrt{3}$, $a/\sqrt{4}$,

$a/\sqrt{8}$, $a/\sqrt{11}$, etc., which are the distances between the 111, 200, 220, and 311 planes.

In the *body-centered cubic lattice* illustrated in Fig. 3-6 there is an additional lattice point in the center of each unit cell. These extra lattice points lie in the 110 planes, and further analysis shows that they always lie on planes for which the sum of the Miller indices $(h + k + l)$ is even. Thus the X rays diffracted from the body-centered lattice points are in phase with those from the corner lattice points for these planes. But inspection will show that the body-centered points lie halfway between planes for which $h + k + l$ is odd. As a result, the X rays scattered by the body-centered points destructively interfere with the X rays scattered by the corner lattice points. If a crystal is oriented at such an angle that there is a first-order reflection from a certain set of planes, the insertion of a plane halfway between these planes will cause destructive interference. Therefore, no 100 reflection is obtained. A similar interference destroys the reflection from the 111 planes. Thus the interplanar spacings found for a body-centered cubic lattice are $a/\sqrt{2}$, $a/\sqrt{4}$, $a/\sqrt{6}$, $a/\sqrt{8}$, etc., which are the distances between the 110, 200, 211, and 220 planes.

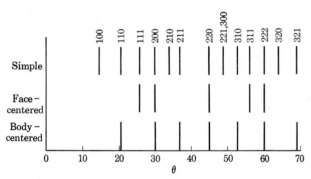

FIG. 3-7. Angles of incidence θ for which reflections will occur for the three types of cubic lattices if $\lambda/a = 0.500$.

The reflections for the three types of cubic crystals are summarized in *Fig. 3-7*, in which the presence of a reflection is indicated by a line at the corresponding angle of incidence. Since the angle of reflection for a real crystal depends upon the length of the unit cell a and the wavelength λ of the X rays used, the ratio λ/a is arbitrarily taken as $\frac{1}{2}$ for the purposes of this illustration. Thus the various types of cubic crystals may be readily distinguished by their diffraction patterns.

X-Ray Powder Photographs. In early studies of X-ray diffraction Bragg studied the reflections from suitably oriented samples of crystalline substances using a movable ionization chamber to detect the X rays. In this method the crystal was rotated by a clockwork mechanism so that the planes of the crystal were sure to be set at the proper angle during part of the time in order to record the reflections. Instead of reflecting X rays from a single large crystal it may be convenient in some types of work to pass the X rays through a large number of small crystals oriented in random directions as proposed originally by Hull and later by Debye and Scherrer. The reflections may be recorded on a

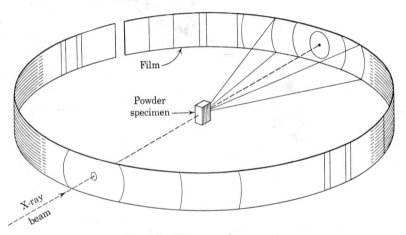

FIG. 3-8. X-ray powder camera.

circular photographic film as illustrated in *Fig. 3-8*. If coarse crystals are used, the powder pattern is seen to be made up of rings of spots each produced by a suitably oriented small crystal. If the crystals are very fine a large number of cones of reflected beams are produced by the different crystal planes. Several photographs of powdered crystals taken in this way are shown in *Fig. 3-9* in which the circular film is stretched out.

For cubic crystals, X-ray powder patterns are all that is required to identify the lattice type. The powder patterns of three substances forming cubic crystals are shown in Fig. 3-9. The reflections for sodium chloride are found to correspond to those expected for a face-centered cubic lattice. The Miller indices have been assigned on this basis. The 100 reflection is missing, and so none of the spacings calculated from the Bragg equation are equal to the length of the side of the unit cell a. But a may be calculated from the angle of any reflection by use of equation 3 and the relation $d = a/\sqrt{h^2 + k^2 + l^2}$. The value of a for sodium chloride is 5.64 A.

The structural units of the face-centered lattice which have thus been found could be sodium chloride molecules, or there might be two separate lattices of atoms penetrating each other, the one consisting of sodium atoms or ions and the other consisting of chlorine atoms or ions. If the lattice were made up of sodium chloride molecules, all units of the lattice would be the same, and the intensities of the X-ray reflections

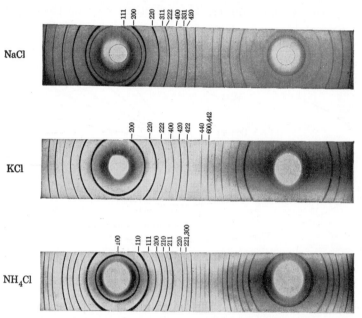

FIG. 3-9. X-ray powder patterns for cubic crystals. The X-ray beam enters through the hole at the right and leaves through the hole at the left (see Fig. 3-8). Courtesy Professor S. Bailey of the University of Wisconsin.

would always decrease progressively from first- to second- to third-order reflections. This is true for the 200, 400, and 600 reflections, but not for the 111, 222, 333 ··· reflections. It may be noted in Fig. 3-9 that the 111 reflection is very weak while 222 is strong and 333 is apparently missing. This fact leads to the requirement of two interpenetrating lattices as shown in *Fig. 3-10*, and evidence will be cited presently to show that these interpenetrating lattices are composed of ions rather than atoms.

The radius of the sodium ion is 0.98 A, and that of the chloride ion is 1.81 A. The square connecting chloride ions is drawn in Fig. 3-10, showing the face-centered lattice of the chloride ions.

Similar squares could be drawn on any part of the faces. A similar square is drawn with dashed lines for the sodium ions, and it is evident that such squares can be drawn anywhere on any of the faces showing the face-centered lattice of the sodium-ion lattice. It is to be noted that these lattices overlap by half the length of the face, so as to give an interpenetrating lattice in which the corners of the sodium cube always come halfway between the corners of the chloride cube and the corners of the chloride cube come halfway between the corners of the sodium cube.

A further examination of Fig. 3-10 shows that the 111 planes which cut diagonally through the cubes in both horizontal and vertical planes include only sodium ions or only chloride ions in a single plane. It may be remembered that the maximum in X-ray reflections occurs when the angle is such that the paths between successive layers of ions are equal to one wavelength of the reflected radiation. If the rays are reflected from these planes at such an angle that the rays from

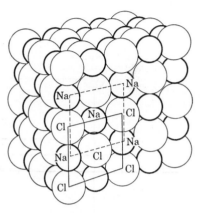

Fig. 3-10. Crystal lattice of sodium chloride; small spheres, sodium ions; large spheres, chloride ions.

successive planes of chloride ions differ in path length by a whole number of wavelengths, the rays coming from successive sodium-ion planes, which are spaced equally between them, will then differ by half a wavelength and cause interference. The interference would be complete except for the fact that the chloride ions have more electrons and scatter X rays more efficiently. In the case of the reflections from the 222 planes, however, there is a difference of a whole wavelength between the rays from the chloride and sodium planes, so that there is no interference, and the 222 reflection is intense. The 333 reflection again corresponds to a difference of one-half wavelength between the two sets of reflecting planes, and this interference, combined with the fact that the third-order spectrum is naturally weaker, leads to its practical disappearance.

The powder pattern for potassium chloride given in Fig. 3-9 is superficially that of a simple cubic lattice. This appears surprising since the structure would be expected to be like that for sodium chloride. Actually the structure is the same as that of sodium chloride, but the reflections look very much like those from a simple cubic structure because the scattering power of the potassium ion is almost exactly equal to that of the chloride ion, since both ions contain the same number of electrons. A more accurate determination of the intensities of reflection would verify the fact that potassium chloride forms a face-centered lattice.

The powder pattern for ammonium chloride given in Fig. 3-9 shows that it has a simple cubic lattice, which can be resolved into two sym-

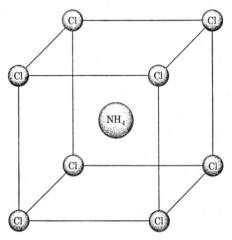

FIG. 3-11.   Ammonium chloride unit cell (interpenetrating simple cubic).

metrically interpenetrating lattices, one of chloride ions and one of ammonium ions. If the center of a chloride ion is taken as the corner of the unit cell, then the ammonium ion lies at the center of the cell as illustrated in *Fig. 3-11*.

Exercise II.   Rather than work with powder patterns it may sometimes be convenient to orient a cubic crystal in such a way as to obtain reflections from the three types of planes illustrated in Fig. 3-6. Show that when this is done the ratios of the distances between the three different sets of planes are:

Simple cubic $d_{100}:d_{110}:d_{111} = 1:0.707:0.578$

Face-centered cubic $d_{200}:d_{220}:d_{111} = 1:0.707:1.155$

Body-centered cubic $d_{200}:d_{110}:d_{222} = 1:1.414:0.578$

For other crystal classes the interpretation is very much more difficult and additional types of X-ray diffraction experiments may be required in order to determine the structure.

Determination of the Wavelength of X Rays.   The diffraction of X rays by crystals can be used as already described to establish the type of lattice for a given crystal. It can be used also to determine quantitatively the distance between planes when the wavelength of the X rays is known; and conversely it can be used to determine the wavelength of the X rays from the interplanar spacing when this can be determined independently.

The distance between planes can be calculated from physical dimensions of cubic crystals and a knowledge of the number of ions which are associated with each unit of the crystal lattice. In the case of the face-centered cubic lattice of chloride ions (Fig. 3-10), the ion at a corner of a unit cell is actually shared by eight adjacent unit cells so that only one-eighth of its mass is associated with one unit cell. There are eight such corner ions per unit cell, each contributing an eighth of its mass to the unit cell, so that the corner ions contribute one chloride ion for each unit cube of the chloride-ion lattice. Each unit cube of the chloride lattice also has one ion on each of its six faces which is shared by an adjacent cube, so that half of the six ions, or three, can be attributed to a given cube. Thus the unit cell of the sodium chloride lattice contains four chloride ions and an equal number of sodium ions.

Since the density of sodium chloride is 2.163 g cm^{-3} the length a of the side of the unit cell which contains four sodium ions and four chlorine atoms may be calculated as follows:

$$2.163 \text{ g cm}^{-3} = \frac{(4 \text{ molecules})(58.45 \text{ g mole}^{-1})}{(6.02 \times 10^{23} \text{ molecules mole}^{-1})a^3}$$

$$a = 5.64 \times 10^{-8} \text{ cm, length of side of the unit cell}$$

Since the distance between 200 planes is one-half the length of the side of this unit cell, $d_{200} = 2.82 \times 10^{-8}$ cm. Bragg's law may now be used to calculate the wavelength of the X rays from a palladium target from the observed angle of reflection (5.9°) from the 200 planes in sodium chloride.

$$\lambda = 2d \sin \theta$$

$$\lambda = 2(2.82 \times 10^{-8} \text{ cm}) \sin 5.9°$$

$$\lambda = 0.581 \times 10^{-8} \text{ cm}$$

X-ray wavelengths are expressed in angstroms, 1 A being equal to 10^{-8} cm, and so the wavelength is 0.581 A. This value is confirmed by measurements of X-ray reflection from finely ruled gratings.

Note this Example too!

Example 1. Potassium crystallizes with a body-centered cubic lattice and has a density of 0.856 g cm^{-3}. Calculate the length of the side of the unit cell a and the distance between 200, 110, and 222 planes.

$$0.856 \text{ g cm}^{-3} = \frac{(2 \text{ molecules})(39.1 \text{ g mole}^{-1})}{(6.023 \times 10^{23} \text{ molecules mole}^{-1})a^3}$$

$$a = 5.34 \times 10^{-8} \text{ cm or } 5.34 \text{ A}$$

$$d = \frac{5.34}{\sqrt{h^2 + k^2 + l^2}}$$

For 200 planes, $d = 5.34/\sqrt{4} = 2.67$ A.
For 110 planes, $d = 5.34/\sqrt{2} = 3.77$ A.
For 222 planes, $d = 5.34/\sqrt{12} = 1.54$ A.

Determination of the Structure of More Complicated Crystals.
Read over For more complicated crystals a different procedure is required for the determination of the structure. The procedure may be divided into the following four steps:

Not too vital

1. The dimensions of the unit cell are determined from the angles of X-ray diffraction.

2. The number of molecules or formula units per unit cell is calculated from the unit cell volume and the molar volume.

3. The space group (page 39) is determined by a study of the intensities of reflections in the X-ray diffraction pattern together with information on the symmetry of the lattice.

4. The positions of the atoms within the unit cell are determined from the intensities of the reflections. This last step requires mathematical methods too complicated to be discussed here. Since it is the electrons that are responsible for the scattering of X rays the crystal structure will be completely solved if the electron density can be found throughout the unit cell. In principle the electron density (number of electrons per unit volume) may be calculated from the diffraction data. Since this calculation is so difficult it is customary to calculate the projection of the actual three-dimensional pattern on an appropriate plane. The computation of electron-density maps is extremely lengthy and has been facilitated by the use of automatic computing equipment.

Such an electron-density map for crystalline maleic acid is shown in *Fig. 3-12.* In the construction of such a map it is necessary to know the phases of the scattered beams. If there is a heavy atom in the unit cell, the structure may be determined directly. Otherwise it is necessary to use a method of successive approximations which starts with an initial assumed trial structure in order to obtain the correct electron-density map. Once the map has been calculated from the intensities

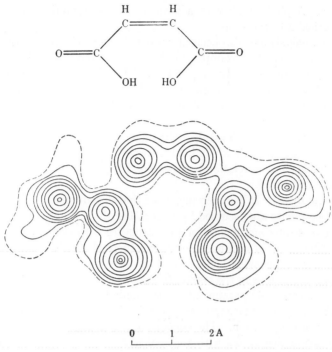

FIG. 3-12.   Electron-density map for crystalline maleic acid. Shahat, *Acta Cryst.*, *5*,
763 (1952).

of X-ray reflections the bond distances and angles may be obtained. A
number of bond distances are summarized on page 84.

Other Applications of X-Ray Diffraction. The X-ray pattern
for an unknown substance may be used to identify it, or the presence of
impurities may be detected, and even measured quantitatively, in a
known substance. This application is greatly facilitated by such tables
as those of the American Society for Testing Materials which give the
d-spacings calculated from the three strongest lines for a very large
number of substances.

Many metallurgical operations can now be studied more scientifically
by means of X rays. Different crystal forms produced by different heat
treatments are readily recognized. Iron carbide in molten iron, for example, when cooled slowly, shows lines that are not present when it is
cooled rapidly. A given alloy or material can be standardized by means
of X rays, the desired product always giving the same pattern.

Even material not ordinarily classed as crystalline may be tested with
X rays, for example, fibers, rubber, shellac, cellulose compounds, and

asbestos. A photograph with a beam of monochromatic X rays gives symmetrical arcs for fibers.

X-ray analysis has also been of great help as a research tool in inorganic chemistry. For example, in the study of the synthetic elements neptunium, plutonium, curium, and americium it was possible to establish quickly the purity of compounds and the chemical composition with exceedingly small amounts of material and without destroying the samples.

Binding Forces in Crystals. Crystals may also be classified according to the type of bonds which hold the crystal together. It will be seen that there is good correlation between bond type and the physical properties of the crystal.

1. *Ionic Bonds.* It has been suggested that in sodium chloride crystals the lattice points are occupied by ions rather than atoms. There are a number of strong arguments for this structure with electrostatic bonding.* Since molten sodium chloride conducts electricity, it is natural to assume that the ions which produce this electric conductivity actually exist as charged ions in the crystal lattice.

Another convincing argument for the ionic lattice of certain crystals depends on the lattice energies as determined from the heat of formation and heat of evaporation. The energy required to separate the units in the crystal lattice agrees with that calculated on the assumption that the units are ions held together by electrostatic forces. It has also been found that in sodium chloride and crystalline salts, in general, the distance between ions in the lattice corresponds to the ionic radius rather than to the atomic radius.

In ionic crystals there is no fixed directed force of attraction. The crystal planes will strongly resist any tendency to slip past each other, but, if sufficient external force is applied to move the planes slightly so as to displace the positive-negative ion positions, the force may be greatly weakened. Accordingly, although the ionic crystals are strong, they are likely to be brittle. They have very little elasticity and cannot easily be bent or worked. The melting points of ionic crystals are generally high (NaCl, 800°C; KCl, 790°C). In ionic crystals some of the atoms may be held together by covalent bonds to form ions having definite positions and orientations in the crystal lattice. For example, in the case of calcium carbonate a carbonate ion does not "belong" to a given calcium ion, but three particular oxygen atoms do belong to a given carbon atom.

Note - almost never is a bonding completely ionic or covalent.

Usually, the bonding is predominantly one or other.

* Friedman and Shuler, in *J. Chem. Education*, **24**, 11 (1947), have summarized the experimental evidence for the ionic structure of such crystals, making use of seven different types of measurements.

2. *Covalent Bonds.* This is the type of bond which is familiar in organic chemistry and involves paired electrons as is discussed in the following section. Crystals held together by covalent bonds in three dimensions are strong and hard and have high melting points. A di-

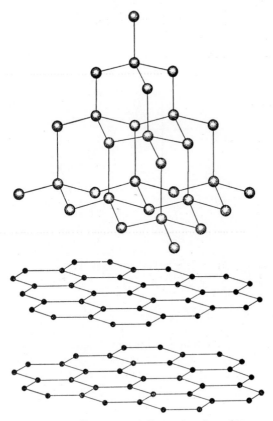

Fig. 3-13. Structures of diamond and graphite.

amond is an example of this type. Each carbon atom is bonded to four others in a tetrahedral arrangement as shown in *Fig. 3-13.* This arrangement is similar to that in organic compounds, and, indeed, the C—C bond distance is the same as in aliphatic compounds (1.54 A). Silicon, ZnS, and AgI also form crystals of the diamond type with covalent bonds.

The great difference between graphite and diamond can be understood in terms of the crystal lattice. Graphite has hexagonal networks in sheets like benzene rings of organic chemistry, as shown at the bottom of

Fig. 3-13. The distances between atoms in the plane is 1.34 A, but the distances between these atomic layer planes is 3.41 A. In two directions, then, the carbon atoms are tightly held as in the diamond, but in the third direction the force of attraction is much less. This gives a structure such that one layer can slip over another. The crystals are flaky, and yet the material is not wholly disintegrated under mechanical rubbing. It is excellent, then, as a lubricant.

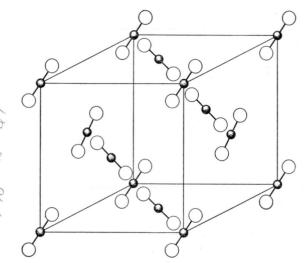

FIG. 3-14.   Structure of carbon dioxide lattice.

In contrast to ionic bonds, covalent bonds have fixed directions. However, covalent crystals are like ionic crystals in that there are no larger groups of atoms that differ from the fundamental units of which the lattice is made, so that the whole crystal may be regarded as the molecule.

3. *Van der Waals' Bonds.* Crystals consisting of neutral molecules are held together by weaker forces of the same type as are involved in gases and necessitate the introduction of van der Waals' *a*. Since such bonds are weak, molecular crystals are soft and possess comparatively low melting points. Examples are carbon dioxide, carbon tetrachloride, argon, and most organic compounds. As an illustration the structure of solid carbon dioxide is given in *Fig. 3-14.*

4. *Hydrogen Bonds.* It has been recognized that in many crystals a hydrogen atom is attracted by rather stong forces to two atoms, instead of only one, so that it may be considered to be acting as a bond between them. Hydrogen bonds are involved in many organic and inorganic

crystals and in the structure of ice and water. They are comparatively
weak bonds. The interaction is essentially electrostatic.

5. *Metallic Bonds.* In crystals of metals in which all the atoms are
of the same kind the arrangement of atoms frequently corresponds to
closest packing of spheres. There are two ways in which spheres of
equal size may be stacked with a minimum of empty space. These are
referred to as cubic close packing and hexagonal close packing. The
most convincing way to see the two possibilities is to stack up layers of
marbles. In these packings each atom is surrounded by twelve other
atoms. Copper, silver, and lead crystallize in the cubic close packing
(which is face-centered cubic), and zinc and magnesium in hexagonal
close packing. The alkali metals and tungsten crystallize in a body-
centered cubic lattice.

A characteristic of metals is that the electrons are held loosely in the
crystal so that they are good conductors of electricity. In contrast to
the other types these crystals can be bent and worked and are
strong.

The bond types in some crystals are intermediate between the above
types, and no sharp demarcation lines may be drawn.

Bonding in Molecules. As pointed out above, a number of different types of bonding are involved in holding together the atoms, ions,
or molecules of crystals, and this brings us to a consideration of the nature of the bonds between atoms in molecules. The theoretical basis
for the valence of various atoms has been developed by quantum mechanics, but some of the simpler ideas may be discussed without the
details of quantum mechanics which will be described later (Chapter 18).
The bonds between atoms or groups of atoms may be broadly classified
as *electrostatic bonds* or *covalent bonds*, although some bonds may be considered to be partly electrostatic and partly covalent in character. An
example of electrostatic bonding has already been encountered in the
crystals of sodium chloride. Electrostatic bonds may also be formed
between an ion and a molecule having a permanent electric dipole. A
molecule is said to have a permanent electric dipole if the positive and
negative charges within the molecule are partially separated so that the
molecule will tend to orient in an electric field. The magnitude of this
separation of charge is measured quantitatively by the dipole moment
(page 78). Complex ions such as $[Ni(NH_3)_4]^{++}$ contain electrostatic
bonds of this *ion-dipole* type. An ion may also induce a dipole moment
in a neutral molecule to form an *ion-induced dipole* bond. Such a bond
is formed in the reaction

$$I^- + I_2 = I_3^-$$

There may also be considerable electrostatic interaction between two dipoles because they may be oriented as $(-+)(-+)$ or $(\mp)(\pm)$. This *dipole-dipole* interaction leads to association of liquids such as water, the alcohols, and other polar substances.

Covalent bonds involve the sharing of electrons between atoms as was proposed by G. N. Lewis in 1916. According to this hypothesis there is a definite tendency for electrons in bonds to be involved in pairs. A pair of electrons held jointly by two atoms may be considered to be effective in completing a stable electronic configuration for each atom. It was recognized by Lewis, by Kossel, and by Langmuir that there is a tendency for an atom to lose or gain electrons in its outer shell in order to have an "octet." Since the rare gases Ne, A, Kr, Xe, and Rn have eight electrons in their outer shells, this is apparently a very stable configuration. The stable configuration of hydrogen and helium is to have two electrons in the outer orbit.

In the following structures each atom supplies one electron to the covalent bond. The electrons in the outer shell are represented by dots.

$$H\cdot + \cdot H = H:H$$

$$:\overset{..}{\underset{..}{Cl}}\cdot + \cdot\overset{..}{\underset{..}{Cl}}: = :\overset{..}{\underset{..}{Cl}}:\overset{..}{\underset{..}{Cl}}:$$

$$
\begin{array}{cccc}
\text{H} & & & \text{R}\\
\overset{..}{\text{H}:\text{C}:\text{H}} & \left[\begin{array}{c} :\overset{..}{O}: \\ :\overset{..}{O}:\overset{..}{Cl}:\overset{..}{O}: \\ :\overset{..}{O}: \end{array}\right]^{-} & & \overset{..+..\,-}{R:N:O:}\\
\text{H} & & & \text{R}
\end{array}
$$

Methane   Perchlorate ion   Trimethylamine oxide

In the case of perchlorate ion one more electron than those supplied by the chlorine and oxygen atoms is required, and so the group as a whole has a charge of -1. In the trimethylamine oxide structure, R has been used to represent the methyl group. The positive and negative signs in this structure indicate that it is found on counting electrons around each atom (dividing shared pairs equally between the bonded atoms) that the oxygen atom has an electric charge of -1 and the nitrogen atom of $+1$. A charge of -1 indicates an extra electron, and a charge of $+1$ indicates that the atom has lost an electron. These charges are formal charges in the sense that the actual distribution of charge in the molecule may be somewhat different. In other words, this simple way of looking at bonds is not sufficient to show in general the actual distribution of electrons within the molecule, and the detailed application of quantum mechanics is required. It will be noted that this latter type of bond results because both electrons of the electron pair between N and O are contributed by N. Such a bond may be referred to as a coordinate covalent bond.

$$x \cdot + \cdot y = x : y \quad \text{(normal covalent bond)}$$

$$x : + y = x : y \quad \text{(coordinate covalent bond)}$$

Double bonds and triple bonds can be represented by the sharing of two pairs or three pairs of electrons, as shown by ethylene and acetylene.

$$
\begin{array}{c}
\text{H} \cdot \qquad \cdot \text{H} \\
: \text{C} :: \text{C} : \\
\text{H} \cdot \qquad \cdot \text{H}
\end{array}
\qquad\qquad \text{H} : \text{C} ::: \text{C} : \text{H}
$$

Some molecules can be represented only by introducing one electron or three electron bonds. Such molecules are abnormal and tend to associate. Nitrogen dioxide and triphenylmethyl are examples.

The tendency to complete an orbit of eight electrons may also lead to an electrostatic bond. For example, in sodium chloride, sodium loses its single valence electron to chlorine, which has seven electrons in its outer shell.

$$\text{Na} \cdot + \cdot \overset{\cdot\cdot}{\underset{\cdot\cdot}{\text{Cl}}} : \ = \ [\text{Na}]^+ + [: \overset{\cdot\cdot}{\underset{\cdot\cdot}{\text{Cl}}} :]^-$$

In hydrogen chloride the electron does not shift completely from one atom to the other, and so HCl is best described by a combination of the ionic structure $[\text{H}]^+ [: \overset{\cdot\cdot}{\underset{\cdot\cdot}{\text{Cl}}} :]^-$ and the covalent structure $\text{H} : \overset{\cdot\cdot}{\underset{\cdot\cdot}{\text{Cl}}} :$.

REFERENCES

Wyckoff, *The Structure of Crystals*, Second Edition, Chemical Catalog Co., New York, 1931.

Stillwell, *Crystal Chemistry*, McGraw-Hill Book Co., New York, 1938; *J. Chem. Education*, 10, 590, 667 (1933); 11, 159 (1934); 13, 415, 469, 521, 566 (1936).

Evans, *An Introduction to Crystal Chemistry*, Cambridge University Press, Cambridge, 1939.

Buerger, *X-Ray Crystallography*, John Wiley & Sons, New York, 1942.

Bunn, *Chemical Crystallography*, Oxford University Press, New York, 1946.

Robertson, *Organic Crystals and Molecules*, Cornell University Press, Ithaca, New York, 1953.

Pauling, *The Nature of the Chemical Bond*, Cornell University Press, Ithaca, New York, 1939.

Seitz, *The Modern Theory of Solids*, McGraw-Hill Book Co., New York, 1940.

PROBLEMS

1. A certain crystal face intercepts the x axis at $\frac{1}{2}a$, the y axis at b, and the z axis at $\frac{1}{2}c$, where a, b, and c are the lengths of the sides of the unit cell. What are the Miller indices of this face?   *Ans.* 212.

2. The X-ray diffraction pattern of a certain crystal is obtained using X rays from a copper target, and it is found that a certain reflection occurs at $10°\,27'$. When a molybdenum target was used the same reflection occurred at $4°\,48'$. Given the wavelength of the X rays from the copper target ($\lambda = 1.540$ A), calculate the wavelength of the X rays from the molybdenum target.   *Ans.* 0.710 A.

3. The density of KCl at 18°C is 1.9893 g cm^{-3}, and the length of a side of the unit cell is 6.29082 A as determined by X-ray diffraction. Calculate Avogadro's number using the values of the atomic weights.   *Ans.* 6.02×10^{23}.

4. The crystal unit cell of MgO is a cube 4.20 A on an edge. Each cell contains the equivalent of 4 atoms of magnesium and 4 of oxygen. What is the density of crystalline magnesium oxide?   *Ans.* 3.62 g cm^{-3}.

5. Tungsten forms body-centered cubic crystals. From the fact that the density of tungsten is 19.3 g cm^{-3} calculate (*a*) the length of the side of this unit cell and (*b*) d_{200}, d_{110}, and d_{222}.
          Ans. (*a*) 3.16 A. (*b*) $d_{200} = 1.58$, $d_{110} = 2.23$, $d_{222} = 0.912$ A.

6. A substance crystallizes in a form like that of sodium chloride. Its density is 1.984 g cm^{-3} and its molecular weight is 74.56. What is the length of the edge of a single cell?   *Ans.* 6.30 A.

7. When an X-ray powder pattern of crystalline copper is taken using X rays from a copper target (the wavelength of the K_α line is 1.5405 A), reflections are found at $\theta = 21.65°$, $25.21°$, $37.06°$, $44.96°$, $47.58°$, and other larger angles. (*a*) What type of cubic crystal is formed by copper? (*b*) What is the length of a side of the unit cell at this temperature? (*c*) What is the density of copper?
          Ans. (*a*) Face-centered. (*b*) 3.616 A. (*c*) 8.93 g cm^{-3}.

8. Write the following structures in terms of the electron theory of valence: (*a*) sulfate ion $SO_4^=$; (*b*) nitrogen N_2; (*c*) ammonium chloride NH_4Cl.

$$\text{\textit{Ans.}} \quad (a)\ \begin{bmatrix} :\ddot{O}: \\ :\ddot{O}:S:\ddot{O}: \\ :\ddot{O}: \end{bmatrix}^= , \quad (b)\ :N:::N: , \quad (c)\ \begin{bmatrix} H \\ H:\ddot{N}:H \\ H \end{bmatrix}^+ :\ddot{Cl}:^-.$$

9. What are the Miller indices for a plane in a crystal which intercepts the x axis at a, the y axis at $\frac{1}{3}b$, and the z axis at $\frac{1}{2}c$?

10. Using X rays with a wavelength of 1.54 A from a copper target it is found that the first reflection from a face of a crystal of potassium chloride at 25° is at $\theta = 14°\,12'$. Calculate (*a*) the length of the side of the unit cell for this interpenetrating face-centered lattice and (*b*) the density of the crystal.

11. Potassium bromide has a lattice equivalent to a face-centered cubic lattice, and the edge of the unit cube is 6.54 A. The unit contains the equivalent of 4 ions of each kind. What is the density of the crystal?

12. Tantalum crystallizes with a body-centered cubic lattice. Its density is 17.00 g cm^{-3}. (*a*) How many atoms of tantalum are there in a unit cell? (*b*) What is the length of a unit cell? (*c*) What is the distance between 200 planes? (*d*) What is the distance between 110 planes? (*e*) What is the distance between 222 planes?

13. Calculate the angles at which reflections would be obtained in Problem 7 if an iron target was used in the X-ray tube rather than copper. Given: λ for the K_α line of iron is 1.937 A.

See fig 3·7 Page 44

14. The X-ray powder pattern for molybdenum has reflections at $\theta = 20.25°$, $29.30°$, $36.82°$, $43.81°$, $50.69°$, $58.00°$, $66.30°$, and other larger angles when Cu K_α X rays are used ($\lambda = 1.5405$ A). (a) What type of cubic crystal is formed by molybdenum? (b) What is the length of a side of the unit cell at this temperature? (c) What is the density of molybdenum?

15. The diamond has a face-centered cubic crystal lattice, and there are 8 atoms in a unit cell. Its density is 3.51 g cm^{-3}. Calculate the first six angles at which reflections would be obtained using an X-ray beam of wavelength 0.712 A.

16. Write the following reactions in terms of the electron theory of valence:

(a) $Zn + S = ZnS$.

(b) $C_2H_4 + Cl_2 = C_2H_4Cl_2$.

(c) $CH_3CO_2H = H^+ + CH_3CO_2^-$.

---

17. (a) Metallic iron at 20° is studied by the Bragg method, in which the crystal is oriented so that a reflection is obtained from the planes parallel to the sides of the cubic crystal, then from planes cutting diagonally through opposite edges, and finally from planes cutting diagonally through opposite corners. Reflections are obtained at $\theta = 11° 36'$, $8° 3'$, and $20° 26'$, respectively. What type of cubic lattice does iron have at 20°? (b) Metallic iron also forms cubic crystals at 1100°, but the reflections determined as described in (a) occur at $\theta = 9° 8'$, $12° 57'$, and $7° 55'$, respectively. What type of cubic lattice does iron have at 1100°? (c) The density of iron at 20° is 7.86 g cm^{-3}. What is the length of a side of the unit cell at 20°? (d) What is the wavelength of the X rays used? (e) What is the density of iron at 1100°?

18. Insulin forms crystals of the orthorhombic type with cell dimensions of 130 $\times$ 74.8 $\times$ 30.9 A. If the density of the crystal is 1.315 g cm^{-3} and there are 6 insulin molecules per unit cell, what is the molecular weight of the protein insulin?

19. Represent the following compounds on the basis of the electron theory of valence: (a) LiH; (b) CH$_4$; (c) HCl; (d) CO; (e) CH$_3$OH.

4

Molecular Structure and
Physical Properties

A physical property, such as molecular weight, which depends on the number and kind of atoms in the molecule is called an *additive* property. A physical property, such as the rotation of polarized light, which depends on the particular arrangement of atoms within the molecule is called a *constitutive* property. A great many physical-chemical properties are additive in part and constitutive in part. The prediction of physical properties from the known constitution is valuable from both a practical and a theoretical viewpoint. Likewise, these physical properties are useful in identifying chemical substances and deciding questions of their molecular structure.

Refractive Index. * When a beam of light passes from one substance into another, as from air into water, the beam is refracted so that it travels in a different direction. The extent to which the beam is refracted depends on the relative concentration of atoms and on their arrangement within molecules. The refractive index, which is a quantitative measure of this refraction of light, is used to determine the concentration of solutions, to identify chemical compounds and to determine their purity, and to determine the molecular structure.

The refractive index n is defined as the ratio of the velocity of light in a vacuum to that in a medium, and it may be calculated from the relation

$$n = (\sin i)/(\sin p) \qquad (1)$$

where i is the angle which the incident light makes with a perpendicular from the surface, and p is the angle of refraction which the light makes after entering. Refractive index measurements are among the oldest and the most accurate measurements of physical chemistry. Refractive

---

* The experimental apparatus used for the several optical measurements and the methods of calculation discussed in this chapter are described in Daniels, Mathews, Williams, and Staff, *Experimental Physical Chemistry*, McGraw-Hill Book Co., New York, 1949, Chapters 2 and 18.

indices can be determined easily to 1 or 2 parts in 10,000 under laboratory conditions if the temperature is kept constant. Usually the angle of refraction is measured with the help of a glass prism on which is placed the liquid or solid. The refractive index depends on the wavelength of the light and on the temperature, which are usually specified with subscripts and superscripts, respectively. Thus, $n_D^{25°}$ indicates a refractive index taken with the monochromatic yellow D light of the sodium arc at a temperature of 25°. Sometimes the wavelength of the light is specified in the subscript. Usually the *refractive index* given in the tables refers to the index of refraction measured with respect to air or more properly to vacuum. The ordinary refractive index measured in air can be converted into absolute refractive index by multiplying by the refractive index of air, which is about 1.00029 under standard conditions.

The refractive index of a fluid varies with temperature and pressure as the number of molecules in the path of the light is changed, but the *specific refraction r* is independent of these variables. On the basis of the electromagnetic theory of light, Lorenz and Lorentz have shown that

$$r = \frac{1}{d} \frac{n^2 - 1}{n^2 + 2} \tag{2}$$

where n is the refractive index and d the density. The *molar refraction Mr* is equal to the specific refraction multiplied by the molecular weight.

Example 1. The refractive index n_D of carbon tetrachloride at 20° is 1.4573, the density at 20° is 1.595 g cm^{-3}, and the molecular weight is 153.84. Calculate the molar refraction.

$$Mr_D = \frac{M(n^2 - 1)}{d(n^2 + 2)} = \frac{(153.84 \text{ g mole}^{-1})(1.4573^2 - 1)}{(1.595 \text{ g cm}^{-3})(1.4573^2 + 2)}$$

$$= 26.51 \text{ cm}^3 \text{ mole}^{-1}$$

The refractive index at 20°, the specific refraction, and molar refraction are given for several common liquids in Table I.

Table I. Molar Refractions

Compound	Formula	n_D^{20}	r_D^{20}	Mr_D^{20}
Carbon tetrachloride	CCl_4	1.4573	0.1724	26.51
Acetone	$(CH_3)_2CO$	1.3571	0.2782	16.15
Benzene	C_6H_6	1.4979	0.3354	26.18
Ethanol	C_2H_5OH	1.3590	0.2775	12.78
Toluene	$C_6H_5CH_3$	1.4929	0.3356	30.92
Chloroform	$CHCl_3$	1.4426	0.1780	21.25
Acetic acid	CH_3COOH	1.3698	0.2154	12.93
Ethyl acetate	$CH_3COOC_2H_5$	1.3701	0.2527	22.25
Water	H_2O	1.3328	0.2083	3.75

The refraction of light is an additive property, but it is also partly a constitutive property depending on the structural arrangement of the atoms within the molecule. The molar refractions of a large number of organic and inorganic compounds have been determined, and it has been found that many atoms and groups of atoms always contribute the same definite amount to the molar refraction of any compound in which they are found. Thus, in a homologous series of aliphatic compounds a difference of CH_2 in composition always produces a difference of 4.618 in the molar refraction. The molar refraction of hexane, C_6H_{14}, is 29.908, and, by subtracting from this value six times the effect of the CH_2 group, it is possible to obtain the atomic refraction of the hydrogen atom, namely, 1.100. Thus,

$$\frac{29.908 - (6)(4.618)}{2} = 1.100$$

From these data the atomic refraction of carbon is readily calculated, thus:

$$4.618 - (2)(1.100) = 2.418$$

Likewise, the atomic refraction of bromine is obtained by subtracting the atomic refractions of two carbons and five hydrogens from the molar refraction of ethyl bromide.

The atomic refractions are affected by the structural features. For example, the molar refraction of BrH_2C—CH_2Br is 26.966, and that of $BrHC$=$CHBr$ is 26.499.* If the atomic refractions of the hydrogen and bromine atoms are subtracted, the value for C—C is 4.836, and for C=C it is 6.569. Since the two carbons together have a value of 4.836, it follows that a double bond between carbon atoms contributes an additional 1.733 to the molar refraction.

Table II has been built up in the manner just indicated, averaging the results for a large number of compounds.

Table II.   Atomic Refractions

Group	Mr_D	Group	Mr_D
CH_2	4.618	Cl	5.967
H	1.100	Br	8.865
C	2.418	I	13.900
Double bond (C=C)	1.733	N (*pri*-amines)	2.322
Triple bond (C≡C)	2.398	N (*sec*-amines)	2.499
O (carbonyl) (C=O)	2.211	N (*tert*-amines)	2.840
O (hydroxyl) (O—H)	1.525	—C≡N	5.459
O (ethers) (R—O—R)	1.643		

* The experimental values available in the literature give 27.0 and 26.3.

This table is useful in determining the structure of molecules as it enables one to select the atom or group of atoms with the proper structural features so that the sum of the atomic refractions will add up to give a total which is equal to the experimentally determined molar refraction.

Example 2. A substance having the analysis C_3H_6O might be either acetone

$$\begin{matrix} CH_3 \\ \diagdown \\ \qquad CO \\ \diagup \\ CH_3 \end{matrix} \quad \text{or allyl alcohol} \quad \begin{matrix} H & H \\ | & | \\ C{=}C{-}C{-}OH \\ | & | & | \\ H & H & H \end{matrix}$$ Determine which of these two substances

it is from the fact that the molar refraction Mr_D is 16.974

Acetone			Allyl Alcohol		
3 carbons	=	7.254	3 carbons	=	7.254
6 hydrogens	=	6.600	6 hydrogens	=	6.600
1 carbonyl oxygen	=	2.211	1 double bond (C=C)	=	1.733
		———	1 hydroxyl oxygen	=	1.525
		16.065			———
					17.112

Since the experimentally determined molar refraction agrees more closely with that calculated for allyl alcohol, the substance is allyl alcohol rather than acetone.

Rotation of Polarized Light. Ordinary light can be *plane-polarized* by passing it through a Nicol prism or a "Polaroid" film with the result that the electromagnetic vibration of the transmitted light is confined to a single plane. A Nicol prism consists of a crystal of double-refracting Iceland spar cut and cemented in such a way that one of the rays is refracted to one side and the remaining one which passes through is plane-polarized. Polaroid films are made by incorporating into a transparent plastic a large number of small crystals of a compound, such as an iodide of quinine, which possesses the property of double refraction, and orienting them all in one direction.

When certain optically active substances are placed in a beam of polarized light, the plane of polarization is rotated either to the right or to the left, and the extent of this optical rotation is measured quantitatively in a *polarimeter*, by noting the angle through which a second Nicol prism must be rotated in order to transmit completely or cut off completely the beam of polarized light.

The extent of the optical rotation depends on several factors, including the nature of the substance; the length of the column through which the light passes; the concentration, if the material is dissolved in a solution; the wavelength of the light; and the temperature.

This statement may be expressed mathematically as

$$\alpha = [\alpha]_\lambda^t l(g/v) \tag{3}$$

where l is the length of the tube in decimeters * through which the light passes, g is the number of grams of optically active material in volume v cubic centimeters, and $[\alpha]_\lambda^t$ is a proportionality constant which depends upon the wavelength of light, the temperature t, and the solvent. This proportionality constant $[\alpha]_\lambda^t$ is called the *specific rotation* and is a characteristic property of a substance.

The *molar rotation* $M[\alpha]_\lambda^t$ is obtained by multiplying the specific rotation by the molecular weight.

The specific rotations are useful for the rapid and accurate analysis of optically active materials, as indicated in the following example.

Example 3.   The value of $[\alpha]_D^{20}$ for lactose is 55.4. What is the concentration, in grams per liter, of a solution of lactose which gives a rotation of 7.24° in a 10-cm cell at 20° with sodium D light?

$$g = \frac{\alpha v}{l[\alpha]_D^{20}} = \frac{(7.24 \text{ deg})(1000 \text{ cm}^3)}{(1 \text{ dec})(55.4 \text{ deg cm}^3 \text{ dec}^{-1} \text{ g}^{-1})}$$

$$= 131 \text{ grams}$$

When certain sugars are dissolved in water the optical rotatory power of the solution changes with time. This phenomenon, which is known as mutarotation, results from the reversible interconversion of various molecular forms of the sugar. Table III gives the optical rotations of

Table III.   Optical Rotations $[\alpha]_D^{20}$ for Mutarotating Sugars

	α Isomer	β Isomer	Equilibrium Mixture
D-Glucose	+112.2	+18.7	+52.7
D-Mannose	+29.3	−17.0	+14.2
D-Lactose	+89.5	+34.9	+55.4
D-Lyxose	+5.6	−72.6	−13.8

the α and β isomers of several sugars and the equilibrium value. The composition of the equilibrium mixture may be calculated from these rotations.

Example 4.   When α-D-glucose ($[\alpha]_D^{20} = +112.2°$) is dissolved in water the optical rotation decreases as β-D-glucose is formed until at equilibrium $[\alpha]_D^{20} = +52.7°$. As expected, when β-D-glucose ($[\alpha]_D^{20} = +18.7°$) is dissolved in water the optical

---

* It would be better to express the length in centimeters, as is done with most other physical-chemical properties, but the tables and the literature record specific rotation using decimeters.

rotation increases until $[\alpha]_D^{20} = +52.7°$ is obtained. Calculate the percentage of the β form in the equilibrium mixture.

If x is the fraction of D-glucose in the β form, the fraction in the α form is $(1 - x)$.

$$x(+18.7) + (1 - x)(+112.2) = 52.7$$

$$x = 0.636 \quad \text{or} \quad 63.6\% \ \beta$$

$$1 - x = 0.364 \quad \text{or} \quad 36.4\% \ \alpha$$

Optical activity is found in only a few chemical compounds, the most important of which contain a carbon atom bonded to four different atoms or groups of atoms so as to give an asymmetric molecule. One

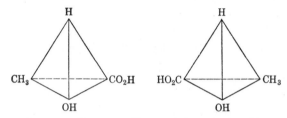

Fig. 4-1. Structure of *levo-* and *dextro-*lactic acid.

of the simplest examples is lactic acid, shown in *Fig. 4-1*. The *dextro* or *d* form rotates the plane of polarized light to the right in a clockwise direction as viewed in a polarimeter, and the *levo* or *l* form rotates it counterclockwise. If the *dextro* and *levo* forms occur together in equal amounts in the same solution, the two rotations offset each other, and no optical activity is observed. Such a mixture is called a *racemic* mixture. As a matter of fact, almost all substances capable of exhibiting optical activity are found in the racemic form when produced in the laboratory. In synthesizing lactic acid, for example, there is equal probability of obtaining either the *dextro* or the *levo* form, and the same numbers of molecules of each are formed.

Although the *dextro* and *levo* forms have nearly the same physical and chemical properties, except for the rotation of polarized light, they can be separated. Microorganisms sometimes will destroy one form more rapidly than the other. For example, a certain mold growing in a racemic mixture of tartaric acid will thrive at the expense of the *dextro* acid and leave the pure *levo* acid. In a second method of separating *dextro* and *levo* optical isomers the racemic mixture is allowed to react chemically with an optically active material, such as an alkaloid. If the *d* form is added to a racemic mixture two compounds *dd* and *dl* will be formed. Since these two compounds are no longer optical isomers they will have different properties, including solubility, so that they can be separated.

Sometimes the two optical isomers crystallize out in crystal forms which are alike except that one crystal form is the mirror image of the other. They can then be separated by hand picking, as was done first by Louis Pasteur in his brilliant researches on the optical activity of tartaric acid.

The specific rotation of some solutes is the same in different solvents, but usually it varies in a manner that is specific for each solvent and solute. Apparently some loose combination with the solvent at certain parts of the molecule changes the rotation. Ionization of the optically active molecule usually leads to a marked change in the specific rotation.

Optical activity is not restricted to asymmetric molecules containing carbon; it has been observed in molecules containing four different groups surrounding an atom of nitrogen, sulfur, cobalt, or tin. In fact it is sometimes found in unsymmetrical molecules which do not contain a single, central atom.

Crystals exhibit two different types of optical activity. In some crystals, as, for example, in sugar, the molecules themselves are optically active. In others, as, for example, in quartz, the crystal rotates the plane of polarized light by virtue of a spiral arrangement of the units in the crystal lattice.

Absorption of Light. The mechanism by which light is absorbed by molecules is discussed more fully in Chapters 18 and 19, but it may be stated here that absorption of light in the visible and ultraviolet regions of the spectrum involves the displacement of electrons within the molecules. Absorption in the infrared region where the wavelengths are longer involves the displacement of atoms within molecules. According to the quantum theory, a beam of light is composed of many units of radiation called photons. The energy of one photon is called a quantum of energy, and it depends on the wavelength of the light, the quantum being large in the ultraviolet, of lesser energy in the blue, and still less in the red and infrared. However, all the photons in monochromatic light of a given wavelength have the same energy.

Only certain displacements of electrons or atoms within the molecule are permissible according to the quantum theory, and, when the photons in a beam of light passing through a given material happen to have about the same energy as the energy required to bring about a permissible change within the molecule, there is a definite probability that the photon will be absorbed and its energy consumed in effecting the displacement inside the molecule.

When white light or polychromatic light containing many different wavelengths is passed into a substance, some of the light may be absorbed, the rest being either transmitted or reflected. A substance appears colored because part of the light is absorbed. For example, a solution of copper ions appears blue because, when white light is passed through it, the red and yellow light are absorbed, and only the blue is transmitted to the eye. The colored light, transmitted or reflected, can be measured by passing it through a spectrometer, which spreads it out into a spectrum by means of a prism or grating.

The color or wavelength λ of light is described in different units as follows:

1 A (angstrom) $= 10^{-8}$ cm

1 mμ (millimicron) $= 10^{-7}$ cm $= 10$ A

Wave number $\tilde{\nu} = \dfrac{1}{\text{Wavelength in cm}}$

Frequency $\nu = \dfrac{\text{Velocity of light}}{\text{Wavelength in cm}} = \dfrac{3.0 \times 10^{10} \text{ cm sec}^{-1}}{\lambda_{\text{cm}}}$

For much work in physical chemistry the use of angstroms is preferred.

Example 5. What are the wavelength in centimeters and in millimicrons, the wave number, and the frequency of blue light which has a wavelength of 4500 A?

$\lambda = (4500 \text{ A})(10^{-8} \text{ cm A}^{-1}) = 4.5 \times 10^{-5}$ cm

$\lambda = (4500 \text{ A})(10^{-1} \text{ m}\mu \text{ A}^{-1}) = 450$ mμ

$\tilde{\nu} = \dfrac{1}{4.5 \times 10^{-5} \text{ cm}} = 22{,}200 \text{ cm}^{-1}$

$\nu = \dfrac{3.0 \times 10^{10} \text{ cm sec}^{-1}}{4.5 \times 10^{-5} \text{ cm}} = 6.66 \times 10^{14} \text{ sec}^{-1}$

The range of electromagnetic radiations usually referred to as light may be divided into three regions: the ultraviolet, the visible, and the infrared. The visible region extends from about 4000 to 8000 A, and light within these limits may be detected by the eye, by photographic plates, and by photoelectric cells (page 544). Lenses, prisms, and absorption cells of ordinary glass may be used for focusing and refracting the light in the spectrometer. Ultraviolet light in the range below 4000 A can be measured with photoelectric cells and with photographic plates. Glass is opaque in the shorter ultraviolet and is replaced with quartz; or with fluorite, CaF_2, in the ultraviolet below 2000 A. The infrared range of the spectrum extends from 8000 A (0.8 μ) to about 350,000 A (35 μ). Because of the limitations of sources and prism materials the region which has been most thoroughly investigated is that below 15 μ. In this region the radiation is measured with thermopiles which register electrically the heat generated when a thin, blackened metal receiver is placed in the path of the light. The optical parts of an infrared spectrometer are usually made from large crystals of sodium chloride or potassium bromide because these materials are transparent to infrared radiation.

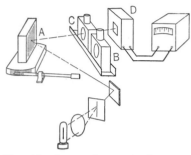

The percentage of light absorbed can be determined by measuring the density of a photographic plate at different parts of the spectrum, but most measurements of light absorption are now made with photocells. The deflection of a sensitive galvanometer or the output of an amplifier is directly proportional to the intensity of light transmitted.

FIG. 4-2. Spectrophotometer for measuring the absorption of light at different wavelengths.

The light is divided into narrow spectral regions by means of optical filters, prisms, or gratings, and the percentage of light transmitted is determined.

The principle of such an instrument is illustrated in the spectrophotometer shown in *Fig. 4-2*. A beam of light is passed through a narrow slit onto an optical grating A, from which it is reflected through a cell C containing the solution, and thence to the photocell D which is connected to the galvanometer. The fraction of the light transmitted, called the *transmittancy*, is calculated by dividing the deflection I of the galvanometer by the deflection I_0 obtained when cell B, containing the solvent, is slid along into the path of the light, thus displacing the cell C. By turning the screw the grating is turned so as to pass any desired wavelength through the cell. In this way the transmittancy I/I_0 can be determined for the different wavelengths, and the spectrum can be mapped. When the desired absorption band is located, the instrument can be set for this wavelength and the transmission determined for different concentrations of absorbing material. The positions of the absorption bands and lines serve for identification and for criteria of purity; the percentage transmissions serve for quantitative analyses of the amount of material present.

Emission spectra of volatilized metals and compounds are readily obtained by means of an arc, a spark, or a flame; they are valuable in qualitative and quantitative analysis. In quantitative estimation of the amounts of material, it is necessary to compare the blackening of the plate with the blackening produced by known amounts of the standard substance volatilized and activated under identical conditions of current and voltage.

Lambert-Beer Law.[*] It was stated that the extent of absorption depends upon the probability that the energy of the quantum will be absorbed by a molecule where it can effect a chemical reaction or where it is dissipated eventually as heat. The probability of absorption is directly proportional to the concentration of absorbing molecules. This probability is expressed mathematically by the equation

$$dI/I = -kcdb \tag{4}$$

where I is the intensity of light, that is, the number of photons per cm^2 per second, and dI is the change in light intensity produced by absorption in a thin layer of thickness db and concentration c.

According to this equation the fraction of light absorbed is proportional to the thickness of the absorbing solution, provided that the thickness and fraction absorbed are small. The proportionality constant k varies with the wavelength of light used and the temperature. A large value of k indicates that the material is very absorbing.

At a given wavelength the intensity of a beam of light after passing through b centimeters of solution is related to the incident intensity I_0 by equation 6, which is obtained by integrating [†] equation 4 between the limits I_0 when $b = 0$ and I at length b.

$$\int_{I_0}^{I} \frac{dI}{I} = -kc \int_{0}^{b} db \tag{5}$$

$$\ln[‡] \frac{I}{I_0} = 2.303 \log \frac{I}{I_0} = -kcb \tag{6}$$

Since it is convenient to use logarithms to the base 10, equation 6 may be written in the form

$$\log \frac{I_0}{I} = A_s = a_s bc \tag{7}$$

[*] A wide variety of conflicting terms have been used in the field of spectrophotometry. An attempt has been made by the Bureau of Standards to introduce a consistent set of terms (*Letter Circular* LC-857, May 19, 1947), and their definitions will be used here since they appear to be the best compromise of the various terms and symbols used in the past.

[†] Details of this simple integration are given in Daniels, *Mathematical Preparation for Physical Chemistry*, McGraw-Hill Book Co., New York, 1928, page 132.

[‡] ln signifies $\log_e$; log signifies $\log_{10}$; 2.303 log $x = \log_e x$.

where the quantity log (I_0/I) is referred to as the *absorbancy* * A_s of the sample. A graphical representation of equation 7 using data on the absorption of blue light by bromine dissolved in carbon tetrachloride is given in *Fig. 4-3.*

The *absorbancy index* a_s† is a characteristic of the solute and depends upon the wavelength of light, the solvent, and the temperature. When the concentration c is expressed in moles per liter and b in centimeters, the term *molar absorbancy index*, a_M, is used.

The scale of a spectrophotometer may be graduated in absorbancy as well as in terms of percentage transmittancy $(100I/I_0)$. It is con-

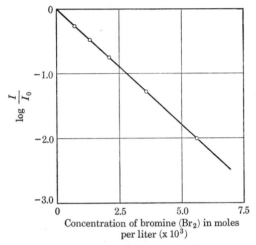

FIG. 4-3.   Graph of log (I/I_0) versus concentration of bromine in carbon tetrachloride at 4360 A for a one centimeter cell.

venient to use the absorbancy scale since the value read on this scale will be directly proportional to concentration if the Lambert-Beer law is obeyed. In order to determine the absorbancy of a solute a cell containing solvent and a nearly identical one containing the solution are placed in the spectrophotometer. With the cell containing solvent in the light beam, the slit width or the amplification of the photocell current is adjusted so that a reading of 100 is obtained. The cell containing the solution is then placed in the light beam and the percentage transmittancy read on a galvanometer or potentiometer.

---

* This quantity has also been called the optical density D.

† This quantity has also been called the extinction coefficient E.

Example 6. The percentage transmittancy of an aqueous solution of sodium fumarate at 250 mμ and 25° is 19.2% for a 5×10^{-4} M solution in a 1-cm cell. Calculate the absorbancy and the molar absorbancy index.

$$A_s = \log (I_0/I) = \log (100/19.2) = 0.716$$

$$a_M = \frac{A_s}{bc} = \frac{0.716}{(1 \text{ cm})(5 \times 10^{-4} \text{ mole l}^{-1})} = 1.43 \times 10^3 \text{ l mole}^{-1} \text{ cm}^{-1}$$

What will be the percentage transmittancy of a 1.75×10^{-4} M solution?

$$\log (I_0/I) = (1.43 \times 10^3 \text{ l mole}^{-1} \text{ cm}^{-1})(1 \text{ cm})(1.75 \times 10^{-4} \text{ mole l}^{-1})$$

$$= 0.250$$

$$I_0/I = 1.778 \quad \text{and} \quad 100I/I_0 = 56.2\%$$

Example 7. When a 1.9-cm absorption cell was used the transmittancy of blue light (4360 A) by bromine in carbon tetrachloride solution was found to be as follows:

Concentration of Br_2					
(c), moles per liter	0.00546	0.00350	0.00210	0.00125	0.00066
Transmittancy, I/I_0	0.010	0.050	0.160	0.343	0.570

Calculate the molar absorbancy index a_M.

In Fig. 4-3, $\log (I/I_0)$ is plotted against concentration, and the constant a_M is calculated from the slope of the line and the thickness of the cell to be 193 l mole^{-1} cm^{-1}.

What percentage of the incident light would be transmitted by 2 cm of solution containing 0.00155 mole of bromine per liter of carbon tetrachloride?

$$\log (I/I_0) = -a_M bc = -(193 \text{ l mole}^{-1} \text{ cm}^{-1})(2 \text{ cm})(1.55 \times 10^{-3} \text{ mole l}^{-1})$$

$$= -0.599$$

$$I/I_0 = 0.252$$

or

$$100I/I_0 = 25.2\%$$

The amount of light absorbed, $(I_0 - I)$, is equal to the difference between the incident light and the transmitted light. In example 7 the absorption is $100 - 25.2 = 74.8\%$. Thus

$$I_0 - I = I_0(1 - 10^{-a_s bc}) \tag{8}$$

In this calculation the reflected light is ignored, but it may be estimated. It amounts to about 4 per cent when a perpendicular beam of light goes from air to glass or glass to air.

For mixtures of independently absorbing substances the absorbancy is given by the equation

$$\log (I_0/I) = A_s = (a_{s1}c_1 + a_{s2}c_2 + \cdots)b \tag{9}$$

where c_1, c_2 $\cdots$ are the concentrations of the substances having absorbancy indices of a_{s1}, a_{s2} $\cdots$. A mixture of n components may be analyzed by measuring A_s at n wavelengths at which the absorbancy indices are known for each substance, provided that these indices are

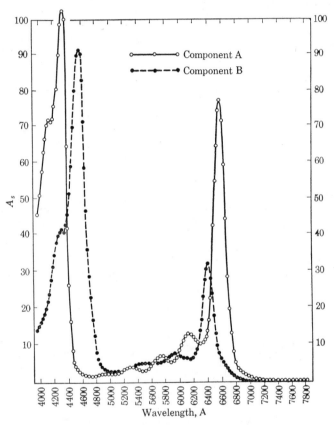

Fig. 4-4. Absorption spectrum of chlorophyll.

sufficiently different. The concentrations of the several substances may then be calculated by solving the n simultaneous equations.

Absorption and Chemical Structure. The absorption of light may be used not only for determining the concentration of a substance but also for identifying it. Since many substances which are not colored in the visible absorb in the infrared and ultraviolet regions of the spectrum, this method is of general applicability. The spectroscope is very widely used for analysis by emission spectra, but it is used also for absorption spectra. Many ions, dyes, and other colored organic and inorganic substances have characteristic absorption spectra. A ketone group (C=O), for example, absorbs between 3000 and 4000 A, depending on the adjacent groups, and again in the infrared at 5.8 μ.

It is often possible to predict the absorption spectra of organic compounds from a knowledge of the structure and the influence of substituted groups. Likewise, the absorption spectra are helpful in deciding questions of chemical constitution. Several spectra, plotted in different ways, are shown in Figs. 4-4 and 4-5.

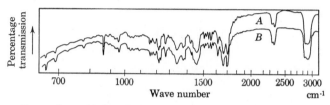

FIG. 4-5. Comparison of infrared absorption spectra for identification. *A*. Oxidation product of 11α-hydroxyprogesterone. *B*. Pure 11-keto progesterone. From Peterson, *Research, 6,* 309 (1953).

Figure 4-4 shows an absorption spectrum of chlorophyll from green leaves showing the two components, chlorophyll A and chlorophyll B, with slightly different absorption maxima.

Figure 4-5 is taken from an investigation by Peterson on the preparation of cortisone and hydrocortisone in which the infrared absorption spectra are used for identification of products.

Infrared Spectroscopy. The measurement of infrared absorption spectra of organic compounds has become of considerable practical importance. Many compounds which do not absorb light in the visible region and do not have very characteristic absorption in the ultraviolet region have very detailed and quite different spectra in the infrared region. An example of some practical importance is shown in *Fig. 4-6*, which gives the spectra for butadiene and four impurities. It can be seen that the impurities absorb strongly at 6.0 microns where butadiene is relatively transparent, so that quantitative analysis is possible.

The infrared absorption spectrum of a compound is an identifying characteristic just like its melting point or boiling point. For such practical applications the infrared spectra for a large number of compounds have been cataloged and are used like "fingerprints." Functional groups within the molecule also have quite characteristic absorption bands. A few such values are shown in Table IV. The wavelengths

Length absorption cell 11 cm

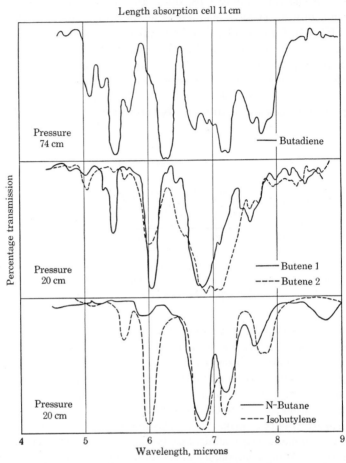

FIG. 4-6.   Infrared transmittancy curves of butadiene and common impurities. From Brady, *Ind. Eng. Chem., Anal. Ed.,* **16**, 422 (1944).

Table IV.   Infrared Absorption Bands for Various Functional Groups

Group	λ, microns	Group	λ, microns
$-NH_2$	2.82–2.99		
$C\equiv C-H$	3.02–3.10	$-\overset{\mid}{\underset{\mid}{C}}-CH_3$	7.20–7.33
$C=O$	5.71–5.98		
$-NH_2$	6.08–6.35		
$C=C$ (aromatic)	6.17–6.30		
	6.60–6.75	$-\overset{\mid}{\underset{\mid}{C}}-O-$	9.05–9.17
CH_2 and CH_3	6.78–7.03		9.32–9.42

at which various groups absorb may vary somewhat, depending upon the structure of the rest of the molecule. The principal functional groups within the molecule may be frequently identified, and such information can be used to identify positively compounds where chemical evidence permits relatively few possible structures. As will be mentioned later the infrared spectra of simpler compounds can be used in the investigation of molecular structure and the force constants of bonds.

Microwave Spectroscopy.[*] The development of generators of microwave frequencies such as the klystron tube for use in radar equipment has made possible the investigation of molecules in the region between the far infrared and ordinary radio frequencies. The microwave region extends from about 1 mm to 30 cm in wavelength. In this region the spectra correspond to changes in rotational energies of molecules. The frequencies at which absorption occurs depend upon the moment of inertia I of the molecule which may be defined for a linear molecule by

$$I = \sum_{i=1}^{n} m_i r_i^2 \qquad (10)$$

where r_i is the distance from the center of mass of the molecule to the atom of mass m_i and n is the number of atoms. Thus, the frequencies of these absorption lines can be interpreted in terms of the masses of the atoms and the interatomic distances. A few molecular dimensions obtained from these measurements are given in Table V. These dimensions are quite accurate because of the high precision of the frequency measurements in the microwave region. Nonlinear molecules, such as NH_3, which have one and only one axis of three-or-more-fold symmetry are referred to as symmetric top molecules. The moments of inertia about the two axes perpendicular to the axis of highest symmetry are equal in this case. All three principal moments of inertia are different for asymmetric top molecules.

The absorption of electromagnetic energy by rotation arises from interaction of the molecular dipole moment (see section on dipole moments) with the electromagnetic field. Thus a molecule must have a permanent dipole moment in order to show absorption in the microwave region. For substances of this type which can be vaporized microwave spectroscopy offers a means for identification and analysis in much the same way that the line emission spectra make possible the identification of elements.

[*] Gordy, Smith, and Trambarulo, *Microwave Spectroscopy*, John Wiley & Sons, New York, 1953.

Table V.[1] Interatomic Distances (A) and Bond Angles from Microwave Spectra

Substance	Bond Distance		Bond Angles	
	Diatomic Molecules			
CO		1.2823		
BrCl		2.138		
NaCl		2.3606		
	Linear Polyatomic Molecules			
HCN	CH	1.064		
	CN	1.156		
NNO	NN	1.126		
	NO	1.191		
HC≡CCN	CH	1.057		
	C—C	1.382		
	C≡C	1.203		
	CN	1.157		
	Symmetric Top Molecules			
CH_3Cl	CH	1.10	HCH	110°
	CCl	1.782		
$CH_3C≡CH$	CH_3	1.097	HCH	108°
	C≡C	1.207		
	C—C	1.460		
	≡CH	1.056		
NH_3	NH	1.016	HNH	107°
	Asymmetric Top Molecules			
SO_3	SO	1.433	OSO	119.33°
CH_2O	CH	1.12	HCH	118°
	CO	1.21		
CH_2Cl_2	CH	1.068	HCH	112°
	CCl	1.7724	ClCCl	111°

[1] Gordy, Smith, and Trambarulo, *Microwave Spectroscopy*, John Wiley & Sons, New York, 1953.

Electron Diffraction. * The arrangements of building units within crystals have been clearly revealed by means of the diffraction of X rays, as already described. A beam of electrons possessing many of the properties of a beam of light of very short wavelength may be produced by

* Brockway, in Weissberger, *Physical Methods of Organic Chemistry*, Interscience Publishers, New York, 1949, Vol. I, Part II; Clark and Wolthuis, *J. Chem. Education*, 15, 64–74 (1938); Pirenne, *The Diffraction of X Rays and Electrons by Free Molecules*, Cambridge University Press, Cambridge, 1946.

accelerating electrons emitted from a heated filament by a powerful electrostatic field, as explained on page 537. These electrons, when moving at high uniform velocities, are deflected by atoms, and the extent of the deflections permits a calculation of the arrangement of atoms and the distance between the atomic nuclei. Space models are constructed which account for the observed deflections in a manner similar to that by which space models are constructed for interpreting photographs obtained from the diffraction of X rays.*

X rays are very penetrating; electron beams at lower voltages are but slightly penetrating. X rays, then, are suitable for studying the

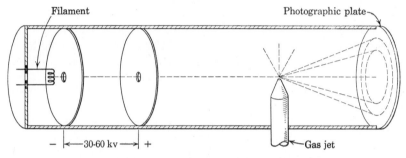

Filament   Photographic plate

— ⟵30-60 kv⟶ +   Gas jet

FIG. 4-7.   Electron-diffraction apparatus for determining molecular structure.

structures of crystals and solids and liquids, but electron diffraction is more suitable for studying gases and adsorbed gases and surface layers. The arrangement of atoms and ions in the crystal determines the crystal lattice, whereas the arrangement and distance of atoms in the individual molecules of a material in the gas phase give the molecular structure. This determination of the distance and angles between atoms in a molecule is now finding important applications in the calculation of chemical equilibria and reaction rates.

In carrying out measurements on molecular structure the beam of electrons is accelerated in a vacuum by a constant voltage of 40,000 volts, which gives the electrons a wavelength of 0.06 A. They are shot out of a small pinhole at a photographic plate about 10 cm away in an apparatus shown in principle in *Fig. 4-7*.

A magnetic lens is used to focus the electron beam on the photographic plate so that a sharper pattern will be obtained. A stream of vapor of the substance to be studied is passed at a low pressure (10^{-5} mm) through the beam. Short exposures, of about a second each, and subsequent development of the plate give rings of varying intensity, depend-

* Pauling and Brockway, *J. Am. Chem. Soc.*, *57*, 2684 (1935).

ing on the positions of atoms within the molecule. The diameters of the rings of different intensities are measured and used to decide which of many possible spatial arrangements of the atoms is the correct one.

An example of the use of these diffraction patterns in studies of molecular structure may be cited. Chemical evidence shows that in 1,2-dichloroethylene the two carbon atoms are joined by a double bond with one hydrogen and one chlorine atom attached to each carbon. If it is assumed that all the atoms lie in a plane, there are two possibilities: in the *cis* form the two chlorine atoms lie on the same side of the carbon double bond; and in the *trans* form they lie on opposite sides. The distances between the two chlorine atoms will be different in the two forms. Electron diffraction patterns show that in the *cis* isomer of dichloroethylene the distance is 3.22 A, and in the *trans* isomer it is 4.27 A. Models of these two molecules are shown in Fig. 4-11 on page 85, and the radii of some of the common elements encountered in organic chemistry as determined by electron diffraction are given in Table VII on page 84. The uncertainty in the bond lengths determined by electron diffraction is about 0.02 A.

Dipole Moments. Nonpolar or electrically symmetrical molecules tend to give nearly perfect gases or ideal solutions, with properties which are proportional to the number of molecules present. The simple laws of physical chemistry involving surface tensions, heats of vaporization and solution, additive volumes, and other phenomena apply much better to the nonpolar substances than to the polar. On the other hand, polar or electrically dissymmetrical molecules tend to give gases and solutions which are not ideal.

Molecules are composed of positively and negatively charged particles in such numbers that they are neutral as a whole. In polar molecules there is a finite distance of separation between what may be termed the centers of gravity of the positive and negative electrical charge, and the polarity of a molecule becomes less as these centers of gravity in a molecule approach each other. When placed in an electric field a polar molecule will tend to orient itself in such a way that the positive part of the molecule points toward the negative electrode and the negative part toward the positive electrode. The force that tends to orient a polar molecule in an electrical field is proportional to the magnitude of the charges and the distance between them.

The *dipole moment* μ is the product of the electric charge and the distance between the two average centers of positive and negative electricity. It serves as a useful quantitative measure of the extent to which a molecule is polar.

In expressing dipole moments, distances are generally given in centimeters and charges in electrostatic units (esu). A dipole consisting of an electron separated from a unit positive charge by a distance of 1 A would have a dipole moment of $(4.80 \times 10^{-10}$ esu$)(10^{-8}$ cm$)$ $= 4.80 \times 10^{-18}$ esu cm or 4.8 debye units. A debye unit is 10^{-18} esu cm.

Example 8. If HCl is considered to be a proton and a chloride ion separated by 1.28 A (calculated from infrared spectra) a dipole moment of $(4.80 \times 10^{-10}$ esu$)$ $(1.28 \times 10^{-8}$ cm$) = 6.14 \times 10^{-18}$ esu cm would be expected. The fact that the experimental value (1.03×10^{-18}) is considerably lower indicates that the charges are not completely separated in HCl.

Experimental measurements of the dipole moment have become of great importance in studying the structure of molecules. The interpretation of solubility and the properties of solutions, of the deviations from the laws for ideal gases and ideal solutions, and of the influence of solvents on reaction rates and equilibrium constants is greatly assisted by knowledge of dipole moments.

The measurement of the dipole moment is complicated by the fact that all molecules, whether polar or nonpolar, possess the property of becoming polarized when placed in an electric field. Even those non-polar molecules whose electric charges are uniformly distributed, as in H_2 or CCl_4, acquire a positive charge at the part nearest the negative electrode and a negative charge at the part nearest the positive electrode. This induced molar polarization is called distortion polarization P_D; the other, a permanent polarization, is called orientation polarization P_μ. The latter quantity can be determined from measurements of dielectric constants in two different ways—by determining the dielectric constant in the gaseous state at several temperatures, or by determining the extent to which the substance in the dissolved state in a solution of a non-polar solvent contributes to the dielectric constant of the solution. By extrapolating the measurements of dielectric constant to infinite dilution, a value is obtained which corresponds to a situation in which the molecules of solute are so far apart that they do not induce dipole moments in each other. The first method is more accurate and simple in theoretical treatment but less convenient in experimental procedure. The quantitative relations follow.

The *dielectric constant* ϵ is a measure of the relative effect of the medium between the two plates on the magnitude of the electrical charge stored by a condenser. The dielectric constant of a vacuum is taken as unity, but for practical purposes the dielectric constant of air is nearly unity. The dielectric constant of a liquid or gas is determined by measuring the electric capacitance * of two metal plates set into a glass vessel and insulated from each other. The capacitance is determined with

* Daniels, Mathews, Williams, and Staff, *Experimental Physical Chemistry*, McGraw-Hill Book Co., New York, 1949.

only dry air between the plates and again with the liquid or gas to be measured between the plates. The capacity of the condenser depends on the size of the plates, the distance between the plates, and the medium between them. The dielectric constant ϵ may be calculated from

$$\epsilon = C_x/C_{\text{air}} \tag{11}$$

where C_x and C_{air} refer to the electric capacitances of the capacitor when filled with the medium being measured and with air, the plate size and distance remaining constant.

The molar polarization P of a substance can be calculated from its experimentally measured dielectric constant ϵ using a formula developed by Clausius and Mosotti on the basis of electromagnetic theory. This formula may be taken as a definition of P, thus,

$$P = \frac{\epsilon - 1}{\epsilon + 2} \times \frac{M}{d} \tag{12}$$

where M is the molecular weight and d is the density. It may be noted that, inasmuch as ϵ is merely a ratio without physical dimensions, the molar polarization has the dimensions of molar volume, M/d.

The total molar polarization is due to two effects as already explained, thus:

$$P = P_D + P_\mu \tag{13}$$

Debye showed how these two quantities can be separated. The induced polarization P_D, produced by the electric field, is unaffected by an increase in temperature, but the permanent or orientation polarization P_μ depends on temperature, because the thermal agitation tends to produce a completely random orientation of the molecules, and at the higher temperatures fewer of the permanent dipoles are oriented in the direction of the field.

It has been shown by Debye * that the dipole moment μ is related to the permanent or orientation polarization P_μ by the formula

$$P_\mu = (\tfrac{4}{3}\pi N \mu^2)/3kT \tag{14}$$

where N is the Avogadro constant 6.02×10^{23}, and k is the Boltzmann constant or gas constant per molecule. The molecular gas constant is related to the molar gas constant by the equation

$$k = \frac{R}{N} = \frac{8.314 \times 10^7 \text{ erg deg}^{-1} \text{ mole}^{-1}}{6.02 \times 10^{23} \text{ molecules mole}^{-1}}$$

$$= 1.38 \times 10^{-16} \text{ erg deg}^{-1} \text{ molecule}^{-1}$$

* Debye, *Polar Molecules*, Chemical Catalog Co., New York, 1929; or Dover Publications, Inc., New York.

The factor $\frac{4}{3}\pi N$ is used in electrodynamics to convert these molecular quantities into molar quantities.

The induced polarization produced by the electric field is proportional to the polarizability or the electric moment per molecule α, induced by an electric field of unit strength. Then,

$$P_D = \frac{4}{3}\pi N\alpha \tag{15}$$

Substituting the values of P_D and P_μ just given into equation 13 gives

$$P = P_D + P_\mu = \frac{4}{3}\pi N\alpha + \frac{4}{3}\pi N\mu^2/3kT \tag{16}$$

In the gaseous state the molecules are so far apart that they do not induce electric effects in adjacent molecules, and α as well as μ may be

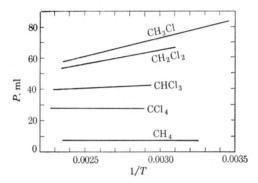

FIG. 4-8. Variation of molar polarization with absolute temperature.

considered constant. When this is the case a plot of P versus $1/T$ is a straight line.

$$P = a + b/T \tag{17}$$

where a and b are constants.

The dielectric constants ϵ and the densities are obtained at several temperatures, and the corresponding total molar polarizations P are calculated with the help of equation 12. These values of P are then plotted against $1/T$, and the slope b of the resulting line described by equation 17 enables one to calculate the dipole moment μ, since $b = 4\pi N\mu^2/9k$. Thus:

$$\mu = \sqrt{9kb/4\pi N} = 0.01282 \times 10^{-18}\sqrt{b} \tag{18}$$

These calculations are illustrated in *Fig. 4-8* for the chlorine-substituted compounds of methane as measured by Sanger.* It is seen that CH_4

* Sanger, *Physik. Z.*, *27*, 562 (1926).

and CCl_4 give horizontal lines when P is plotted against $1/T$. The slope is zero, and the dipole moment is zero. This is to be expected, because the molecules are symmetrical. The sloping lines for $CHCl_3$, CH_2Cl_2, and CH_3Cl show that these molecules have dipole moments owing to the unsymmetrical arrangement of the electronegative chlorine atoms. The steeper the slope, the greater is the dipole moment.

According to the second method for the determination of μ, already mentioned, the dipole moment μ can be determined by extrapolating the molar polarization P of the solute to infinite dilution, all the measurements being made at constant temperature. At optical frequencies for which $\epsilon = n^2$ there is no orientation polarization, and therefore the total polarization is equal to P_D and can be calculated from

$$P_D = \left(\frac{n^2 - 1}{n^2 + 2}\right)\frac{M}{d}$$

Then, the permanent molar polarization P_μ of the solute can be obtained from the measured molar polarization P_∞ at infinite dilution and the known refractive index of the solute, thus:

$$P_\mu = P_\infty - \left(\frac{n^2 - 1}{n^2 + 2}\right)\frac{M}{d} \tag{19}$$

Once P_μ has been determined, the value of μ can be determined from equation 14 as follows:

$$\mu = 0.01282 \times 10^{-18}\sqrt{P_\mu T}$$

Dipole moments of several typical substances are given in Table VI.

Table VI.   Dipole Moments

In esu cm

$AgClO_4$	4.7×10^{-18}	CCl_4	0	SO_2	1.61×10^{-18}
$C_6H_5NO_2$	4.23	C_6H_5Cl	1.73×10^{-18}	HCl	1.03
$(CH_3)_2CO$	2.8	C_6H_5OH	1.70	HBr	0.79
H_2O	1.84	C_2H_5OH	1.70	HI	0.30
CH_4	0	$C_6H_5NH_2$	1.56	N_2O	0.14
CH_3Cl	1.85	NH_3	1.46	CO	0.12
CH_3Br	1.45	H_2S	1.10	CS_2	0
CH_3I	1.35	H_2	0	C_2H_4	0
CH_2Cl_2	1.59	Cl_2	0	C_2H_6	0
$CHCl_3$	1.15	CO_2	0	C_6H_6	0

Carbon dioxide and water might have structures corresponding to a symmetrical linear molecule, to an unsymmetrical linear molecule, or to a triangle as shown in *Fig. 4-9.* The dipole moments recorded in Table VI show that carbon dioxide has zero moment, and the molecule must be symmetrical and linear. If it were unsymmetrical or triangular there would be a permanent dipole moment. On the other hand, water has a pronounced dipole moment and it cannot have the symmetrical linear structure. Measurements of band spectra show that it has the triangular form rather than the unsymmetrical linear form.

To a certain extent dipole moments of groups of atoms may be added as vectors in molecules, but there are deviations which are important

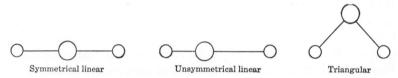

Symmetrical linear   Unsymmetrical linear   Triangular

FIG. 4-9. Possible structures of carbon dioxide. The symmetrical linear model is the only one consistent with the observed dipole moment of carbon dioxide.

aids in determining the molecular structure.* Vectors have the property of direction as well as magnitude, which is represented by their length. Vectors are added in a special way.

The *cis* and *trans* isomers of dichloroethylene have been discussed already in connection with electron diffraction. Measurements of dipole moments are also significant. The *cis* isomer with the two chlorines

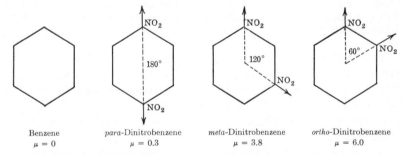

Benzene   *para*-Dinitrobenzene   *meta*-Dinitrobenzene   *ortho*-Dinitrobenzene
$\mu = 0$ $\mu = 0.3$ $\mu = 3.8$ $\mu = 6.0$

FIG. 4-10. Dipole moments of the dinitrobenzenes in debye units.

on one side of the carbon-carbon double bond has a dipole moment of 1.56×10^{-18}, whereas the more symmetrical *trans* isomer has a dipole moment of only 0.3×10^{-18}.

The dinitrobenzenes, shown in *Fig. 4-10*, are interesting. The arrows indicate the vectors and show that the dipole moment increases progressively as the molecule becomes more unsymmetrical.

* Additional examples of the use of dipole moments are given by Smyth, *Dielectric Behavior and Structure*, McGraw-Hill Book Co., New York, 1955; Sidgwick, *The Covalent Link in Chemistry*, Cornell University Press, Ithaca, N. Y., 1933, pages 138–198.

Molecular Models. The distances between atoms and bond angles may be determined from measurements of electron diffraction, X-ray diffraction, and molecular spectra.

It has been found that the distance between two kinds of atoms connected by a covalent bond of a given type (single, double, etc.) is nearly the same in different molecules. The distance between two atoms is taken to be equal to the sum of the bond radii of the two atoms. Since the C—C bond distance is 1.54 A in many compounds the radius for a carbon single bond is taken to be 0.77 A. Since the C≡C distance in acetylene is 1.20 A, the radius for a carbon triple bond is taken to be 0.60 A. By consideration of the bond distances in many compounds Pauling has been able to build up tables of bond radii which are useful in describing the structure of molecules.

Table VII. Bond Radii

angstroms		angstroms	
Hydrogen	0.30	Nitrogen (nitrate) (single)	0.70
Carbon (single bond)	0.77	Chlorine	0.99
Carbon (double bond)	0.67	Bromine	1.14
Carbon (triple bond)	0.60	Iodine	1.33
Oxygen (single bond)	0.66	Nitrogen (cyanide)	0.55
Oxygen (double bond)	0.57	Carbon (benzene) (C—C)	0.69
Nitrogen (amino)	0.70	Carbon (benzene) (C—H)	0.77
Nitrogen (nitrate) (double)	0.65		

The single bond of carbon has a bonding radius of 0.77 A, and hydrogen has a bonding radius of 0.30 A, and so the separation for C—H is 0.30 + 0.77 = 1.07 A. Similarly, the interatomic distance for C—C is 0.77 + 0.77 = 1.54 A. When double bonds are present, all the adjacent bonds lie in a single plane. Thus ethylene and benzene have planar structures.

If it is necessary to write several structures in order to account for the observed properties of a compound the system is considered to be *resonating* between these structures. Benzene is probably the most familiar example since it cannot be represented by a structure with fixed single and double bonds. The structure of benzene is not exactly intermediate in character between the several Kekule structures with alternating double and single bonds in the 6-member ring because as a consequence of resonance it is stabilized by a certain amount of energy, the *resonance energy*. As a result of resonance, the carbon-carbon bond distance in benzene (1.39 A) is intermediate between the C—C bond distance in aliphatic hydrocarbons (1.54 A) and the usual C=C distance (1.33 A).

Whenever the interatomic distance is not equal to the sum of the bond radii, it may be concluded that there is something abnormal, such as a strained structure or the existence of more than one molecular structure brought about by rapid oscillation of the electrons between different

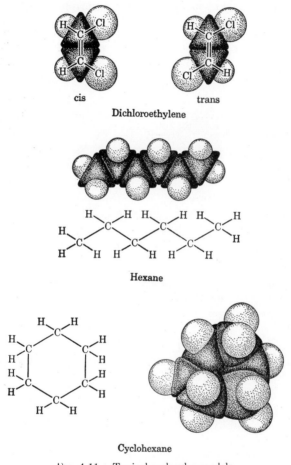

cis   trans

Dichloroethylene

Hexane

Cyclohexane

FIG. 4-11.   Typical molecular models.

positions.   Conjugated double bonds are good examples of such resonating structures.   Butadiene, for example, has the structure

$$\underset{\substack{| \\ H}}{H} - C = C - C = C - H$$

and illustrates this type of resonance.   It is found that in butadiene the carbon-carbon distances are not exactly equal to the sum of the normal bond radii. When resonance occurs, the compounds are more stable than would otherwise be expected, and they have abnormally low heats of reaction; that is, an extra amount of energy is required to pull the atoms apart when new compounds are formed.

Models are available * in which nearly 1 cm represents 1 A, and the faces of the atoms are cut so as to give the correct bond angles. Models of molecules may then be built up which represent the actual relations on a large scale, and certain deductions can be drawn from these models. Models are shown in *Fig. 4-11* for the *cis* and *trans* forms of dichloroeth-

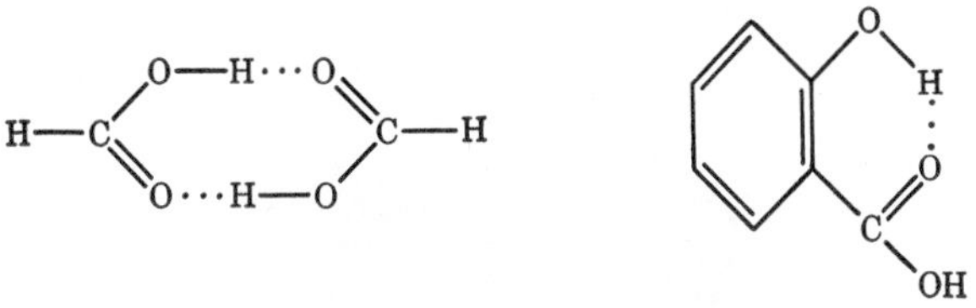

Formic acid dimer   Salicylic acid

FIG. 4-12.   Examples of hydrogen bonding.

ylene, and the reasons for the difference in dipole moments is readily apparent.

Hexane, which is shown also in Fig. 4-11, has a long, snakelike structure which can move around in various positions, but the probabilities of free motions of the cyclohexane shown just below it are greatly reduced. This reduction of the probable motions leads to a decrease in entropy, which is discussed on page 132.

For compounds containing groups like —COOH, —OH and —NH$_2$ it is frequently necessary to consider so-called *hydrogen bonding*. Under certain conditions an atom of hydrogen is attracted by two atoms instead of only one, so that it may be considered to be acting as a bond between them. The hydrogen atom is unique, owing to the fact that, when its electron becomes detached, only the nucleus of very small diameter is left. In formic or acetic acid vapor hydrogen bonds, formed as illustrated in *Fig. 4-12*, are sufficiently strong to lead to an appreciable concentration of dimerized molecules in the vapor phase. Benzoic and other carboxylic acids have been shown to be associated to double molecules in certain nonpolar solvents such as benzene and carbon tetrachloride. In salicylic acid an intramolecular hydrogen bond can be formed as illustrated in Fig. 4-12. This bonding tends to release the hydrogen of the carboxyl group, and as a result salicylic acid with

* Fisher-Hirschfelder-Taylor atomic models.

its OH and carboxyl groups adjacent is a much stronger acid than its *meta* and *para* isomers, in which these groups are farther apart.

REFERENCES

Brode, *Chemical Spectroscopy*, John Wiley & Sons, New York, 1947.

Gilman, *Organic Chemistry*, John Wiley & Sons, New York, 1943, Vol. 2, Chapters 20 and 21.

Pauling, *The Nature of the Chemical Bond*, Cornell University Press, Ithaca, N. Y., 1939.

Selwood, *Magnetochemistry*, Interscience Publishers, New York, 1943.

Harrison, Lord, and Loofbourow, *Practical Spectroscopy*, Prentice-Hall, New York, 1948.

Barnes, Gore, Liddel, and Williams, *Infrared Spectroscopy*, Reinhold Publishing Corp., New York, 1944.

Weissberger, *Physical Methods of Organic Chemistry*, Interscience Publishers, 1949, Vol. I, Part II (chapters on refractometry, spectrophotometry, polarimetry, electron diffraction, and dipole moments).

Mellon, *Analytical Absorption Spectroscopy*, John Wiley & Sons, New York, 1950.

Smyth, *Dielectric Behavior and Structure*, McGraw-Hill Book Co., New York, 1955.

PROBLEMS

1. From the atomic refractions, calculate the refractive index n_D at 20° of trimethylcarbinol $(CH_3)_3COH$. The density is 0.7864 g cm^{-3}. The experimentally determined value of n_D is 1.3878.   *Ans.* 1.385.

2. The specific rotation $[\alpha]_D$ of a solution of *d*-ethoxysuccinic acid in water is 33.02° at 17°C. Calculate the concentration of this compound in grams per liter in a solution which has a rotation of 2.02° when measured in a polarimeter at 17°C in which the container of the solution is 20 cm long.   *Ans.* 30.6 g/l.

3. When α-D-mannose $([\alpha]_D^{20} = +29.3°)$ is dissolved in water, the optical rotation decreases as β-D-mannose is formed until at equilibrium $[\alpha]_D^{20} = +14.2°$. This process is referred to as mutarotation. As expected, when β-D-mannose $([\alpha]_D^{20} = -17.0°)$ is dissolved in water the optical rotation increases until $[\alpha]_D^{20} = +14.2°$ is obtained. Calculate the percentage of α form in the equilibrium mixture.
                                    Ans. 67.4%.

4. For acetone vapor at 50° the value of k in the expression $I = I_0\,e^{-klc}$ is 6.63 for light of 3130 A, where c is expressed in moles per liter and l is in centimeters. What per cent of light will be absorbed by acetone vapor at 100 mm pressure at 50° when a beam of light of 3130 A is passed through a cell 15 cm long?
                                    Ans. 39.1%.

5. A solution of a dye containing 1 g per 100 ml transmits 80 per cent of the blue light at 4356 A in a glass cell 1 cm thick. (*a*) What per cent of light will be absorbed by a solution containing 2 g per 100 ml in a cell 1 cm thick? (*b*) What concentration will be required to absorb 50 per cent of the light? (*c*) What per cent of light will be transmitted by a solution of the dye containing 1 g per 100 ml in a cell 5 cm thick? (*d*) What thickness should the cell be in order to absorb 90 per cent of the light with solution of this concentration?
                                    Ans. (*a*) 36.0%. (*b*) 3.10 g/100 ml.
                                    (*c*) 32.7%. (*d*) 10.3 cm.

6. Calculate the moments of inertia in g cm^2 for (a) hydrogen, (b) chlorine, and (c) carbon dioxide using bond distances from Table VII.

$Ans.$ (a) 0.030×10^{-39}, (b) 11.5×10^{-39}, (c) 8.19×10^{-39} g cm^2.

7. The molar polarization P of ammonia varies with temperature as follows:

t, °C	19.1	35.9	59.9	113.9	139.9	172.9
P, ml mole^{-1}	57.57	55.01	51.22	44.99	42.51	39.59

(a) Plot P against $1/T$, and determine the dipole moment of ammonia. (b) If the density of ammonia gas at 59.9° and 1 atm is 0.632 g per liter (0.000632 g per ml), what is the dielectric constant of ammonia under these conditions?

$Ans.$ (a) 1.596×10^{-18} esu cm.   (b) 1.0059.

8. By extrapolation the molar polarization of pyridine oxide, C_5H_5NO, in an infinitely dilute solution in dioxane is found to be 411 ml mole^{-1} at 25°. The molar refraction of C_5H_5NO is 28 ml mole^{-1}, and this is approximately equal to P_D. Calculate the dipole moment $Ans.$ 4.33×10^{-18} esu cm.

---

9. Calculate the molar refraction of diethyl ether, $(C_2H_5)_2O$. The refractive index n_D at 17.1° is 1.35424, and the density at 17.1° is 0.7183 g per ml. Compare the molar refraction with the sum of the atomic refractions.

10. A solution of l-mandelic acid in water containing 1.56 g in 100 ml rotated polarized light 4.91° in a polarimeter which had a cell 20 cm long. The D line of sodium was used as a light source. Calculate the specific rotation.

11. The specific rotation of l-leucine is $[\alpha]_D^{25} = -14.0°$. If the specific rotation of a mixture of d and l forms is $[\alpha]_D^{25} = +2.3$, calculate the fraction of l form in the mixture.

12. For light having a wavelength of 400 mμ calculate (a) the wavelength in angstroms, (b) the frequency, and (c) the wave number.

13. The following absorption data are obtained for solutions of oxyhemoglobin in pH 7 buffer at 575 mμ in a 1-cm cell.

g/100 ml	% Transmission
0.03	53.5
0.05	35.1
0.10	12.3

Calculate the per cent transmission for a solution containing 0.01 g per 100 ml assuming that Beer's law is obeyed.

14. Using data from page 70, calculate what concentration of bromine in a cell 5 cm long will be necessary to absorb 50 per cent of the blue light (4360 A) passing through it.

15. The dielectric constants and densities of germanium tetrachloride at various temperatures are tabulated. Calculate the molar polarizations at these temperatures. What do these data suggest about the dipole moment of germanium tetrachloride?

$t°$	0	20	30	40	50
ϵ	2.491	2.443	2.417	2.395	2.370
d, g ml^{-1}	1.9226	1.8762	1.8533	1.8296	1.8063

16. The molar polarization of silicobromoform $SiHBr_3$ is 46 ml mole^{-1} at 25°. The induced polarizability α may be taken as 1.308×10^{-23}. Calculate the dipole moment of this molecule.

_____

17. The refractive index of n-heptyl fluoride $CH_3(CH_2)_5CH_2F$ is 1.3861 at 20°, and the density is 0.804 g cm^{-3}. What is the refractive index of fluorotrichloromethane CCl_3F at 20° if the density is 1.494 g cm^{-3}?

18. Calculate from the atomic refractions the refractive index n_D at 20° of allyl ethyl ether $(C_2H_5)O(C_3H_5)$. The density is 0.7651 g cm^{-3}. The experimental value of n_D is 1.3881.

19. The specific rotation of ethyl l-lactate $[\alpha]_D^{20}$ is 14.52. The density of the liquid is 1.030 g cm^{-3}. A tube 20 cm long is used for an experimental measurement. Calculate the percentage of error in the value of $[\alpha]$ caused by (a) an error of 0.1° in the angle, (b) an error of 0.01 in the density, (c) an error of 0.5 mm in the length of the tube.

20. A preparation of l-proline when dissolved in water gave a concentration of 23 g per liter at 20° and rotated polarized light from the D line of sodium through $-3.05°$, as measured with a polarimeter in a cell 20 cm long. The specific rotation at 20° of pure l-proline is $-84.9°$. What conclusions can be drawn as to the purity of the product if it is assumed that any impurities are optically inactive?

21. Calculate the wavelength in angstroms, the wave number, and the frequency of light with a wavelength of 6.5 microns.

22. In order to test the validity of Beer's law in the determination of vitamin A, solutions of known concentration were prepared and treated by a standard procedure with antimony trichloride in chloroform to produce a blue color. The per cent transmission of the incident filtered light for each concentration in a given cell is as follows:

Concentration micrograms per milliliter	% Transmission
1.0	66.8
2.0	44.7
3.0	29.2
4.0	19.9
5.0	13.3

Plot these data so as to give a straight line. A solution, when treated in the standard manner with antimony chloride, transmitted 35 per cent of the incident light in the same cell. What was the concentration of vitamin A in the solution?

23. A certain solution of a blue dye absorbs 25 per cent of the red light in a thickness of 1 cm. (a) How much of the light will be absorbed by 2 cm of solution? (b) How much will be absorbed by 10 cm of solution? (c) What depth of solution will be required to absorb only 10 per cent of the light?

24. In synthesizing ethyl (l-ethyl propenyl) allylcyanoacetate,

$$
\begin{array}{c}
C_2H_5 \\
| \\
CH_3CH{=}C \qquad CN \\
\diagdown C \diagup \\
\diagup \quad \diagdown \\
CH_2{=}CH{-}CH_2 \qquad COOC_2H_5
\end{array}
$$

none of whose physical constants were known, a product was obtained having a refractive index n_D^{25} of 1.4617 and a density of 0.9704 g cm^{-3} at 25°. What conclusions can be drawn as to the purity of the compound?

25. The following data for a sample of linseed oil at 25° were found experimentally: Refractive index n_D = 1.4792; density = 0.9260 g cm^{-3}; molecular weight M = 783 (polymerized); the molar polarization of linseed oil extrapolated to infinite dilution in benzene = 263 ml mole^{-1}. Calculate the dipole moment of the linseed oil at 25°.

26. Calculate the dipole moment of fluorobenzene, using a plot of P versus $1/T$, from the following molar polarizations measured by McAlpine and Smyth [*J. Chem. Phys.*, *3*, 55 (1935)]:

T, °K	343.6	371.4	414.1	453.2	507.0
P, ml mole^{-1}	69.9	66.8	62.5	59.3	55.8

27. If the error in the measurement of per cent transmission is a constant per cent transmission, it may be shown that concentrations may be measured most accurately if the concentration is such that the per cent transmission is 36.8 per cent. Calculate the concentration of sodium fumarate solution required to give 36.8 per cent transmission if a 2-cm cell is used. The molar absorbancy index for sodium fumarate in water at 25° is 1.43 × 10^3 cm^{-1} M^{-1} at 250 mμ.

28. Write resonating structures for benzene and naphthalene showing the electron pairs.

29. Write possible resonating structures for (*a*) the carboxyl group and (*b*) nitrous oxide (N_2O).

5

Heat, Work, and Heat Capacity

Thermodynamics. The quantitative relations between heat and other forms of energy are studied in the science of thermodynamics. Thermodynamics has been used in physics for a century, and it has found extensive applications in engineering; but its practical application in chemistry is a considerably later development. The present chapter provides an introduction to the simple concepts of heat and work. It is followed by a chapter on heat measurements in chemical reactions and then by a chapter on chemical thermodynamics. Throughout the study of solutions and chemical equilibria, thermodynamics will be applied to correlate and explain the observed facts.

Forms of Energy. Electrical and mechanical energy and other forms of energy can be converted completely into heat, and a specified amount of energy always produces the same amount of heat.

The *cgs* unit of energy is the *erg*, which is the work done when a force of 1 dyne acts through a distance of 1 cm. The unit force, the *dyne*, gives a mass of 1 gram an acceleration of 1 cm sec^{-2}. Since an erg of energy is such a small quantity, a larger unit, the *joule*, which is equal to 10^7 ergs, is a more convenient unit. Experiments by Rumford (1798), Davy (1799), Joule (1849), and many recent investigators have shown that a given amount of work always produces the same amount of heat. In some of these experiments a measured amount of work was used in stirring a liquid while the rise in temperature was measured, and in others a known quantity of electricity was passed through a heating coil of known resistance immersed in a liquid containing a thermometer.

The unit of heat used most frequently in physical chemistry is the calorie. The 15° calorie is the heat required to raise the temperature of a gram of water from 14.5° to 15.5°.* The *calorie* as now used by American physical chemists is arbitrarily defined as being equal to 4.1840 absolute joules.* This value is used throughout this book. The *kilocalorie* is equal to 1000 calories.

* The 15° calorie is equal to 4.1855 absolute joules.

Energy may be stored in a given system by virtue of position, as, for example, a stone above the earth's surface, or a spring under compression; or by virtue of chemical properties due to the arrangement of atoms and electrons within a molecule. Energy may also exist in other forms, such as the kinetic energy of a moving ball or molecule.

This energy may be released, under the proper conditions, to do work: to push a piston in an engine cylinder or to send a current of electricity through the windings of an electric motor. The energy may be converted into heat, thus raising the temperature of the system itself or of the surroundings. Energy, work, and heat are all expressed in the same units: calories, joules, or ergs.

Although symbols are employed to represent the total energy stored in a system, it should be borne in mind that usually it is not necessary to know the total amount of this energy.

Generally, we are concerned only with the change in energy that takes place during the operation we are studying. For example, in the burning of coal we are interested in the energy released by changing the carbon and oxygen into carbon dioxide, and we are not often concerned with the energy that may still reside in carbon dioxide by virtue of its temperature above absolute zero, or by virtue of the arrangement of the atoms and electrons within the molecule, or by the stability of the nuclei of the atoms. Again, we calculate that the energy required to lift a kilogram weight through 10 cm against the force of gravity * is

$$(1000 \text{ g})(980.7 \text{ cm sec}^{-2})(10 \text{ cm}) = 9.807 \times 10^6 \text{ ergs}$$

and that after the lifting operation the weight possesses 9.807×10^6 ergs of energy more than it had before. We are not concerned with the energy that the weight possesses by virtue of its distance from the center of the earth. When the weight falls back to its original level, the potential energy of position is converted into kinetic energy of motion; and, when it is stopped by collision with the ground, this kinetic energy is converted into heat energy.

Energy may be expressed as the product of two factors—an intensity factor and a capacity factor. Examples are given in Table I.

It is evident that the different energies may be compared but that no relation exists between the intensity factors alone or between the capacity factors alone. For example, electric energy may be converted quantitatively into heat energy, but the rise in temperature cannot be calculated from the voltage unless the number of coulombs and the heat

* The force of gravity varies somewhat with latitude and distance above sea level and with the composition and density of the earth's crust, but the value 980.7 cm sec^{-2} is used for the calculations of this book.

Table I. Intensity and Capacity Factors of Energy Involved in Various Processes

Energy	Intensity	Capacity
Mechanical (ergs)	Force (dynes)	Change in distance (cm)
Surface (ergs)	Surface tension (dynes per cm)	Change in area (cm²)
Volume expansion (ergs)	Pressure (dynes per cm²)	Change in volume (cm³)
Heat (calories)	Difference in temperature (degrees)	Heat capacity (calories per degree)
Electric (joules)	Difference in potential (volts)	Coulombs (amperes × seconds)
Kinetic (ergs)	Square of velocity (cm sec⁻¹)²	½ Mass (g)
Potential (ergs)	Height × acceleration (cm sec⁻¹)²	Mass (g)
Moving of charged particles (electron volts)	Volts	Electronic charge

capacity of the system are known. It is clear also that the same quantity of work can be accomplished by a small quantity of water passing through a turbine from a great height as by a large quantity of water falling through a short distance.

The First Law of Thermodynamics. According to the first law of thermodynamics, *the sum of all the energies in an isolated system is constant.* In other words, energy may be transformed from one form into another, but it cannot be created or destroyed.

Our confidence in the first law of thermodynamics rests largely on the fact that no exceptions to it have yet been found. At first sight one might think that the energy expended in lifting a piece of iron is destroyed if the iron is dissolved in sulfuric acid, but the iron in the resulting ferrous sulfate is at a higher level and possesses potential energy equal to the energy expended in the lifting. If energy is expended in compressing a steel spring and the spring is dissolved in acid, the energy appears to be lost; but more heat is evolved by a compressed spring than by an uncompressed spring.

Even the new developments in nuclear reactions do not contradict the first law, for, according to the theory of relativity, mass may be converted into energy, and the large evolution of energy produced by reactions between atomic nuclei in nuclear reactions (page 627) is due to the actual decrease in mass. Einstein showed that if there is a change in mass, Δm,

$$\text{Energy} = \Delta mc^2 \tag{1}$$

where c is the velocity of light $(3 \times 10^{10}$ cm sec⁻¹). Thus 1 gram of

matter is equivalent to 9×10^{20} ergs of energy. It is evident that the
law of the conservation of energy and the law of the conservation of
mass are essentially the same and that no violation of thermodynamics
occurs when matter is converted into energy, or energy into matter.
However, nuclear transformations and changes in total mass are not
involved in ordinary chemical and physical phenomena, and their discussion is reserved for Chapter 20.   Equation 1 is of no importance in
most chemical phenomena.

A change in the energy of a system will be brought about if the system
does work, or has work done on it, or if it absorbs or evolves heat.   The
work is designated by w.   A positive value of w indicates that the work
is done by the system on its surroundings, and a negative value shows
that the surroundings are doing work on the system, as, for example,
when a gas is compressed by the application of external pressure.   The
heat exchange is designated by q; a positive value shows that heat is
being absorbed by the system from its surroundings, and a negative
value shows that the system is giving out heat to its surroundings.

In *chemical* thermodynamics we are not ordinarily interested in the
energy which a system has by virtue of its distance from the center of
the earth or by virtue of any movement of the system through space.
We are interested in the *internal energy E*, which includes many complicated factors such as attractions between molecules and motions of
electrons, atoms, and molecules.   Chemical changes are accompanied by
rearrangements which lead to a change in the internal energy.

The symbol Δ always indicates a change, and in physical chemistry it
refers to the difference between the values of a property in the initial
and the final states.   For example, if E_1 represents the internal energy
in the initial state and E_2 the internal energy in the final state, in the
reaction

$$\text{state}_1 \rightarrow \text{state}_2$$

then

$$\Delta E = E_2 - E_1$$

The initial state 1 is taken as the state which happens to be written down
at the left of a chemical equation and the final state 2 is designated as
the state written at the right.   This convention applies to any chemical
or physical change.

Since energy can be neither created nor destroyed, it follows that the
internal energy of the final state must be equal to the internal energy
of the initial state plus the energy added in the form of heat or any kind
of work.   Then,

$$E_2 = E_1 + (q - w)$$

or

$$E_2 - E_1 = \Delta E = q - w \tag{2}$$

This equation may be regarded as a mathematical formulation of the first law of thermodynamics.

It is important to realize that E_1 and E_2 are thermodynamic quantities that are characteristic of the state of the system. ΔE is the same, irrespective of the path followed in going from state 1 to state 2. The quantities q and w, however, can vary greatly with the experimental conditions. The initial and final *states* of a system are important for thermodynamics, and they must be clearly distinguished from the *process* by which the system passes from one state to the other.

If there is no change of internal energy (as in the isothermal expansion of an ideal gas) the work done must be exactly equal to the heat absorbed. Again, if there is a chemical reaction and the internal energy of the system decreases, that is, E_2 is less than E_1, the released energy may appear as heat evolved and work done. Nothing is stated regarding the relative amounts of heat and work, but the two taken together $(q - w)$ must be equal to the change in internal energy. Under special conditions it is possible to have either q or w or both equal to zero.

For infinitesimal changes, equation 2 is written

$$dE = dq - dw \qquad (3)$$

but there is an important reservation which must be made regarding the use of dq and dw. Changes in internal energy E, like changes in pressure or volume, depend only on the initial and final state and are independent of the intermediate stages. Mathematically they are classed as perfect differentials, and

$$\int_{E_1}^{E_2} dE = E_2 - E_1 = \Delta E$$

On the other hand, q and w do not represent differences between initial and final states. They refer to processes rather than states, and their values depend on the manner in which the change is carried out. The terms dq and dw are not perfect differentials, and their integrals should not be written as the differences between initial and final values (for example, as $q_2 - q_1$), but simply as q or w.

Reversible Processes. Vaporization of a Liquid. When a gas increases in volume, it pushes back the surrounding atmosphere and does work. Imagine that a liquid is placed in a cylinder provided with a weightless, frictionless piston and that it is set into a large reservoir at the boiling temperature of the liquid. The fact that no machine can be built with a weightless frictionless piston in no way affects the conclusions drawn from this idealized process. The vapor pressure of the liquid at this temperature is exactly equal to the atmospheric pressure, and the whole system is in a state of equilibrium. If now the temperature of the reservoir is raised by an infinitesimal amount, the vapor pressure of the liquid will be slightly greater, and the piston will be pushed back against the atmospheric pressure. As the volume increases, more liquid evaporates and the pressure in the cylinder is thus maintained constant; heat flows in from the reservoir to maintain the temperature constant and offset the cooling caused by vaporization.

The work done is the product of the external resisting pressure and the increase in volume. The increase in volume is the distance through which the piston is driven out multiplied by the cross-sectional area of the piston. If the liquid in the cylinder is water and the pressure is 1 atm the temperature will be 100°, and when 1 mole has been evaporated, the increase in volume can be calculated on the assumption that the vapor behaves as an ideal gas and that the volume of the liquid (0.018 liter) is negligible:

$$w = p\,\Delta V = (1 \text{ atm})(22.41 \text{ l mole}^{-1})\,\frac{373.1 \text{ deg}}{273.1 \text{ deg}} = 30.6 \text{ l-atm mole}^{-1}$$

Since it is assumed that the ideal gas laws are obeyed, RT may be substituted for $p\,\Delta V$. Then,

$$w = RT = (0.08205 \text{ l-atm deg}^{-1} \text{ mole}^{-1})(373.1 \text{ deg})$$

$$= 30.6 \text{ l-atm mole}^{-1}$$

or

$$w = RT = (1.987 \text{ cal deg}^{-1} \text{ mole}^{-1})(373.1 \text{ deg}) = 741.3 \text{ cal mole}^{-1}$$

The work done in this process depends only on the temperature and is independent of the cross-sectional area of the piston or the pressure or volume. In very exact work it is not legitimate to consider a vapor at its boiling point as a perfect gas, and then the volume change must be measured experimentally or calculated with more exact equations of state.

The energy consumed in doing this external pressure-volume work comes from heat absorbed from the reservoir by the evaporating liquid. A great deal more energy must be absorbed from the reservoir, however, in order to separate the molecules from their neighboring molecules in the liquid. To vaporize a gram of water at 373.1°K and atmospheric pressure, 539 cal is required. This corresponds to 18.02×539 or 9713 cal per mole. Then, under these conditions of constant pressure the total heat absorbed is equal to the sum of the two quantities as given by equation 4.

$$q = \Delta E + w \qquad (4)$$

Then

$$\Delta E = q - w = 9713 - 741 = 8972 \text{ cal mole}^{-1}$$

This process of absorbing heat and doing external work is reversible in the example just given, because at any time the vaporization can be stopped by decreasing the temperature by an infinitesimal amount or by increasing the pressure slightly, thus making internal and external pressures exactly equal. Increasing the pressure still further by an infinitesimal amount causes the vapor to condense and give back the heat of vaporization to the reservoir. A *reversible process*, then, is defined as one that can be reversed at will by making infinitesimal changes in temperature or pressure or other variables.

After a mole of water has been evaporated by decreasing the pressure, it can be condensed again by increasing the pressure, and thus the whole system may be restored to its original condition. Such a process, which involves a series of changes and restores the system to its original condition, is called a *cycle*. A *reversible cycle* is a cycle that is carried out by applying infinitesimal changes under conditions such that the system is at all times practically in a state of equilibrium.

Maximum Work by Isothermal Expansion. The maximum work that can be done by the *isothermal expansion* of a perfect gas is an important quantity in theoretical chemistry. Imagine a gas enclosed in a cylinder fitted with a frictionless and weightless piston and placed in a thermostat at the temperature T. The external pressure on the piston is decreased by a small amount, Δp, and the gas expands by an amount Δv. In this expansion the pressure of the gas in the cylinder decreases until it becomes equal to the external pressure, and then the piston ceases to rise. This process differs from the one described previously on page 96, where the gas was in contact with *liquid* at its boiling point so that the pressure in the cylinder was maintained constant. A second decrease in pressure produces a second expansion Δv, and, as the pressure is decreased in successive amounts, the volume undergoes a series of expansions. In each little expansion the work done is the external pressure multiplied by Δv, and the total work done in expanding from the *initial* volume v_1 to the *final* volume v_2 is equal to the sum of the work done in each expansion.

The maximum work w_{max} is obtained when the Δv's are made infinitesimally small, and under these conditions the exact value is readily obtained by integral calculus,* thus:

$$w_{\text{max}} = w_{\text{rev}} = \int_{v_1}^{v_2} p\, dv \qquad (5)$$

Only if the work done is maximum work can sufficient energy be stored to reverse the process, compressing the gas and restoring the original conditions. Under the conditions for maximum work the internal pressure can be substituted for the external or resisting pressure, because the two can never differ by more than an infinitesimal amount dp, and the system is then always practically in a state of equilibrium; that is, it is a reversible process.

If 1 mole of a perfect gas is taken, $pV = RT$, or $p = RT/V$, and

$$w_{\text{max}} = \int_{V_1}^{V_2} \frac{RT}{V}\, dV$$

Since R and T are constants, integration gives

$$w_{\text{max}} = RT \int_{V_1}^{V_2} V^{-1}\, dV = RT \ln \frac{V_2}{V_1} = RT\, 2.303 \log \frac{V_2}{V_1} \qquad (6)$$

Exercise I. Show that for n moles of a perfect gas the reversible work of expansion is

$$w_{\text{max}} = nRT\, 2.303 \log (v_2/v_1)$$

The maximum work done by a gas in expansion is equal to the minimum work required to compress the gas, and the calculation is made by simply interchanging the limits of integration and using the smaller volume for the upper limit. In integrations, the upper limit always refers to the final state and the lower limit refers to the initial state. The signs then take care of themselves. The negative value obtained for w in compression means that work is done on the gas by its surroundings.

Example 1. What is the maximum work which can be obtained by the isothermal expansion of 1 mole of an ideal gas at $0°$ from 2.24 liters to 22.4 liters?

$$w_{\text{max}} = 2.303RT \log (V_2/V_1) = (2.303)(1.987)(273.1) \log 10 = 1250 \text{ cal}$$

Then 1250 cal is also the minimum amount of work required to compress the gas from 22.4 to 2.24 liters at $0°$.

The maximum work for 1 mole of gas may be calculated in terms of pressures instead of volumes since $p_1 V_1 = p_2 V_2$ and $V_2/V_1 = p_1/p_2$. Then,

$$w_{\text{max}} = RT \ln (p_1/p_2) = -RT\, 2.303 \log (p_2/p_1)$$

* The significance of this equation may be found in Daniels, *Mathematical Preparation for Physical Chemistry*, McGraw-Hill Book Co., New York, 1928, pages 162-164.

Enthalpy. In many cases the only work done is pressure-volume work, that is $dw = p\,dv$. If there is no volume change, dv is zero and dw is therefore zero. Then for processes in which the volume is kept constant and no electric or other work is done, equation 2 can be written

$$q_v{}^* = \Delta E + 0 = \Delta E \tag{7}$$

In words, the *heat absorbed in a process, measured under conditions of constant volume, is equal to the internal energy increase*. According to this equation, if no outside work is done, the heat evolved is equal to the decrease in the internal energy.

Constant-pressure processes are generally more common in chemistry than constant-volume processes, because most operations are carried out in open vessels. Under conditions of constant pressure equation 2 may be written

$$q_p = \Delta E + p\,\Delta v \tag{8}$$

It is convenient to introduce a new quantity, the enthalpy,† H, which is defined by

$$H = E + pv \tag{9}$$

Like the internal energy E, it depends only on the state of the system and is not affected by the process involved in going from the initial state to the final state. Then

$$\Delta H = \Delta E + \Delta(pv)$$

or at constant pressure

$$\Delta H = \Delta E + p\,\Delta v$$

Substitution in equation 8 yields

$$\Delta H = q_p \tag{10}$$

In words, *the heat absorbed in a process at constant pressure is equal to the change in enthalpy* if the only work done is that of the pressure-volume type.

When pressure-volume work is the only type of work (electrical and other types being excluded) it is easy to visualize ΔE and ΔH; in a *constant-volume* calorimeter the evolution of heat is a measure of the decrease in internal energy E, and in a *constant-pressure* calorimeter the evolution of heat is a measure of the decrease in enthalpy, H.

---

* A subscript below a quantity indicates that the property indicated by the subscript is kept constant; thus, q_v shows that the process is restricted to constant volume.

† Enthalpy (pronounced enthal′py) is often referred to as heat content.

Heat Capacity. Heat can be absorbed not only by physical and chemical changes but also in raising the temperature. The *specific heat* of a substance is defined as the quantity of heat required to raise the temperature of 1 gram of the substance 1 degree centigrade. Since chemical calculations are more frequently carried out on a molar basis it is convenient to use the *molar heat capacity C*, which is the specific heat times the molecular weight.

When a substance is heated under conditions of constant volume, the molar heat capacity C_v is given by

$$C_{v \text{ average}} = \frac{q_v}{T_2 - T_1} = \frac{E_2 - E_1}{T_2 - T_1} \tag{11}$$

or more exactly by

$$C_v = \left(\frac{\partial E}{\partial T}\right)_v{}^* \tag{12}$$

The heat capacity at constant pressure is given by the equation

$$C_p = \left(\frac{\partial H}{\partial T}\right)_p \tag{13}$$

The heat capacity at constant volume C_v includes only the heat absorbed in increasing the internal energy, but the heat capacity at constant pressure C_p is larger because it includes in addition the work done in expansion.

Any two of the three variables, temperature, pressure, and volume, suffice to define the condition of a substance if E is a function only of T, p, and v. The change in the internal energy of a mole of gas may, therefore, be expressed by the fundamental equation of partial differentiation,

$$dE = \left(\frac{\partial E}{\partial T}\right)_v dT + \left(\frac{\partial E}{\partial v}\right)_T dv \tag{14}$$

where temperature and volume are the variables chosen. The derivative $(\partial E/\partial T)_v$ represents the heat absorbed per degree by the gas at constant volume and, therefore, according to equation 12, it may be replaced by C_v. Equation 14 now assumes the form:

$$dE = C_v \, dT + \left(\frac{\partial E}{\partial v}\right)_T dv \tag{15}$$

---

* The partial differential ∂ (Appendix, page 653) indicates that only the temperature is allowed to change and all other possible variables are held constant while the temperature changes. The subscript v emphasizes the fact that the volume is one of the possible variables which is kept constant.

But, since $dE = dq - dw$,

$$dq = C_v \, dT + \left(\frac{\partial E}{\partial v}\right)_T dv + dw$$

The work done when the volume of a mole of gas, liquid, or solid increases by an amount dv at pressure p is $p \, dv$. Hence,

$$dq_p = C_v \, dT + \left(\frac{\partial E}{\partial v}\right)_T dv + p \, dv$$

This equation means in words that the heat absorbed when a substance is heated slightly at constant pressure is equal to the sum of three quantities: (1) the temperature increase multiplied by the heat capacity at constant volume; (2) the volume increase multiplied by the rate at which the internal energy increases with volume, all other factors being held constant; (3) the work done in expansion.

Internal Energy of Gases. When an ideal gas expands into a vacuum in a closed system, there is no absorption or evolution of heat from the system as a whole. Imagine two vessels in a constant-temperature bath connected with a valve. The first is filled with an ideal gas under pressure, and the second is evacuated. When the valve is opened the gas rushes from the first into the second. The first becomes cooler by the expansion of the gas, and the second becomes warmer on account of the compression of the gas. When equilibrium is reached, however, and the same pressure is established throughout the two vessels, the heating and cooling effects will exactly balance, and there will be no change in the average temperature of the whole tank. There is neither evolution nor absorption of heat in the system as a whole. Moreover, since the total volume of the system, consisting of the two vessels, remains unchanged, no external work can be done against the atmosphere.

Since $q = 0$ and $w = 0$, it follows, from equation 2, that ΔE must be zero. In other words, the internal energy of an ideal gas is independent of the volume, and

$$\left(\frac{\partial E}{\partial v}\right)_T = 0 \tag{16}$$

This equation gives an important criterion for an ideal gas. Another criterion, given earlier, is that

$$pv = nRT$$

In most real gases there is an attractive force between the molecules and equation 16 does not apply. The experiment in which a gas expands into an evacuated vessel does not allow accurate measurements to be made, and instead a stream of gas is forced through a thermally insulated porous plug. The issuing gas at a reduced pressure usually has a reduced temperature also. This cooling effect, known as the Joule-Thomson effect, is caused by the work done by the expanding gas as its molecules are forced farther apart against the intermolecular attraction. In hydrogen and helium, at temperatures far above their boiling tem-

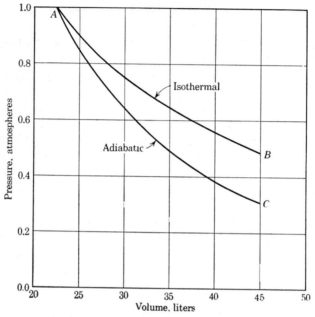

Fig. 5-1.   Isothermal and adiabatic expansion of a gas.

peratures, the attractive forces between molecules are so small that this cooling effect does not occur. In fact under certain conditions a heating effect is observed.

Adiabatic Expansion of a Gas. An *adiabatic* process is one in which there is no loss or gain of heat, that is, one in which the system under investigation is thermally insulated from its environment. When a mole of gas expands adiabatically to a larger volume and a lower pressure, the volume is smaller than it would be after an isothermal expansion to the same pressure, because in the adiabatic expansion the external work done cools the gas and leads to a shrinkage in volume, as shown in *Fig. 5-1*.

One mole of helium at *A* occupying 22.4 liters under 1 atm and at 0° expands isothermally to *B*, where the volume is 44.8 liters at 0.5 atm still at $0°$. When the mole of helium at A expands adiabatically toward C, at 0.5 atm it occupies 33.6 liters and the temperature falls to $-66°$. If it is allowed to expand still further to 44.8 liters at C, the temperature drops to $-101°$ and the pressure becomes 0.32 atm. The work done by the isothermal reversible expansion of the gas, represented by the area under AB, is larger than the work done by the adiabatic expansion, represented by the area under AC, indicating that the heat absorbed from the surroundings in the isothermal expansion supplies extra energy for doing work. The energy for the adiabatic expansion comes only from the cooling of the gas itself.

In the adiabatic expansion of a gas the temperature falls, but there is no exchange of heat with the surroundings, and $dq = 0$. Then, by the first law,

$$dE = dq - dw = -dw = -p \, dv$$

According to equations 15 and 16, $dE = C_v \, dT$ for the expansion of 1 mole of an ideal gas, and so

$$C_v \, dT = -p \, dV$$

Since, for 1 mole of an ideal gas, $p = RT/V$, it follows that

$$C_v \, dT = -RT \, (dV/V)$$

and

$$C_v \, (dT/T) = -R \, (dV/V)$$

If V_1 is the volume of the gas at the initial temperature T_1, and V_2 is the volume at the final temperature T_2, and if C_v is constant, integration between these limits gives

$$C_v \ln (T_2/T_1) = -R \ln (V_2/V_1) \qquad (17)$$

According to this equation, when 1 mole of an ideal gas having a heat capacity C_v expands reversibly and adiabatically, V_2 is greater than V_1, and, accordingly, T_2 must be less than T_1. In other words, the gas cools. It is evident also that adiabatic compression of the gas produces an increase in temperature. In solving problems it is necessary, of course, to express C_v and R in the same units.

Example 2. If a gas is compressed so rapidly that there is no opportunity to transfer heat to the container, the operation will be adiabatic. Calculate the temperature increase of a mole of helium which is compressed adiabatically from 44.8 liters at $0°$ to 22.4 liters.   The molar heat capacity C_v of helium is constant and equal to 3.00 cal per degree.

$$C_v \ln (T_2/T_1) = -R \ln (V_2/V_1)$$

$$(3.00)(2.303) \log (T_2/273.1) = (-1.987)(2.303) \log (22.4/44.8)$$

$$\log T_2 = -(1.987/3.00)(\log \tfrac{1}{2}) + \log 273.1$$

$$T_2 = 432.4°K$$

$$\text{Increase in temperature} = 432.4 - 273.1 = 159.3°$$

Exercise II. Starting with equations 17 and 21, show that for an adiabatic expansion

$$C_p \log (T_2/T_1) = R \log (p_2/p_1)$$

Heat Capacity of Gases.   When a monatomic gas, such as helium or mercury vapor, is heated at constant volume, the heat energy supplied is used only to augment the translational kinetic energy of the molecules.   Since there is no change in volume, there can be no work done against the atmosphere, and, since there is only one atom in the molecule, there can be no absorption of vibrational or rotational energy within the molecule.

According to the fundamental kinetic equation given on page 28,

$$pv = \tfrac{2}{3} \text{ kinetic energy} \qquad (18)$$

or

$$\text{Kinetic energy} = \tfrac{3}{2}\, pv$$

But, for 1 mole of an ideal gas,

$$pV = RT = 1.987T$$

Therefore,

$$\text{Kinetic energy of 1 mole} = \tfrac{3}{2}RT = 2.98T \text{ calories} \qquad (19)$$

If $2.98T_2$ represents the kinetic energy at temperature T_2, and $2.98T_1$ at temperature T_1, the difference in kinetic energy is $2.98(T_2 - T_1)$ cal. If now the difference in temperature is made exactly $1°$, the difference in kinetic energy is 2.98 cal, and this is the value of the molar heat capacity at constant volume C_v, defined as the number of calories necessary to raise 1 mole of the gas through $1°$.   For gases in which the energy can be absorbed only by increasing the translational velocity,

$$C_v = \tfrac{3}{2}R = 2.98 \text{ cal deg}^{-1} \text{ mole}^{-1} \qquad (20)$$

It has been found that monatomic gases have a molar heat capacity C_v of 2.98 cal deg^{-1} mole^{-1} in perfect agreement with this formula.

When a gas is heated at constant pressure, the gas expands and does work against the atmosphere.   Heat must be introduced into the gas to do this work as well as to raise the temperature. This work is equal to $p \, \Delta V$. If V_2 is the molar volume at T_2, and V_1 is the molar volume at T_1, and $T_2 - T_1 = 1°$, then for an ideal gas, in which the internal energy is independent of the volume,

$$C_p - C_v = p \, \Delta V = p(V_2 - V_1) = R(T_2 - T_1) = R$$

$$= 1.987 \text{ cal deg}^{-1} \text{ mole}^{-1} \qquad (21)$$

Since $C_v \doteq 2.98$ for monatomic gases, and $C_p = C_v + R$, it follows that $C_p = 4.97$, and the ratio γ of the two heat capacities is

$$\gamma = C_p/C_v = 4.97/2.98 = 1.67 \qquad (22)$$

Again, this relation is in excellent agreement with the experimental data for monatomic gases such as argon and helium, as shown in Table II.

Table II. Molar Heat Capacities of Gases

In cal deg^{-1} mole^{-1} at 25°

Gas	C_p	C_v	$C_p/C_v = \gamma$
Argon, A	4.97	2.98	1.67
Helium, He	4.97	2.98	1.67
Mercury, Hg	4.97	2.98	1.67
Hydrogen, H_2	6.90	4.91	1.41
Oxygen, O_2	7.05	5.05	1.40
Nitrogen, N_2	6.94	4.95	1.40
Chlorine, Cl_2	8.25	6.14	1.34
Nitric oxide, NO	7.11	5.11	1.39
Carbon monoxide, CO	6.97	4.97	1.40
Hydrogen chloride, HCl	7.05	5.01	1.41
Carbon dioxide, CO_2	8.96	6.92	1.29
Nitrous oxide, N_2O	9.33	7.29	1.28
Sulfur dioxide, SO_2	9.4	7.3	1.29
Ammonia, NH_3	8.63	6.57	1.31
Methane, CH_4	8.60	6.59	1.31
Ethane, C_2H_6	12.71	10.65	1.19
Dimethyl ether, C_2H_6O	15.89	13.75	1.16

For polyatomic molecules the values of C_v are greater than 3 cal deg^{-1} mole^{-1} because such molecules possess rotational and vibrational energy in addition to translational energy. Although the interpretation of heat capacity requires the use of quantum mechanics (Chapter 18) several simple ideas based on classical physics are helpful. According to the principle of equipartition of energy each degree of translational freedom and each degree of rotational freedom can contribute $\frac{1}{2}R$ or 1 cal deg^{-1} mole^{-1} to the heat capacity. Since the translational motion of a gas molecule may be resolved into components along three perpendicular axes, the gas molecule is said to have three degrees of translational freedom. Thus, translational motion contributes 3 cal deg^{-1} $mole^{-1}$, and this is the heat capacity of a monatomic gas.

For a rigid diatomic molecule there are two rotational degrees of freedom because any rotatory movement may be represented in terms of rotation in two perpendicular planes. Therefore, C_v would be ex-

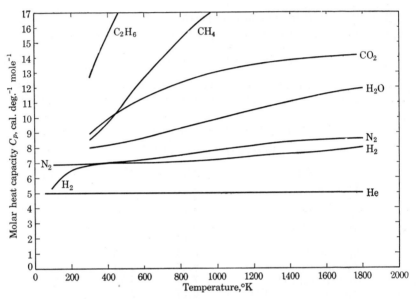

FIG. 5-2.   Influence of temperature on the heat capacity of gases.

pected to be $3 + 2(\frac{1}{2})R = 5$ cal deg^{-1} $mole^{-1}$ and $C_p = 7$ cal deg^{-1} $mole^{-1}$, which is in excellent agreement with what is found for H_2, O_2, N_2, NO, CO, and HCl at $25°$ as may be seen in Table II. Interestingly enough, diatomic hydrogen gas behaves as a monatomic gas below $60°K$, and γ is found to have a value of 1.66. The reason rotational energy becomes negligible at these low temperatures is not forthcoming from classical physics but is explained by quantum mechanics. Some of the degrees of freedom become "frozen" at low temperatures. However, larger values of heat capacities are obtained for these molecules at high temperatures as illustrated in *Fig. 5-2*.

This increase results from the increasing vibrational energy of the molecules. According to classical physics each mode of vibrational energy should contribute R cal deg^{-1} $mole^{-1}$ to the heat capacity because there is potential energy as well as kinetic energy associated with vibration, each contributing $\frac{1}{2}R$ cal deg^{-1} mole^{-1}. Thus it is expected that maximum values of $C_v = 7$ and $C_p = 9$ cal deg^{-1} mole^{-1} might be reached for diatomic molecules at high temperatures. For a linear triatomic molecule such as CO_2 there are still only two degrees of rotational freedom, but there are four degrees of vibrational freedom because vibrations in linear triatomic molecules may be resolved into four simple types of vibration. Thus CO_2 might be expected to have a C_p value of 15 cal deg^{-1} mole^{-1} at very high temperatures where all these types of vibration will occur. At lower temperatures some of these degrees of freedom are lost because the quanta of energy available are too small to cause certain types of motion. In general, the more complex the molecule, the greater is its molar heat capacity, the greater is the temperature effect, and the smaller is γ, although this ratio cannot become smaller than 1. A table of constants for calculating the heat capacities of common gases at temperatures in the range 300–1500°K is given on page 123.

Heat Capacity of Solids. Dulong and Petit in 1819 found that at room temperature *the product of the specific heat c_p and the atomic weight of the solid elements is a constant,* approximately 6.4 cal deg^{-1}. This law of Dulong and Petit played an important part in the determination of atomic weights because it could be used to select the multiple of the known equivalent weight required to give the atomic weight.

Example 3. Estimate the specific heat c_p of zinc at constant pressure at room temperature from the fact that its atomic weight is 65.38.

$$65.38 \, c_p = 6.4$$

$$c_p = 0.098 \text{ cal deg}^{-1} \text{ g}^{-1}$$

The heat capacity of a solid at constant volume is a more significant quantity than the heat capacity at constant pressure. In the latter case, there are secondary effects depending on the thermal expansion and compressibility which tend to mask the more fundamental relation. Lewis and Gibson * found that the atomic heat capacity at constant volume and room temperature is 5.90 cal deg^{-1} g-atom^{-1} within 0.09 for all the elements heavier than potassium for which data were available.

Boltzmann showed that this value for C_v for a solid is in accord with the expectation for an ideal solid in which the atoms oscillate about equilibrium positions and do not interact in any way with their neighbors. Such a solid would have $\frac{3}{2}RT$ of translational energy, as does an ideal monatomic gas, and, in addition $\frac{3}{2}RT$ of potential energy, or a total of $\frac{6}{2}RT$. Thus C_v is expected to be very close to 6 cal deg^{-1}

* Lewis and Gibson, *J. Am. Chem. Soc., 39,* 2554 (1917).

mole^{-1}. Although the values for metals and elements are close to this at room temperature, it is found that in all cases the value of C_v decreases with the temperature and approaches zero at 0°K as shown in *Fig. 5-3*. The explanation of the low values of C_v at low temperatures again requires quantum mechanics. It has been shown by Debye that at temperatures below 50°K the heat capacity should be proportional to T^3. This relation is useful for calculating values of C_v at temperatures where it is difficult to obtain experimental data.

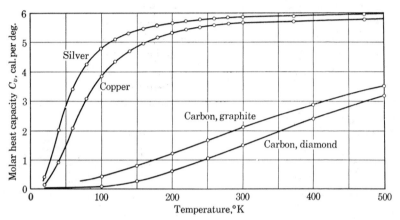

Fig. 5-3. Molar heat capacity of solid elements as a function of temperature.

The influence of temperature on the heat capacity of crystals is shown in Fig. 5-3 for three different elements. Near the absolute zero of temperature, all the crystals increase in heat capacity slowly, in agreement with theory, and, then, at higher temperatures, the heat capacity increases rapidly with the temperature as new vibrations are brought into action and new degrees of freedom are released. Finally, at sufficiently high temperatures, the limiting value of 5.9 is reached. It is reached at low temperatures for those elements like copper which are soft and malleable and have large atomic weights and low melting points. These properties indicate that the atoms are held together rather loosely in the crystal and can vibrate internally in all possible directions with an expenditure of energy which is available at temperatures well below room temperature. Carbon, however, has strong crystal forces as evidenced by the fact that it has a very high melting point. Moreover, it has a low atomic weight. These properties lead to atomic vibrations of such high energy that it is necessary to heat carbon to a very high temperature before there is enough energy to bring all the vibrations into play. Accordingly, the full heat capacity of 5.9 cal deg^{-1} g atom^{-1}

at constant volume is not reached even at moderately high temperatures.
The molar heat capacities of crystalline compounds can be estimated approximately by adding up the molar heat capacities of the elements. For example, the molar heat capacity of lead sulfide, PbS, is 12.3 at room temperature, and the sum of the gram-atomic heat capacities of lead and sulfur is 6.3 + 5.5 or 11.8.

REFERENCES

Lewis and Randall, *Thermodynamics and the Free Energy of Chemical Substances*, McGraw-Hill Book Co., New York, 1923.

Glasstone, *Thermodynamics for Chemists*, D. Van Nostrand Co., New York, 1947.

Rossini, *Chemical Thermodynamics*, John Wiley & Sons, New York, 1950.

Paul, *Principles of Chemical Thermodynamics*, McGraw-Hill Book Co., New York, 1951.

Klotz, *Chemical Thermodynamics*, Prentice-Hall, New York, 1950.

PROBLEMS

1. Thirty-five liters of hydrogen are produced at a total pressure of 1 atm by the action of acid on a metal. Calculate the work done by the gas in pushing back the atmosphere in (a) l-atm, (b) calories, (c) joules, and (d) ergs.
   Ans. (a) 35 l-atm. (b) 847 cal. (c) 3540 joules. (d) 3540 × 10⁷ ergs.

2. A 900-gram weight falls 120 meters. (a) How many ergs of heat are liberated when it strikes the ground? (b) How many joules? (c) How many calories? (d) How many liter-atmospheres?
   Ans. (a) 1.059 × 10¹⁰ ergs. (b) 1059 joules. (c) 253.1 cal. (d) 10.45 l-atm.

3. One hundred grams of liquid benzene is vaporized at its boiling point 80.2° at 760 mm. The heat of vaporization at constant pressure is 94.4 cal per gram. Calculate (a) w; (b) q; (c) ΔH; (d) ΔE. (e) Is w the maximum work that can be performed? *Ans.* (a) 898, (b) 9440, (c) 9440, (d) 8542 cal, (e) Yes.

4. Calculate the work done when a mole of sulfur dioxide gas expands isothermally and reversibly at 27° from 10 atm to 1 atm: (a) assuming that the gas is an ideal gas. (b) Would an attractive force between molecules of the gas tend to make the work done larger or smaller? *Ans.* (a) 1370 cal mole⁻¹. (b) Smaller.

5. Calculate the quantity of heat required to raise 1 mole of CO_2 from 0°C to 300°C (a) at constant pressure and (b) constant volume. Given

$$C_p = 6.40 + 10.2 \times 10^{-3}T - 35 \times 10^{-7}T^2$$

Ans. (a) 3020, (b) 2420 cal.

6. One mole of argon at 25° and 1 atm pressure is allowed to expand to a volume of 50 liters (a) isothermally, and (b) adiabatically. Calculate the final pressure in each case, assuming ideal gas behavior. *Ans.* (a) 0.489, (b) 0.303 atm.

7. Lead chloride is found by chemical analysis to contain 74.5 per cent lead and 25.5 per cent chlorine. The atomic weight of chlorine is 35.45. The specific heat of lead is approximately 0.0309 cal g⁻¹. Using this information, decide among the

possible formulas such as Pb_2Cl, $PbCl$, $PbCl_2$, $PbCl_3$, Pb_2Cl_4, etc., and calculate the atomic weight of lead.   *Ans.* $PbCl_2$ or Pb_2Cl_4, etc.; 207.2.

8. How much work is done when a man weighing 75 kg (165 lb) climbs the Washington monument, 555 ft high? How many kilocalories must be supplied to do this muscular work, assuming that 25 per cent of the energy produced by the oxidation of food in the body can be converted into muscular mechanical work?

9. A mole of ammonia gas is condensed at its boiling point $-33.4°C$ by the application of a pressure infinitesimally greater than 1 atm. To evaporate a gram of ammonia at its boiling point requires the absorption of 327 cal. Calculate (a) w; (b) q; (c) ΔH; (d) ΔE.

10. One hundred grams of benzene vapor (free from liquid benzene) at 80.2° and 760 mm is expanded reversibly and isothermally by reducing the pressure to 100 mm. Assume that benzene vapor acts as an ideal gas. (a) What is the maximum work that can be obtained by this expansion? (b) What is the maximum work that can be obtained by expanding 100 grams of benzene isothermally at 100° from 760 mm to 100 mm?

11. One mole of hydrogen at 25° and 1 atm is compressed adiabatically into a volume of 5 liters. Calculate (a) the final temperature, (b) the final pressure, and (c) the work done if carried out reversibly.

12. How many calories of heat is required to raise the temperature of 10 grams of argon (a monatomic gas) through 10° (a) at constant volume, (b) at constant pressure?

13. Ten liters of mercury vapor, which is monatomic, expands adiabatically at 600°C from 3 atm until the pressure is 1 atm. What will be the temperature of the mercury vapor after the adiabatic expansion?

14. (a) Estimate from Dulong and Petit's relation the specific heat of iron at room temperature. (b) Assuming that the atomic heats of solids are roughly additive, estimate the specific heat of silver iodide.

15. Prove for a piston moving in a cylinder that the work done equals the pressure times the cross-sectional area times the distance, using the fundamental relation that work equals force times distance.

16. Show that for an isothermal expansion of an ideal gas $\Delta H = 0$.

17. Estimate the maximum rise in temperature of a 500-kg iron weight when it hits a hard iron surface after falling through 500 meters (neglecting air resistance and assuming that half the heat goes into the iron weight). The atomic weight of iron is 55.85.

18. The specific heat of zinc is 0.0978 cal deg^{-1} g^{-1} and it has been established that 10.00 grams of zinc combine with 10.85 grams of chlorine to form a stable zinc chloride. What is the atomic weight of zinc, and what is the formula for the zinc chloride if the valence of chlorine is 1 and its atomic weight 35.45?

19. Calculate the molar heat capacity of glycol, $(CH_2OH)_2$, at 2° from the following data. One hundred grams of glycol was weighed into a copper container equipped with an electric heater and a sensitive resistance thermometer. The copper container or calorimeter was suspended by fine cords inside a metal shield which was in turn suspended inside an outer container which could be evacuated. The shield carried heaters and thermocouples by means of which its temperature was kept so close to that of the calorimeter that the heat leak to the calorimeter was negligible.

The apparatus was immersed in an ice bath, and, after it had cooled to nearly $0°$, it was evacuated. With the shield maintained at the temperature of the calorimeter, 955 absolute joules was required to heat the calorimeter from $0.500°$ to $3.500°$. The heat capacity of the calorimeter was found to be 20.00 cal per deg at $2°$.

20. One hundred liters of water vapor at $100°$ and $\frac{1}{2}$ atm is compressed isothermally and reversibly to 1 atm and further until the volume is 10 liters. Neglecting the volume of the water condensed in comparison with the volume of the vapor and assuming that the vapor behaves as an ideal gas, calculate the work done and the heat evolved.

21. Ten cubic feet of oxygen under pressure is allowed to expand reversibly under adiabatic conditions to a volume of 30 cu ft. Considering oxygen to be an ideal gas with the heat capacity given in Table II, calculate the final temperature if the initial temperature is $25°$.

22. The specific heat of neon at constant volume is 0.149 cal deg^{-1} g^{-1} and the ratio $c_p/c_v = 1.66$. How many atoms are there in a molecule of neon?

23. One mole of an ideal gas is confined in a cylinder by a piston. The pressure is p, the volume is V, and the cylinder is immersed in a thermostat at temperature T. The following cycle is carried out: (1) The temperature of the thermostat is raised $1°$, the pressure being kept constant; (2) the pressure is gradually increased until the volume is decreased to the original value V, with no change in temperature; and (3) the temperature of the thermostat is lowered $1°$, the volume being kept constant. Make a table showing the initial and final pressure, volume, and temperature, and q, w, and ΔE, for each step. Since ΔE for the cycle is 0, show that $C_p - C_v = R$.

24. Estimate how many more calories of heat will be required to heat 100 g of aluminum from $25°$ to $300°$ than will be required to heat the same weight of silver through the same temperature interval.

25. For the adiabatic expansion of a perfect gas show that

$$pV^\gamma = \text{constant} \quad \text{and} \quad TV^{R/C_v} = \text{constant}$$

26. Develop a formula for calculating $C_p - C_v$ for a gas which follows van der Waals' equation.

27. A perfect monatomic gas passes from a large pipe into an evacuated cylinder through a valve which is opened slowly enough to keep the pressure in the pipe sensibly constant. The gas in the main is at pressure p and temperature T. Develop a formula for calculating the temperature of the gas in the cylinder when its pressure reaches the pressure p of the pipe, if the gas loses no heat during the process.

28. What is the minimum number of calories of work required to compress isothermally 1 mole of ammonia at 1 atm and $150°$ to a volume of 10 liters: (a) assuming that it follows the ideal gas laws, (b) assuming that it follows van der Waals' equation with $a = 4.170$ liters^2 atm mole^{-2} and $b = 0.03707$ liter mole^{-1}.

6

Thermochemistry

Definitions. Thermochemistry is concerned with the heat that accompanies chemical reaction. Thermochemical data are usually expressed by writing the equation for the chemical reaction and giving the value of ΔH after the reaction. In writing equations, solids, liquids, and gases are designated by (s), (l), and (g), respectively, following each of the reactants and products. Thus,

$$C(\text{graphite})(s) + O_2(g) \rightarrow CO_2(g) \qquad \Delta H_{298} = -94,052 \text{ cal mole}^{-1}$$

ΔH is equal to the heat of reaction at constant pressure in reactions where pressure-volume work is the only work done. In chemical equations it is the change in enthalpy when the reactants, that is, the chemical compounds written at the left of the equation, react to give the reaction products written at the right of the equation. The absolute values of the enthalpy are unknown and unnecessary. In the oxidation of carbon, heat is evolved, and the enthalpy is thereby decreased, so that ΔH has a negative value. As a matter of fact, most ordinary chemical reactions evolve heat. They are *exothermic* reactions and have negative values of ΔH. At temperatures much higher than ordinary room temperatures the heat-absorbing or *endothermic* reactions are more common.

Another convention used in the thermochemistry of solutions is the symbol aq (*aqua*, water) signifying a large excess of water, so large that the addition of more water has no measurable effect on the heat evolved.

Calorimetric Measurements. Calorimeters are used for measuring the heat changes that accompany chemical reactions. In the most common type, the reaction is allowed to take place in a reaction chamber surrounded by a weighed quantity of water in an insulated vessel, and the rise in temperature is measured with a sensitive thermometer. The product of the rise in temperature and the total heat capacity of the water and calorimeter is a measure of the heat evolved. The heat capacity of the surrounding water is obtained by weighing the water; the heat capacity of the calorimeter is obtained by measuring a reaction of known heat evolution or by introducing a measured quantity of heat with an electric heater. The best reactions to measure are those which proceed rapidly, thus minimizing any errors due to cooling; and those which run to completion, thus assuring that the heat value obtained applies to the reaction assumed and that none of the reacting materials remain unreacted.

The water in the calorimeter must be stirred adequately to insure uniform temperature throughout, but the heat of stirring must be kept to a minimum so that corrections from this source will be small. The evaporation of the water must be kept very small also. The heat lost from the hotter calorimeter to its surrounding jacket may be calculated by plotting the temperature of the calorimeter against time, and extrapolating this cooling curve back to the time at which the heat-evolving reaction started. The difference between this extrapolated temperature and the initial temperature gives a fair estimate of the temperature rise which would have been obtained if there had been no loss of heat from the calorimeter during the period of observation.

In adiabatic calorimetry the cooling correction is rendered unnecessary by experimental devices which eliminate or greatly reduce the transfer of heat. Vacuum-walled vessels are used to minimize the heat losses, or the outer jacket is heated electrically at an experimentally controlled rate such that the jacket is always kept at the same temperature as the calorimeter.

Heat of Combustion. The heat evolved in the complete oxidation of a substance is known as the *heat of combustion*. The values are given in terms of heats of combustion per gram or as heats of combustion per mole. Since only rapid, complete reactions are suitable for thermochemical measurement, heats of combustion have been by far the most common data of thermochemistry.

It is essential to burn everything to its highest stage of oxidation to insure that a definite reaction is being measured which will give reproducible results. For this purpose the material is ignited electrically in a heavy steel bomb containing oxygen under a pressure of 25 atm.* All carbon is burnt to carbon dioxide, and all hydrogen to water. As yet the halogen-containing compounds present difficulties, and the heat of combustion of a substance like ethyl chloride is not known with high accuracy because the products formed are not always definite.

---

* Experimental details may be found in Daniels, Mathews, Williams, and Staff, *Experimental Physical Chemistry*, McGraw-Hill Book Co., New York, 1949, pages 38–43.

A great deal of our present thermochemical knowledge goes back to the data of Thomsen and Berthelot of the last century. Richards made accurate calorimetric measurements early in this century, and more recently many accurate data have come from Rossini and others.* Several compilations of accurate thermochemical data have been published by the Bureau of Standards, and the values in Table I have been obtained from this source.

Table I.[1]   Heats of Combustion [to $H_2O(l)$ and $CO_2(g)$] at Constant Pressure and 25°C

	ΔH	
Substance	in kcal mole^{-1}	in kcal g^{-1}
Hydrogen, $H_2(g)$	-68.3174	-33.8876
Graphite, $C(s)$	-94.0518	-7.8311
Carbon monoxide, $CO(g)$	-67.6361	-2.4147
Methane, $CH_4(g)$	-212.798	-13.2651
Ethane, $C_2H_6(g)$	-372.820	-12.3992
Propane, $C_3H_8(g)$	-530.605	-12.0335
n-Butane, $C_4H_{10}(g)$	-687.982	-11.8373
iso-Butane, $C_4H_{10}(g)$	-686.342	-11.8091
n-Pentane, $C_5H_{12}(g)$	-845.16	-11.7146
n-Hexane, $C_6H_{14}(l)$	-995.01	-11.5468
n-Heptane, $C_7H_{16}(l)$	-1151.27	-11.4899
n-Octane, $C_8H_{18}(l)$	-1307.53	-11.4471
Ethylene, $C_2H_4(g)$	-337.234	-12.0217
Propylene, $C_3H_6(g)$	-491.987	-11.6923
1-Butene, $C_4H_8(g)$	-649.757	-11.5813
Acetylene, $C_2H_2(g)$	-310.615	-11.9302
Cyclopentane, $C_5H_{10}(l)$	-786.54	-11.2155
Cyclohexane, $C_6H_{12}(l)$	-936.88	-11.1327
Benzene, $C_6H_6(l)$	-780.98	-9.9987
Toluene, $C_7H_8(l)$	-934.50	-10.1428

[1] From Rossini, Pitzer, Taylor, Ebert, Kilpatrick, Beckett, Williams, and Werner, "Selected Values of Properties of Hydrocarbons," *Circular of the National Bureau of Standards* C 461, U. S. Government Printing Office, Washington, D. C., 1947.

Heats of combustion are useful in calculating other thermochemical data. Also they have practical as well as theoretical importance. The heating value of fuel is an important matter. The purchaser of coal should be interested in its heat of combustion as well as in its weight.

* Rossini, *Bur. Standards J. Research*, **12**, 735 (1934); Richardson and Parks, *J. Am. Chem. Soc.*, **61**, 3543 (1939); Huffman and Ellis, *J. Am. Chem. Soc.*, **57**, 41 (1935), and later papers.

The dietician must know among other factors the number of calories obtainable from various foods.

Thermochemical Calculations. Lavoisier and Laplace recognized in 1780 that the heat absorbed in decomposing a chemical compound must be equal to the heat evolved in its formation under the same conditions. Hess pointed out in 1840 that the over-all heat of a chemical reaction at constant pressure is the same, regardless of the intermediate steps involved. These are both corollaries of the first law of thermodynamics, the law of conservation of energy. They follow from the experience of the preceding chapter, since the enthalpy change ΔH for a reaction depends only on the initial and final states and is not affected by the path of the reaction. A specific example follows:

The total amount of heat evolved in the oxidation of methane to CO_2 and H_2O is the same whether the combustion is carried out in a single step or in a stepwise fashion.

$$CH_4(g) + \tfrac{1}{2}O_2(g) \rightarrow CH_3OH(l) \qquad \Delta H = -39.1 \text{ kcal}$$

$$CH_3OH(l) + \tfrac{1}{2}O_2(g) \rightarrow CH_2O(l) + H_2O(l) \qquad \Delta H = -39.0 \text{ kcal}$$

$$CH_2O(l) + \tfrac{1}{2}O_2(g) \rightarrow CH_2O_2(l) \qquad \Delta H = -70.1 \text{ kcal}$$

$$CH_2O_2(l) + \tfrac{1}{2}O_2(g) \rightarrow CO_2(g) + H_2O(l) \qquad \Delta H = -64.6 \text{ kcal}$$

If these four reactions and their ΔH's are added the intermediate compounds cancel out since they occur in equal quantities on each side of the arrow. The over-all reaction and over-all ΔH can then be obtained.

$$CH_4(g) + 2O_2(g) \rightarrow CO_2(g) + 2H_2O(l) \qquad \Delta H = -212.8 \text{ kcal}$$

This method of adding together several known thermochemical reactions is frequently used to obtain the heat of reactions that have not yet been measured or that cannot be measured by direct experimental methods. For example, it is not practical to measure the heat evolved when carbon burns to carbon monoxide in a limited amount of oxygen because the product will be an uncertain mixture of carbon monoxide and carbon dioxide. However, it is a simple matter to burn the carbon completely to carbon dioxide in an excess of oxygen and to measure the heat of this complete reaction. Thus, for graphite

$$C(s) + O_2(g) \rightarrow CO_2(g) \qquad \Delta H = -94.0518 \text{ kcal}$$

The heat evolved when carbon monoxide burns to carbon dioxide can be readily measured also:

$$CO(g) + \tfrac{1}{2}O_2(g) \rightarrow CO_2(g) \qquad \Delta H = -67.6361 \text{ kcal}$$

Writing these equations in such a way as to obtain the desired reaction $C + \frac{1}{2}O_2 \rightarrow CO$, adding, and canceling

$$C(s) + O_2(g) \rightarrow CO_2(g) \qquad \Delta H = -94.0518 \text{ kcal}$$
$$CO_2(g) \rightarrow CO(g) + \frac{1}{2}O_2(g) \qquad \Delta H = 67.6361 \text{ kcal}$$

$$C(s) + \frac{1}{2}O_2(g) \rightarrow CO(g) \qquad \Delta H = -26.4157 \text{ kcal}$$

It will be noticed that, since the second reaction has been reversed, the sign of ΔH is changed from minus to plus. This indicates that 67.6361 kcal would be absorbed if the reaction $CO_2(g) \rightarrow CO(g) + \frac{1}{2}O_2(g)$ occurred.

The indirect calculation of heats of reaction is illustrated with other examples.

Example 1. Calculate the heat change involved when 1 mole of monoclinic sulfur undergoes transition into rhombic sulfur at room temperature. Although there is a natural transition at room temperature, the change is too slow for accurate calorimetric measurements. Accordingly, the two different forms are subjected to a reaction, the heat of which can be measured accurately, and the difference in heat of reaction is equal to the heat of transition.

$$S(\text{monoclinic})(s) + O_2(g) \rightarrow SO_2(g) \qquad \Delta H = -71.03 \text{ kcal}$$
$$SO_2(g) \rightarrow S(\text{rhombic})(s) + O_2(g) \qquad \Delta H = 70.96 \text{ kcal}$$

$$S(\text{monoclinic})(s) \rightarrow S(\text{rhombic})(s) \qquad \Delta H = -0.07 \text{ kcal}$$

As a general rule, the denser of the two forms requires more energy to pull the atoms apart, and the heat of any reaction involving this material is accordingly less, if other factors remain the same. The rhombic form is more dense at 25° than the monoclinic, and it evolves 70 cal less than the monoclinic variety.

Example 2. What is the heat of reaction when sulfuric acid is formed from its elements?

It is not possible to mix hydrogen and oxygen and sulfur in a calorimeter and produce sulfuric acid directly, but reactions capable of direct calorimetric measurements can be selected in such a way that, when added together, they will give the desired over-all reaction.

Sulfur is burnt in a stream of oxygen in a calorimeter at room temperature. Sulfur dioxide is oxidized with oxygen with a platinum catalyst at a high temperature, and the corrections are made to give the heat of reaction at room temperature. Other necessary reactions are included. Then

$$S(s) + O_2(g) \rightarrow SO_2(g) \qquad \Delta H = -70.96 \text{ kcal}$$
$$SO_2(g) + \frac{1}{2}O_2(g) \rightarrow SO_3(g) \qquad \Delta H = -23.49 \text{ kcal}$$
$$SO_3(g) + H_2O(l) \rightarrow H_2SO_4(l) \qquad \Delta H = -31.14 \text{ kcal}$$
$$H_2(g) + \frac{1}{2}O_2(g) \rightarrow H_2O(l) \qquad \Delta H = -68.32 \text{ kcal}$$

$$S(s) + 2O_2(g) + H_2(g) \rightarrow H_2SO_4(l) \qquad \Delta H = -193.91 \text{ kcal}$$

Heats of Formation. The most convenient way to record thermo-chemical data for the indirect calculation of heats of reaction is in the form of tables giving the heats of formation of the chemical compounds. Although the absolute values of enthalpy of the compounds are not known, the over-all change in enthalpy during a chemical reaction can be calculated from the *heats of formation* on the basis of the convention that the enthalpies of the elements are arbitrarily taken as zero. For example, it follows from the reaction

$$C(s) + O_2(g) \rightarrow CO_2(g) \qquad \Delta H = -94.0518 \text{ kcal}$$

that the heat of formation of carbon dioxide is -94.0518 kcal, because 94.0518 kcal of heat is evolved when a mole of carbon dioxide gas is produced from its elements, and the elements are arbitrarily assigned a zero value. The symbol $\Delta H°_f$ is used for the heat of formation of a compound from its component elements at constant pressure; it is the difference in enthalpy of the compound and the elements from which it is formed. The enthalpy of the elements will vary, depending on their physical state, and it is conventionally agreed that the standard states for which H is taken as zero are the naturally occurring states of the elements under 1 atm pressure and at the temperature of the reaction. In the example given, oxygen is a gas at atmospheric pressure, and carbon is a solid. If two or more allotropic forms can exist at the specified temperature, it is necessary to specify the form. In this book graphite is always taken as the standard state for carbon and rhombic sulfur as the standard state for sulfur. Unless the temperature is specified, it is assumed to be 25°C, because this has come to be accepted as the standard temperature for physical chemical measurements.

The heats of formation or enthalpies of formation of many inorganic and organic compounds have been compiled by the Bureau of Standards, and a few selected values have been collected in Table II.

The calculation of heats of reaction is simplified by using the heats of formation when they are available. The change in enthalpy of a given reaction ΔH is obtained by subtracting the heats of formation $\Delta H°_f$ of the reactants from those of the products.

$$Fe_2O_3(s) + 2Al(s) \rightarrow Al_2O_3(s) + 2Fe(s)$$

$$-196.5 \qquad 0 \qquad -399.1 \qquad 0$$

where the heats of formation of the compounds are given below each compound. Then for the isothermal reaction at 25°

$$\Delta H = (-399.1 + 0) - (-196.5 + 0) = -202.6 \text{ kcal}$$

Table II.[1]   Heat of Formation at 25°

$\Delta H°_f$ in kcal mole^{-1}

Elements and Inorganic Compounds

$O_3(g)$	34.0	$CO(g)$	-26.4157
$H_2O(g)$	-57.7979	$CO_2(g)$	-94.0518
$H_2O(l)$	-68.3174	$PbO(s)$	-52.5
$HCl(g)$	-22.063	$PbO_2(s)$	-66.12
$Br_2(g)$	7.34	$PbSO_4(s)$	-219.50
$HBr(g)$	-8.66	$Hg(g)$	14.54
$HI(g)$	6.20	$Ag_2O(s)$	-7.306
S(monoclinic)	0.071	$AgCl(s)$	-30.362
$SO_2(g)$	-70.96	$Fe_2O_3(s)$	-196.5
$SO_3(g)$	-94.45	$Fe_3O_4(s)$	-267.0
$H_2S(g)$	-4.815	$Al_2O_3(s)$	-399.09
$H_2SO_4(l)$	-193.91	$UF_6(g)$	-505
$NO(g)$	21.600	$UF_6(s)$	-517
$NO_2(g)$	8.091	$CaO(s)$	-151.9
$NH_3(g)$	-11.04	$CaCO_3(s)$	-288.45
$HNO_3(l)$	-41.404	$NaF(s)$	-136.0
$P(g)$	75.18	$NaCl(s)$	-98.232
$PCl_3(g)$	-73.22	$KF(s)$	-134.46
$PCl_5(g)$	-95.35	$KCl(s)$	-104.175
C(s, diamond)	0.4532		

Organic Compounds

Methane, $CH_4(g)$	-17.889	Propylene, $C_3H_6(g)$	4.879
Ethane, $C_2H_6(g)$	-20.236	1-Butene, $C_4H_8(g)$	0.280
Propane, $C_3H_8(g)$	-24.820	Acetylene, $C_2H_2(g)$	54.194
n-Butane, $C_4H_{10}(g)$	-29.812	Formaldehyde, $CH_2O(g)$	-27.7
iso-Butane, $C_4H_{10}(g)$	-31.452	Acetaldehyde, $C_2H_4O(g)$	-39.76
n-Pentane, $C_5H_{12}(g)$	-35.00	Methanol, $CH_3OH(l)$	-57.02
n-Hexane, $C_6H_{14}(g)$	-39.96	Ethanol, $C_2H_6O(l)$	-66.356
n-Heptane, $C_7H_{16}(g)$	-44.89	Formic acid, $CH_2O_2(l)$	-97.8
n-Octane, $C_8H_{18}(g)$	-49.82	Acetic acid, $C_2H_4O_2(l)$	-116.4
Benzene, $C_6H_6(g)$	19.820	Oxalic acid, $C_2H_2O_4(s)$	-197.6
Benzene, $C_6H_6(l)$	11.718	Carbon tetrachloride, $CCl_4(l)$	-33.3
Ethylene, $C_2H_4(g)$	12.496	Glycine, $C_2H_5O_2N(s)$	-126.33

[1] These data have been obtained from Rossini, Wagman, Evans, Levine, and Jaffe, "Selected Values of Chemical Thermodynamic Properties," *Circular of the National Bureau of Standards* 500, U. S. Government Printing Office, Washington, D. C., 1952, and Rossini, Pitzer, Taylor, Ebert, Kilpatrick, Beckett, Williams, and Werner, "Selected Values of Properties of Hydrocarbons," *Circular of the National Bureau of Standards* C 461, U. S. Government Printing Office, Washington, D. C., 1947.

Similarly, the heat of formation may be calculated from the measured heat of combustion. For example, when acetylene is burned

$$HC\equiv CH(g) + 2\tfrac{1}{2}O_2(g) \rightarrow 2CO_2(g) + H_2O(l) \qquad \Delta H = -310.615 \text{ kcal}$$

$$\Delta H = -310.615 = 2\ \Delta H°_{f,CO_2} + \Delta H°_{f,H_2O} - \Delta H°_{f,\text{acetylene}}$$

$$= -188.104 + (-68.3174) - \Delta H°_{f,\text{acetylene}}$$

$$\Delta H°_{f,\text{acetylene}} = 54.194 \text{ kcal}$$

In other words, if hydrogen and carbon could combine at 25° to form acetylene, 54.194 kcal of heat would be absorbed per mole of acetylene formed.

Because the heats of formation are obtained by taking differences between heats of combustion a fairly small percentage error in the large heats of combustion may introduce a large percentage error in their difference.

Example 3. What per cent error in the calculation of the heat of formation of *n*-butane will be introduced by an error of 0.2 per cent in the heat of combustion of *n*-butane?

$$C_4H_{10}(g) + 6\tfrac{1}{2}O_2(g) \rightarrow 4CO_2(g) + 5H_2O(l) \qquad \Delta H = -687.982 \text{ kcal}$$

$$\Delta H°_{f,n\text{-butane}} = 687.982 - 4(94.0518) - 5(68.3174)$$

$$= -29.812 \text{ kcal}$$

An error of 0.2 per cent in the heat of combustion would be 1.4 kcal. An error of 1.4 kcal in the heat of formation of *n*-butane is an error of $(100)(1.4)/(29.8)$ or 4.7 per cent.

Reactions at Constant Pressure and Constant Volume. As explained on page 96, when a reaction occurs at constant volume, no work is involved, but, if the system is allowed to expand during the reaction, it does work against the atmosphere, and a smaller quantity of heat is evolved. If the system contracts, the heat evolved in a reaction at constant pressure is greater than that at constant volume by an amount equal to the work done on the system by the surroundings. If the products and the reactants have the same volume, the heats of reaction at constant pressure are the same as those at constant volume.

The general equation relating ΔH and ΔE, which has been derived on page 99, is

$$\Delta H = \Delta E + p\,\Delta v = \Delta E + \Delta nRT \qquad (1)$$

where ΔH is the heat of reaction at constant pressure, ΔE is the heat of reaction at constant volume, and $p\,\Delta v$ is the work done by the system. Since liquids and solids occupy very small volumes, the term $p\,\Delta v$ usually includes only the volumes of gases. The change in the number of moles of gas is denoted by Δn, that is, the number of moles of gaseous products minus the number of moles of gaseous reactants. Writing ΔnRT for $p\,\Delta v$ is exact only when the gases are ideal, but for practical purposes it is satisfactory for all gases at atmospheric pressure.

Heats of reaction are usually given for conditions of constant pressure because most reactions are studied at constant pressure. Heats of combustion of liquids and solids, however, are usually measured at constant volume, and equation 1 is useful in converting one into the other. In combustion there usually is a decrease in the number of moles of gas during the reaction and an evolution of heat. In such a case ΔH will have a larger negative value than ΔE, as illustrated in the following example.

Example 4. The heat of combustion of *n*-heptane at constant volume and 25° is 1148.93 kcal mole^{-1}.

$$C_7H_{16}(l) + 11O_2(g) \rightarrow 7CO_2(g) + 8H_2O(l) \qquad \Delta E = -1148.93 \text{ kcal mole}^{-1}$$

What is the value of ΔH, that is, the heat of reaction at constant pressure?

$$\Delta H = \Delta E + \Delta nRT = -1,148,930 - (4)(1.987)(298.1)$$

$$= -1,148,930 - 2369$$

$$= -1,151,299 \text{ cal mole}^{-1} \quad \text{or} \quad -1151.30 \text{ kcal mole}^{-1}$$

Thermochemical Constants. Thermochemical data are necessary for many calculations of theoretical significance in the predictions of chemical equilibria and reaction rates. It will be shown on page 140, for example, that, when specific heat curves of reactants and products are known down to absolute zero, then a knowledge of the heat of reaction permits a simple and accurate calculation of the equilibrium constant of a chemical reaction. In many of these calculations the heats of reactions constitute the least satisfactory part of our available data.

The compilations of the Bureau of Standards (see references of Table II) have largely superseded the older standard sources [*][†] of thermochemical data, although some classes of compounds have not yet been included. The addition and subtraction of heats of formation values from different tables may lead to errors since different tables may be based on slightly different values for the heats of combustion of elements and compounds. A single table is self-consistent; that is, the same heat of reaction is obtained when it is figured by two different paths. Projects of the American Petroleum Institute under the direction of Dr. F. D. Rossini have placed emphasis on the accumulation of heats of formation of the hydrocarbons. High purity of the compounds is as important as exact measurements in calorimetry. Heats of hydrogenation and bromination of unsaturated organic compounds have been determined accurately by Kistiakowsky [‡] and his co-workers.

* Bichowsky and Rossini, *The Thermochemistry of the Chemical Substances*, Reinhold Publishing Corp., New York, 1936.

† *International Critical Tables*, McGraw-Hill Book Co., New York, 1929.

‡ Kistiakowsky, Ruhoff, Smith, and Vaughan, *J. Am. Chem. Soc.*, *58*, 146 (1936), and other articles.

Heats of ionic reactions including neutralizations are determined simply in a calorimeter. When zinc deposits copper from a copper sulfate solution, for example,

$$Zn + Cu^{++} \rightarrow Cu + Zn^{++} \qquad \Delta H = -53 \text{ kcal}$$

When dilute solutions of ions are mixed, there is no thermal change unless a reaction takes place. For example, when dilute solutions of sodium bromide and sodium nitrate are mixed, no heat is evolved or absorbed. However, when sodium bromide and silver nitrate are mixed, there is an evolution of 20 kcal per mole due to the heat of precipitation of silver bromide. Moreover, in dilute solutions the heat of precipitation of silver bromide is the same at the same temperature whether the starting materials are potassium bromide and silver sulfate or any other ionized bromide and ionized silver salt.

It is possible to prepare a table of heats of formation of the different positive and negative ions from which heats of ionic reaction can be calculated. The heat of the reaction $\frac{1}{2}H_2 \rightarrow H^+ + e$ is usually taken arbitrarily as zero, and the heats of formation of other ions are then obtained by difference from known ionic reactions.

A scheme for estimating heats of formation and heat capacities has been developed by Andersen, Beyer, and Watson.* Each compound is regarded as a fundamental group which is modified by replacing its atoms with new groups. For example, a paraffin hydrocarbon is derived from methane by successive substitutions of CH_3 groups for hydrogen atoms. Definite values of $\Delta(\Delta H^\circ_f)$ are assigned to various group replacements such as OH, C_6H_5, NH_2, Cl, and to the replacement of single bonds by multiple bonds.

If experimental data cannot be found directly or indirectly by combining several equations, one is forced to make guesses based on the heats of reaction of similar compounds for which data are available.

As a last resort, heats of reaction can be estimated from a table of bond energies such as Table III. The bond energy is the energy required to break the bond and yield atoms. The use of such a table is based on the approximate assumption that the energy of a given bond between two atoms is the same regardless of other bonds to these atoms.

The heat of a reaction may be estimated by adding the bond energies for the bonds that are broken and subtracting from this total the bond

* Hougen and Watson, *Chemical Process Principles*, Vol. II, John Wiley & Sons, New York, 1947, page 758.

Table III.[1] Bond Energies

kcal mole^{-1}

Bond	ΔH of Bond Dissociation	Bond	ΔH of Bond Dissociation
C—C	80.5	O—O	34
C=C	145	O—H	109.4
C≡C	198	H—H	103.2
C—H	98.2	N—N	37
C—Cl	78	N—H	92.2
C—O	79	H—Cl	102.1
C=O	173	Cl—Cl	57.1
C—Br	54	Br—Br	46

[1] Pitzer, *Quantum Chemistry*, Prentice-Hall, New York, page 170, 1953.

energies for the new bonds formed in the reaction. This may be illustrated with the reaction

$$
\begin{array}{ccc}
\text{H} \ \ \text{H} & & \text{H} \ \ \text{H} \\
| \ \ \ | & & | \ \ \ | \\
\text{C}=\text{C} + \text{H}-\text{H} \rightarrow & \text{H}-\text{C}-\text{C}-\text{H} \\
| \ \ \ | & & | \ \ \ | \\
\text{H} \ \ \text{H} & & \text{H} \ \ \text{H}
\end{array}
$$

H—H	bond is broken	$\Delta H =$	103.2 kcal
C=C	bond is broken	$\Delta H =$	145 kcal
C—C	bond is formed	$\Delta H =$	− 80.5 kcal
2(C—H)	bonds are formed	$\Delta H =$	−196.4 kcal

$$\Delta H = -\ 29\ \ \text{kcal}$$

According to these estimates the hydrogenation of ethylene should evolve 29 kcal per mole. The experimentally determined value is 32.73 kcal per mole.

Variation of Heat Capacity with Temperature. In the preceding chapter it was shown that the heat capacity of a monatomic gas at constant pressure is 5.0 cal mole^{-1} deg^{-1} at all temperatures and that the heat capacity of polyatomic gases, as illustrated in Fig. 5-2 on page 106, is greater than this and increases with the temperature. Empirical equations giving the molar heat capacities of a number of gases as a function of temperature are recorded in Table IV. Usually the heat capacity can be expressed as a parabolic function of the absolute temperature with an equation containing two or three constants.

Table IV.[1]   **Molar Heat Capacity of Gases at Constant Pressure in Calories Degree^{-1} Mole^{-1}**

$$C_p = a + bT + cT^2$$

Gas	a	$b \times 10^3$	$c \times 10^7$
H_2	6.9469	−0.1999	4.808
N_2	6.4492	1.4125	−0.807
O_2	6.0954	3.2533	−10.171
Cl_2	7.5755	2.4244	−9.650
CO	6.3424	1.8363	−2.801
CO_2	6.3957	10.1933	−35.333
HCl	6.7319	0.4325	3.697
HBr	6.5776	0.9549	1.581
H_2O	7.1873	2.3733	2.084
CO_2	6.3957	10.1933	−35.333
NH_3	6.189	7.887	−7.28
CH_4	3.422	17.845	−41.65
C_2H_6	1.375	41.852	−138.27
C_3H_8	0.410	64.710	−225.82

[1] The constants are applicable in the range 300 to 1500°K.   Spencer and Justice, *J. Am. Chem. Soc.*, *56*, 2311 (1934); Spencer and Flannagan, *ibid.*, *64*, 2511 (1942).

These heat-capacity equations are important in many practical calculations, but data from which to determine them are very meager, particularly for the more complex molecules and at the higher temperatures. Important progress has been made in deriving them from spectroscopic data with the aid of statistical mechanics (page 567). For the simple molecules the calculations are often more accurate than the calorimetrically determined data, especially at elevated temperatures.

To calculate accurately the quantity of heat absorbed at constant *↱* pressure when the temperature of a substance is increased, it is necessary to integrate the equation $dH = C_p\, dT$ between the desired temperature limits.

$$\Delta H = H_{T_2} - H_{T_1} = \int_{T_1}^{T_2} C_p\, dT = \int_{T_1}^{T_2} (a + bT + cT^2)\, dT$$

$$= \int_{T_1}^{T_2} a\, dT + \int_{T_1}^{T_2} bT\, dT + \int_{T_1}^{T_2} cT^2\, dT \tag{2}$$

Example 5.   Calculate the amount of heat required to raise the temperature of 1 mole of oxygen from 300°K to 1000°K at constant pressure.

$$C_p = 6.0954 + 3.2533 \times 10^{-3}T - 1.0171 \times 10^{-6}T^2$$

$$\Delta H = \int_{300}^{1000} C_p \, dT = \int_{300}^{1000} (6.0954 + 3.2533 \times 10^{-3}T - 1.0171 \times 10^{-6}T^2) \, dT$$

$$= (6.0954)(700) + \frac{3.2533 \times 10^{-3}}{2}(1000^2 - 300^2)$$

$$- \frac{1.0171 \times 10^{-6}}{3}(1000^3 - 300^3)$$

$$= 4267 + 1480 - 330 = 5417 \text{ cal}$$

When the temperature is limited to a narrow range or the change of heat capacity with temperature is small, it is satisfactory to use the average heat capacity rather than the integrated heat capacity. Then the heat absorbed is given by the expression

$$\Delta H = C_{p \text{ avg}}(T_2 - T_1) \tag{3}$$

These equations for the heat capacities at constant pressure can be transformed into the corresponding equations at constant volume C_v by subtracting 1.987 cal deg^{-1} mole^{-1} from the first term, in agreement with the relation developed in the preceding chapter, $C_p - C_v = R$.

Variation of Heat of Reaction with Temperature. It has been shown that, for a mole of any substance,

$$\left(\frac{\partial H}{\partial T}\right)_p = C_p$$

Also, the change in enthalpy for a reaction may be written

$$\Delta H = \Sigma H_{\text{products}} - \Sigma H_{\text{reactants}}$$

where the summation sign Σ indicates the sum of the heats of formation.

Differentiating with respect to temperature at constant pressure yields

$$\left(\frac{\partial(\Delta H)}{\partial T}\right)_p = \Sigma \left(\frac{\partial H}{\partial T}\right)_{p,\text{products}} - \Sigma \left(\frac{\partial H}{\partial T}\right)_{p,\text{reactants}}$$

$$= \Sigma C_{p,\text{products}} - \Sigma C_{p,\text{reactants}}$$

$$= \Delta C_p \tag{4}$$

and, since the term ΔH is used for the heats of reaction *at constant pressure*, it is unnecessary to specify further the constancy of the pressure.

Then, equation 4 may be written as

$$\frac{d\,\Delta H}{dT} = \Delta C_p \tag{5}$$

If we remember that ΔH is equal to the heat of reaction at constant pressure, this equation may be stated in words as follows: *The change in heat of reaction at constant pressure per degree rise in temperature is equal to the heat capacity of the products minus the heat capacity of the reactants.* This differential equation can be expressed in words in this manner because 1 degree is such a small quantity that it may be put equal to dT.

For larger temperature differences, equation 5 must be integrated between the two temperatures, T_1 at which ΔH is ΔH_{T_1}, and a higher temperature T_2 at which ΔH is ΔH_{T_2}:

$$\Delta H_{T_2} - \Delta H_{T_1} = \int_{\Delta H_{T_1}}^{\Delta H_{T_2}} d\,\Delta H = \int_{T_1}^{T_2} \Delta C_p\, dT \tag{6}$$

If ΔC_p is practically independent of temperature, over the temperature range from T_1 to T_2, equation 6 becomes

$$\Delta H_{T_2} - \Delta H_{T_1} = \Delta C_p(T_2 - T_1) \tag{7}$$

and

$$\frac{\Delta H_{T_2} - \Delta H_{T_1}}{T_2 - T_1} = \Delta C_p \tag{8}$$

These simple formulas 6 and 8 are very useful for calculating the heat of reaction at a given temperature when it is known at another temperature and when the heat capacities of the reactants and products are known or can be calculated.

If the heat capacity changes with temperature, it is necessary to know ΔC_p as a function of temperature, and then the heat of reaction at different temperatures can be calculated by equation 6 from the standard rules of integration as illustrated in example 6.

Example 6. Calculate the heat of combustion of hydrogen at $400°$ from a knowledge of the heat of reaction at $25°$.

$$2H_2(g) + O_2(g) \rightarrow 2H_2O(l) \qquad \Delta H_{298} = -136,635 \text{ cal}$$

First, ΔH is calculated for the same reaction at $100°$, using the molar heat capacities for H_2 and O_2 from Table IV, and assuming that the molar heat capacity of liquid water is 18 cal deg^{-1} mole^{-1} throughout this temperature range.

When liquid water changes to steam at $100°$ there is a large absorption of heat. Moreover, the heat capacity of liquid water below $100°$ is much different from that of steam above $100°$. Accordingly the calculation has to be carried out in three steps.

$$\Delta H_{373} = \Delta H_{298} + \int_{298}^{373} \Delta C_p \, dT$$

$$= \Delta H_{298} + \int_{298}^{373} [(2)(18) - 2(6.9469 - 0.1999 \times 10^{-3}T + 4.808 \times 10^{-7}T^2)$$

$$- (6.0954 + 3.2533 \times 10^{-3}T - 10.171 \times 10^{-7}T^2)] \, dT$$

$$= -136,635 + 1138$$

$$= -135,497 \text{ cal}$$

At temperatures just above $100°$ the product is steam instead of liquid water, and sufficient heat is absorbed to vaporize the water, namely 539.7 cal g^{-1}.

$$2H_2O(l) \rightarrow 2H_2O(g) \qquad \Delta H_{373} = 2(18.016)(539.7) = 19,445 \text{ cal}$$

Then

$$2H_2(g) + O_2(g) \rightarrow 2H_2O(g) \qquad \Delta H_{373} = -135,497 + 19,445$$

$$= -116,052 \text{ cal}$$

Finally, for this reaction at $673°$, further calculation must be made using the molar heat capacities of steam, hydrogen, and oxygen.

$$\Delta H_{673} = \Delta H_{373} + \int_{373}^{673} [2(7.1873 + 2.3733 \times 10^{-3}T + 2.084 \times 10^{-7}T^2)$$

$$- 2(6.9469 - 0.1999 \times 10^{-3}T + 4.808 \times 10^{-7}T^2)$$

$$- (6.0954 + 3.2533 \times 10^{-3}T - 10.171 \times 10^{-7}T^2)] \, dT$$

$$= -116,052 - 1352 = -117,404 \text{ cal}$$

REFERENCES

Bichowsky and Rossini, *The Thermochemistry of the Chemical Substances*, Reinhold Publishing Corp., New York, 1936.

Wenner, *Thermochemical Calculations*, McGraw-Hill Book Co., New York, 1941.

Daniels, Mathews, Williams, and Staff, *Experimental Physical Chemistry*, McGraw-Hill Book Co., New York, 1949.

Lewis and Randall, *Thermodynamics and the Free Energy of Chemical Substances*, McGraw-Hill Book Co., New York, 1923.

International Critical Tables, McGraw-Hill Book Co., New York, 1929.

Parks and Huffman, *Free Energy of Some Organic Compounds*, Reinhold Publishing Corp., New York, 1932.

Hougen and Watson, *Chemical Process Principles*, Vol. II, John Wiley & Sons, New York, 1947.

Rossini, Pitzer, Taylor, Ebert, Kilpatrick, Beckett, Williams, and Werner, "Selected Values of Properties of Hydrocarbons," *Circ. Natl. Bur. Standards* C 461, U. S. Government Printing Office, Washington, D. C., 1947.

Rossini, Wagman, Evans, Levine, and Jaffe, "Selected Values of Chemical Thermodynamic Properties," *Circ. Natl. Bur. Standards* 500, U. S. Government Printing Office, Washington, D. C., 1952.

PROBLEMS

1. In a bomb calorimeter, the combustion of 1.753 grams of sucrose produces a temperature rise of 2.907°. The heat of combustion of sucrose is 1349.6 kcal mole^{-1}. (a) What is the total heat capacity of the water and the calorimeter? (b) If the calorimeter contains 1850 grams of water (specific heat = 1.0 cal deg^{-1} g^{-1}), what is the effective heat capacity of the calorimeter? In this problem, corrections for the oxidation of the wire and residual nitrogen may be neglected.

Ans. (a) 2378, (b) 528 cal deg^{-1}.

2. Using data on heats of formation, calculate the heats of combustion (ΔH) at 25° of the following substances to $H_2O(l)$ and $CO_2(g)$: (a) n-butane, (b) methanol, (c) acetic acid. *Ans.* (a) −687.982, (b) −173.67, (c) −208.3 kcal mole^{-1}.

3. Calculate the heat of formation for 1 mole of $HI(g)$ from the following data:

(a)	$H_2(g) + Cl_2(g) \rightarrow 2HCl(g)$	$\Delta H = -44.20$ kcal
(b)	$HCl(g) + aq \rightarrow HCl(aq)$	$\Delta H = -17.31$
(c)	$HI(g) + aq \rightarrow HI(aq)$	$\Delta H = -19.21$
(d)	$KOH(aq) + HCl(aq) \rightarrow KCl(aq)$	$\Delta H = -13.74$
(e)	$KOH(aq) + HI(aq) \rightarrow KI(aq)$	$\Delta H = -13.67$
(f)	$Cl_2(g) + 2KI(aq) \rightarrow 2KCl(aq) + I_2(s)$	$\Delta H = -52.42$

Ans. 5.94 kcal.

4. The combustion of oxalic acid in a bomb calorimeter yields 673 cal g^{-1} at 25°C. Calculate ΔE and ΔH for the combustion of 1 mole of oxalic acid ($M = 90.0$).

Ans. $\Delta E = -60.57$, $\Delta H = -59.68$ kcal mole^{-1}.

5. (a) Estimate from heats of formation and bond energies the heat of dissociation of HCl gas into atoms. (b) Estimate the heats of the following reactions at constant pressure assuming that all reactants and products are in the gaseous state:

$$C_2H_4 + Cl_2 \rightarrow C_2H_4Cl_2$$

$$C_2H_6 + 2Cl_2 \rightarrow C_2H_4Cl_2 + 2HCl$$

Ans. (a) 102, (b) −34 and −49 kcal mole^{-1}.

6. Calculate ΔH at 1000°K for the reaction $CH_4(g) + 2O_2(g) \rightarrow CO_2(g) + 2H_2O(g)$

Ans. −191.430 kcal.

7. For $(CH_3)_2CO$, $\Delta H°_f$ is −61.4 kcal mole^{-1} at 25°. (a) Calculate the heat of combustion at constant pressure. (b) Calculate the heat evolved when 2 grams of acetone is burnt under pressure in a closed bomb at 25°.

Ans. (a) 425.7 kcal mole^{-1}. (b) 14.64 kcal.

8. For the compound $CHClF_2$,

$$C_v = 10.44 + 0.0230t$$

where C_v = cal mole^{-1} deg^{-1} and t = °C. This relationship holds from 35 to 135°. Calculate the change in internal energy ΔE of the gas in going from 35 to 135°.

Ans. 1240 cal mole^{-1}

---

9. In an adiabatic calorimeter, 0.4362 gram of naphthalene caused a rise of 1.707° in temperature. The heat capacity of the calorimeter and water was 2460 cal per

deg. If corrections for the wire and residual nitrogen are neglected, what is ΔE for the combustion of naphthalene per mole?

10. The heat of combustion at constant pressure and 25° of liquid carbon disulfide CS_2 is 246.6 kcal per mole. (a) Calculate the heat of combustion per mole at constant volume in a closed bomb. (b) Calculate the heat of formation $\Delta H°_f$ of liquid carbon disulfide.

11. Calculate the heat of formation of $PCl_5(s)$, given the heats of the following reactions at 25°.

$$2P(s) + 3Cl_2(g) \rightarrow 2PCl_3(l) \qquad \Delta H = -151,800 \text{ cal}$$

$$PCl_3(l) + Cl_2(g) \rightarrow PCl_5(s) \qquad \Delta H = -32,810 \text{ cal}$$

12. From the table of the heats of formation calculate the heats of combustion at constant pressure at 25° of (a) CO, (b) H_2, (c) C_2H_6, and (d) C_2H_5OH.

13. Compute the heat of reaction per mole of lead, in the smelting of lead,

$$PbS + O_2 \rightarrow Pb + SO_2$$

from the data on the heats of formation and the equations

(a) $PbS + 2O_2 \rightarrow PbSO_4$ and $PbSO_4 + PbS \rightarrow 2Pb + 2SO_2$

Check the calculation, using the equations

(b) $2PbS + 3O_2 \rightarrow 2PbO + 2SO_2$ and $2PbO + PbS \rightarrow 3Pb + SO_2$

The heat of formation of PbS is -22.3 kcal $mole^{-1}$.

14. Estimate the molal heat of combustion ΔH of n-nonane, C_9H_{20}, from the data on n-heptane, n-hexane, and n-octane.

15. The equation for the molar heat capacity of n-butane is

$$C_p = 4.64 + 0.0558T$$

Calculate the heat necessary to raise the temperature of 1 mole from 25 to 300°.

16. Using data in this chapter and C_p for carbon

$$C_p = 2.673 + 0.002617T - \frac{1.169 \times 10^5}{T^2}$$

calculate ΔH for the following reaction at 600°K:

$$H_2O(g) + C(s) \rightarrow CO(g) + H_2(g)$$

17. Calculate the heat evolved in the reaction $H_2 + Cl_2 \rightarrow 2HCl$ at 1023° and constant pressure.

———————————

18. The heat of formation of nitric oxide from nitrogen and oxygen has been calculated from spectroscopic data. A direct calorimetric determination is desirable, however. It has been found that phosphorus will burn completely to P_2O_5 in nitric oxide leaving nitrogen, if the phosphorus is thoroughly ignited with a hot arc. Calculate the heat of formation of NO from the following data.

Phosphorus was burnt in a calorimeter in a stream of nitric oxide for 12.00 minutes and produced 1.508 grams of H_3PO_4. The calorimeter was surrounded by 1386 grams of water. The observed temperature rise was 2.222°, and the cooling correction amounted to 0.037°. The correction for the heat of stirring was 11.1 cal evolved per minute. The heat capacity of the calorimeter, as determined with an electric heater, was 244 cal per deg.

The same experiment was repeated, in which the nitric oxide was replaced by a mixture of half nitrogen and half oxygen. The amount of H_3PO_4 produced was 2.123 grams. Time, 10.00 minutes. Observed temperature rise, 2.398°. Cooling correction, 0.032°. Correction for heat of stirring, 12.2 cal per minute. Weight of water, 1386 grams. Heat capacity of calorimeter, 244 cal per deg. What is the heat of formation of NO?

19. (a) Calculate the heat evolved when 1 gram of ethylene is exploded at constant pressure at 25° with an excess of air. (b) Calculate the heat evolved when 1 gram of ethylene is exploded with an excess of pure oxygen at 20 atm pressure in a closed bomb.

20. One hundred grams of iron is dissolved in dilute acid at 25°, giving a ferrous salt. Will more heat be evolved when the reaction is carried out in an open beaker or in a closed bomb? How much more?

21. Calculate the heat evolved at 25° in the reaction $3Mg + Fe_2O_3 \rightarrow 3MgO + 2Fe$. When magnesium is oxidized to MgO, $\Delta H = -145,700$ cal.

22. Calculate the molar heat of combustion of carbon monoxide at constant pressure and 1327°C.

23. As a rough approximation, the molar heat capacity of a solid is the same as the sum of the atomic heat capacities of the solid elements of which the solid compound is formed. What general statement can be made regarding the influence of temperature on the heat of reactions of solids to give solids, as, for example, the reaction $Fe + S \rightarrow FeS$?

24. One British thermal unit (Btu) is the heat required to raise the temperature of 1 lb of water 1°F. Calculate the number of British thermal units evolved by the complete combustion at constant pressure and 25° of 1 cu ft of water gas ($\frac{1}{2}CO$ and $\frac{1}{2}H_2$ by volume) measured at 25° and 1 atm.

25. How many grams of cane sugar ($C_{12}H_{22}O_{11}$) must be oxidized to give the same number of calories of *heat* as the number of calories of work done by a 160-lb (59.8-kg) man in climbing a mountain 1 mile (1.609 km) high? The heat of combustion of $C_{12}H_{22}O_{11}$ is 1349.7 kcal per mole. It is found empirically that only about 25 per cent of the heat value of food can be converted into useful work by men or animals, and accordingly the calculated grams of sugar could be multiplied roughly by 4 to give the amount of sugar which would actually be oxidized.

26. In some of the published tables of heats of formation and other thermodynamic properties diamond is taken as the standard state of carbon instead of graphite. Derive a relation between the heats of formation based on these two choices of the standard state of carbon, for a substance containing n carbon atoms per mole.

27. For the following reaction $\Delta H = 47.16$ kcal:

$$CH_3COONa(aq) \rightarrow CH_2CO(g) + NaOH(aq)$$

Calculate the heat of formation of ketene, $CH_2CO(g)$, obtaining additional data from tables of thermochemical data not given in this book.

28. Show that, in measuring the isothermal heat of a reaction, no error is introduced if the temperature rises, provided that the products are cooled to the original temperature of the reactants.

7

Thermodynamics

Spontaneous and Nonspontaneous Processes. We are familiar with the fact that many processes occur spontaneously, that is, when they are simply left to themselves. Water runs downhill; gases expand from regions of high pressure to regions of low pressure; chemical reactions proceed to equilibrium; and heat flows from hot bodies to cooler bodies. For any spontaneous process it is possible to devise, in principle at least, a mechanism for getting useful work from the process. Thus, falling water can turn a water wheel; an expanding gas can push a piston; a chemical reaction may be harnessed in a battery; and hot and cold reservoirs may be used to run a heat engine. Thus, it is apparent that as a spontaneous process occurs a system loses ability to do useful work.

It is a matter of experience that spontaneous processes do not reverse themselves. That is, water does not run uphill; gases do not flow from regions of low pressure to regions of high pressure; spontaneous chemical reactions do not reverse themselves; and heat does not flow from a colder body to a hotter body. An exception to this statement is encountered when systems containing only a few molecules or particles are investigated. For example, in investigating Brownian motion (page 502) with an ultramicroscope it is sometimes found that the tiny particles occasionally move from the region of low concentration to the region of higher concentration. However, with systems containing very large numbers of molecules or particles the probability that a large number of molecules will move from the region of low concentration to the region of higher concentration is negligibly small and has never been observed.

In another example, if one end of a tube of gas is hot and the other end cold, heat will flow from the hot end to the cold and in so doing could do work. But after the motions of molecules have become averaged throughout, and the whole tube is at a uniform temperature, it is extremely improbable that the more rapidly moving molecules would

130

all move to one end, causing the tube to become hot at one end and cold at the other.

The term *nonspontaneous* is applied to the reverse of a spontaneous process, e.g., water flowing uphill. Nonspontaneous processes can be made to occur only by supplying energy from outside the system. For example, energy is required to pump water uphill or to compress a gas. Since the energy required can only be supplied by a spontaneous process, it is apparent that a spontaneous process may be reversed only by harnessing, in some way, energy from another spontaneous process.

When a spontaneous process occurs by itself no useful work is obtained, e.g., as when a gas expands into a vacuum. The maximum amount of work is obtained from a spontaneous process when it is carried out reversibly, that is, in such a way that at any time it may be reversed by an infinitesimal change. In the case of an expanding gas the pressure on the piston could be made just infinitesimally smaller than the pressure of the gas, or infinitesimally larger, so that the direction of movement of the piston could be reversed by an infinitesimally small change of the applied pressure. Actually, it is not possible to obtain the maximum work from any system with a real machine because of losses due to friction and the fact that a truly reversible process must be carried out infinitely slowly. However, the concept of the maximum work from a reversible process is a very useful one.

Thus, processes may be classified according to whether they are spontaneous (or natural), nonspontaneous (or unnatural), or reversible. Reversible processes do not actually occur in nature, although we can closely approximate them experimentally by infinitesimal alterations of pressure, temperature, voltage, etc., so that a spontaneous process occurs which differs only infinitesimally from the reversible process considered.

The Second Law of Thermodynamics. The first law of thermodynamics given on page 94 specifies that, when heat is converted into work, a definite quantitative relationship exists between the heat converted and the work done, but it has nothing to say with regard to whether a given process is possible. Although work can be transformed completely into heat, it does not follow that heat can be transformed completely into work. The second law gives information as to the limitations that govern the transformation of heat into work and is directly concerned with the question of whether or not a given process is possible.

The second law of thermodynamics may be stated in many different ways which appear to be quite different but really amount to the same thing. Since it has proved impossible to devise a cyclic process for removing heat from a reservoir and converting it into work without transferring heat from a hot to a cold reservoir, a statement of this fact may be taken as the second law of thermodynamics. However, such a statement does not appear to be directly applicable in answering the question of whether or not a certain chemical reaction or physical process is spontaneous. In order to state the second law in a form applicable to chemical systems, it is necessary to introduce the quantity *entropy*.

Entropy. The entropy, designated by S, is a function of the state of the system. Thus, its value, like that of the internal energy E, depends upon the condition of the system and not upon its past history. *The entropy change for an infinitesimal reversible process is given by*

$$dS = dq_{rev}/T \tag{1}$$

where dq_{rev} is the heat absorbed from the surroundings in a reversible process.

For a process that occurs spontaneously the entropy change is greater than the heat change divided by the absolute temperature.

$$dS > dq/T \tag{2}$$

For a nonspontaneous or unnatural process the entropy change is less than the heat change divided by the absolute temperature.

$$dS < dq/T \tag{3}$$

A finite process may be divided into infinitesimal steps. If all the steps in the process are reversible, the total change in entropy is given by

$$\Delta S = \Sigma \frac{dq_{rev}}{T} \tag{4}$$

where Σ indicates that dq_{rev}/T is added up for all the steps. Thus, the difference in entropy between two states can be calculated if the substance can be brought reversibly from one to the other. The amount of work done w and the heat absorbed q may change, depending on how the experiment is carried out, but ΔS will always be the same provided only that the initial and final states are the same.

The entropy change for an irreversible process can be calculated then by carrying out the same process reversibly, i.e., going from the same initial state to the same final state by a series of reversible steps and measuring the heat absorbed and the temperature in each step. For example, a mole of gas at 10 atm pressure at 25° might be expanded to a larger volume at 1 atm at 25° by reducing the pressure to 1 atm in a single step. The heat absorbed could not be used to calculate the entropy change because the process is not reversible. The process can be carried out reversibly, however, by expanding the gas against a constantly decreasing pressure which is always slightly less than the pressure of the gas itself. Under these conditions the process is reversible, and the heat absorbed can be used to calculate the entropy increase which accompanies the expansion of the gas. Frequently, in order for the process to be reversible, the steps must be infinitesimally small steps, and the total entropy change is then obtained by integration.

All systems tend to approach a state of equilibrium, and, according to the second law of thermodynamics, entropy can be used as a quantitative measure of the extent to which this equilibrium has been reached. Consider first an isolated system, thermally insulated so that no heat q can be gained or lost. If a given process is carried out reversibly, it follows from equation 1 that $dS = dq_{rev}/T$, and, since $dq_{rev} = 0$,

$$dS = 0 \tag{5}$$

If the process is not carried out reversibly, equation 2 is applicable, and, since q is still zero in this isolated system,

$$dS > 0 \tag{6}$$

The more nearly reversible the process is, the closer will dS approach zero. The increase in entropy that accompanies a process taking place in an isolated system may thus be considered a measure of the approach of the system to a state of equilibrium.

From a slightly different point of view, the entropy of a system may be regarded as a function of the probability of the thermodynamic state, the state of equilibrium being the most probable; and the tendency for the entropy of an isolated system to increase corresponds to the tendency of the system, if left alone, to go to a state of maximum probability, that is, to equilibrium. According to this idea, *entropy is a measure of the disorder of a system*. The more the molecules in a system are distributed in a disordered or random manner, the more probable is the arrangement, and the greater is the entropy. As the entropy of a system increases, it loses its capacity for spontaneous change.

Entropy Calculations. A few concrete examples of entropy calculations will now be presented. The transfer of heat from one body to another at constant temperature is a reversible process if the direction of heat flow can be reversed by infinitesimal changes in the temperature of one of the bodies. The fusion of a solid at its melting point or the evaporation of a liquid at a constant pressure equal to its vapor pressure are examples of isothermal reversible processes in which the entropy change is readily visualized and easily calculated. When T is constant, integration of equation 1 yields

$$S_2 - S_1 = \Delta S = q_{rev}/T \qquad (7)$$

Since the heat gained by the system is equal to that lost by the surroundings, the entropy change for the surroundings is the negative of the entropy change for the system, and ΔS, for both the system and surroundings taken together, is zero.

Example 1. n-Hexane boils at 68.74°C, and the heat of vaporization is 6896 cal mole^{-1}. The vaporization process is isothermal and reversible, and so the entropy change may be calculated as follows:

$$\Delta S = q_{rev}/T = 6896/341.8 = 20.18 \text{ cal deg}^{-1} \text{ mole}^{-1}$$

The molar entropy of a vapor is always greater than that of the liquid with which it is in equilibrium.

Entropy has the dimensions of energy divided by absolute temperature, and the usual units are calories deg^{-1} mole^{-1}.

The entropy increase involved in raising the temperature of a substance may be calculated since the temperature change may be carried out in a reversible manner. The heat absorbed is equal to the heat capacity C multiplied by the increase in temperature, and, if the changes are kept infinitesimally small, the heat absorbed is $C\,dT$ and

$$dS = \frac{C\,dT}{T} \qquad (8)$$

As the temperature is raised, each infinitesimal absorption of heat must be divided by the temperature at which the absorption takes place, a calculation which is readily made with the help of calculus. Integrating between the limits T_1 and T_2 gives

$$\int_{S_1}^{S_2} dS = \int_{T_1}^{T_2} \frac{C\,dT}{T} \qquad (9)$$

If C is constant,

$$S_2 - S_1 = C(\ln T_2 - \ln T_1) = C \ln \frac{T_2}{T_1} = 2.303C \log \frac{T_2}{T_1} \qquad (10)$$

This formula is equally applicable for constant pressure or constant volume. If the heating is carried out at constant pressure, C_p is used; if it involves constant volume, C_v is used. Chemical operations usually involve constant pressure.

Example 2. Calculate the increase in entropy involved in heating a gram-atomic weight of silver at constant volume from 0 to 30°C. The value of C_v over this temperature range is 5.85 cal deg^{-1} mole^{-1}.

$$\Delta S = S_2 - S_1 = (2.303)(5.85) \log \tfrac{303}{273} = 0.605 \text{ cal deg}^{-1} \text{ mole}^{-1}$$

Example 3. When a mole of supercooled water freezes isothermally at $-10°$C, what is the change in entropy? The process is irreversible. In order to calculate the entropy change, the process must be carried out in steps, every one of which is reversible, and the absorption or evolution of heat must then be measured in each reversible step. Thus,

$$\text{H}_2\text{O}(l) \text{ at } -10° \rightarrow \text{H}_2\text{O}(l) \text{ at } 0° \qquad \Delta S = \int_{263}^{273} C_{\text{liq}} \frac{dT}{T}$$

$$\text{H}_2\text{O}(l) \text{ at } 0° \rightarrow \text{H}_2\text{O}(s) \text{ at } 0° \qquad \Delta S = q_{\text{rev}}/T$$

$$\text{H}_2\text{O}(s) \text{ at } 0° \rightarrow \text{H}_2\text{O}(s) \text{ at } -10° \qquad \Delta S = \int_{273}^{263} C_{\text{ice}} \frac{dT}{T}$$

The crystallization of liquid water at 0°C evolves 80 cal g^{-1}. The specific heat of water is 1.0 cal deg^{-1} and that of ice 0.5 cal deg^{-1} over this range. Then the total entropy change when 1 mole of liquid water at $-10°$C changes to ice at $-10°$C is calculated as follows:

$$\Delta S = (18 \text{ g mole}^{-1})(1.0 \text{ cal g}^{-1})(2.303) \log \frac{273}{263} + \frac{(18 \text{ g mole}^{-1})(-80 \text{ cal g}^{-1})}{273 \text{ deg}}$$

$$+ (18 \text{ g mole}^{-1})(0.5 \text{ cal g}^{-1})(2.303) \log \frac{263}{273}$$

$$= 0.67 - 5.28 - 0.34 = -4.95 \text{ cal deg}^{-1} \text{ mole}^{-1}$$

The crystallization of water at $-10°$C is a spontaneous process, and the fact that the value of ΔS calculated above is negative may be surprising. This emphasizes the fact that it is the entropy change for the whole system, including the surroundings, and not merely that for the water, which indicates whether the process is spontaneous or not. The entropy change of the surroundings may be calculated by considering that the water is in contact with a large reservoir at $-10°$C. The heat evolved by the water upon freezing is absorbed by the reservoir without a significant rise in temperature. Since the absorption of heat by the reservoir is reversible the change in entropy of the reservoir is given by

$$\Delta S = (18 \text{ g mole}^{-1})(75 \text{ cal g}^{-1})/(263 \text{ deg})$$

$$= 5.13 \text{ cal deg}^{-1} \text{ mole}^{-1}$$

where 75 cal g^{-1} is the heat of fusion of water at $-10°$C. Thus, the entropy change for the reservoir is positive, and, since it is greater than that lost by the ice, the entropy for the water plus surroundings increases during this spontaneous process.

Conversion of Heat into Work. The concept of entropy may be used to derive the relation between the heat supplied to a heat engine, like a steam engine, and the maximum amount of work done. Such an engine carries out a cyclic process, and the Carnot cycle which has been

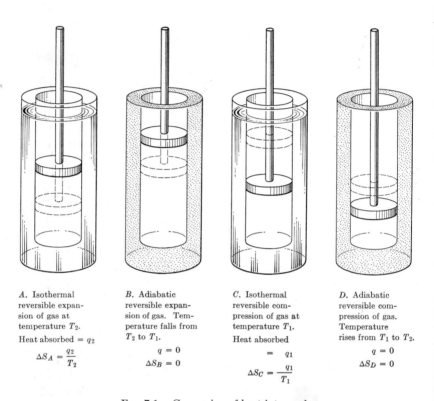

| A. Isothermal reversible expansion of gas at temperature T_2. Heat absorbed = q_2 $$\Delta S_A = \frac{q_2}{T_2}$$ | B. Adiabatic reversible expansion of gas. Temperature falls from T_2 to T_1. $$q = 0$$ $$\Delta S_B = 0$$ | C. Isothermal reversible compression of gas at temperature T_1. Heat absorbed $$= q_1$$ $$\Delta S_C = \frac{q_1}{T_1}$$ | D. Adiabatic reversible compression of gas. Temperature rises from T_1 to T_2. $$q = 0$$ $$\Delta S_D = 0$$ |

FIG. 7-1. Conversion of heat into work.

of great importance in the development of thermodynamics is an idealized cyclic process consisting of four steps. The four steps, which are illustrated in *Fig. 7-1*, are: *A*, a reversible isothermal expansion at temperature T_2; *B*, a reversible adiabatic expansion to a lower temperature T_1; *C*, a reversible isothermal compression at temperature T_1; and *D*, a reversible adiabatic compression to temperature T_2 and the original volume and pressure. Heat has been transferred from a reservoir at temperature T_2 to a reservoir at a lower temperature T_1, and more work is obtained in the expansion at temperature T_2 than is required to compress the gas at temperature T_1. Since the gas has been returned to its initial state, the total entropy change for the four steps is zero. Then

$$\Delta S = \Delta S_A + \Delta S_B + \Delta S_C + \Delta S_D = \frac{q_2}{T_2} + 0 + \frac{q_1}{T_1} + 0 = 0$$

and

$$\frac{q_2}{T_2} + \frac{q_1}{T_1} = 0 \tag{11}$$

For the complete cycle ΔE is zero also, and, by the first law, the work done per cycle is given by

$$w = q_2 + q_1 \tag{12}$$

Solving equation 11 for q_1 and substituting in equation 12, we obtain

$$w_{max} = q_2(T_2 - T_1)/T_2 \tag{13}$$

wherein we have explicitly indicated that the work obtained is a maximum, since the process is reversible.

This important equation, which may be regarded as a mathematical statement of the second law of thermodynamics, is independent of the properties of the substance in the engine and of the engine itself. It shows that the maximum fraction of heat which can be converted into work, that is, w_{max}/q_2, is equal to the difference in temperature divided by the higher absolute temperature. If the condenser could be placed at absolute zero, all the heat would be available for doing work and the maximum efficiency would be unity. This equation, 13, finds important applications in engineering.

Example 4. What is the maximum work that can be obtained from 1000 cal of heat supplied to a water boiler at 100° if the condenser is at 20°?

$$w_{max} = q_2 \frac{T_2 - T_1}{T_2} = (1000) \frac{373.1 - 293.1}{373.1} = 214 \text{ cal}$$

If the boiler temperature is raised to 150° by the use of superheated steam under pressure, how much more work can be obtained?

$$w_{max} = (1000) \frac{423.1 - 293.1}{423.1} = 307 \text{ cal}$$

$$307 - 214 = 93 \text{ cal more}$$

Mercury engines have been successfully operated, and their thermodynamic efficiency is higher than that of steam engines because the boiler temperature is 723°K; but the advantage is offset by the initial cost of mercury, the great weight, and the danger from poisoning by mercury vapor.

In gasoline engines and Diesel engines the temperatures of the explosions are much higher than the temperatures of steam in steam engines and the efficiencies are accordingly higher. Gas turbines now operate with high efficiencies up to 1000°C, which is about the limit of high-temperature steels, and efforts are being made to find suitable materials of construction that will permit the use of still higher temperatures.

A relation of the same form as equation 13 was derived by Carnot for an ideal gas. The second law as derived in equation 13 is general, whereas the Carnot cycle is derived only for an ideal gas.

The temperature used in deriving equation 13 was introduced in equations 1 and 2 and called the thermodynamic absolute temperature without further discussion, whereas the temperature used in the derivation of Carnot leading to the same relation is the absolute temperature of ordinary usage, defined in terms of the properties of ideal gases. Both approaches lead to the same formula, which shows that the two scales of absolute temperature are the same.

Exercise I. Derive equation 13 by considering a Carnot cycle carried out with 1 mole of an ideal gas. In a reversible isothermal expansion from V_1 to V_2 the work done is given by

$$w = RT \ln (V_2/V_1)$$

and the heat absorbed is equal to the work done since $\Delta E = 0$. In a reversible adiabatic expansion the work done is given by

$$w = \int_{T_1}^{T_2} C_v \, dT$$

The relationship between the temperature change and volume change in a reversible adiabatic expansion is given by

$$C_v \ln (T_2/T_1) = -R \ln (V_2/V_1)$$

The Third Law of Thermodynamics. The most orderly arrangement imaginable is a crystal, with its symmetrical lattice, at absolute zero. Here the entropy should be very small, and, in fact, according to the *third law of thermodynamics, the entropy of most crystals may be taken as zero at the absolute zero.*

There is as yet no direct, conclusive proof of the validity of the third law, but it has been checked and cross-checked in many different ways. It is important because it makes possible the determination of the absolute entropies of chemical compounds and the calculation of chemical equilibria, as is explained on page 261. The idea on which the third law is based was first proposed by T. W. Richards in 1902. The law was propounded by Nernst and was fully developed and applied to chemical problems by G. N. Lewis and his associates in 1923.

In calculating entropy, the entropy is taken as zero at the absolute zero for a perfect crystalline substance; as the temperature rises, the molecules and parts of molecules absorb heat in various vibrational, rotational, and translational motions and thus increase in energy. The higher the temperature, the greater is the disordered motion, the greater is the amount of heat that has been absorbed, and the greater is the entropy of the substance.

If the entropy at absolute zero is taken as zero, according to the third law, the entropy at any higher temperature may be calculated from

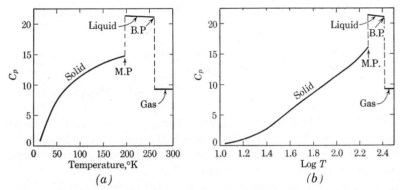

FIG. 7-2.   Heat capacity of sulfur dioxide at constant pressure (cal deg^{-1} mole^{-1}).

heat capacity measurements and heats of transition from one crystalline form to another by use of equations 9 and 7.   If there are no transitions, the entropy at temperature T is given by

$$S° = \int_0^T \frac{C\,dT}{T} = \int_0^T C\,d\ln T = 2.303 \int_0^T C\,d\log T \qquad (14)$$

Thus, the entropy may be obtained by plotting the heat capacity versus $\log T$ and determining the area under the curve from absolute zero to temperature T.   The area of such a plot ($\int y\,dx$) may be determined by counting squares under the curve or by use of a planimeter. If base 10 logarithms are used this area is multiplied by 2.303 to give the entropy in cal deg^{-1} mole^{-1}.   Whenever there is a change in state or a transition between two crystalline forms the entropy change is calculated by equation 7 and must be added to that obtained from the plot of C versus $\log T$.

As an illustration of the determination of the absolute entropy of a substance, the measured heat capacities for SO_2 are shown as a function of T and of $\log T$ in *Fig. 7-2a* * and *b*.   Solid SO_2 melts at 197.64°K, and

* Giauque and Stephenson, *J. Am. Chem. Soc.*, *60*, 1389 (1938).

the heat of fusion is 1769.1 cal mole^{-1}. The liquid vaporizes at 263.08°K, and the heat of vaporization is 5960 cal mole^{-1}. The calculation of the entropy at 25°C is summarized in Table I.

Table I.   The Entropy of Sulfur Dioxide

Temperature, °K	Method of Calculation	ΔS, cal deg^{-1} mole^{-1}
0–15	Debye function (C_p = constant T^3)	0.30
15–197.64	Graphical	20.12
197.64	Fusion, 1769.1/197.64	8.95
197.64–263.08	Graphical	5.96
263.08	Vaporization, 5960/263.08	22.66
263.08–298.1	From C_p of gas	1.25

$$S°_{298.1} = 59.24$$

Specific heat measurements down to these very low temperatures are made with special calorimeters in which the substance is heated electrically in a carefully insulated system and the input of electrical energy and the temperature are measured accurately.

Table II gives the entropies, $S°$, at 1 atm pressure and 25°C for a number of elements and compounds. Data of this type can be used in the calculation of equilibrium constants as shown later in Chapter 10. By means of statistical mechanics it is possible to calculate absolute entropies for simple molecules with great accuracy utilizing spectroscopic data, and these values are in good agreement with those obtained calorimetrically.

Example 5.   Calculate the entropy change for the formation of water vapor at 25° from oxygen and hydrogen.

$$\tfrac{1}{2}O_2(g) + H_2(g) \rightarrow H_2O(g)$$

$$\Delta S° = 45.106 - 31.211 - \tfrac{1}{2}(49.003)$$

$$= -10.606 \text{ cal deg}^{-1} \text{ mole}^{-1}$$

An increase in entropy is produced by mixing two substances, and so the entropy of a mixture at absolute zero is greater than zero.

Free Energy.   In discussing processes that occur at constant temperature and pressure it is convenient to introduce the free energy * F which is defined in terms of the other thermodynamic properties by

$$F = E + pV - TS = H - TS \qquad (15)$$

---

* This is sometimes referred to as the Gibbs free energy and represented by G, but the symbol F is used generally in the United States.

Table II.[1]   Entropies at 25°

$S°$ in cal deg^{-1} mole^{-1}

Elements and Inorganic Compounds

$O_2(g)$	49.003	C(s, diamond)	0.5829
$O_3(g)$	56.8	C(s, graphite)	1.3609
$H_2(g)$	31.211	$CO(g)$	47.301
$H_2O(g)$	45.106	$CO_2(g)$	51.061
$H_2O(l)$	16.716	Pb(s)	15.51
He(g)	30.126	$PbO_2(s)$	18.3
$Cl_2(g)$	53.286	$PbSO_4(s)$	35.2
$HCl(g)$	44.617	Hg(g)	41.80
$Br_2(g)$	58.639	Hg(l)	18.5
$Br_2(l)$	36.4	Ag(s)	10.206
$HBr(g)$	47.437	AgCl(s)	22.97
$HI(g)$	49.314	Fe(s)	6.49
S(rhombic)	7.62	$Fe_2O_3(s)$	21.5
S(monoclinic)	7.78	$Fe_3O_4(s)$	35.0
$SO_2(g)$	59.40	Al(s)	6.769
$SO_3(g)$	61.24	$Al_2O_3(s)$	12.186
$H_2S(g)$	49.15	$UF_6(g)$	90.76
$N_2(g)$	45.767	$UF_6(s)$	54.45
$NO(g)$	50.339	Ca(s)	9.95
$NO_2(g)$	57.47	CaO(s)	9.5
$NH_3(g)$	46.01	$CaCO_3(s)$	22.2
$HNO_3(l)$	37.19	Na(s)	12.2
P(g)	38.98	NaF(s)	14.0
P(s, white)	10.6	NaCl(s)	17.3
$PCl_3(g)$	74.49	K(s)	15.2
$PCl_5(g)$	84.3	KF(s)	15.91
		KCl(s)	19.76

Organic Compounds

Methane, $CH_4(g)$	44.50	Propylene, $C_3H_6(g)$	63.80
Ethane, $C_2H_6(g)$	54.85	1-Butene, $C_4H_8(g)$	73.48
Propane, $C_3H_8(g)$	64.51	Acetylene, $C_2H_2(g)$	47.997
n-Butane, $C_4H_{10}(g)$	74.10	Formaldehyde, $CH_2O(g)$	52.26
iso-Butane, $C_4H_{10}(g)$	70.42	Acetaldehyde, $C_2H_4O(g)$	63.5
n-Pentane, $C_5H_{12}(g)$	83.27	Methanol, $CH_3OH(l)$	30.3
n-Hexane, $C_6H_{14}(g)$	92.45	Ethanol, $C_2H_6O(l)$	38.4
n-Heptane, $C_7H_{16}(g)$	101.64	Formic acid, $CH_2O_2(l)$	30.82
n-Octane, $C_8H_{18}(g)$	110.82	Acetic acid, $C_2H_4O_2(l)$	38.2
Benzene, $C_6H_6(g)$	64.34	Oxalic acid, $C_2H_2O_4(s)$	28.7
Benzene, $C_6H_6(l)$	41.30	Carbon tetrachloride, $CCl_4(l)$	51.25
Ethylene, $C_2H_4(g)$	52.45	Glycine, $C_2H_5O_2N(s)$	26.1

[1] These data have been obtained from Rossini, Wagman, Evans, Levine, and Jaffe, "Selected Values of Chemical Thermodynamic Properties," *Circular of the National Bureau of Standards* 500, U. S. Government Printing Office, Washington, D. C. 1952, and Rossini, Pitzer, Taylor, Ebert, Kilpatrick, Beckett, Williams, and Werner, "Selected Values of Properties of Hydrocarbons," *Circular of the National Bureau of Standards* C 461, U. S. Government Printing Office, Washington, D. C., 1947.

The free-energy change upon going from an initial state to a final state is

$$(F_2 - F_1) = (E_2 - E_1) + (p_2V_2 - p_1V_1) - (T_2S_2 - T_1S_1)$$

$$\Delta F = \Delta E + \Delta(pV) - \Delta(TS) \tag{16}$$

If the temperature and pressure are held constant,

$$\Delta F = \Delta E + p\,\Delta V - T\,\Delta S \tag{17}$$

For a reversible isothermal process, ΔE may be replaced by

$$\Delta E = q_{\text{rev}} - w_{\text{max}} = T\,\Delta S - w_{\text{max}} \tag{18}$$

where w_{max} is the maximum work done since the process is carried out reversibly. Substitution of 18 into 17 leads to

$$-\Delta F = w_{\text{max}} - p\,\Delta V \tag{19}$$

This equation is helpful in visualizing ΔF. When the temperature and pressure are kept constant, the decrease in free energy is equal to the maximum work that can be done by the process other than pressure-volume work. The actual amount of work obtained from a physical-chemical change depends upon the way in which it is carried out, but only when it is carried out reversibly is the maximum work obtained. The free-energy change for a process depends only upon the initial and final states.

For an isothermal process the change in free energy is obtained from equation 15

$$\Delta F = \Delta H - T\,\Delta S \tag{20}$$

This is a very important equation, as will be seen in later chapters. The quantities ΔH and ΔS can be determined by direct calorimetric measurements, and then it is easy to calculate ΔF. The free-energy change in turn is useful in calculating such things as the voltages of electrical cells and the equilibrium constants of chemical reactions. When equation 20 is written as $\Delta H = \Delta F + T\,\Delta S$ it is evident that the change in enthalpy at constant temperature is expressed in terms of two other quantities—the maximum available work excluding external pressure-volume expansion work plus the heat absorbed when the process is carried out reversibly.

There is an additional thermodynamic quantity A, the work function or Helmholtz free energy, which is of interest since

$$-\Delta A = w_{\text{max}} \tag{21}$$

for an isothermal reversible process. The work function is defined in terms of the other thermodynamic quantities by

$$A = E - TS \quad \text{or} \quad \Delta A = \Delta E - \Delta(TS)$$

Equation 21 may be proved by holding T constant and combining this equation with equation 18.

Influence of Pressure on Free Energy. By differentiating equation 15 we obtain the change in free energy resulting from changes in E, V, p, S, and T.

$$dF = dE + p\,dV + V\,dp - T\,dS - S\,dT \tag{22}$$

Since $dE = dq - dw$, substitution of $T\,dS$ for dq for a reversible process, and restriction to pV work, leads to

$$dE = T\,dS - p\,dV$$

and so

$$dF = V\,dp - S\,dT \tag{23}$$

Therefore, if the temperature is held constant the variation of free energy with pressure is given by

$$\left(\frac{\partial F}{\partial p}\right)_T = V \tag{24}$$

And if the pressure is held constant the variation of free energy with temperature is given by

$$\left(\frac{\partial F}{\partial T}\right)_p = -S \tag{25}$$

If the molar volume V is known as a function of pressure the change of free energy per mole with pressure may be calculated. This will be illustrated for (a) an ideal gas and (b) a liquid or solid for which the volume remains constant over a moderate change in pressure.

For an ideal gas,

$$\left(\frac{\partial F}{\partial p}\right)_T = \frac{RT}{p} \tag{26}$$

$$\int_{F_1}^{F_2} dF = \int_{p_1}^{p_2} \frac{RT\,dp}{p}$$

$$\Delta F = F_2 - F_1 = RT \ln \frac{p_2}{p_1} \tag{27}$$

Since this equation applies to 1 mole of gas, the right side may be multiplied by n, the number of moles of gas, if $n \neq 1$. This equation applies only to a change at constant temperature and for an ideal gas, but it gives the change in free energy whether the process is carried out reversibly or irreversibly. The free energy, like E, H, A, and S, depends only upon the state of the system and is independent of the manner in which that state was reached.

Example 6. Calculate the free-energy change for the expansion of 2 moles of ideal gas from 1 atm to $\frac{1}{10}$ atm at 25°.

$$\Delta F = (2 \text{ moles})(1.987 \text{ cal deg}^{-1} \text{ mole}^{-1})(298 \text{ deg})(2.303) \log \tfrac{1}{10}$$

$$= -2720 \text{ cal}$$

If volume is independent of pressure

$$\int_{F_1}^{F_2} dF = V \int_{p_1}^{p_2} dp$$

$$\Delta F = F_2 - F_1 = V(p_2 - p_1) \tag{28}$$

Gibbs-Helmholtz Equation. The fact that the rate of change in free energy with temperature at constant pressure is equal to the negative of the entropy (equation 25) makes it possible to derive a very useful relation between the change in free energy and the change in enthalpy for a process. From equation 25

$$-\Delta S = -(S_2 - S_1) = \left(\frac{\partial F_2}{\partial T}\right)_p - \left(\frac{\partial F_1}{\partial T}\right)_p = \left[\frac{\partial(\Delta F)}{\partial T}\right]_p$$

Substitution into equation 20 yields

$$\Delta F = \Delta H + T\left[\frac{\partial(\Delta F)}{\partial T}\right]_p \tag{29}$$

which was derived independently by Gibbs and Helmholtz. The use of this equation will be illustrated later.

Exercise II. Show that equation 29 can be written in the form

$$\left[\frac{\partial(\Delta F/T)}{\partial(1/T)}\right]_p = \Delta H$$

indicating that ΔH may be obtained from the slope of a plot of $\Delta F/T$ versus $1/T$.

Thermodynamics of a Chemical Reaction. The significance of the five thermodynamic quantities E, H, A, F, and S in a chemical reaction is illustrated for the reaction

$$\text{Zn} + 2\text{H}^+ \rightarrow \text{Zn}^{++} + \text{H}_2$$

which is carried out irreversibly by adding zinc dust to an acid in an open calorimeter in a thermostat. One mole of hydrogen is evolved, and work pV or RT is done against the atmosphere. The heat evolved at constant pressure q_p gives a measure of ΔH for the reaction. The heat evolved at constant volume q_v is greater than that at constant pressure by RT because none of the chemical energy is consumed in pressure-volume work or any other kind of work and it is all converted into heat q_v. Then $\Delta E = q_v$ because $\Delta E = q - w$, and at constant volume $w = 0$.

In order to obtain ΔA, ΔF, and ΔS experimentally it is necessary to carry out the reaction reversibly and measure the work done, which will then be the maximum work. It is possible to carry out this reaction reversibly by setting up a battery in which a zinc electrode dips in a solution containing zinc ions and a hydrogen electrode dips in a solution containing hydrogen ions. The two solutions are connected through a tube of solution or a porous plate. This battery will run a motor and do work that can be measured. More work is obtained when the operation is carried out slowly with small electrical currents which give but little loss of energy as heat. The maximum work obtainable can be calculated accurately by measuring the voltage with a potentiometer (described on page 415) under conditions such that practically no current is flowing. The zinc can be converted into zinc ions by letting the battery operate slowly, or the zinc ions can be converted into zinc by opposing a slightly higher voltage, and thus the criterion for reversibility is met.

The decrease in work content, $-\Delta A$, is equal to the maximum work, w_{max}, done by the operation of the battery, including both the electrical work and the pressure-volume work against the atmosphere. The pressure-volume work is done anyway, no matter how much electrical work is done. But $-\Delta F$ is measured by the maximum work minus the pressure-volume work, i.e., $w_{max} - RT$. The measurements of electrical work do not include the pressure-volume work, and so the maximum electrical work provides a direct and simple way for measuring ΔF. Then, for this reaction of zinc and acid, $-\Delta F$ = maximum electrical work and $\Delta A = \Delta F - RT$.

Thus, the reaction of zinc with an acid may be carried out under two extreme conditions. In the first case, no electrical work was done and all the energy went into heat at constant volume, or into heat and pressure-volume work at constant pressure. In the second case, all the work possible went into electrical work, but still some of the chemical energy went into pressure-volume work, and there was some exchange of heat with the surroundings even when the cell was operating reversibly. This heat accompanying the reversible operation of the electrochemical cell divided by the absolute temperature gives the value of ΔS for the reaction. The fact that this heat is very small and is delivered over such a long interval of time means that a calorimetric measurement of the operating cell is not a suitable method for determining ΔS. However, ΔS can be calculated from the values of ΔF and ΔH. Often these hypothetical experiments lead to useful concepts and formulas. The large and easily measured heat evolved when zinc is added directly to acid in a calorimeter is useless for the calculation of entropy because the reaction carried out in this way is not reversible.

The reaction may be carried out so as to obtain some electrical work but not the maximum work. Thus, q may vary between q_{rev} and ΔH, and w may vary between w_{max} and 0, but ΔE, ΔH, ΔA, ΔF, and ΔS are always the same, no matter how the reaction is carried out.

Criteria of Chemical Equilibrium. Early attempts to discover a relation between thermodynamics and the direction of spontaneous chemical reactions led Berthelot in 1879 to the false conclusion that the evolution of heat in a chemical reaction is a measure of chemical affinity. The mere existence of spontaneous reactions which absorb heat and the general reversibility of all reactions under suitable conditions show that this suggestion cannot be right.

It has been shown earlier (page 133) that the entropy is a useful criterion of equilibrium for an isolated system. If for an infinitesimal change dS is greater than zero, the process is spontaneous. A finite process which may be thought of as consisting of a number of small steps with entropy change dS will be spontaneous if $\Delta S > 0$. That is, the entropy of an isolated system tends to increase to a maximum. For a change carried out at equilibrium in an isolated system, $\Delta S = 0$. The entropy change is not a convenient criterion for a spontaneous process in the case of chemical reactions since reactions are generally carried out at constant temperature and pressure rather than in an isolated system.

For a system that is not isolated but is kept in contact with its environment at constant temperature and pressure, the free-energy change provides a more convenient thermodynamic criterion for equilibrium and for spontaneous changes. According to the equation

$$ - \Delta F = w_{\mathrm{max}} - p \, \Delta V $$

when a system is in a state of equilibrium and no net work is obtainable from a given change

$$ \Delta F = 0 \tag{30} $$

According to this equation, at constant temperature and pressure, *if there is no change in free energy in going from one state to another, the system is in a state of equilibrium.* For spontaneous processes tending irreversibly toward equilibrium at constant temperature and pressure

$$\Delta F < 0$$

Thus, at constant temperature and constant pressure, if ΔF for a reaction or a process has a negative value, the system can change spontaneously. In other words, the free energy tends to decrease to a *minimum* value. If $\Delta F > 0$, the process will not take place spontaneously. It is evident that the reverse process would take place spontaneously, however, since for the reverse process ΔF would be less than zero.

These considerations of free energy as a criterion for equilibrium or spontaneous reaction can be illustrated with a mixture of ice and water. Both ice and water have the same free energy per mole at 0° and 1 atm pressure, and there is no tendency for the ice to melt or the water to freeze in a mixture at 0° and 1 atm. On the other hand, the free energy of water supercooled to −10°C is higher per mole than that of ice at −10°, both being under a pressure of 1 atm. The change of water to ice at this temperature and pressure is accompanied by a decrease in free energy, and, hence, it is a spontaneous change. The change in the reverse direction, that is, ice changing to water at −10°, cannot take place spontaneously because there would then be an increase in free energy, that is, $\Delta F > 0$.

If the processes are carried out at constant volume instead of at constant pressure, the work content is a more useful thermodynamic quantity, and, by reasoning similar to that already outlined, the criterion for an equilibrium process is that

$$\Delta A = 0$$

and, for a spontaneous process, that

$$\Delta A < 0$$

These several relations are summarized in Table III.

Table III. Criteria for Equilibrium and Spontaneous Processes

	Spontaneous	Equilibrium	Not Spontaneous
ΔS ($q = 0$)	+	0	−
ΔF (T and p constant)	−	0	+
ΔA (T and V constant)	−	0	+

Although these criteria may show that a certain process is a natural or spontaneous one, it does not necessarily follow that the process will take place with an appreciable speed. Thus, a mixture of 1 mole of carbon and 1 mole of oxygen at 1 atm pressure and 25° has a free energy greater than that of 1 mole of carbon dioxide at 1 atm and 25°, and so it is possible for the carbon and oxygen to combine to form carbon dioxide at this constant temperature and pressure. However, thermodynamics has nothing to say about the time that will be required, and carbon may exist for a very long time in contact with oxygen; but the reaction is theoretically possible. The reverse process—the decomposition of carbon dioxide—involves an increase in free energy, and it can occur only with the aid of an outside agency or by heating to a very high temperature where the free-energy change has the opposite sign.

A qualitative principle known as the theorem of Le Châtelier has been useful in predicting the direction in which a change may be expected. According to this theorem, if a system at equilibrium is disturbed, the system will shift in such a way as to minimize the effect of the disturbance. For example, if pressure is applied to ice, the ice melts to give liquid water, which has a smaller volume. Other examples are given in later chapters.

Thermodynamic Calculations. The various thermodynamic quantities q, w, H, F, S, E, and A are understood best through the quantitative relations which connect them. In this section simple physical processes are considered. Applications to chemical processes will be found later throughout the book. In considering the application of thermodynamic formulas to a given problem, the various restrictions under which the formulas were derived must be borne in mind, and it is well to consider: (a) What are the initial and final states? (b) Is the process reversible or not? (c) Is it isothermal or not? (d) Is it isobaric or not; that is, is it carried out at constant pressure?

Example 7. One mole of steam is compressed reversibly to liquid water at the boiling point 100°. The heat of vaporization of water at 100° and 760 mm is 539.7 cal g^{-1}. Calculate w and q and each of the thermodynamic quantities ΔH, ΔE, ΔF, ΔA, and ΔS.

$$w = p\,\Delta V = p(V_{\text{liq}} - V_{\text{vap}}) \cong^* -pV_{\text{vap}} = -RT$$

$$= -(1.987 \text{ cal deg}^{-1}\text{ mole}^{-1})(373 \text{ deg}) = -741 \text{ cal mole}^{-1}$$

$$q_p = \Delta H = -(539.7 \text{ cal g}^{-1})(18.0 \text{ g mole}^{-1}) = -9720 \text{ cal mole}^{-1}$$

$$\Delta E = \Delta H - p\,\Delta V = -9720 + 741 = -8979 \text{ cal mole}^{-1}$$

* The symbol $\cong$ is used to indicate an approximate equality.

$$\Delta F = \int V \, dp = 0$$

$$\Delta A = -w_{\text{max}} = 741 \text{ cal mole}^{-1}$$

$$\Delta S = \frac{q_{\text{rev}}}{T} = \frac{-9720 \text{ cal mole}^{-1}}{373 \text{ deg}} = -26.0 \text{ cal deg}^{-1} \text{ mole}^{-1}$$

ΔF may be calculated in another way.

$$\Delta F = \Delta H - T \, \Delta S = -9720 \text{ cal mole}^{-1} - (373 \text{ deg})(-26.0 \text{ cal deg}^{-1} \text{ mole}^{-1})$$

$$= 0$$

Example 8. One mole of an ideal gas at 27.0° changes its pressure from 10 to 1 atm by expanding isothermally and reversibly against a pressure that is gradually reduced. Calculate each of the thermodynamic quantities. Calculations with the simple gas equation show that the volume expands from 2.462 to 24.62 liters.

The process is carried out isothermally and reversibly, but the pressure is not constant.

$$w_{\text{max}} = RT \ln \frac{V_2}{V_1} = (1.987 \text{ cal deg}^{-1} \text{ mole}^{-1})(300.1 \text{ deg})(2.303) \log \frac{24.62}{2.462}$$

$$= 1373 \text{ cal mole}^{-1}$$

$$\Delta A = -w_{\text{max}} = -1373 \text{ cal mole}^{-1}$$

Since the internal energy of an ideal gas is not affected by a change in volume,

$$\Delta E = 0$$

$$q = \Delta E + w = 0 + 1373 = 1373 \text{ cal}$$

$$\Delta H = \Delta E + \Delta(pV) = 0 + 0 = 0$$

since PV is constant for an ideal gas at constant temperature.

$$\Delta F = \int_{10}^{1} V \, dp = RT[\ln p]_{10}^{1} = (1.987 \text{ cal deg}^{-1} \text{ mole}^{-1})(300.1 \text{ deg})(2.303)(-1)$$

$$= -1373 \text{ cal mole}^{-1}$$

$$\Delta S = \frac{q_{\text{rev}}}{T} = \frac{1373 \text{ cal mole}^{-1}}{300.1 \text{ deg}} = 4.58 \text{ cal deg}^{-1} \text{ mole}^{-1}$$

Also,

$$\Delta S = \frac{\Delta H - \Delta F}{T} = \frac{0 - (-1373)}{300.1 \text{ deg}} = 4.58 \text{ cal deg}^{-1} \text{ mole}^{-1}$$

Example 9. One mole of an ideal gas expands isothermally at 27° into an *evacuated* vessel until the pressure drops from 10 to 1 atm; that is, it expands from a vessel of 2.462 liters into a connecting vessel such that the total volume is 24.62 liters. Calculate the change in thermodynamic quantities.

This process is isothermal, but it is *not* reversible, and the pressure is not constant.

$w = 0$ because the system as a whole is closed and no external work can be done.

$q = 0$ because there is no heat change in the vessel as a whole during the expansion of an ideal gas.

ΔA and ΔF cannot be calculated directly from w, because the work is not maximum work, and ΔS is not equal to q/T, because the heat is not measured in a reversible process. But these quantities are independent of the path, and their differences between initial and final state are identical with those of Example 8 carried out under conditions which permit their calculation. Then,

$$\Delta F = -1373 \text{ cal mole}^{-1} \qquad \Delta A = -1373 \text{ cal mole}^{-1} \qquad \Delta H = 0 \qquad \Delta E = 0$$

$$\Delta S = 4.58 \text{ cal deg}^{-1} \text{ mole}^{-1}$$

Open Systems. So far, systems have been considered in which the number of moles of the various components do not change. In order to extend the thermodynamic equations to open systems, that is, systems in which matter may enter or leave, it is necessary to write the second law of thermodynamics (see equation 22) as

$$dE = T \, dS - p \, dV + \mu_1 \, dn_1 + \mu_2 \, dn_2 + \cdots + \mu_n \, dn_n \qquad (31)$$

where the number of moles of component 1 is represented by n_1, etc.

The differential coefficients $\mu_1 \cdots \mu_n$ were first introduced by Gibbs and are called the *chemical potentials* of the various constituents. From equation 31 the chemical potential of component i is defined by

$$\mu_i = \left(\frac{\partial E}{\partial n_i} \right)_{S,V,n_1 \cdots n_n} \qquad (32)$$

The chemical potential may also be defined in other ways, depending upon what is held constant. For example, introduction of equation 31 into equation 22 leads to

$$dF = V \, dp - S \, dT + \mu_1 \, dn_1 + \mu_2 \, dn_2 + \cdots + \mu_n \, dn_n \qquad (33)$$

Therefore,

$$\mu_i = \left(\frac{\partial F}{\partial n_i} \right)_{T,p,n_1 \cdots n_n} \qquad (34)$$

which shows that the chemical potential of a substance i is equal to the rate of change in the free energy of the system with number of moles n_i of this component while the temperature, the pressure, and the number of moles of all other components are held constant.

Equilibrium between Phases. We are familiar with the fact that for two phases, as ice and water, to be in equilibrium they must be at the same temperature and pressure. This will be proved, and an additional condition for equilibrium between phases may be derived from equation 33. If an infinitesimal quantity of heat is transferred from a phase α to a phase β which are in equilibrium, the condition for equilibrium is

$$dS = 0 \qquad \text{or} \qquad dS_\alpha + dS_\beta = 0$$

where the phases are designated by subscripts. Since the process is reversible

$$(- dq/T_\alpha) + (dq/T_\beta) = 0$$

or

$$T_\alpha = T_\beta \tag{35}$$

The fact that the pressure must be the same in two phases at equilibrium may be proved by considering that phase α increases in volume by an infinitesimal volume δV and phase β decreases by the same amount. If the temperature and volume of the whole system are held constant,

$$dA_\alpha + dA_\beta = 0 \quad \text{or} \quad -p_\alpha \, \delta V + p_\beta \, \delta V = 0$$

and so

$$p_\alpha = p_\beta \tag{36}$$

An additional restriction may be derived by considering the transfer of a small quantity of substance i from phase α to phase β which are in equilibrium. If the temperature of the whole system and the pressures of the various phases are kept constant, then by equation 30

$$dF_\alpha + dF_\beta = 0$$

or using equation 33

$$-\mu_{i\alpha} \, \delta n_i + \mu_{i\beta} \, \delta n_i = 0$$

or

$$\mu_{i\alpha} = \mu_{i\beta} \tag{37}$$

Thus, the chemical potential of a component is the same in all phases at equilibrium.

If phases α and β are not in equilibrium and a small quantity δn_i of species i is transferred from phase α to phase β in the direction of approaching equilibrium, we have at constant temperature and pressure

$$dF_\alpha + dF_\beta < 0$$

$$-\mu_{i\alpha} \, \delta n_i + \mu_{i\beta} \, \delta n_i < 0$$

If δn_i is positive

$$\mu_{i\alpha} > \mu_{i\beta}$$

Thus, a substance will tend to pass spontaneously from the phase where it has the higher chemical potential to the phase where it has the lower chemical potential. In this respect the chemical potential is like other kinds of potential, electrical, gravitational, etc., in that the spontaneous change is always in the direction from high to low potential.

The relationship between the chemical potential of a perfect gas and its pressure is particularly simple. Since the chemical potential is merely the free energy per mole, it is, according to equation 27,

$$\mu = \mu_0 + RT \ln p \qquad (38)$$

where p is the partial pressure of the gas and μ_0 is a constant which depends upon an arbitrarily chosen standard state of the component and upon the temperature. In order to make equation 38 applicable to non-ideal gases, p must be replaced by the activity which is to be discussed on p. 268.

REFERENCES

Glasstone, *Thermodynamics for Chemists*, D. Van Nostrand Co., New York, 1947.

Lewis and Randall, *Thermodynamics and the Free Energy of Chemical Substances*, McGraw-Hill Book Co., New York, 1923.

Hougen and Watson, *Chemical Process Principles*, Vol. II, *Thermodynamics*, John Wiley & Sons, New York, 1947.

Rossini, *Chemical Thermodynamics*, John Wiley & Sons, New York, 1950.

Gibbs, *The Collected Works of J. Willard Gibbs*, Yale University Press, New Haven, Conn., 1948.

Guggenheim, *Modern Thermodynamics by the Methods of Willard Gibbs*, Methuen & Co., London, 1933.

Klotz, *Chemical Thermodynamics*, Prentice-Hall, New York, 1950.

PROBLEMS

1. Calculate the entropy changes for the following processes: (a) Melting of 1 mole of aluminum at its melting point 660°C. ($\Delta H_{\text{fusion}} = 1.91$ kcal g atom^{-1}.) (b) Evaporation of 2 moles of liquid oxygen at its boiling point, -182.97°C. ($\Delta H_{\text{vap}} = 1.630$ kcal mole^{-1}.) (c) Heating of 10 grams of H_2S from 50° to 100°. ($C_p = 7.15 + 0.00332 \, T$.) *Ans.* (a) 2.05, (b) 36.2, (c) 0.351 cal deg^{-1}.

2. Calculate the molal entropy of liquid chlorine at its melting point, 172.12°K, from the following data obtained by Giauque and Powell:

T, °K	15	20	25	30	35	40	50	60
C_p, cal deg^{-1} mole^{-1}	0.89	1.85	2.89	3.99	4.97	5.73	6.99	8.00

T, °K	70	90	110	130	150	170	172.12
C_p, cal deg^{-1} mole^{-1}	8.68	9.71	10.47	11.29	12.20	13.17	m.p.

Heat of fusion = 1531 cal per mole.

A plot of C_p/T against T is most convenient for the graphical integration. Below 15° it may be assumed that C_p is proportional to T^3. *Ans.* 25.8 cal deg^{-1} mole^{-1}.

3. A mole of steam is condensed at 100°, and the water is cooled to 0° and frozen to ice. What is the entropy change of the water? Consider that the average specific heat of liquid water is 1.0 cal deg^{-1} g^{-1}. Heats of vaporization and fusion are 539.7 and 79.7 cal per gram, respectively. *Ans.* $\Delta S = -36.9$ cal deg^{-1} mole^{-1}.

4. One liter of an ideal gas at 300°K has an initial pressure of 15 atm and is allowed to expand isothermally to a volume of 10 liters. Calculate (a) the maximum work which can be obtained from the expansion; (b) ΔE; (c) ΔH; (d) ΔF; (e) ΔA. *Ans.* (a) 836, (b) 0, (c) 0, (d) -836, (e) -836 cal.

5. Using atomic and molecular entropies from Table II, calculate ΔS for the following reactions at 25°:

(a) $H_2(g) + \frac{1}{2}O_2(g) \rightarrow H_2O(l)$

(b) $H_2(g) + Cl_2(g) \rightarrow 2HCl(g)$

(c) Propane(g) + Ethane$(g) \rightarrow$ n-Pentane(g) + $H_2(g)$

(d) Methane$(g) + \frac{1}{2}O_2(g) \rightarrow$ Methanol(l)

$Ans.$ (a) -38.996, (b) 4.737, (c) -4.88, (d) -38.7 cal deg^{-1}.

6. Calculate the free-energy changes for the reactions in the preceding problem by use of heats of formation data in Table II, page 118.

$Ans.$ (a) -56.690, (b) -45.536, (c) 11.51, (d) -27.59 kcal.

7. One mole of an ideal gas is allowed to expand reversibly and isothermally (25°C) from a pressure of 1 atm to a pressure of 0.1 atm. (a) What is the change in free energy? (b) What would be the change in free energy if the process occurred irreversibly? $Ans.$ (a) -1364, (b) -1364 cal.

8. Theoretically, how high could a gallon of gasoline lift an automobile weighing 2800 lb against the force of gravity, if it is assumed that the cylinder temperature is 2200°K and the exit temperature 1200°K? (Density of gasoline = 0.80 g cm^{-3}; 1 lb = 453.6 g; 1 ft = 30.48 cm; 1 liter = 0.2642 gal. Heat of combustion of gasoline = 11,200 cal g^{-1}.) $Ans.$ 17,000 ft.

9. Derive an expression for the difference in entropy of 1 mole of an ideal gas with constant heat capacities at a temperature T_1 and pressure p_1 and at temperature T_2 and pressure p_2 by calculating the entropy changes when 1 mole of the gas is heated from T_1 to T_2 at constant pressure p_1 and then is isothermally and reversibly compressed from p_1 to p_2. $Ans.$ $\Delta S = C_p \ln (T_2/T_1) - R \ln (p_2/p_1)$.

10. Ten grams of helium is compressed isothermally and reversibly at 100°C from a pressure of 2 atm to 10 atm. Calculate (a) q, (b) w, (c) ΔF, (d) ΔA, (e) ΔH, (f) ΔE, (g) ΔS.

$Ans.$ (a) -2983, (b) -2983, (c) $+2983$, (d) $+2983$, (e) 0, (f) 0 cal (g) -8.00 cal deg^{-1}.

11. Calculate each of the quantities listed in Problem 10 for the isothermal compression of the helium not reversibly, but with a pressure of 10 atm applied directly. $Ans.$ $q = w = -7410$ cal, ΔE, ΔF, ΔH, ΔA, and ΔS are the same as in 10.

---

12. Calculate the molar entropy of CS_2 at 25° from the following heat capacity data and the heat of fusion, 1049.0 cal mole^{-1}, at the melting point (161.11°K).

T, °K	15.05	20.15	29.76	42.22
C_p, cal deg^{-1} mole^{-1}	1.65	2.87	4.96	6.97

T, °K	57.52	75.54	89.37	99.00	108.93
C_p, cal deg^{-1} mole^{-1}	8.50	9.57	10.31	10.98	11.59

T, °K	119.91	131.54	156.83	161–298
C_p, cal deg^{-1} mole^{-1}	12.07	12.58	13.53	18.04

13. Calculate the entropy changes for the following processes at 25°.

(a) S(rhombic) $\rightarrow$ S(monoclinic)

(b) Ethanol$(l) + \frac{1}{2}O_2(g) \rightarrow$ Acetaldehyde(g) + $H_2O(l)$

(c) n-Hexane$(g) \rightarrow$ Benzene(g) + $4H_2(g)$

14. Calculate the theoretical maximum efficiency with which heat can be converted into work in the following hypothetical turbines: (a) Steam at 100° with condenser at 40°. (b) Mercury vapor at 360° with condenser at 140°. (c) Steam at 400° and condenser at 150°. (d) Air at 800° and exit at 400°. (e) Air at 1000° and exit at 400°, special alloys being used. (f) Helium at 1500° and exit at 400°, heat from atomic energy being used.

15. (a) Calculate the external work done against the atmosphere when 1 mole of toluene is vaporized at its boiling point, 111°. The heat of vaporization at this temperature is 86.5 cal per gram. For the vaporization of 1 mole, calculate (b) q, (c) ΔH, (d) ΔE, (e) ΔF, (f) ΔA, (g) ΔS.

16. One mole of NH_3 (considered to be a perfect gas) initially at 25° and 1 atm pressure is heated at constant pressure until the volume has trebled. Calculate (a) q, (b) w, (c) ΔH, (d) ΔE, (e) ΔS. See Table IV, page 123.

17. One mole of nitrobenzene $C_6H_5NO_2$ is vaporized at 210°. The heat of vaporization at this temperature is 79.1 cal per gram. Calculate (a) q, (b) w, (c) ΔH, (d) ΔE, (e) ΔF, (f) ΔA, (g) ΔS.

18. A thermostat was maintained at a temperature of 96.9°. The air in the room was at 26.9°. During a certain length of time 1000 cal of heat leaked through the thermostat insulation into the room. (a) What was the entropy change of the material in the thermostat? (b) What was the entropy change of the air in the room? (c) Was the process reversible or irreversible?

---

19. Calculations with the Debye formula show the molal entropy of silver iodide to be 1.5 cal deg^{-1} $mole^{-1}$ at 15°K. From the following data for the molar heat capacity at constant pressure, calculate the molal entropy of silver iodide at 298.1°K:

$T°$	C_p	$T°$	C_p	$T°$	C_p	$T°$	C_p
21.00	3.82	64.44	9.36	145.67	11.92	258.79	13.05
30.53	5.23	88.58	10.60	170.86	12.15	273.23	13.26
42.70	7.09	105.79	11.19	198.89	12.49	287.42	13.48
52.15	8.20	126.53	11.60	228.34	12.76	301.37	13.64

20. What is the change in entropy when 1 mole of water vapor is heated from 300° to 600°C at constant pressure?

21. Calculate the change in entropy if 350 grams of water at 5° are mixed with 500 grams of water at 70°, assuming that the specific heat is 1.00 cal deg^{-1} g^{-1}.

22. In the reversible isothermal expansion of an ideal gas at 300°K from 1 liter to 10 liters, where the gas has an initial pressure of 20 atm, calculate (a) ΔS for the gas, (b) ΔS for all systems involved in the expansion, (c) ΔA for the gas, (d) ΔA for all systems involved in the expansion.

23. Show that the coefficient of performance of a refrigeration machine, defined as the ratio of the heat absorbed by the refrigeration fluid at the low temperature T_2 to the work done by the compressor on the fluid, is $T_2/(T_1 - T_2)$ for reversible operation. The cycle consists of absorption of heat by the fluid in the evaporator at T_2, reversible adiabatic compression which raises the temperature to T_1, rejection of heat in the condenser at T_1, and reversible adiabatic expansion which lowers the temperature to T_2. How much work must be done in a refrigerating machine, operating in a Carnot cycle between 0 and 25°, in order to freeze 100 kg of water?

24. Calculate the change in entropy of a mole of water when it is cooled at 1 atm from vapor at 200° to liquid at 25°.

25. Calculate the differences between the atomic entropies of Hg(l) and Hg(s) at −50°. The melting point of Hg is −39°, and the heat of fusion is 560 cal per gram-atom. The heat capacity per gram-atom of Hg(l) may be taken as $7.1–0.0016T$, and that of Hg(s) as 6.4 cal per degree.

26. Calculate (a) w, (b) ΔA, and (c) ΔF when 1 mole of liquid water is evaporated at its boiling point 100° at 1 atm and then expanded in its vapor state to 50 liters at 100°.

27. One mole of an ideal gas in 22.4 liters is expanded isothermally and reversibly at 0° to a volume of 224 liters and $\frac{1}{10}$ atm. Calculate (a) w, (b) q, (c) ΔH, (d) ΔF, (e) ΔS for the gas.

One mole of an ideal gas in 22.4 liters is allowed to expand irreversibly into an evacuated vessel such that the final total volume is 224 liters. Calculate (f) w, (g) q, (h) ΔH, (i) ΔF, (j) ΔS for the gas.

Calculate (k) ΔS for all the systems involved in (e), and calculate (l) ΔS for all the systems involved in (j).

28. Discuss the advantages and disadvantages of using diphenyl instead of water for an engine. Diphenyl boils at 254.6° and melts at 70.5°.

29. An ideal gas expands isothermally and reversibly from a state of p_1 and v_1 to a state of p_2 and v_2. Calculate the work done by the gas and also the $\int v \, dp$ term. What is the change in the product of p and v?

An actual gas which obeys the relation $p(v - b) = RT$, where b is a constant, under certain conditions expands isothermally and reversibly from a state of p_1 and v_1 to a state of p_2 and v_2. Calculate the work done and also the term $\int v \, dp$. What is the change in the product of p and v? What general conclusion can be drawn from these results?

30. A 2-liter container at 0° contains H_2S (assumed to be an ideal gas) at 1 atm pressure. The gas is heated to 100°, the external pressure remaining 1 atm. Calculate (a) the heat absorbed, (b) the work done, (c) ΔE, (d) ΔH, and (e) ΔS. For H_2S, $C_p = 7.15 + 0.00332T$.

31. (a) Calculate the least work that would have to be performed in order to extract 100 cal of heat from an ice bath at 0°, when the surroundings are at 25°. (b) How much heat at 25° could be obtained from the ice bath on the expenditure of 10 cal of work?

32. An isothermal irreversible process takes place at 300°K so that the net gain in entropy for all systems involved is +10.0 entropy units. Calculate the minimum amount of work which would have to be transformed into heat at 300°K to restore the systems involved to their previous state.

33. One-half mole of an ideal monatomic gas initially at 25° and occupying a volume of 2 liters is allowed to expand adiabatically against a constant pressure of 1 atm until external and internal pressures are equal. The gas is then compressed isothermally and reversibly until its volume is 2 liters at the lower temperature. Calculate (a) q, net heat absorbed, (b) w, net work done, (c) ΔE, (d) ΔH, and (e) ΔS.

34. One hundred and fifty grams of ice is added to a kilogram of water at 25° in an isolated system. Calculate the change in entropy if the heat of fusion is 1435 cal mole^{-1} and $C_p = 18$ cal deg^{-1} mole^{-1} for water.

8

The Liquid State

Theory of Liquids. A liquid has no definite shape, but it does retain a definite volume under given conditions. The distance between molecules is much less in liquids than in gases, as illustrated by the fact that a mole of liquid water at 100° occupies 18.8 ml, but when vaporized it occupies about 30,200 ml at 1 atm pressure. This closer proximity of molecules in the liquid state and a corresponding restriction of their movements result in a lesser fluidity and make the effect of changing pressure and temperature much less in a liquid than in a gas.

The internal energy in the vapor state is greater than in the liquid state because it is necessary to supply energy in order to overcome the force of attraction that holds the molecules close together in the liquid.

A liquid may be regarded as a condensed gas or as a melted solid, and each point of view is important. The theory of liquids is in a much less satisfactory state than the theories of gases and crystals, but important progress is being made in our understanding of the structure of liquids.

Liquefaction of Gases. More than a century ago, Faraday liquefied practically all the gases that condense at moderate pressures and not too low temperatures. He inverted a sealed-off U tube and heated one end while the other was immersed in a freezing mixture. When crystals of chlorine hydrate were heated in this tube, the liberated chlorine gas was put under such a high pressure that it condensed to yellow, liquid chlorine in the cold end of the tube.

The following principles are involved in the liquefaction of gases: (1) the gas must be below its critical temperature; (2) the pressure must be great enough to cause liquefaction, and the lower the temperature, the lower is the required pressure; (3) the incoming gas is cooled by the outgoing gas which has been cooled by expansion; (4) the gas is cooled by doing external work in an engine; and (5) the gas is cooled by expanding against the force of attraction between the molecules.

Air was first liquefied in large amounts in 1895. The Linde process, still largely used, makes use only of the cooling effect produced by the expansion of the gas against the molecular attraction; the Claude process conserves some of the energy of expansion by operating an external engine with the compressed air as it expands.

The liquefaction of gases finds extensive applications. Ammonia, sulfur dioxide, and "Freon" (CF_2Cl_2) are among the gases used in refrigeration and air conditioning. The use of solid carbon dioxide (Dry Ice) is widespread. Many gas mixtures can be separated by liquefaction. Examples are: oxygen and nitrogen from air; helium from natural gas; propane and butane for household cooking from petroleum products; and neon and argon for electric lights from air.

Oxygen is now widely used for welding and other operations, and it would find much greater application if it could be made more cheaply.

The important specific heat measurements at low temperatures are dependent on liquid nitrogen (b.p. $77.3°K$), liquid hydrogen (b.p. $20.4°K$) and liquid helium (b.p. $4.2°K$). The advantages of using liquid helium are readily apparent, but few laboratories have been equipped to produce liquid helium because of the costly and cumbersome equipment required. A compact laboratory apparatus for liquefying helium is now available,* however, and is making measurements in the neighborhood of absolute zero practical. In this apparatus the helium is compressed to 225 pounds per square inch and a temperature of $78°K$ is reached by causing the helium gas to do work in an expansion engine. A temperature of $10°K$ is obtained by allowing the gas to do work in a second expansion engine, and liquid helium is obtained at $4°K$ in the last step, which is a Joule-Thomson expansion (page 102). Interesting new phenomena can be studied, such as superconductivity (the disappearance of electrical resistance) and the extraordinary ability of helium to flow, apparently without friction, at temperatures below $2.2°K$.

Vapor Pressure of Liquids. According to the kinetic theory there is a continuous flight of molecules from the surface of a liquid into the free space above it. At the same time molecules of gas or vapor † return to the surface of the liquid at a rate depending on the concentration of the vapor. Eventually, a condition of equilibrium is established between the liquid and its vapor, when the rate of escape is exactly equal to the rate of condensation of vapor. The vapor is then said to be *saturated*. The pressure exerted by vapor in equilibrium with the liquid is known as the *vapor pressure*. The equilibrium between a liquid and its vapor is dependent on the temperature. For every temperature below the critical temperature there is a certain pressure at which vapor

---

* The Collins Helium Cryostat is produced by the Arthur D. Little Co.

† A vapor is generally defined as an easily liquefiable gas as distinguished from permanent gases such as nitrogen and hydrogen, which must be cooled far below room temperature before becoming liquid at atmospheric pressure.

and liquid may exist in equilibrium in all proportions; and, conversely, for every pressure below the critical pressure, there is a certain temperature at which vapor and liquid may exist in equilibrium in all proportions. In the special case where the pressure is 760 mm, this temperature is the standard boiling point of the liquid. The vapor pressure of a liquid is a constant quantity at any temperature and is independent of

Table I. Vapor Pressures of Liquids in Millimeters of Mercury

$t°C$	Water	Ethanol	Benzene	n-Hexane	Acetone	Ethyl Ether	n-Octane
0	4.58	12.2	28.5	47.3		185.3	2.9
20	17.54	43.9	76.7	121.6	184.8	442.2	10.4
40	55.32	135.3	179.9	278.6	421.5	921.3	30.8
60	149.38	352.7	384.6	555.9	866.0		77.5
80	355.1	812.6	749.9	1059			174.8
100	760.0		1380	1841			353.6

the amounts of liquid and vapor present, but it increases as the temperature is raised. Table I gives the vapor pressures of several typical liquids from 0 to 100°.

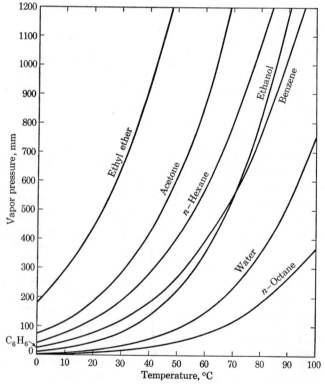

Fig. 8-1.   Vapor-pressure-temperature curves for seven common liquids.

These data are plotted in *Fig. 8-1* on rectangular coordinates, and in *Fig. 8-2* the logarithms of the vapor pressures in millimeters are plotted against the reciprocals of the absolute temperatures. The reciprocals of the absolute temperatures have been multiplied by 10^4 for con-

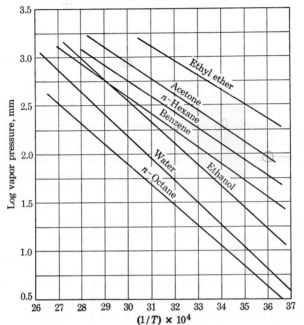

FIG. 8-2.   Log p vs. $1/T$ curves for the liquids shown in Table I.

venience in plotting. Thus, 0°C or 273.1°K gives for $1/T$ a value of 0.00366 or 36.6×10^{-4}, as shown at the extreme right.

These graphs follow, as a first approximation, the equation

$$\log p = A + (B/T) \tag{1}$$

where p is the vapor pressure and A and B are constants. The theoretical justification for this empirical equation will be given shortly.

Example 1. Draw the best straight line through the points obtained by plotting log vapor pressure of iodobenzene against the reciprocal of the absolute temperature. At 70° the vapor pressure is 13.65 mm, at 110° it is 73.88 mm, and at 170° it is 479.7 mm.

(a) Find the equation for this straight line.

$$\log p = A + (B/T) = 8.041 - (2370/T)$$

(b) Calculate the vapor pressure at 0°.

$$\log p = (-2370/273.1) + 8.041 = -0.637 \qquad p = 0.231 \text{ mm}$$

(c) Calculate the boiling point, that is, the temperature at which the vapor pressure is 760 mm.

$$\log 760 = (-2370/T) + 8.041$$

$$T = \frac{2370}{8.041 - \log 760} = 459.3°\text{K or } 186.2°\text{C}$$

Measurement of Vapor Pressure. The boiling temperatures of a liquid may be determined at various pressures using a vacuum or pressure pump to change the pressure and a manometer to measure it. The thermometer is not immersed in the liquid, because the liquid may become superheated. It is supported so that the vapor condenses on it and bathes the thermometer bulb with liquid, which is in equilibrium with the vapor at the measured pressure. In another method the liquid is allowed to drip slowly over the thermometer bulb while it is heated by the condensation of vapor. There is no danger of superheating the liquid above its normal boiling temperature if the heat is supplied only by the condensing vapor. In the so-called static method the pressure exerted by the vapor in equilibrium with the liquid is measured directly. A bulb containing the liquid is attached to a manometer and trap and immersed in a thermostat. After the substance has been degassed by freezing under vacuum and then melted, the manometer reads the vapor pressure of the material at the temperature of the thermostat.

The *gas-saturation method* is an accurate and convenient method for determining the vapor pressure of a liquid. A current of pure dry air or other gas is bubbled slowly through a weighed amount of the liquid whose vapor pressure is to be determined. The liquid is maintained at constant temperature, and its loss in weight is measured. The vapor may be removed from the gas stream in an absorption tube and weighed, or the liquid in the vessel may be weighed before and after. In passing through the saturating vessel the air vaporizes an amount of liquid directly proportional to the vapor pressure of the liquid. The accuracy of this method depends, of course, on having the gas completely saturated with vapor, and, in order to give ample contact with the liquid, the gas is often passed through two or more vessels of liquid in series.

If v is the volume which contains g grams of the vaporized liquid having the molecular weight M, and p is the pressure of the vapor in equilibrium with the liquid at the temperature T, then the vapor pressure p of the liquid is calculated from the ideal gas laws by the formula

$$p = (g/Mv)RT \qquad (2)$$

For approximate calculations the volume v occupied by the vapor may be taken as the volume of the dry air measured before it becomes saturated with the vapor. For more accurate calculations or for high vapor pressures, allowance must be made for the fact that the total volume of the gases is increased by the introduction of the vapor. The volume v, of both air and vapor through which the vapor molecules are distributed, is $v'P/(P - p)$, where v' is the volume of the pure air before saturation, P is the barometric pressure, and p is the vapor pressure of the liquid. Then,

$$p = \frac{g}{M}\frac{RT}{v} = \frac{g}{M}\frac{RT(P - p)}{v'P}$$

$$p\left(1 + \frac{g}{M}\frac{RT}{v'P}\right) = \frac{g}{M}\frac{RT}{v'}$$

Or, solving for p,

$$p = \frac{gRT/Mv'}{1 + (gRT/Mv'P)} \tag{3}$$

Example 2. When liquid bromobenzene was vaporized at 30.0° by passing 20.00 liters of dry air through it, the loss in weight of the liquid was 0.9414 gram. The barometric pressure was 760 mm. The molecular weight is 157.0. Approximately, what is the vapor pressure at this temperature?

$$p = \frac{gRT}{Mv} = \frac{(0.9414 \text{ g})(0.08205 \text{ l-atm deg}^{-1} \text{ mole}^{-1})(303.1 \text{ deg})}{(157.0 \text{ g mole}^{-1})(20.00 \text{ l})}$$

$$= 0.00746 \text{ atm}$$

$$p = (0.00746 \text{ atm})(760 \text{ mm atm}^{-1})$$

$$= 5.67 \text{ mm}$$

A more exact answer is obtained by use of equation 3:

$$p = \frac{5.67 \text{ mm}}{1 + (5.67 \text{ mm}/760 \text{ mm})} = 5.62 \text{ mm}$$

The difference between the use of equation 2 and equation 3 is much more pronounced with materials of high vapor pressure.

The Clapeyron Equation. The theoretical explanation of the empirical relation between vapor pressure and temperature was developed by Clapeyron in 1834. Consider a liquid in equilibrium with its vapor at a temperature T and a pressure equal to the vapor pressure p at that temperature. If some of the liquid is vaporized at this equilibrium pressure and temperature, by equation 30 of Chapter 7,

$$\Delta F = 0$$

Since the free energy of the whole system does not change in this case, the free energy of a mole of liquid F_l is the same as the free energy of a mole of vapor F_v.

$$F_l = F_v \tag{4}$$

If the temperature is raised to $T + dT$, the pressure must be increased to $p + dp$, the vapor pressure at this higher temperature, in order for the two phases to be in equilibrium. Under these conditions the free energy of 1 mole of the liquid and of 1 mole of the vapor will be $F_l + dF_l$ and $F_v + dF_v$, respectively, and, since the change in free energy of the system must be zero for vaporization of the liquid at this new equilibrium pressure and temperature,

$$F_l + dF_l = F_v + dF_v$$

Therefore, subtracting equation 4 gives

$$dF_l = dF_v \tag{5}$$

By differentiating equation 15 of Chapter 7,

$$F_l = H_l - T_l S_l = E_l + p_l V_l - T_l S_l$$

we obtain

$$dF_l = dE_l + p_l\, dV_l + V_l\, dp_l - T_l\, dS_l - S_l\, dT_l \tag{6}$$

For a reversible process,

$$dq = T\, dS$$

and by the first law of thermodynamics, under constant pressure,

$$dE_l = dq - dw = T_l\, dS_l - p_l\, dV_l$$

Substituting for dE_l in equation 6, we obtain

$$dF_l = V_l\, dp_l - S_l\, dT_l \tag{7}$$

This relation gives the increase in free energy of 1 mole of the liquid when the pressure is increased by dp_l and the temperature by dT_l; V_l is the volume and S_l the entropy of 1 mole of liquid at pressure p_l and temperature T_l. A similar equation holds for the vapor:

$$dF_v = V_v\, dp_v - S_v\, dT_v \tag{8}$$

The subscripts on dp and dT may be dropped in equations 7 and 8 since the temperature and pressure of the two phases are the same.

Setting these two equations equal, as justified by equation 5, gives

$$V_l \, dp - S_l \, dT = V_v \, dp - S_v \, dT$$

or, on rearranging,

$$\frac{dp}{dT} = \frac{S_v - S_l}{V_v - V_l} \tag{9}$$

Also, by equation 7 of Chapter 7, we have

$$S_v - S_l = \frac{\Delta H_{\text{vap}}}{T} \tag{10}$$

where ΔH_{vap} is the heat of vaporization of a mole of the liquid at this temperature and pressure. Substituting equation 10 into equation 9, we obtain the Clapeyron equation:

$$\frac{dp}{dT} = \frac{\Delta H_{\text{vap}}}{T(V_v - V_l)} \tag{11}$$

This equation gives the rate of change of the vapor pressure of a liquid with temperature, dp/dT, in terms of the molar heat of vaporization ΔH_{vap}, molar volume V_l of the liquid, and molar volume V_v of the vapor at the temperature T and pressure p.

In using this equation it is necessary to have the units consistent; that is, the heat term must be expressed in the same units as the product of pressure and volume change. If the pressure is given in atmospheres and the volume in liters, the heat is expressed in liter-atmospheres; or, if the pressure is converted into dynes cm^{-2}, the heat is expressed in ergs.

Example 3. What is the rate of change of the vapor pressure of water at 100°? The heat of vaporization is 539.7 cal per gram, the molar volume (that is, the volume occupied by 1 mole of liquid water) is 18.78 ml, and the molar volume of steam is 30.199 liters, all at 100°C and 1 atm. The factor for converting calories to l-atm may be obtained as follows:

$$\frac{0.08205 \text{ l-atm deg}^{-1} \text{ mole}^{-1}}{1.987 \text{ cal deg}^{-1} \text{ mole}^{-1}} = 0.04129 \text{ l-atm cal}^{-1}$$

$$\frac{dp}{dT} = \frac{\Delta H_{\text{vap}}}{T(V_v - V_l)} = \frac{(539.7 \text{ cal g}^{-1})(18.01 \text{ g mole}^{-1})(0.04129 \text{ l-atm cal}^{-1})}{(373.1 \text{ deg})(30.199 \text{ l mole}^{-1} - 0.01878 \text{ l mole}^{-1})}$$

$$= 0.0356 \text{ atm deg}^{-1}$$

$$= (0.0356 \text{ atm deg}^{-1})(760 \text{ mm atm}^{-1}) = 27.1 \text{ mm deg}^{-1}$$

Equation 11 is applicable not only to the effect of pressure on the temperature of vaporization but also to its effect on the temperature of fusion, sublimation, and changes from one crystalline form to another. For an equilibrium between solid and liquid, dp/dT gives the influence of pressure on the melting point.

$$\frac{dp}{dT} = \frac{\Delta H_{fus}}{T(V_l - V_s)}$$

Here ΔH_{fus} is the molar heat of fusion and V_l and V_s are the molar volumes of the liquid and solid.

Example 4. Calculate the change in the freezing point of water produced by an increase in pressure of 1 atm. At $0°$ the heat of fusion of ice is 79.7 cal per gram or 3.291 l-atm per gram, the density of water is 0.9998 g per ml, and the density of ice is 0.9168. The reciprocals of the densities, 1.0002 and 1.0908, are the volumes in milliliters of 1 gram, and the molar volumes are obtained by multiplying by 18.01. The volume change upon freezing $(v_l - v_s)$ is therefore -9.06×10^{-5} liter per gram. For small changes dp/dT may be replaced by $\Delta p/\Delta t$. Then

$$\frac{\Delta p}{\Delta T} = \frac{\Delta H_{fus}}{T(V_l - V_s)}$$

$$= \frac{(3.291 \text{ l-atm g}^{-1})(18.01 \text{ g mole}^{-1})}{(273.1 \text{ deg})(-9.06 \times 10^{-5} \text{ l g}^{-1})(18.01 \text{ g mole}^{-1})}$$

$$= -133 \text{ atm deg}^{-1}$$

In other words, 133 atm is the pressure required to lower the freezing point of water $1°$; and the reciprocal,

$$\Delta T/\Delta p = -1/133 = -0.0075 \text{ deg atm}^{-1}$$

shows that an increase in pressure of 1 atm lowers the freezing point $0.0075°$. The negative sign indicates that an increase of pressure causes a decrease in temperature, a relation which follows by Le Châtelier's theorem from the fact that the specific volume of ice is greater than that of water at the freezing point.

The Clausius-Clapeyron Equation. Clausius showed how the Clapeyron equation may be simplified by assuming that the vapor obeys the ideal gas law. The volume of a mole of liquid V_l is negligible in comparison with V_v and may be dropped out. For example, with water at $100°$, V_v is 30.2 liters and V_l is 0.0188 liter. Then RT/p may be substituted for V_v, and

$$\frac{dp}{dT} = \frac{\Delta H_{\text{vap}}}{T(V_v - V_l)} = \frac{p \, \Delta H_{\text{vap}}}{RT^2}$$

On rearrangement this becomes

$$\frac{1}{dT} \frac{dp}{p} = \frac{\Delta H_{\text{vap}}}{RT^2} \tag{12}$$

or

$$\frac{d \ln p}{dT} = \frac{\Delta H_{\text{vap}}}{RT^2} \tag{13}$$

Since R is a constant, integrating on the assumption that ΔH_{vap} is a constant yields

$$\int d \ln p = \int \frac{\Delta H_{\text{vap}}}{R} T^{-2} \, dT$$

$$\ln p = - \frac{\Delta H_{\text{vap}}}{R} \frac{1}{T} + C \tag{14}$$

where C is the integration constant. This is the equation of a straight line, and, when $\ln p$ is plotted against $1/T$, a straight line results, the slope of which is numerically equal to $- \Delta H_{\text{vap}}/R$. When logarithms to the base 10 are plotted, the slope is $- \Delta H_{\text{vap}}/2.303R$. The theoretical justification for the empirical relation given in equation 1 is now apparent.

The slope of the line can be used for calculating the heat of vaporization, thus:

$$\Delta H_{\text{vap}} \text{ (in calories)} = -(\text{slope of line})(2.303)(1.987) \tag{15}$$

Frequently, it is more convenient to use a formula obtained by integrating between limits, p_2 at T_2 and p_1 at T_1, as follows:

$$\int_{p_1}^{p_2} d \ln p = \int_{T_1}^{T_2} \frac{\Delta H_{\text{vap}}}{R} T^{-2} \, dT$$

$$\ln p_2 - \ln p_1 = \frac{\Delta H_{\text{vap}}}{R} \left[- \frac{1}{T_2} - \left(- \frac{1}{T_1} \right) \right]$$

$$\log \frac{p_2}{p_1} = \frac{\Delta H_{\text{vap}}(T_2 - T_1)}{(2.303)(1.987) T_2 T_1} \tag{16}$$

Using this equation it is possible to calculate the heat of vaporization from the vapor pressures at two different temperatures; and, if the heat of vaporization and the vapor pressure at one temperature are known, the vapor pressure at any other temperature can be calculated. Any units of pressure may be taken as long as they are the same units for both pressures, and any units of heat may be used as long as ΔH_{vap} and R are taken in the same units.

Equation 16 derived here for the relation between vapor pressure, temperature, and heat of vaporization is a special case of a general formula for any equilibrium involving temperature which will be derived on page 255. Equilibrium constants of any type replace the equilibrium vapor pressures, and the heat of the chemical reaction or physical change replaces the heat of vaporization.

Exercise I. When a solid is converted into vapor the process is known as sublimation. The heat of sublimation at a given temperature is equal to the heat of fusion plus the heat of vaporization. Derive an equation similar to equation 16 for the sublimation pressure of solids at different temperatures.

The unintegrated expression is most convenient in correcting boiling points for barometric fluctuations. For *small* changes in pressure the change in boiling point with pressure is given approximately by the formula

$$\frac{\Delta T}{\Delta p} = \frac{RT^2}{\Delta H_{\mathrm{vap}}p} \tag{17}$$

Since formula 16 for calculating the heat of vaporization was derived on the assumption that the vapor behaved as an ideal gas, the results obtained by its use are no more accurate than the calculations involving the formula $pv = nRT$.

Another approximation is involved in the assumption of the constancy of the heat of vaporization. If the data are sufficiently exact and the temperature range sufficiently great, it will be seen that the lines are not exactly straight. The lines are straight if the heat capacities of the vapor and liquid are both the same, making the heat of vaporization constant, and if the vapor is an ideal gas. When the line is curved, it is possible to determine the heat of vaporization at any temperature by drawing a tangent to the curve at that temperature. In general, the slope of the log p versus $1/T$ plot becomes steeper, that is, the heat of vaporization becomes greater, at the lower temperatures where more energy is required to pull the molecules away from each other and put them into the gas phase.

A more exact equation may be obtained by the addition of another term, thus:

$$\log p = (A/T) + B \log T + \text{constant} \tag{18}$$

The vapor pressures of a large number of substances can be represented by this formula, even up to the critical temperature, with only small errors. The evaluation of the three constants from data at three temperatures by solving simultaneous equations requires accurate data. The reason for adding a term in log T is indicated by Exercise II.

Exercise II. If it is assumed that the vapor follows the ideal gas law, show that equation 18 can be derived from thermodynamics, and state the physical significance of the constant B.

$$\Delta H_{vap} = \Delta H^{\circ}_{vap} + \int_0^T (C_{p,vap} - C_{p,liq})\, dT = \Delta H^{\circ}_{vap} + \Delta C_p \int_0^T dT$$

$$= \Delta H^{\circ}_{vap} + \Delta C_p T$$

where ΔH_{vap} is the molar heat of vaporization at temperature T, and C_p is the heat capacity at constant pressure, which is independent of temperature. The constant ΔH°_{vap} is a hypothetical heat of vaporization at absolute zero.

Substituting into equation 13 yields

$$\frac{d \ln p}{dT} = \frac{\Delta H_{vap}}{RT^2} = \frac{\Delta H^{\circ}_{vap} + (\Delta C_p)T}{RT^2} = \frac{\Delta H^{\circ}_{vap}}{RT^2} + \frac{\Delta C_p}{RT}$$

$$\log p = \frac{-\Delta H^{\circ}_{vap}}{2.303RT} + \frac{\Delta C_p}{R} \log T + \text{constant}$$

The constant B in equation 18 then is equal to the difference between the heat capacity of the vapor and liquid at constant pressure, divided by the gas constant. This conclusion is only an approximation because the deviations from the ideal gas law still introduce an appreciable error which is not corrected in this derivation.*

There are several useful relations and simple methods of graphing which enable one to estimate the vapor pressure of a liquid at specified temperatures.† ‡ The log p versus $1/T$ graphs are nearly straight lines and the slopes do not vary greatly, particularly for compounds of the same general type. The boiling point of a liquid at 760 mm pressure or at a reduced pressure is usually known, so that one point on the line is readily available. On a log p versus $1/T$ graph a line is then drawn parallel to that of another, similar liquid whose vapor pressure is known at various temperatures. Thus it is easy to draw in a log p versus $1/T$ graph that will give fairly reliable values of the vapor pressure at different temperatures.

Empirical Relationships. A rough relationship was given in Table II of Chapter 2, where it was seen that the standard boiling point (that is, the temperature at which the vapor pressure becomes equal to 1 atm) is equal in many cases to about two-thirds of the critical tem-

---

* One of the most successful empirical vapor-pressure equations is the Antoine equation, which contains an additional constant C.

$$\log p = A - \left(\frac{B}{t + C}\right)$$

where t is temperature in degrees centigrade.

† Watson, *Ind. Eng. Chem.*, *23*, 360 (1931).

‡ Germann and Knight, *Ind. Eng. Chem.*, *26*, 467 (1934).

perature, both expressed in absolute temperatures. In this way a very approximate estimate of the critical temperature can be obtained from the boiling point of a given liquid.

Another empirical rule for liquids enables one to estimate the heat of vaporization of a liquid from the temperature at which the liquid boils. According to Trouton's approximate relation, if T denotes the standard boiling point, and ΔH_{vap} the heat of vaporization of 1 mole of liquid, then,

$$\Delta H_{vap}/T \cong 21 \text{ cal deg}^{-1} \text{ mole}^{-1} \tag{19}$$

In words, the ratio of the molar heat of vaporization to the absolute boiling temperature of a liquid is constant, approximately 21. The relation is shown over a wide range of temperature in Table II.

Trouton's empirical rule has some theoretical significance. The molar heat of vaporization divided by the absolute temperature gives the in-

Table II. Heats of Vaporization

Substance	Boiling Temperature, °C at 760 mm	ΔH_{vap}, kcal mole^{-1}	$\Delta H_{vap}/T$, cal deg^{-1} mole^{-1}
O_2	-182.97	1.630	18.07
H_2	-252.77	0.216	10.6
H_2O	-100.00	9.7171	26.040
He	-268.944	0.020	4.7
HF	19.9	1.8	6.1
Cl_2	-34.06	4.878	20.40
HCl	-85.05	3.86	20.5
SO_2	-10.02	5.955	22.63
H_2S	-60.34	4.463	20.97
N_2	-195.82	1.333	17.24
NH_3	-33.43	5.581	23.28
CH_3OH	64.7	8.43	24.95
CCl_4	76.7	7.17	20.5
$CHCl_3$	61.2	7.02	20.99
CS_2	46.25	6.40	20.0
C_2H_5OH	78.5	9.22	26.22
PbI_2	872	24.8	21.7
Methane (CH_4)	-161.49	1.955	17.51
Ethane (C_2H_6)	-88.63	3.517	19.06
n-Butane	-0.50	5.352	19.63
n-Hexane	68.742	6.896	20.17
n-Octane	125.66	8.360	20.96
Benzene	80.10 ✓	7.353	20.81
Toluene	110.62	8.00	20.85
Cyclohexane	80.74	7.19	20.30
Methylcyclohexane	100.94	7.58	20.26
Acetic acid	118.3	5.82	14.8

crease in entropy when a liquid is converted into a vapor. The change from liquid to vapor leads to increasing disorder, that is, to more random motion of the molecules. The change of entropy is very small at the critical temperature because the liquid and gas are indistinguishable. Accordingly, at their critical temperatures all liquids would have almost zero heat of vaporization and all would be alike. Most liquids behave alike not only at their critical temperatures but also at equal fractions of their critical temperatures, and we have seen (p. 18) that the standard boiling points of many liquids are roughly equal fractions of the critical temperatures. Hence, different liquids should have about the same entropy of vaporization at their boiling points provided that the molecules in liquid and vapor are the same and that no change is involved other than vaporization of the molecules.

When, in addition to the normal force of attraction, there are other forces which hold molecules together in the liquid state, the heat of vaporization becomes abnormally large. Water, alcohols, ammonia, and other substances with large dipole moments (page 78) require an extra amount of energy for separation of the molecules into the gas phase. Hydrogen and helium, which boil only a little above absolute zero, might well be expected to show large departures from this rule. Acetic acid and carboxylic acids, in general, are abnormal in that the vapor consists of double molecules. An examination of Table II shows that acetic acid does show a marked deviation from the behavior predicted on the basis of Trouton's rule.

The extra attraction that exists between molecules with large dipole moments leads to abnormal behavior not only with respect to Trouton's rule but also with respect to other physical-chemical relationships which correlate the behavior of normal liquids—relationships involving such phenomena as surface tension, viscosity, heat capacity, vapor pressures, and behavior on mixing with other liquids.

For "normal" liquids, the molecules of which do not have particularly large dipole moments, Example 5 gives an indication of the approximation to be expected.

Example 5. The boiling point of *n*-heptane is 98°. Estimate roughly (*a*) the heat of vaporization per gram and (*b*) the critical temperature.

(*a*) $\Delta H_{\text{vap}} \cong 21T = (21 \text{ cal deg}^{-1} \text{ mole}^{-1})(371 \text{ deg}) = 7800 \text{ cal mole}^{-1}$

$$\frac{(7800 \text{ cal mole}^{-1})}{(100 \text{ g mole}^{-1})} = 78 \text{ cal g}^{-1}$$

(*b*) $T_c \cong \frac{3}{2}T_b = \frac{3}{2}(371) = 557°\text{K or } 284°\text{C}$

The experimentally determined heat of vaporization is 76.4 cal g^{-1}, and the critical temperature is 266°.

The direct measurement of the volume of a liquid at its critical temperature is difficult. It is possible, however, to obtain this value graphically from determinations of the density of the liquid at several temperatures together with that of the saturated vapor in equilibrium with the liquid. At higher temperatures the density of the liquid becomes less, and the density of the saturated vapor in equilibrium with the liquid becomes greater. The higher vapor pressure is responsible

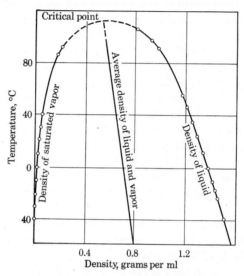

FIG. 8-3. Densities of liquid and saturated vapor of CCl_2F_2 showing equality of the two at the critical temperature.

for the increased vapor density. The two densities approach each other and become equal at the critical temperature. The mean of the densities of any substance in the liquid and vapor states, when plotted against the corresponding temperature, lies on a straight line. This behavior is indicated by the graph shown in *Fig. 8-3.** This relation, pointed out first by Cailletet and Mathias, is expressed mathematically in equation 20,

$$(d_l + d_v)/2 = A T + B \qquad (20)$$

where d_l and d_v are the densities of the liquid and saturated vapor, respectively, and A and B are constants. The measurements are carried as close to the critical point as is experimentally convenient, and then the curve is extrapolated as shown by the dotted lines in Fig. 8-3. The

* From measurements of Bichowsky and Gilkey on CCl_2F_2, *Ind. Eng. Chem.*, *23*, 365 (1931).

intersection of the straight line of equation 20 with this extrapolated curve gives the critical density.

Surface Tension. The surface of a liquid possesses special properties which are due to the unbalanced forces of molecular attraction at the surface. The molecules at the surface are pulled inward by the other molecules of the liquid, and the liquid tends to adjust itself to give the minimum surface area. This fact explains many common phenomena, including the spherical shape of raindrops, the rise of water in a capillary tube, and the movement of water in blotting paper or in the soil. The surface tension of a liquid, γ, is the force per centimeter on the surface of a liquid which opposes the expansion of the surface area. This definition is illustrated in *Fig. 8-4*, where the force f is pulling on a movable bar against a liquid film which is stretched like a soap-bubble film on a wire frame. Then

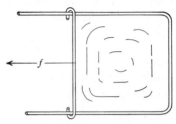

Fɪɢ. 8-4. Illustration of the surface tension of a liquid.

$$\gamma = f/2l \qquad (21)$$

where l is the length of the bar in centimeters, and the factor 2 is introduced because there are two liquid surfaces, one at the front and one at the back. The surface tension is expressed in dynes per centimeter and is equal to the surface energy expressed in ergs per square centimeter of surface.

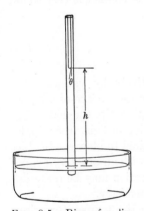

Fɪɢ. 8-5. Rise of a liquid in a capillary tube.

Some liquids, like water, wet the walls of a glass capillary tube; others, like mercury, do not. When a liquid wets the tube, the liquid adhering to the walls pulls the body of the liquid up; but when the liquid does not adhere, the liquid is depressed. In the first instance the surface of the liquid in the tube, called the meniscus, is concave to the horizontal plane. In the second it is convex.

The most accurate method for determining the surface tension of a liquid consists in measuring the height to which it rises in a capillary tube.

A capillary tube of radius r, as shown in *Fig. 8-5*, is immersed in a vessel of liquid whose density is d. The liquid wets the tube, and the liquid rises. It continues to rise until the surface tension tending to pull the liquid upward is counterbalanced by the force of gravity pulling it downward. The height to which the meniscus rises at this equilibrium point is denoted by h. The meniscus is curved, and the average height of the column of liquid is the significant quantity. In ordinary work the height to the bottom of the meniscus is taken, but it is more exact to add to this height a correction equal to one-third of the radius. Then the downward force $= \pi r^2 h d g$, where g is the acceleration of gravity.

The surface makes an angle θ with the walls, and only the vertical component of this force is effective in pulling the liquid upward in the capillary. It acts along the whole length of the surface. Thus, the upward force is

$$2\pi r \gamma \cos \theta$$

At equilibrium the upward and downward forces are equal, and

$$2\pi r \gamma \cos \theta = \pi r^2 h d g$$

or

$$\gamma = \frac{h d g r}{2 \cos \theta} \qquad (22)$$

For many liquids, including water, the angle of contact is very small, θ is nearly 0, and $\cos \theta$ is practically 1. Then,

$$\gamma = \tfrac{1}{2} h d g r \qquad (23)$$

Surface tension can be measured quantitatively by various other means, including the pulling of a wire ring from the surface of a liquid, the weighing of drops which fall from a special glass tip, the determination of the shape of a hanging drop, the reflection of light from ripples on the surface of a liquid, and the pressure required to blow gas bubbles in the liquid. When the liquid is in contact not with air or its own vapor but with an immiscible liquid, the interfacial tension may be quite different. This property is important in colloid chemistry.

The surface tension of a liquid decreases as the temperature rises, and the molecular agitation increases. The surface tensions of a few common liquids, measured in air, at different temperatures, are shown in Table III. The surface tensions of liquid metals and molten salts are large in comparison with those of organic liquids. For example, the surface tension of mercury at $0°C$ is 480.3 dyne cm^{-1}, and that of silver at $800°C$ is 800 dyne cm^{-1}.

Table III.   Surface Tension of Liquids in Dynes per Centimeter

Temperature, °C	H_2O	CCl_4	C_6H_6	$C_6H_5NO_2$	C_2H_5OH	CH_3COOH
0	75.64	29.0	31.6	46.4	24.0	29.5
25	71.97	26.1	28.2	43.2	21.8	27.1
50	67.91	23.1	25.0	40.2	19.8	24.6
75	63.5	20.2	21.9	37.3	....	22.0

Exercise III. The surface area of a sphere of liquid containing 1 mole is proportional to $(M/d)^{2/3}$, where M is the molecular weight, and this area multiplied by the surface tension depends upon the temperature. Plot $\gamma(M/d)^{2/3}$ for some substance against $(T_c - T)$, where T_c, the critical temperature, is the temperature at which surface tension should disappear. Ramsay and Shields found that a nearly straight line was produced and that the slope of the line was about 2 for most liquids. Liquids with high dipole moments which give abnormally high heats of vaporization by Trouton's rule give also abnormally low values for the slope of this line.

The Parachor. At the critical temperature the difference between liquid and gas tends to disappear, and since all gases are alike it may be inferred that all liquids will tend to be similar if studied at their critical temperatures. It is inconvenient to make measurements of molar volumes, for instance, at the critical temperature but since the boiling points are approximately two-thirds of the critical temperatures a comparison of molar volumes of liquids at the boiling points should be significant. As a first approximation the molar volumes at the boiling points, easily obtained from measurements of density, are equal to the sum of the gram-atomic volumes of the elements if allowance is made for structural features such as double bonds.

It should be still better to compare the molar volumes of liquids under conditions of similar surface tensions where the forces tending to pull the molecules together are the same. Sugden * defined the term molar parachor P by an equation which can be simplified to

$$P = (M/d)\gamma^{1/4} \tag{24}$$

where M is the molecular weight, d is the density, and γ the surface tension of the liquid. He pointed out that the molar parachor is equal to the sum of the gram-atomic parachors just as the molar refraction is equal to the sum of the gram-atomic refractions. Atomic and structural parachors are obtained in a similar manner by taking differences. In the molar parachors the structural features play a part, so that the

* Sugden, *J. Chem. Soc.*, *125*, 1177 (1924); *The Parachor and Valency*, George Routledge & Sons, London, 1930.

physical measurements can be used in helping to decide questions of molecular structure. A summary of the values is given in Table IV.

Table IV. Atomic and Structural Parachors

C	4.8	Br	68.0	Double bond	23.2
H	17.1	I	91.0	Triple bond	46.6
O	20.0	N	12.5	5-membered ring	8.5
Cl	54.3	S	48.2	6-membered ring	6.1

Example 6. Parachlorotoluene, $ClC_6H_4CH_3$ or

has a surface tension of 32.24 dynes cm^{-1} at 25°. Its density at this temperature is 1.065 g cm^{-3}.

What is the value of the molar parachor?

$$P = \frac{M}{d}\,\gamma^{\frac{1}{4}} = \frac{126.5}{1.065}\,(32.24)^{\frac{1}{4}} = 283$$

What is the value calculated from the atomic and structural parachors?

$$P_{calc} = 54.3 + (7)(4.8) + (7)(17.1) + (3)(23.2) + (1)(6.1) = 283.3$$

The parachor seems to give quite accurate results in correlating structure with the physical properties of organic compounds.*

Viscosity. Viscosity is the resistance that a fluid exhibits to the flow of one layer over another. Although it is possible to change the shape of any liquid by the application of force, the extent of this change of shape depends on the magnitude of the force and the length of time of its application and on the viscosity of the liquid. The viscosity varies greatly, being high for materials like heavy lubricating oils and low for liquids like benzene and water.

The force required to slip two parallel surfaces in a liquid past one another with a definite velocity will depend directly on the viscosity of the liquid and on the areas of the surfaces and inversely on the perpendicular distance between the two surfaces.

The unit of viscosity is the *poise*, named after Poiseuille, who pioneered in the study of viscosity. If a force of 1 dyne will cause a flat surface 1 cm^2 in area to move relative to another such surface at a distance of 1 cm with a velocity of 1 cm sec^{-1}, the fluid between the planes is said to have a viscosity of 1 *poise*.

* Quayle, Owen, and Estes, *J. Am. Chem. Soc., 60,* **2716** (1938).

The coefficient of viscosity η of a liquid can be determined directly in poises by passing a liquid through a tube of small diameter and making use of the following formula: *

$$\eta = \frac{P\pi r^4 t}{8vl} \qquad (25)$$

where t is the time required for v ml of liquid to flow through a capillary tube of length l and radius r under an applied pressure P.

Exercise IV. Find the cgs units of viscosity.

$$\eta = \frac{(\text{dyne cm}^{-2})(\text{cm}^4)(\text{sec})}{(\text{cm}^3)(\text{cm})} = \text{dyne sec cm}^{-2}$$

$$= \text{g cm}^{-1} \text{sec}^{-1}$$

The quantitative measurement of absolute viscosity by this method is difficult. Accordingly, indirect measurements are usually made in which the viscosity of a liquid is determined relative to another liquid

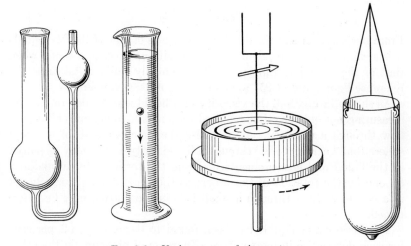

Fig. 8-6. Various types of viscometers.

whose viscosity is already known. This determination of physical-chemical constants by making relative measurements and comparing them with similar measurements of a standard substance is a common procedure. The absolute measurements of the standard substance may well take years of research with expensive equipment and highly spe-

* The derivation of this formula is given in specialized textbooks such as Barr's *A Monograph on Viscometry*, Oxford University Press, Oxford, 1931.

cialized techniques, whereas the relative measurements can often be made quickly and easily and with a high degree of accuracy.

In a simple viscometer such as that illustrated on the left in *Fig. 8-6* the pressure that causes flow through the capillary depends upon the difference in height h of liquid levels in the two tubes, the density of the liquid d_1, and the acceleration of gravity g. Thus, equation 25 may be rearranged to

$$\eta_1 = \left(\frac{hg\pi r^4}{8lv}\right) d_1 t_1$$

Then if the same volume of a second liquid of viscosity η_2 and density d_2 takes t_2 seconds to flow through the same capillary,

$$\eta_2 = \left(\frac{hg\pi r^4}{8lv}\right) d_2 t_2$$

In taking the ratio of these equations the height h cancels if the same volume of the two liquids has been used, and so do the other apparatus constants, so that

$$\eta_1/\eta_2 = d_1 t_1/d_2 t_2 \tag{26}$$

From measurements of the densities and times of flow of the two liquids it is a simple matter to calculate the viscosity η_1 of the first liquid when that of the second is known. Quite commonly water is taken as the reference liquid, and at 25° η_2 has a value of 0.00895 poise.

As shown in Fig. 8-6, the viscosity of a liquid may be determined by measuring not only the time required for a measured volume of liquid to flow through a capillary tube but also the time required for a heavy sphere (ball bearing) to fall through a liquid; or two disks may be placed in the liquid and measurements made on the torsional force produced on one by the rotation of the other; or the time required for a liquid in a cup to run out through a small hole in the bottom may be determined.

The viscosity of liquids has been found to decrease 1 to 2 per cent for each degree rise in temperature. Increase of pressure, on the other hand, causes the viscosity of liquids to increase, the change in viscosity being greater at higher pressures than at low. The viscosities of a few liquids at different temperatures are shown in Table V.

Table V.   Viscosity of Liquids in Poises

	0°	25°	50°	75°
Water	0.01793	0.00895	0.00549	0.00380
Ethanol	0.0179	0.0109	0.00698	. . . .
Benzene	0.0090	0.0061	0.0044	. . . .

The viscosity of an ideal gas would increase as the temperature increases. Viscosities of most liquids decrease. The flow of a liquid involves the shift of molecules from one position to another. Such shifts require energy, and since more kinetic energy is available at higher temperatures the liquid can flow more rapidly at the higher temperature. The variation of viscosity with temperature is such that it may be represented quite well by

$$\log \eta = A + (B/T)$$

where A and B are constants.

It should be pointed out that the phenomenon of viscosity is fundamentally different from the other phenomena discussed here such as vapor pressure and surface tension. It does not involve equilibrium conditions as the other phenomena do. It involves time as a factor and could properly be included in a later chapter on chemical kinetics.*

Some properties are brought out best by considering the *fluidity*, ϕ, which is defined as the reciprocal of viscosity. It is a measure of the tendency of the liquid to flow, whereas η is a measure of the resistance to flow. The fluidities of mixtures of nonpolar liquids are in general additive. Thus,

$$\phi = m\phi_1 + n\phi_2 \tag{27}$$

where m and n are the volume fractions of the two liquids. Mixtures of associated liquids or liquids with large dipole moments which exhibit some interaction may give widely varying viscosities. In fact, mixtures of some liquids have viscosities greater than either pure liquid alone.

Viscosity is an important property in both practical and theoretical work. In biology and physiology the viscometer is useful in the study of the properties of blood and other animal fluids, and in the realm of technology it has been applied successfully to the solution of a wide variety of problems presented by the paint, rubber, glue, textile, and other industries.

Viscosity is an important factor which must be considered in the design of chemical-engineering equipment, because the cost of pumping is often considerable, and these costs depend greatly on the viscosity of the liquids or gases. The data given in Table V and the derivation of the fundamental equation itself depend on the assumption that the liquid (or gas) is flowing without turbulence, that is, with one hypothetical layer slipping smoothly past another. When a fluid is forced

---

* Glasstone, Laidler, and Eyring, *Theory of Rate Processes*, McGraw-Hill Book Co., New York, 1940.

rapidly through a tube or around curves or obstacles, as in packed absorption towers, the flow of liquid or gas changes from smooth or laminar flow to turbulent flow, and, under this condition, the viscosity may increase greatly. This increase from normal to high viscosity due to turbulence may occur rather suddenly as the velocity is increased.

REFERENCES

Glasstone, *Textbook of Physical Chemistry*, D. Van Nostrand Co., New York, 1946, Chapter VII.

Bingham, *Fluidity and Plasticity*, McGraw-Hill Book Co., New York, 1922.

Rideal, *An Introduction to Surface Chemistry*, Second Edition, The Macmillan Co., New York, 1930.

Weissberger, *Physical Methods of Organic Chemistry*, Vol. I, Interscience Publ., New York, 1949, Chapters IV, V, VIII, and IX.

Timmermans, *Physico-Chemical Constants of Pure Organic Compounds*, Elsevier Publishing Co., New York, 1950.

PROBLEMS

1. n-Propyl alcohol has the following vapor pressures at the indicated temperatures:

t, °C	40	60	80	100
p, mm	50.2	147.0	376	842.5

Graph these data so as to obtain a nearly straight line, and calculate (a) the heat of vaporization and (b) the boiling point at 760 mm.
                    Ans. (a) 10.9 kcal mole^{-1}. (b) 97°C.

2. If the vapor pressure of toluene is 60 mm at 40.3° and 20 mm at 18.4°, calculate (a) the vapor pressure at 25° and (b) the heat of vaporization.
                    Ans. (a) 28.4 mm. (b) 9110 cal mole^{-1}.

3. In an industrial operation 10,000 cu ft of air is blown through a chamber per minute. The air at 25° and 40 per cent relative humidity is dried by removal of the water in an adsorbing agent. Calculate how many kilocalories of heat will be required per hour to regenerate the adsorbing agent by evaporating the water (582 cal per gram). The vapor pressure of water at 25° is 23.7 mm; 1 cu ft = 28.316 liters.   *Ans.* 90,600 kcal.

4. The heat of vaporization of ether is 88.39 cal per gram at its boiling point, 34.5°. (a) Calculate the rate of change of vapor pressure with temperature dp/dT, near the boiling point. (b) What is the boiling point at 750 mm? (c) What is the vapor pressure at 36.0°?   *Ans.* (a) 26.5 mm per deg. (b) 34.1°C. (c) 800 mm.

5. Trouton's rule is useful in estimating the vapor pressure of substances for which only the normal boiling point is known. For example, aniline boils at 185°C. At what temperature would you expect the liquid to boil in a vacuum-still at 20 mm pressure?   *Ans.* 68°C.

6. The surface tension of toluene at 20° is 28.4 dyne cm^{-1}, and its density at this temperature is 0.866 g cm^{-3}. What is the radius of the largest capillary that will permit the liquid to rise 2 cm?   *Ans.* 0.0335 cm.

7. Chlorobenzene, C_6H_5Cl or Cl—C

H H
C=C

CH, has a surface tension of 33.19

C—C
H H

dynes per centimeter at 25°. Its density at this temperature is 1.106 g cm^{-3}. (a) If the density of the vapor at this temperature is neglected, what is the value of the parachor? (b) What is the value calculated from the atomic and structural para-chors?   Ans.   (a) 244.1   (b) 244.3.

8. If it takes 10 minutes to drain a capillary pipet at 25° when filled with water, how long will it take to drain it when it is filled with ethanol (density = 0.789 g cm^{-3})?
Ans.   15.4 minutes.

9. Propene has the following vapor pressures at the following absolute tempera-tures:

T, °K	150	200	250	300
p, mm	3.82	198.0	2074	10,040

Graph these data so as to obtain a nearly straight line, and determine the vapor pressure at 225 °K.

10. The normal boiling point of cyclohexane is 80.7 °C, and the heat of vaporization is 7.19 kcal mole^{-1}. Calculate (a) the boiling point at 650 mm pressure, and (b) the vapor pressure at 25°.

11. The vapor pressure of solid benzene is 2.24 mm at −30° and 24.5 mm at 0°; and the vapor pressure of liquid benzene is 26.73 mm at 0° and 118.5 mm at 30°. Calculate from these data (a) the melting point of benzene and (b) the heat of fusion of benzene.

12. From the data of the tables given in this chapter estimate the temperature at which ethanol has a vapor pressure of 92.5 mm.

13. (a) How many tons of water can be evaporated from a square mile of moist land on a windy summer day, if it is assumed that the limiting factor is the supply of solar heat, which amounts to about 1.3 cal per minute per square centimeter for a 10-hour day? The temperature is 25°, the vapor pressure of water is 23.7 mm, and the heat of vaporization 582 cal per gram. One mile = 1.609 kilometers. (b) How many liters of air is required to hold this much water if the temperature is 25° and the barometric pressure is 740 mm?

14. Ten liters of air was bubbled through carbon tetrachloride at 20°. The loss in weight of the liquid was 8.698 grams. Calculate the vapor pressure of carbon tetrachloride by the approximate formula and by the more exact formula.

15. Ethylene dibromide, CH_2Br—CH_2Br, at 25° has a density of 2.170 g cm^{-3} and a surface tension of 38.2 dyne cm^{-1}. Calculate the parachor, and compare it with the sum of the atomic parachors.

16. At 30°, the density of boron triethyl, $B(C_2H_5)_3$, is 0.6774 g cm^{-3}, and its sur-face tension is 19.84 dynes per centimeter. Using the atomic parachors of carbon and hydrogen, calculate the atomic parachor of boron.

17. The critical temperature of carbon tetrachloride is 283.1°. The densities in grams per milliliter of the liquid d_l and vapor d_v at different temperatures are as follows:

t	100°	150°	200°	250°	270°	280°
d_l	1.4343	1.3215	1.1888	0.9980	0.8666	0.7634
d_v	0.0103	0.0304	0.0742	0.1754	0.2710	0.3597

What is the critical molar volume of carbon tetrachloride?

18. Acetone has a density of 0.790 g cm^{-3} at 20° and rises to a height of 2.56 cm in a capillary tube having a radius of 0.0235 cm. What is the surface tension of the acetone at this temperature?

19. The water flow time for a viscometer of the type illustrated on the left in Fig. 8-6 is 59.2 seconds at 25°. If 46.2 seconds is required for the same volume of ethyl benzene (density = 0.867 g cm^{-3}) to flow through the capillary, calculate its absolute viscosity in poises at 25°.

---

20. A room 5 by 10 by 4 meters is filled with air containing some water vapor. The temperature is 20°, and the relative humidity is 60 per cent. The vapor pressure of water at 20° is 17.36 mm. (The relative humidity is the partial pressure of water vapor divided by the vapor pressure of the liquid water at that temperature.) How many grams of water are contained in the air of this room?

21. A block of ice is placed in a lake of pure water, forced 100 ft below the surface, and maintained in a quiet steady position. What will be the temperature of the surface of the ice? Assume that the densities of the ice and water are not changed by the pressure. At atmospheric pressure the melting point of ice is 0°. The densities of ice and water are 0.9106 and 1.000 g cm^{-3}, respectively.

22. From the data of the tables given in this chapter calculate the vapor pressure of diethyl ether at 60°.

23. The vapor pressure of 2,2-dimethyl-1-butanol is given by the expression

$$\log p = (-4849.3/T) - 14.701 \log T + 53.1187$$

where p is expressed in millimeters of mercury. Calculate the heat of vaporization (a) at 25°, and (b) at the boiling point, 136.7°.

24. What is the boiling point of water on a mountain where the barometer reading is 660 mm?

25. It is proposed to operate a large calcium oxide-lined furnace at a temperature of 2100°C. The volatility of the calcium oxide, CaO, may be a difficulty. Air is blown continuously through the furnace at a rate of 1000 cu ft (28,320 liters) per minute (measured at 0°C and 760 mm pressure). Assuming that, if the sublimation pressure of the calcium oxide is large enough to give a loss of more than 5 kg per day, the process will be impractical, calculate the maximum permissible sublimation pressure (vapor pressure) in millimeters of the CaO, if the process is to be practical. Assume that the air becomes saturated with CaO vapor.

26. At 0° ice absorbs 80 cal per gram in melting; water absorbs 597 cal per gram in vaporizing. (a) What is the heat of sublimation of ice at this temperature? (b) At 0° the vapor pressure of both ice and water is 4.6 mm. What is the rate of change of vapor pressure with temperature dp/dT for ice at this temperature? (c) Estimate the vapor pressures of ice and of liquid water at −5°.

27. Liquid mercury has a density of 13.690 g per ml, and solid mercury has a density of 14.193 g per ml, both being measured at the melting point −38.87°C under 1 atm pressure. The heat of fusion is 2.33 cal per gram. What are the melting

points of mercury (a) under a pressure of 10 atm and (b) under 3540 atm? The observed melting point under 3540 atm is $-19.9°C$.

28. The boiling point of n-butyl chloride is $77.96°C$. (a) Using this as the only experimental datum available, estimate the vapor pressure at 50°, and compare with that calculated from the empirically determined equation (in which p is expressed in centimeters):

$$\log p = -(1763/T) + 6.912$$

(b) Calculate the heat of vaporization per gram.

29. The densities of vapor and liquid methyl ether at various temperatures are as follows:

t	30°	50°	70°	100°	120°
d_l	0.6455	0.6116	0.5735	0.4950	0.4040
d_v	0.0142	0.0241	0.0385	0.0810	0.1465

If the critical temperature of this substance is $126.9°C$, what is its critical volume

30. Plot log of viscosity of mercury against the reciprocal of the absolute temperature from the following data, and estimate the viscosity of mercury at 50°.

t	0°	20°	35°	98°	203°
η	0.01661	0.01547	0.01476	0.01263	0.01079

31. A certain liquid boils under atmospheric pressure (760 mm) at $t°$. Estimate (a) the critical temperature of the substance, (b) its molar heat of vaporization, and (c) its boiling point at 720 mm pressure. How accurate would you expect these estimates to be?

32. Plot the logarithm of the vapor pressure of mercury against $1/T$ for values of T between 0 and 360° (from reference tables), and draw tangents at two different temperatures. Show that the heat of vaporization changes with the temperature. If mercury vapor is monatomic, what can be stated regarding the specific heat of liquid mercury?

33. Mercury does not wet a glass surface. Draw a figure analogous to Fig. 8-5, page 171, for mercury and glass, and calculate the relative positions of the mercury surfaces, if the diameter of the capillary is 0.1 mm. The density of mercury is 13.5 g per ml. The surface tension of mercury at 25° is 520 dynes per centimeter.

34. Show that the observed boiling point T_0, °K, at a barometric pressure of p mm may be corrected approximately to the corrected boiling point T_{corr}, °K, at 760 mm by the following equation:

$$T_{corr} = T_0 + (T_0/8000)(760 - p)$$

9

Solutions

A *solution* may be defined as a system of different chemical substances which has the same chemical composition and physical properties in every part. If the system is composed of only two chemical substances, it is called a *binary solution*, as for example a solution of alcohol in water. In this chapter we shall be concerned with solutions of liquids, solids, or gases in liquids. That substance which is present in larger quantity is usually called the *solvent* and the other the *solute*, but the designation is quite arbitrary. For example, if a little alcohol is dissolved in a large quantity of water the water is called the solvent and alcohol is the solute, but if a little water is contained in an excess of alcohol the water is the solute and the alcohol the solvent.

The quantitative prediction of solubility on the basis of physical properties of the solute and solvent is possible for only a limited number of solutions. In general, it can be stated that similar substances such as benzene and toluene will dissolve in each other and that dissimilar substances like benzene and water will dissolve only slightly.

Also, if a substance tends to react with a liquid it is likely to dissolve to form a solution. For example, if a crystal of sodium chloride is placed in an evacuated vessel at room temperature there will be practically no tendency for the salt to vaporize. However, if the vessel is filled with water a considerable quantity of salt will dissolve in the water and spread throughout the solution which fills the vessel. A large amount of energy is required to pull the sodium and chloride ions apart from the crystal lattice, but this energy is supplied by the interaction of the electrically charged ions and the molecules of the water, which have high dipole moments. Sodium chloride will not dissolve, however, in benzene or carbon tetrachloride, because these liquids have no appreciable dipole moment, and no attractive force exists between them and the sodium or chloride ions.

The Composition of Solutions. The composition of a solution can be expressed in a variety of different ways, each of which has advantages for a particular purpose.

182

Volume concentrations are used in volumetric analysis because it is convenient to introduce with each milliliter of solution a definite number of molecules. A *molar solution* contains 1 mole of solute in a liter of solution. A *normal solution* contains the combining or equivalent weight in grams in a liter of solution, but it is necessary to specify whether the solution is normal with respect to neutralization or oxidation or other reaction and to what stage the oxidation or neutralization is carried.

Weight concentrations are used in physical chemistry because they are not influenced by temperature, whereas the volume concentrations are subject to variations caused by changes in density. A *molal solution* contains 1 mole of solute dissolved in 1000 grams of solvent. The symbol m is usually used to indicate molal concentrations, and M to indicate molar concentrations. One may be converted into the other when the density of the solution is known.

Mole fractions are used in theoretical work because many physical properties of solutions are expressed most simply in terms of the relative numbers of molecules. The *mole fraction* N of a substance in a solution is defined as the number of moles of that substance divided by the total number of moles of all the substances comprising the solution. If a solution contains n_A moles of the substance A and n_B moles of the substance B, then the mole fractions are defined as follows:

$$\text{Mole fraction of } A = N_A = n_A/(n_A + n_B) \tag{1}$$

$$\text{Mole fraction of } B = N_B = n_B/(n_A + n_B) \tag{2}$$

It is obvious that the mole fraction of A plus the mole fraction of B must be equal to 1. If several different substances are involved, the denominator always contains the total number of moles of all kinds.

Percentage by weight is often used in technical work to express the composition of a solution.

Example 1. A solution of acetic acid containing 80.8 grams of acetic acid ($M = 60.1$) per liter of solution at $20°$ has a density of 1.0097 g cm^{-3}. The calculation of four different ways of expressing the concentration is illustrated as follows:

Molar concentration:

$$\frac{80.8 \text{ g/l}}{60.1 \text{ g/mole}} = 1.34 \text{ mole/l}$$

Molal concentration:

$$\frac{80.8/60.1}{1009.7 - 80.8} \times 1000 = 1.45 \text{ mole/1000 g H}_2\text{O}$$

Mole fraction:

$$\text{Mole fraction acetic acid} = \frac{80.8/60.1}{80.8/60.1 + (1009.7 - 80.8)/18} = 0.025$$

Mole fraction water = 0.975

Percentage by weight:

$$\frac{80.8}{1009.7} \times 100 = 8.00\% \text{ acetic acid}$$

$$\frac{1009.7 - 80.8}{1009.7} \times 100 = 92.00\% \text{ water}$$

Vapor Pressure of Ideal Solutions. An ideal gas, discussed on page 4, is one in which there is no attraction between molecules and no change in internal energy when the volume is changed. In the case of liquids an *ideal solution* is one in which the interaction between components of the solution is the same as the interactions between the molecules of each component. That is, if a solution of A and B is ideal the interaction between A and B molecules must be the same as between A molecules and other A molecules or B molecules and other B molecules. When this is true no heat is evolved or absorbed on mixing and a number of the properties, such as vapor pressure, can be calculated by averaging the properties of the pure liquids. The volume of the solution is exactly equal to the sum of the volumes of the liquids which are mixed together. When 100 ml of water is added to 100 ml of water the volume is obviously 200 ml because the interaction of the molecules is not changed by the addition. Likewise if 100 ml of methanol is added to 100 ml of ethanol the volume of the solution will be 200 ml and no heat will be evolved because the attractions between ethanol molecules and methanol molecules are so much alike that no change is produced by the mixing.

On the other hand, if 100 ml of sulfuric acid is added to 100 ml of water the final volume is 182 ml and there is an evolution of a considerable quantity of heat. The sulfuric acid and the water interact, and the sulfuric acid ionizes, with the result that the sulfuric acid and the water in the solution do not have the same properties they had as pure liquids. Solutions of this type which involve the evolution or absorption of heat, and in which the properties of the dissolved liquids are different from those of the liquids in the pure state, are *nonideal solutions*.

The vapor pressure of a pure liquid depends on the rate of escape of molecules from the surface of the liquid, and, when the liquid is mixed with another liquid, the concentration is decreased, and the rate of escape from the surface diminished. Moreover, in an ideal solution, where the character of a dissolved liquid is the same in solution as it is in the pure state, the partial vapor pressure of one component is directly proportional to the fraction of molecules of that component in the mixture. In symbols,

$$p_A = \frac{n_A}{n_A + n_B} \, p_A{}^\circ = N_A p_A{}^\circ \qquad (3)$$

where p_A is the partial vapor pressure of component A, $p_A{}^\circ$ is the vapor pressure of the pure substance, and $n_A/(n_A + n_B)$, or N_A, is the mole fraction of component A. Likewise, in an ideal solution the vapor pressure of the other component would be given by the expression

$$p_B = N_B p_B{}^\circ$$

The simple relation expressed in equation 3 was discovered empirically in 1884 by Raoult in studying the special case of a solvent in dilute solutions. *Raoult's law* may be expressed as follows:

$$p_{\text{solvent}} = N_{\text{solvent}} \, p^\circ{}_{\text{solvent}}$$

where $p^\circ{}_{\text{solvent}}$ is the vapor pressure of the pure solvent. When the mole fraction of the solvent is large the other component has such a small mole fraction that it does not appreciably affect the nature of the liquid solvent and accordingly the solution is practically ideal in agreement with equation 3.

Equation 3 is the equation for a straight line, and it is evident from *Fig. 9-1* that the partial vapor pressure of benzene over solutions of benzene and toluene does in fact give a straight line when it is plotted against the mole fraction of benzene. It is clear also from this diagram that the partial vapor pressure of toluene is directly proportional to the mole fraction of toluene. The experimental data, from which these graphs have been plotted, are recorded as p_{obs} in Table I, and the values of p_{calc} are obtained by calculation using equation 3.

Table I.[1] Partial Pressures of Benzene and Toluene in the Vapor in Equilibrium with Liquid Solutions at 20° (in millimeters)

Mole Fraction Benzene in Liquid Solution	Benzene		Toluene		Total	
	p_{obs}	p_{calc}	p_{obs}	p_{calc}	p_{obs}	p_{calc}
0.00	0	0	22	22	22	22
0.27	18	20	17	16	35	36
0.44	34	33	12	12	46	45
0.55	41	41	11	10	52	51
0.67	49	50	8	7	57	57
1.00	75	75	0	0	75	75

[1] Bell and Wright, *J. Phys. Chem.*, *31*, 1884 (1927).

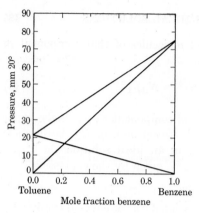

FIG. 9-1. Toluene-benzene; partial and total pressures at 20°.

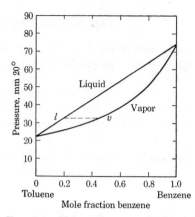

FIG. 9-4. Toluene-benzene; liquid and vapor compositions at 20°.

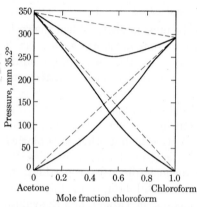

FIG. 9-2. Acetone-chloroform; partial and total pressures at 35.2°.

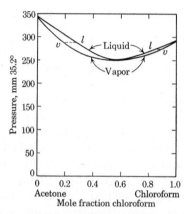

FIG. 9-5. Acetone-chloroform; liquid and vapor compositions at 35.2°.

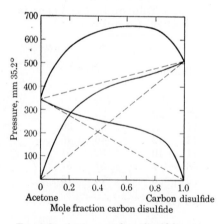

FIG. 9-3. Acetone-carbon disulfide; partial and total pressures at 35.2°.

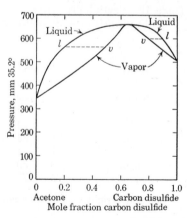

FIG. 9-6. Acetone-carbon disulfide; liquid and vapor compositions at 35.2°.

The uppermost line gives the total vapor pressure of the solution at each mole fraction of the liquid solution as obtained by adding together the partial vapor pressures of the benzene and toluene.

The partial vapor pressures p_{obs} can be measured by the gas-saturation method described on page 160 in which a known volume of air or other gas is passed slowly through the solution to saturate it at a given temperature with vapor in equilibrium with the solution. The vapor is condensed from the gas stream in a cold U tube or trap, and the amount of each liquid is determined by chemical analysis or with a refractometer. The partial vapor pressures p_{obs} are then calculated from the weight of each liquid vaporized and the volume of gas passed through. The calculated values p_{calc} in an ideal solution are easily obtained by equation 3 from the mole fraction as shown in example 2.

Example 2. The vapor pressures of pure benzene and toluene at 20° are 74.7 mm and 22 mm, respectively. Calculate the partial pressures of benzene and toluene and the total vapor pressure above a solution having a mole fraction of 0.80 benzene.

$$p_{benzene} = (0.80)(74.7) = 59.8 \text{ mm}$$
$$p_{toluene} = (0.20)(22) \quad = \quad 4.4 \text{ mm}$$

$$p_{total} \qquad\qquad\quad = 64.2 \text{ mm}$$

It is to be noted that, for the extensive property, volume, it is necessary to specify the quantity of solution taken, but that for the intensive property, vapor pressure, a small quantity of solution in equilibrium with the vapor gives the same vapor pressure as a large quantity and the total quantity need not be specified—only the mole fraction.

Vapor Pressure of Nonideal Solutions. In a nonideal solution of A and B the attractive force between A and B is different from that between A and A or B and B. If the A-B interaction is stronger than the A-A and B-B interactions, the vapor pressure of the solution will be less than expected from equation 3. The tendency of each of the components to pass into the vapor phase is reduced if the components have a special attraction for each other. An example of such a negative deviation from Raoult's law is the system acetone-chloroform for which data are given in Table II and *Fig. 9-2.*

Exercise I. Show by calculating a couple of points on the dashed lines of Fig. 9-2 that these straight lines give the partial vapor pressures and the total vapor pressure that the solutions of chloroform and acetone would have if they were ideal solutions.

There are other types of nonideal solutions in which there is little attraction between A and B but the presence of B molecules decreases the A-A attraction and likewise the A molecules decrease the B-B

Table II.[1] **Partial Pressures of Acetone and Chloroform in the Vapor in Equilibrium with Liquid Solutions at 35.2° (in millimeters)**

Mole Fraction Chloroform in Liquid Solution	Chloroform		Acetone		Total	
	p_{obs}	p_{calc}	p_{obs}	p_{calc}	p_{obs}	p_{calc}
0	0	0	344	344	344	344
0.2	34	59	270	275	304	334
0.4	82	117	183	207	265	324
0.6	148	177	102	137	250	314
0.8	225	236	42	67	267	303
1.00	293	293	0	0	293	293

[1] Zawidzki, *Z. physik. Chem.*, *35*, 129 (1900).

attraction. In such cases the lessened attraction results in a greater tendency to escape from the liquid, and the partial vapor pressures are greater than those calculated on the basis of an ideal solution. Such positive deviations from Raoult's law are shown in Table III and *Fig. 9-3.*

Table III.[1] **Partial Pressures of Acetone and Carbon Disulfide in the Vapor in Equilibrium with Liquid Solutions at 35.2° (in millimeters)**

Mole Fraction CS_2 in Liquid Solution	Carbon Disulfide		Acetone		Total	
	p_{obs}	p_{calc}	p_{obs}	p_{calc}	p_{obs}	p_{calc}
0	0	0	344	344	344	344
0.2	280	102	290	275	570	377
0.4	378	206	255	204	633	410
0.6	425	306	230	138	655	444
0.8	460	410	190	67	650	477
1.00	512	512	0	0	512	512

[1] Zawidzki, *Z. physik. Chem.*, *35*, 129 (1900).

Hydrogen Bonding. For the acetone-chloroform solutions described in the preceding section the observed partial pressures are considerably less than those calculated from Raoult's law. The acetone molecules are held back in solution by the chloroform molecules more than by other acetone molecules; and the chloroform molecules are held back more by the acetone molecules. This may be interpreted as being due to a specific interaction between chloroform and acetone. The tendency of these two substances to form a compound is due to the formation of

a hydrogen bond (page 86) between the oxygen of the acetone and the
hydrogen of chloroform.

$$\begin{array}{ccc}
Cl & & CH_3 \\
| & & | \\
Cl-C-H\cdots O=C & & \\
| & & | \\
Cl & & CH_3
\end{array}$$

Although hydrogen can form only one covalent bond the very small size
of the hydrogen atom without its electron shell makes it possible to form
an additional bond, largely ionic, with an electronegative atom such as
F, O, or N. Hydrogen is unique in its ability to form bonds of this sort
since in no other element can the atom acquire nuclear dimensions by
the loss of a single electron. Fluorine forms very strong hydrogen bonds,
oxygen weaker ones, and nitrogen still weaker ones. The hydrogen
fluoride ion, $[HF_2]^-$, is held together by a strong hydrogen bond. The
unusual properties of water are due to a large extent to the formation
of hydrogen bonds. When water is vaporized these hydrogen bonds
are broken, but in formic and acetic acids the hydrogen bonds are sufficiently strong so that double molecules of the type illustrated exist in
the vapor as described on page 86.

$$CH_3-C \begin{array}{c} O\cdots H-O \\ \diagup \qquad \diagdown \\ \diagdown \qquad \diagup \\ O-H\cdots O \end{array} C-CH_3$$

Exercise II. Look up the melting points and boiling points of H_2S, H_2Se, and H_2Te,
and plot them versus the atomic weight of the heavy atom. Considering this trend
of values show that the melting point and boiling point of water might be approximately -100 and $-80°C$ were it not for hydrogen-bond formation.

This attractive force due to the formation of a hydrogen bond occurs
not only in solutions of acetone and chloroform but in many other solutions containing ketones, esters, or carboxylic acids and partially halo-
genated hydrocarbons or other compounds containing hydrogen. Since
CS_2 cannot form a hydrogen bond with acetone negative deviations
would not be expected in this system and are not found as illustrated in
Fig. 9-3. In fact in this system there are large positive deviations indicating that the attraction between the two components is less than that
between the molecules in pure CS_2 or pure acetone.

Vapor Composition of Binary Solutions. If an ideal solution
could be found which is composed of two liquids with identical vapor
pressures at a given temperature, the composition of the vapor would
be the same as the composition of the solution. Examples of liquids

which practically meet these conditions are found among solutions of isotopically different compounds (page 613), such as $C^{12}HCl_3$ and $C^{13}HCl_3$; but if one of the liquids has a higher vapor pressure than the other at a given temperature it will have proportionally more of its molecules in the gas phase.

If A and B form ideal solutions the composition of the vapor may be readily calculated. The partial pressure of A in the vapor is $p_A = p_A{}^\circ N_{A,\text{liq}}$, and the partial pressure of B in the vapor is $p_B = p_B{}^\circ N_{B,\text{liq}}$. Since the mole fraction in the vapor is the same as the pressure fraction in the vapor, the mole fraction of A in the vapor is

$$N_{A,\text{vapor}} = \frac{p_A{}^\circ N_{A,\text{liq}}}{p_A{}^\circ N_{A,\text{liq}} + p_B{}^\circ N_{B,\text{liq}}} \qquad (4)$$

The "vapor" curve in *Fig. 9-4* may be obtained from calculations of this type. It will be noted that the top or "liquid" line in Fig. 9-4 is the same as in Fig. 9-1. This "liquid" line gives the total pressure of the vapor which exists in equilibrium with the *liquid*, which has the composition indicated on the horizontal axis. The "vapor" curve is obtained by plotting the total pressure of the vapor along the vertical axis and the mole fraction of the *vapor* along the horizontal axis. The vapor curve gives the pressures at which vapors of a given composition first show a tendency to form a liquid phase when the pressure is increased.

In Fig. 9-4 liquid of composition l (0.20 mole fraction benzene) has a total vapor pressure of 33 mm and is in equilibrium with vapor of composition v (0.42 mole fraction benzene). The horizontal line connecting these two points is referred to as a *tie line* since it connects the compositions of phases which are in equilibrium.

Exercise III. Calculate the mole fraction of benzene in the vapor over a benzene-toluene solution containing 0.60 mole fraction benzene and check this point with Fig. 9-4.

For nonideal solutions, which are much more common than ideal solutions, the line for the total vapor pressure is no longer a straight line. *Figure 9-5* shows the composition of the liquid and vapor for solutions of acetone and chloroform which have lower vapor pressures than they would if the solution were ideal. It may be compared with Fig. 9-2. *Figure 9-6* shows the liquid and vapor curves for solutions of acetone and carbon disulfide which have vapor pressures greater than they would have if the solution were ideal.

Boiling Temperatures of Binary Solutions. The discussions of the preceding few pages and Figs. 9-1 to 9-6 have been concerned with the vapor pressures of binary solutions of different concentrations at specified constant temperatures. It is often of more practical impor-

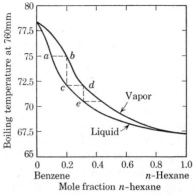

FIG. 9-7. Benzene-n-hexane boiling points; liquid and vapor compositions.

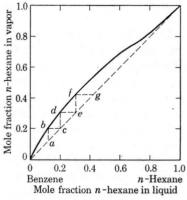

FIG. 9-10. Benzene-n-hexane; composition vapor-composition liquid.

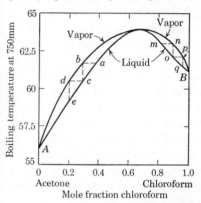

FIG. 9-8. Acetone-chloroform boiling points; liquid and vapor compositions.

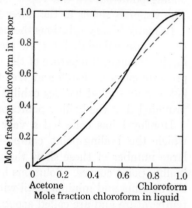

FIG. 9-11. Acetone-chloroform; composition vapor-composition liquid.

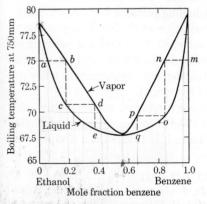

FIG. 9-9. Ethanol-benzene boiling points; liquid and vapor compositions.

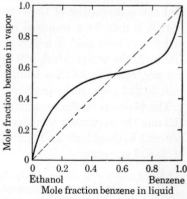

FIG. 9-12. Ethanol-benzene; composition vapor-composition liquid.

tance to hold the pressure constant (at atmospheric pressure for example) and to plot the boiling temperatures against the compositions of the liquid and vapor phases. *Figures 9-7, 9-8,* and *9-9* illustrate this type of graph for benzene and *n*-hexane which give an ideal solution with no maximum or minimum evident in the curve, for acetone-chloroform which gives a maximum in the boiling-point curve, and for ethanol-benzene which gives a minimum in the boiling-point curve. It is evident that these curves are similar to those of Figs. 9-4 to 9-6 but reversed. The higher the vapor pressure, the lower is the boiling temperature; and the presence of a minimum in the vapor-pressure curve leads to a maximum in the boiling-point curve. Whereas in vapor-pressure curves the liquid curve was always above the vapor curve, in boiling-point curves the vapor curve is always above the liquid curve. The vapor is richer in the lower boiling component or azeotrope.

In many binary solutions the boiling temperatures are higher or lower than those calculated for an ideal solution because each of the two liquids changes the nature of the other, as has been discussed for vapor-pressure curves. Ewell and Welch * have shown that most solutions of ketones and alkyl halides exhibit maxima in their boiling-point curves provided that the boiling points of the two liquids are not too far apart.

Horsley † has collected a very complete list of 14,000 solutions for which the boiling-point composition graphs have been studied. A large number of these show the presence of maxima or minima in the boiling-point curves. Solutions having concentrations corresponding to the maxima and minima distil without change in composition or boiling temperature and are called azeotropic solutions or azeotropes.

A few examples of azeotropes are given in Table IV.

The system hydrochloric acid-water has been studied extensively, and the composition of the constant-boiling mixture is so reproducible that it is used as a standard in quantitative analysis. If any solution of hydrochloric acid is boiled for a sufficient time under a pressure of 760 mm, the temperature will gradually rise to 108.58° and remain stationary, and the solution boiling at this constant temperature will contain 20.222 per cent hydrochloric acid by weight.

The position of the maximum changes somewhat with pressure. At 700 mm the maximum temperature is 106.42° at a composition of 20.360 per cent hydrochloric acid, and at 600 mm it is 102.21° at a composition of 20.638 per cent.

* Ewell and Welch, *J. Am. Chem. Soc.,* *63,* 2475 (1941).

† Horsley and co-workers, *Azeotropic Data,* Advances in Chemistry Series, American Chemical Society, Washington, D. C. (1952), 324 pages; "Table of Azeotropes and Non-Azeotropes," *Anal. Chem., 19,* 508–600 (1947).

Table IV. Binary Azeotropic Solutions at 1 Atm Pressure [1]

Component A	B.P. of A, °C	Component B	B.P. of B, °C	B.P. of Azeotrope, °C	Weight Per Cent, A
		Maximum Boiling Azeotropes			
HCl	−80	H_2O	100	108.584	20.222
$CHCl_3$	61.2	CH_3COCH_3	56.40	64.43	78.5
$CHCl_3$	61.2	$CH_3CO_2CH_3$	57.05	64.8	77
$CHCl_3$	61.2	$HCO_2C_2H_5$	54.15	62.7	87
CH_3CO_2H	118.5	$(CH_2)_4O_2$	101.35	119.5	77
CH_3CO_2H	118.5	C_5H_5N	115.5	140	53
		Minimum Boiling Azeotropes			
H_2O	100	$CHCl_3$	61.2	56.12	2.8
H_2O	100	CH_3CH_2OH	78.3	78.174	4.0
H_2O	100	$CH_3CH_2CH_2OH$	82.3	80.3	12.6
H_2O	100	C_6H_6	80.2	69.25	8.83
CCl_4	76.75	CH_3CH_2OH	78.3	65.08	84.15
$CHCl_3$	61.2	CH_3OH	64.7	53.43	87.4

[1] Horsley, *Azeotropic Data*, Advances in Chemistry Series, American Chemical Society, Washington, D. C., 1952.

For hydrochloric acid and water, the minimum in the vapor-pressure curve, or maximum in the boiling-point curve, is due to the ionization of hydrochloric acid. Water and pure hydrochloric acid have high vapor pressures, but the electrically charged hydrogen and chloride ions cannot escape from the solution. It is shown in the next chapter that they lower the vapor pressure of the water. In small amounts, hydrochloric acid added to water lowers the vapor pressure through its ions; but in large amounts, it increases the vapor pressure by adding to the solution the more volatile hydrochloric acid molecules, a fact which can be realized from the sharp odor of hydrochloric acid in the concentrated solutions.

Maxima and minima are not confined to vapor-pressure and boiling-point curves, but they are sometimes found when freezing points, densities, viscosities, and other properties are plotted against composition. *They are not found in ideal solutions.* Whenever a maximum exists, there must be at least two opposing factors, one tending to increase the magnitude of the property and the other tending to decrease it as the concentration is changed.

It was thought at one time that maxima of this type correspond to definite chemical compounds, and indeed a maximum in a freezing-point curve may indicate the formation of a chemical compound, as explained in a later chapter. The composition of 20.22 per cent HCl in the constant-boiling mixture corresponds very closely to the formula $HCl \cdot 8H_2O$, but the relation is accidental. It has been proved that such mixtures are not definite chemical compounds since the composition of the azeotropic mixture changes with pressure. Usually, these maxima do not come at compositions corresponding to any chemical formula, and, if maxima in two different properties occur in the same mixture, they often occur at different compositions.

Distillation of Binary Solutions. When a solution of two liquids is partially vaporized, that component which has the higher partial vapor pressure tends to concentrate in the vapor, thus producing a difference in composition between the liquid and the vapor which is in equilibrium with it. This vapor may be condensed, and the vapor obtained by heating this condensate is still further enriched in the more volatile component. This process of successive vaporization and condensation is called *fractional distillation*.

In Fig. 9-7 it is seen that a solution of 0.9 mole fraction benzene and 0.1 mole fraction *n*-hexane reaches the boiling point at 75° under atmospheric pressure as indicated by point *a*. The vapor that comes off is richer in the more volatile compound, and it has the composition *b*. A small amount of this vapor may be condensed by lowering the temperature along the line *bc*. If a small amount of this condensed liquid is vaporized the first vapor formed will have the composition corresponding to *d*. This process of vaporization and condensation may be continued many times, with the result that the vapor becomes rich in hexane and the remaining liquid becomes rich in benzene, because the solution has lost more hexane than benzene. In this way it is possible by continued fractional distillation to separate the two liquids.

The binary solutions may exhibit a maximum in their boiling points as shown in Fig. 9-8. A series of fractional distillations of a solution rich in acetone will give pure liquid acetone in the distillate and the constant-boiling mixture or azeotrope in the residue. At atmospheric pressure this azeotrope boils at 64.43° and has a composition of 0.64 mole fraction chloroform. The steps along *abcde* indicate a hypothetical distillation as discussed above. From solutions rich in chloroform it is possible to obtain pure chloroform in the distillate and the constant-boiling azeotrope in the residue as indicated by the lines *mnopq*. When the constant-boiling mixture is reached the temperature and the composition remain constant, because the vapor and liquid have the same composition. Although the constancy of boiling point of an organic liquid is often used as a criterion of purity it is well to supplement this test with other tests such as freezing-point constancy.

Exercise IV. Discuss the fractional distillation of ethanol-benzene mixtures with the help of Fig. 9-9.

The efficiency with which two liquids can be separated by fractional distillation is a matter of practical importance. Each vaporization and condensation represented by the lines *abcde* and *mnopq* on Figs. 9-7 to 9-9 corresponds to an idealized process in that only a small amount of

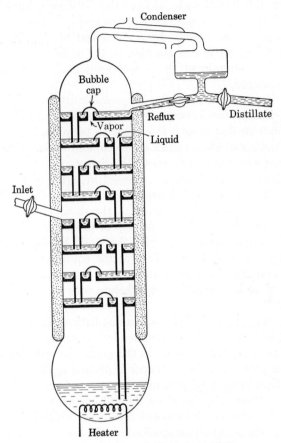

FIG. 9-13. Bubble-cap fractionating column.

vapor is condensed and only a small amount of it is revaporized. It is more practical to effect the separation by means of a distillation column such as the bubble-cap tower illustrated in *Fig. 9-13*.

Each layer of liquid on the plates of the column is equivalent to the boiling liquid in a distilling flask, and the liquid on the plate above it is equivalent to the condenser. The vapor passes upward through the bubble caps, where it is partially condensed in the liquid and mixed with it. Part of the resulting solution is vaporized in this process and is condensed in the next higher layer, while part of the liquid overflows and runs down the tube to the next lower plate. In this way there is a continuous flow of redistilled vapor coming out the top and a continuous flow of recondensed liquid returning to the boiler at the bottom. To make up for this loss of material from the distilling column fresh solution is fed into the column, usually at the middle. The column is well insulated, or it is surrounded by a controlled heating jacket so that there will not be general condensation on the walls. The whole system reaches a steady state in which the composition of liquid on each plate remains unchanged.

A distillation column may also be packed with material which will provide efficient contact between liquid and vapor and will occupy only a small volume so that there is free space to permit a large throughput of vapor. Helices of glass, spirals of screen, and various types of packing * are used with varying degrees of efficiency.

The efficiency of a column is expressed in terms of the number of theoretical plates to which it is equivalent. A *theoretical plate* may be considered as a hypothetical section of the distilling column of such length that the vapor leaving at the top of the section has had opportunity to come into equilibrium with the liquid leaving at the bottom of the section. It may be visualized as the equivalent of a layer in a 100 per cent efficient bubble-cap tower, that is, one in which the vapor leaving the plate is in complete equilibrium with the circulating liquid on the plate.

The number of theoretical plates in a distillation column under actual operating conditions may be determined by the method of McCabe and Thiele as illustrated in *Fig. 9-10*. In this graph the mole fraction of the more volatile component in the vapor is plotted against its mole fraction in the liquid at a total pressure of 1 atm and the boiling temperature of the solution. Any point on the full line such as b or d gives on the vertical axis the actual composition of vapor which is in equilibrium with liquid of the composition specified on the horizontal axis.

Suppose that in distilling a solution of benzene and n-hexane with a certain distillation column it is found that distillate of composition g is obtained when the composition of the liquid in the boiler is given by a. Such a distillation is equivalent to three simple vaporizations and condensations as indicated by the steps abc, cde, and efg. Since three such steps can be drawn between a and g, and since the distilling pot itself corresponds to one theoretical plate, the column has two theoretical plates.

* Daniels, Mathews, Williams, and Staff, *Experimental Physical Chemistry*, McGraw-Hill Book Co., New York, 1949; Carney, *Laboratory Fractional Distillation*, The Macmillan Co., New York, 1949.

Exercise V. The graphs of *Figs. 9-11 and 9-12* are similar to that of Fig. 9-10, except that they apply to binary mixtures having a maximum boiling point and a minimum boiling point, respectively. Explain how they are constructed and how they may be used for determining the efficiency of a distilling column.

A fractionating column operating at total reflux obviously would not be practical for separating liquids. Although some liquid must be distilled out, the higher the reflux ratio, i.e., the ratio of liquid returned to the distilling column to the vapor distilled out per unit time, the greater

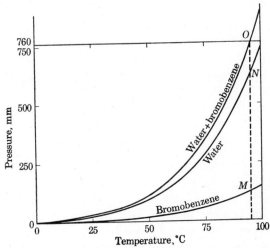

FIG. 9-14. Pressure-temperature graph for immiscible liquids, water and bromobenzene.

is the efficiency of separation. An ordinary distilling flask and unpacked column may be equivalent to one or two theoretical plates, but, when it is well packed, with special packing which presents a large area of the flowing liquid to the vapor, it is possible to have the equivalent of a theoretical plate every inch or so. Fractionating columns of 10 to 20 theoretical plates operating at a reflux ratio of 10 to 1 effectively separate liquids which have boiling points so close together that they cannot be separated in a simple distillation flask. Marked improvements have been made in laboratory distillations and purifications as well as in industrial distillations. The demands of the petroleum industry have given an impetus to the development of the theory and practice of fractional distillation.

Immiscible Liquids. The vapor-pressure relations of two immiscible liquids are shown in *Fig. 9-14*. Each exerts its own vapor pressure independently of the other. The total vapor pressure is obviously the sum of the vapor pressures of the two liquids if neither liquid dissolves in the other, and the vapor pressure and composition of the vapor are constant at constant temperature, independent of the composition of the liquid mixture.

In the example shown, the total vapor pressure reaches atmospheric pressure O at 95°, and both liquids distil together at this temperature. When either one of the liquids has completely distilled away at this temperature, the vapor pressure drops to that of the remaining liquid, M or N.

Since the pressure of a gas is proportional to the number of molecules the ratio of the partial pressures of A and B is the same as the ratio of the number of moles.

$$p_A/p_B = n_A/n_B \tag{5}$$

The number of moles can be calculated by dividing the weight in grams by the molecular weight, giving

$$\frac{p_A}{p_B} = \frac{w_A/M_A}{w_B/M_B}$$

or

$$\frac{w_A}{w_B} = \frac{p_A M_A}{p_B M_B} \tag{6}$$

This formula is useful in calculating the relative weights w_A and w_B of the two liquids which are condensed out in distillation.

A common laboratory and industrial operation which makes use of this relation is *steam distillation*. The steam is blown through a liquid which is immiscible with water, and the condensing steam carries with it quantities of the other liquid.

If an organic substance is immiscible with water and unaffected chemically by steam, it is possible to effect a purification by steam distillation even though the vapor pressure is relatively low. It is the low molecular weight and the cheapness of water which render it so suitable for distillations of this kind.

Example 3. Calculate the molecular weight of nitrobenzene from the fact that when a mixture of nitrobenzene and water is distilled at a pressure of 731.9 mm the distillation temperature is 98.2° and the weight ratio of nitrobenzene to water in the distillate is 0.188. The vapor pressures of water and nitrobenzene at this temperature are known to be 712.4 mm and 19.5 mm, respectively.

$$M_A = \frac{w_A p_B}{w_B p_A} M_B$$

$$= \frac{(0.188)(712.4)(18.0)}{(19.5)} = 123 \text{ g mole}^{-1}$$

The behavior of partially miscible liquids is similar to completely miscible liquids as long as there is only one liquid layer. When the mutual solubility is exceeded and two layers are formed, the vapor-pressure relations resemble those of the immiscible liquids.

Solutions of Gases in Liquids. When a dissolved substance evaporates into a closed space, the concentration of its molecules in the vapor phase increases, and the rate at which these molecules return to the solution increases until a dynamic equilibrium is attained. The solute can be a permanent gas just as well as a liquid or a solid, and it then seems more natural to look at the phenomenon as the solution of a gas in the solvent rather than as the solute escaping from the solution to give a definite vapor pressure.

The solubility of gases was first expressed quantitatively by Henry. Raoult's law $p_{\text{solvent}} = p^\circ_{\text{solvent}} N_{\text{solvent}}$ applies to solutions so dilute that the properties of the solvent are almost the same as those of the pure solvent. Henry's law is similar and applies to the solute. It states that the partial pressure of the solute is proportional to its mole fraction in the solution; thus

$$p_{\text{solute}} = K N_{\text{solute}} \tag{7}$$

In an ideal solution Henry's law, as well as Raoult's, is an exact law, and equation 7 becomes identical with equation 3. Moreover, the proportionality constant K becomes identical with the vapor pressure of the pure solute.

In nonideal solutions the value of K in Henry's law is determined by measuring the vapor pressure of the solute in dilute solutions at known mole fractions. Then,

$$K = p_{\text{solute}}/N_{\text{solute}} \tag{8}$$

In practice, the law is not exact, and the properties of the dissolved solute, including its escaping tendency, change as the concentration changes, and so K changes.*

The solubilities of a few gases are given in Table V in terms of Henry's constant K, in which the concentration of molecules in the gas phase, expressed in millimeters of pressure, is divided by the concentration of the gas in solution expressed in mole fractions.

Sometimes gas solubilities are expressed in terms of Bunsen coefficients, which give the number of liters of gas reduced to 0° and 760 mm

---

* If the "constant" K changes, the most significant value to take is the one obtained by plotting a few values of p/N against N for the solute and extrapolating it to infinite dilution as shown on page 271. The intercept of the curve at $N = 0$ gives the value of K to be taken for thermodynamic calculations.

Table V.   Henry's Law Constants for Gases at 25°

$$K = \frac{p_A}{N_A} = \frac{\text{Pressure of gas } A \text{ in millimeters}}{\text{Mole fraction gas } A \text{ in solution}}$$

Solvent

Gas	Water	Benzene
H_2	5.34×10^7	2.75×10^6
N_2	6.51×10^7	1.79×10^6
O_2	3.30×10^7	
CO	4.34×10^7	1.22×10^6
CO_2	1.25×10^6	8.57×10^4
CH_4	$31.4 \ \times 10^6$	4.27×10^5
C_2H_2	1.01×10^6	
C_2H_4	8.67×10^6	
C_2H_6	$23.0 \ \times 10^6$	

pressure which will dissolve in 1 liter of the solvent under a pressure of 760 mm at a specified temperature.

Example 4. Express the solubility of carbon dioxide in water at 1 atm pressure and 25° in terms of moles n per liter, assuming that a liter of solution contains practically 1000 grams of water.

$$K = 1.25 \times 10^6 = \frac{760}{n_{CO_2}} \left(n_{CO_2} + \frac{1000}{18.02} \right)$$

The number of moles of carbon dioxide n_{CO_2} may be considered negligible in comparison with the number of moles of water, 1000/18.02. Then,

$$n_{CO_2} = \frac{(760)(55.55)}{1.25 \times 10^6} = 3.38 \times 10^{-2} \text{ mole per liter}$$

The Bunsen solubility coefficient for carbon dioxide may be calculated from this value, giving

$$(3.38 \times 10^{-2} \text{ mole l}^{-1})(22.41 \text{ l mole}^{-1}) = 0.757$$

As a first approximation, the volume of gas which dissolves is independent of the pressure above the solution, because the number of moles of dissolved gas changes directly as the pressure, and the volume of the gas above the solution changes inversely as the pressure.

Henry's law, like most of the laws of solutions, is not exact except in very dilute solutions. Up to a pressure of 1 atm it holds within 1 to 3 per cent with many gases.

Dalton showed that the solubility of the individual gases in a mixture of gases is directly proportional to their partial pressures, the solubility of each gas being nearly independent of the presence of the others. The solubility of oxygen in water is nearly twice as great as that of nitrogen, and, since the solubility of one gas is unaffected by the presence of the other, the dissolved air is considerably richer in oxygen than the air above water.

The theoretical explanation of the solubility of inert gases in liquids has not yet been developed. A few empirical facts regarding the subject will be helpful in eventually formulating a satisfactory theory:

(a) The order of increasing solubility of gases in a liquid usually remains the same in different liquids.

(b) The increase in volume caused by the solution of a mole of the gas in a solvent is nearly equal to the corresponding value of b in the equation of van der Waals.

(c) The solubility of a gas in liquids is usually decreased by an increase in temperature. There are numerous exceptions, however, especially with the solvents liquid ammonia, molten silver, and many organic liquids.

(d) The solubility of gases in water is usually decreased by the addition of other solutes, particularly electrolytes. The extent of this "salting out" varies considerably with different salts, but with a given salt the relative decrease in solubility is the same for different gases. For example, if a certain salt reduces the solubility of oxygen in water to 80 per cent of its value, it will also reduce the solubility of nitrogen in water to about 80 per cent of its value.

The solubility of the unreactive gases is probably caused by an attractive force between the solute molecules and the solvent molecules due to dipole-induced dipoles, more generally referred to as van der Waals' forces. Even though a molecule is electrically neutral as a whole, there are parts of the molecule that are positively charged and other parts that are negatively charged, as indicated by the existence of a dipole moment. These electrically charged parts are able to induce electric charges of the opposite sign in molecules in the immediate neighborhood. For example, helium molecules can certainly have no unbalanced electric forces, and the attractive force due to electric dipoles which they induce in each other is so weak that it is overcome by the slight thermal agitation which exists at 4°K, the boiling point of helium. Water molecules, on the other hand, have a considerable dipole moment, and, although the molecule as a whole is neutral, the charged parts induce an opposite charge in a neighboring helium molecule, and a force of attraction is set up between the two, causing some helium to be dissolved in water.

The solubility of gases and other solutes is affected by the addition of large quantities of salts. Sometimes the salting-out effect can be explained on the hypothesis that it is caused by the hydration of the salt.

A portion of the water combines with the salt, and the water thus removed from the role of solvent is no longer free to absorb gas. More specifically, the water molecules with their electric dipoles can be considered to be partially oriented with respect to the ions or dipoles of the dissolved salt and to be less free to induce dipoles in the molecules of gas.* Sometimes the salts interact with solute as, for example, in the salting-in of hydrochloric acid, which leads to a greater solubility.

It is common observation that a glass of cold water, when warmed to room temperature, shows the presence of many small air bubbles. The rate of escape of the molecules of dissolved gas from the liquid is increased more by an increase in temperature than is the rate at which molecules of the gas phase strike the surface and dissolve in the liquid leading to a decreased solubility. From an energy standpoint, the forces of attraction that cause the gas molecules to crowd into the liquid are partially offset by the increased kinetic energy at the higher temperatures.

Partial Molal Quantities. The concept of partial molal quantities, developed by G. N. Lewis, has helped considerably in the quantitative study of solutions. In ideal solutions, the volume of the solution is equal to the sum of the volumes of the components, but this is not true for nonideal solutions. For example, when a mole of methanol is added to water the increase in volume is less than the molar volume of liquid methanol and depends upon the concentration of the final solution. This problem may be treated mathematically by the methods of differential calculus.

If a solution consists of n_1 moles of component 1 and n_2 moles of component 2 the change in volume produced by the addition, at constant temperature and pressure, of an infinitesimal number of moles of 1, dn_1, and an infinitesimal number of moles of 2, dn_2, is

$$dV = \left(\frac{\partial V}{\partial n_1}\right)_{n_2,T,p} dn_1 + \left(\frac{\partial V}{\partial n_2}\right)_{n_1,T\,p} dn_2 \tag{9}$$

$$= \overline{V}_1\, dn_1 + \overline{V}_2\, dn_2$$

where $\overline{V}$ is the partial molal volume, i.e.,

$$\overline{V}_1 = \left(\frac{\partial V}{\partial n_1}\right)_{n_2,T,p} \tag{10}$$

The bar above the symbol of any property is used to designate the par-

* The influence of salting-out on the dipole of a second substance has been measured by Williams and Albright, *Trans. Faraday Soc.*, *33*, 247 (1937).

tial property defined in a manner similar to that of equation 10.   In words, the partial molal volume of component 1 is the rate of change in volume of the solution produced by the addition of small amounts of 1 (so that the composition remains essentially constant) at constant temperature and pressure.   Or it may be visualized as the increase in volume produced by adding one mole of the component to a large quantity of the solution, a quantity so large in fact that the addition does not appreciably change the concentration of the solution.   The partial

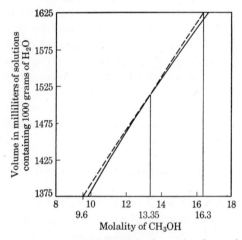

Fɪɢ. 9-15.   Determination of partial molal volumes by the method of tangents.

molal volume depends upon the concentration of the solution.   For example, a mole of methanol weighs 32.04 grams and occupies 40.47 ml at 20°.   When it is added to a large reservoir of pure methanol, the volume is increased 40.47 ml, but, when it is added to a large reservoir of an aqueous solution of 13.35 molal methanol, the increase is only 37.3 ml.

An obvious method for determining the partial molal volume of a solute consists in plotting the volume of the solution against the number of moles of solute contained in 1000 grams of the solvent (that is, against the molality), and determining the slope of the curve as shown in *Fig. 9-15*.   The slope of the curve $\partial V/\partial n_2$ at any molality gives the rate of change in volume with the number of moles of solute added, and this is by definition the partial molal volume of the solute.   In Fig. 9-15 the tangent is drawn to the curve at a molality of 13.35, and it is found to have a slope of $(1625 - 1375)/(16.30 - 9.60)$ or 37.3 ml mole^{-1}, which is the partial molal volume of the methanol at this molality.

The partial molal volume of water is determined in a similar manner by drawing tangents to the curve obtained by plotting the molal volume of the solution against the molality of the water in the methanol-water solution.

Other specialized graphical methods are available for obtaining partial molal quantities with greater precision than is possible by this simple graphical determination of tangents.* Sometimes calculated quantities are plotted in such a way that the errors of graphing apply only to a correcting term rather than to the whole quantity.

Other properties such as partial molal free energies or partial molal heat capacities or partial molal enthalpies may be determined in the same way as partial molal volumes. The partial molal free energy $\overline{F}$ of a given component is equal to the chemical potential (page 150) and is useful in deriving formulas for the thermodynamic behavior of solutions because it has the same value in every phase which is in equilibrium.

After the partial molal volumes have been determined, the volume of the whole solution can be obtained at any concentration by addition, as shown by equation 11,

$$n_1\overline{V}_1 + n_2\overline{V}_2 + n_3\overline{V}_3 + \cdots = V \qquad (11)$$

where V is the volume of the whole solution, and where n_1, n_2, n_3, etc., refer to the number of moles of the different components and $\overline{V}$ to the corresponding partial molal volumes.

Heat of Solution. The heat effect which accompanies the dissolving of a mole of solute is known as the *molal heat of solution*. It changes with the concentration all the way from an infinitely dilute solution to a saturated solution as is illustrated in *Fig. 9-16*. This figure gives the heat absorbed when n_2 moles of sodium bromide is dissolved in 1000 grams of water.† The addition of 1 mole of this solute to 1000 grams of water absorbs 830 cal of heat, and it might be expected that the addition of 2 moles to 1000 grams of solvent would absorb 1660 cal. However, there is an interaction of the solute ions with the solvent which gives a heat effect that is not directly proportional to the amount of solute added. In concentrated solutions, the solvent molecules behave quite differently from those in the pure solvent, and, of course, there is an interaction between solute molecules when the concentration is large. In sodium bromide, shown in Fig. 9-16, the addition of 2 moles of solute to 1000 grams of solvent absorbs 1390 cal, the addition of 3

---

* Lewis and Randall, *Thermodynamics and the Free Energy of Chemical Substances*, McGraw-Hill Book Co., New York, 1923, page 38.

† Harned and Crawford, *J. Am. Chem. Soc.*, **59**, 1903 (1937).

moles absorbs 1790 cal, and the addition of more solute gives a continuously decreasing absorption of heat per mole dissolved. When the solution becomes saturated at 9.0 molal, the further addition of solute produces no further effect because no more can dissolve.

The *integral heat of solution* is defined as the heat absorbed when 1 mole of solute is dissolved in a sufficient quantity of the solvent to give the specified concentration. In Fig. 9-16, the integral heats of solution at 1, 2, and 3 molal are, respectively, 830, 1390/2 or 695, and 1790/3 or

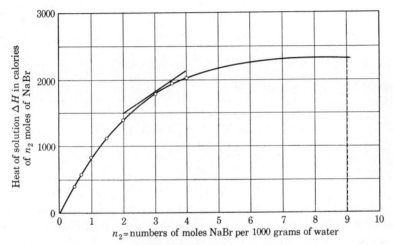

FIG. 9-16.   Heat of solution of sodium bromide in water.

597 cal mole^{-1}. It is possible also to calculate the heat absorbed when a given number of moles is added to a solution of specified concentration. Thus, according to Fig. 9-16, the addition of 1 mole of sodium bromide to a volume of a 1-molal solution containing 1 mole of sodium bromide absorbs 1390 − 830 or 560 cal of heat.

The partial molal or *differential heat of solution* is defined as $d(\Delta H)/dn_2$, where ΔH is the heat of solution of n_2 moles of solute in 1000 grams of solvent. It is the heat of solution of a mole of solute in a quantity of solution so large that the addition of the 1 more mole of solute does not change appreciably the concentration of the solution. It is illustrated by the tangent at 3.0-molal solution, which has a slope of 330 cal per mole.

The partial molal heat of solution in the pure solvent is the limiting slope of the curve as n_2 approaches zero. It represents the heat absorbed when a mole of solute is dissolved in an infinitely large amount of pure solvent to form an infinitely dilute solution. For sodium bro-

mide at infinite dilution $d(\Delta H)/dn_2 = 900$ cal per mole. The slope of
the curve when n_2 is the molality of the saturated solution represents
the heat absorbed when a mole of solute is dissolved in a large amount
of nearly saturated solution.

The integral heats of solution are recorded for a number of solutes in
Table VI. This table gives values of ΔH when 1 mole of the substance

Table VI.[1]   Integral Heats of Solution in Water at 25°

Solute	Moles H_2O	ΔH, kcal/mole	Solute	Moles H_2O	ΔH, kcal/mole
$HCl(g)$	5	-15.31	$NH_4NO_3(s)$	5	4.24
	200	-17.74		200	6.08
	10,000	-17.92	$CH_3CO_2H(l)$	200	-0.32
	∞	-17.96	$CuSO_4(s)$	200	-16.20
$HBr(g)$	200	-20.05	$KOH(s)$	5	-11.53
$HI(g)$	200	-7.02		200	-13.04
$H_2SO_4(l)$	200	-17.91	$KCl(s)$	200	4.20
$HNO_3(l)$	200	-7.84	$NaOH(s)$	5	-9.03
$NH_3(g)$	200	-8.28		200	-10.11
$CH_3OH(l)$	10	-1.43	$NaCl(s)$	200	1.02

[1] *Circular of the National Bureau of Standards* 500, 1952.

is dissolved in the number of moles of water specified. When ΔH is
positive, heat is absorbed; when it is negative, heat is evolved.

Usually, heat is absorbed when a crystalline salt dissolves, because
in the solution process the atoms or ions are torn apart from each other
in the crystal lattice. If this process is not offset by other processes, it
might be expected that as much heat would be absorbed as is absorbed
in the fusion of the crystal. In fact, the heat of solution of a substance
in a solvent to give an ideal solution is exactly equal to the heat of fusion. Combinations with the solvent can evolve heat which partially
or wholly offsets this cooling effect.

The importance of this attraction of the solvent for the solute in the
process of solution may be illustrated by the dissolving of sodium chloride. In the crystal lattice of sodium chloride, positive sodium ions and
negative chloride ions attract each other strongly. The energy required
to separate them is so great that nonpolar solvents like benzene or carbon tetrachloride will not dissolve sodium chloride; but a solvent like
water, which has a high dielectric constant and a large dipole moment,
combines with the ions and in so doing evolves a large amount of heat.
In this way, the large energy required for breaking up the crystal lattice
is made available. With sodium chloride the heat of interaction with
the solvent just about offsets the heat of separation of the ions, and

there is very little heat effect. With some substances the energy of combination with the solvent more than offsets the energy required to separate the units of the solute, and heat is actually evolved.

When a solution is diluted by the addition of more solvent, there is a heat change corresponding to the difference in the integral heat of solution at the two concentrations. As the dilution is increased, the thermal effect produced by the addition of more solvent becomes less and less and ultimately approaches zero.

The data of Professor T. F. Young of the University of Chicago presented in Table VII give unusually exact information regarding the heat

Table VII.   Heats of Solution of Sodium Chloride in Water at 25°

ΔH in calories for $n_1 H_2O + n_2 NaCl$ = solution

Molality	$\dfrac{\Delta H}{KgH_2O}$	$\dfrac{d(\Delta H)}{dn_2}$	$\dfrac{\Delta H}{n_2}$	$\dfrac{n_1}{n_2}$	$\dfrac{d(\Delta H)}{dn_1}$
0.0000	0.00	923	923	∞	−0.0000
0.0100	9.62	979	962	5551	−0.0029
0.0225	21.98	997	977	2467	−0.008
0.0900	90.4	1018	1004	617	−0.023
0.2500	251.2	986	1005	222.0	+0.086
0.4900	478.7	909	977	113.3	0.61
1.0000	898	737	898	55.51	2.90
3.2400	1934	280	597	17.13	18.5
4.8400	2323	244	480	11.47	21.6
6.0025	2659	350	443	9.25	10.1

of solution and heat of dilution $d(\Delta H)/dn_1$ for sodium chloride over a wide range of concentrations. It is interesting to note that there is a change of sign in the heat of dilution as the solution becomes dilute.

REFERENCES

Hildebrand and Scott, *Solubility of Non-Electrolytes*, Reinhold Publishing Corp., New York, 1950.

Robinson and Gilliland, *The Elements of Fractional Distillation*, McGraw-Hill Book Co., New York, 1939.

Carney, *Laboratory Fractional Distillation*, The Macmillan Co., New York, 1949.

Weissberger, *Physical Methods of Organic Chemistry*, Interscience Publishers, New York, 1949, Chapter IV, Vol. I, Part I.

PROBLEMS

1. The density of an aqueous solution of sodium chloride containing 8.000 grams of salt per 100 grams of solution is 1.0541 g/ml at 25°C. Calculate the concentration of this solution on the (a) molar, (b) molal, and (c) mole fraction scales.

Ans.   (a) 1.44.   (b) 1.49.   (c) 0.0261.

2. Ethanol and methanol form a solution which is nearly ideal. The vapor pressure of ethanol is 44.5 mm, and that of methanol is 88.7 mm, at 20°. (a) Calculate the mole fractions of methanol and ethanol in a solution obtained by mixing 100 grams of each. (b) Calculate the partial pressures and the total vapor pressure of the solution. (c) Calculate the mole fraction of methanol in the vapor.

Ans. (a) $N_{CH_3OH} = 0.590$; $N_{C_2H_5OH} = 0.410$.
(b) $p_{C_2H_5OH} = 18.25$; $p_{CH_3OH} = 52.32$; $p_{total} = 70.57$ mm.
(c) 0.741.

3. The following table gives the mole per cent of n-propanol ($M = 60.1$) in aqueous solutions and in the vapor at the boiling point for the solution at 760 mm pressure.

Mole % n-Propanol

Liquid	Vapor	B.P., °C
0	0	100.0
2.0	21.6	92.0
6.0	35.1	89.3
20.0	39.2	88.1
43.2	43.2	87.8
60.0	49.2	88.3
80.0	64.1	90.5
100.0	100.0	97.3

With the aid of a graph of these data calculate the composition of the first drop of distillate when the following solutions are distilled with a simple distilling flask: (a) 87 grams of n-propanol and 211 grams of water; (b) 50 grams of n-propanol and 5.02 grams of water. Ans. (a) $N_p = 0.37$. (b) $N_p = 0.59$.

4. The solubilities of carbon monoxide and nitrous oxide in water are 0.757 and 0.539, respectively, where solubilities are expressed in volume of gas under standard conditions per volume of solution. The solubility of carbon monoxide in 1.0 molal $Mg(NO_3)_2$ is 0.559. Calculate the solubility of nitrous oxide in 1.0 molal $Mg(NO_3)_2$. The experimental value is 0.385.

Ans. 0.398 volume per volume of solution.

5. The boiling point of the immiscible liquid system naphthalene-water is 98° under a pressure of 733 mm. The vapor pressure of water at 98° is 707 mm. Calculate the weight per cent of naphthalene in the distillate. Ans. 20.7%.

6. If the partial specific volume $\bar{v}$ is independent of concentration it is equal to the apparent specific volume, which may be calculated from

$$\bar{v} = \frac{100 - \left(\dfrac{100d_s - g}{d_0}\right)}{g}$$

where g is the number of grams of solute in 100 ml of solution, d_s is the density of the solution, and d_0 is the density of the solvent. The density of a solution of serum albumin containing 1.54 grams of protein per 100 ml is 1.0004 g cm^{-3} at 25°C ($d_0 = 0.99707$ g cm^{-3}). Calculate the apparent specific volume. Ans. 0.785 cm^3 g^{-1}.

7. Using the following data for cadmium nitrate in water, plot the total heats of solution, ΔH, against the molality m, and determine the differential heat of solution of cadmium nitrate in a 4-molal solution.

m (molality)	1.063	1.799	2.821	4.251	6.372	9.949
ΔH (joules)	-34.2	-56.7	-88.3	-126.0	-174.4	-228.5

Ans. -26 joules mole^{-1}.

---

8. A solution of KNO_3 contains 192.6 grams of salt per liter of solution. The density of the solution is 1.1432 g cm^{-3}. Calculate the concentration in terms of (a) molality, (b) molarity, (c) mole fraction, (d) weight per cent.

9. At 25° the vapor pressures of chloroform and carbon tetrachloride are 199.1 and 114.5 mm, respectively. If the two liquids form an ideal solution, (a) what is the composition of the vapor in equilibrium with a mixture containing 1 mole of each; (b) what is the vapor pressure of the mixture?

10. Ethylene dibromide and propylene dibromide form very nearly ideal solutions. Plot the partial vapor pressure of ethylene dibromide ($p° = 172$ mm), the partial vapor pressure of propylene dibromide ($p° = 127$ mm), and the total vapor pressure of the solution versus the mole fraction of ethylene dibromide. What will be the composition of the vapor in equilibrium with a solution containing 0.75 mole fraction ethylene dibromide?

11. The following table gives mole per cent acetic acid in aqueous solutions and in the equilibrium vapor at the boiling point of the solution at 1 atm. Calculate the

B.P. (°C)		118.1	113.8	107.5	104.4	102.1	100.0
Mole %	Liquid	100	90.0	70.0	50.0	30.0	0
Acetic acid	Vapor	100	83.3	57.5	37.4	18.5	0

number of theoretical plates for the column required to produce an initial distillate of 28 mole per cent acetic acid from a solution of 80 mole per cent acetic acid.

12. The vapor pressure of the immiscible liquid system diethylaniline-water is 760 mm at 99.4°. The vapor pressure of water at that temperature is 744 mm. How many grams of steam are necessary to distil 100 grams of diethylaniline?

13. At 20°, 1 volume of water absorbs 0.03405 volume of oxygen under atmospheric pressure and 0.01696 volume of nitrogen under atmospheric pressure. When air (20.9 per cent oxygen and 79.1 per cent nitrogen by volume) is dissolved in water under atmospheric pressure, what is the percentage (by volume) of oxygen and of nitrogen in the dissolved gases?

14. When 1 mole of water was added to an infinitely large amount of an aqueous methanol solution having a mole fraction methanol 0.40, the volume of the solution increased 17.35 ml. When 1 mole of methanol was added to such a solution, the volume increased 39.01 ml. Calculate the volume of a solution containing 0.40 mole of methanol and 0.60 mole of water.

15. Plot enough of the data of Table VII to determine graphically the partial molal heat of solution of sodium chloride in 0.8-molal sodium chloride solution.

16. Calculate the partial molal volume of zinc chloride in 1-molal $ZnCl_2$ solution using the following data:

Per cent by weight of $ZnCl_2$	2	6	10	14	18	20
Density, grams per milliliter	1.0167	1.0532	1.0819	1.1275	1.1665	1.1866

17. For solutions of n-propanol and water the following partial pressures are measured at 25°. Draw a complete pressure-composition diagram, including the total pressure. What is the composition of the vapor in equilibrium with a solution containing 0.5 mole fraction n-propanol?

$N_{n\text{-propanol}}$	p_{H_2O}	$p_{n\text{-propanol}}$
0	23.76	0
0.020	23.5	5.05
0.050	23.2	10.8
0.100	22.7	13.2
0.200	21.8	13.6
0.400	21.7	14.2
0.600	19.9	15.5
0.800	13.4	17.8
0.900	8.13	19.4
0.950	4.20	20.8
1.000	0.00	21.76

18. Ten grams of pure acetic acid, $HC_2H_3O_2$, is dissolved in 100 grams of water. The density of the solution at 20° is 1.0123 g cm^{-3}. Calculate the concentration of acetic acid in terms of (a) per cent by weight, (b) molality, (c) molarity, (d) mole fraction.

19. Prove that, for ideal solutions of two volatile liquids A and B,

$$P = p_A + p_B = p_A° + N_B(p_B° - p_A°)$$

Check this equation against a graph for the total vapor pressure of an ideal solution.

20. Benzene and toluene form a solution which is nearly ideal. At 80° the vapor pressures of benzene and toluene are as follows: vapor pressure of benzene = 753 mm; vapor pressure of toluene = 290 mm. For a solution containing 0.5 mole fraction of benzene and 0.5 mole fraction of toluene, what is the composition of the vapor at 80°?

21. It has been established that the refractive index of a solution of carbon tetrachloride in benzene is a linear function of the mole fraction of either component. For benzene, $n_D^{18} = 1.5024$. For carbon tetrachloride, $n_D^{18} = 1.4618$. Calculate the per cent by weight of CCl_4 in a solution of the two having a refractive index at 18° of 1.4807.

22. At 25° and 1 atm pressure, the solubility of oxygen, O_2, in water is 0.001225 mole per liter. How many grams are dissolved in a lake which is 1 mile in diameter with an average depth of 20 ft, if complete equilibrium with the air is assumed?

23. From the data given below construct a complete temperature-composition diagram for the system ethanol-ethyl acetate. The data apply to 760 mm. A solution containing 0.8 mole fraction of ethanol, EtOH, is distilled completely at 760 mm. (a) What is the composition of the first vapor to come off? (b) That of the last drop of liquid to evaporate? (c) What would be the values of the above quantities if the distillation were carried out in a cylinder provided with a piston so that none of the vapor could escape?

$N_{ethanol}$ Liquid	$N_{ethanol}$ Vapor	Tempera- ture	$N_{ethanol}$ Liquid	$N_{ethanol}$ Vapor	Tempera- ture
0	0	77.15	0.563	0.507	72.0
0.025	0.070	76.7	0.710	0.600	72.8
0.100	0.164	75.0	0.833	0.735	74.2
0.240	0.295	72.6	0.942	0.880	76.4
0.360	0.398	71.8	0.982	0.965	77.7
0.462	0.462	71.6	1.000	1.000	78.3

24. A 10-liter tank of methane at 740 mm total pressure and 25° contains 1 liter of water. How many grams of methane are dissolved in the water?

25. The integral heat of solution of 1 mole of H_2SO_4 in n moles of water is given by the formula:

$$\Delta H_{solution} = \frac{-18,070n}{n + 1.798} \text{ cal}$$

Calculate ΔH for the following reactions: (a) Solution of 1 mole of H_2SO_4 in 5 moles of water. (b) Solution of 1 mole of H_2SO_4 in 10 moles of water. (c) Solution of 1 mole of H_2SO_4 in a large excess of water, 100,000 moles for example. (d) Addition of a large excess of water to a solution containing 1 mole of H_2SO_4 in 10 moles of water. (e) Addition of 5 moles of water to a solution containing 1 mole of H_2SO_4 in 5 moles of water.

26. Two 2-liter vessels are connected with a tube and stopcock of negligible volume. Initially the first bulb contains 10 grams of water and is at 10°. The other bulb contains NH_3 at a pressure of 5 atm and is at 0°. Calculate the total pressure in the system when the stopcock is opened and the whole apparatus is brought to equilibrium at 25°. The solubility of NH_3 in water at 25° is 27.011 moles per 1000 grams of H_2O at one atmosphere pressure. Neglect second-order effects.

27. In the system isopropyl ether-isopropanol the vapor and liquid have the following compositions at the boiling point:

Mole Fraction Isopropyl Ether

In liquid	0	0.084	0.19	0.44	0.66	0.75	0.78	0.88	0.95	1.00
In vapor	0	0.30	0.45	0.64	0.73	0.76	0.78	0.84	0.91	1.00

Plot the data, and state whether this system exhibits a minimum or maximum boiling point. If so, which? What is the composition of this mixture of maximum or minimum boiling point? With a rough sketch show what the temperature-composition diagram would look like.

28. The total vapor pressure of a solution containing 3 per cent by weight of ethanol, C_2H_5OH, in water is 760 mm at 97.11°. The vapor pressure of pure water at this temperature is 685 mm. Using Raoult's law and Henry's law, calculate the partial pressure at 97.11° of ethanol and water over a solution containing 0.02 mole fraction of ethanol.

10

Solutions of Nonvolatile Solutes

In the preceding chapter binary solutions are studied, in which both liquids are volatile and the total pressure is the sum of the partial pressures of the components of the solution. The experimental measurements and the theoretical calculations are much simpler if only one component is volatile, as, for example, in a solution of sugar in water. The partial vapor pressure of the water becomes the total pressure of the solution because the sugar exerts no vapor pressure. The present chapter is concerned with this type of solution in which the solute is nonvolatile.

The solute reduces the escaping tendency of the solvent and consequently the vapor pressure. Because the vapor pressure is lowered, the boiling point is raised and the freezing point is lowered. The phenomenon of osmosis is connected also with the lowering of the vapor pressure. All four of these properties are interrelated, and they are used for calculating molecular weights and other properties of dissolved substances. These properties are sometimes called colligative properties.

Lowering of the Vapor Pressure. Raoult's law is the fundamental formula for connecting the vapor pressure of the solvent with its concentration. As given in the last chapter, this equation

$$p_{solvent} = N_{solvent} p^{\circ}{}_{solvent}$$

is applicable to ideal solutions, but it holds reasonably well for nonideal solutions also if they are dilute, because the solvent is only slightly changed from its normal behavior.

The difference between two quantities often can be determined experimentally more accurately than the absolute value of one of them. According to this principle, the difference between the vapor pressure of a solution and that of the pure solvent can be determined and calculated more accurately than the vapor pressure of the solution. Raoult's law may be written in the form

$$p = N_1 p^{\circ} = \frac{n_1}{n_1 + n_2} p^{\circ} \tag{1}$$

212

where p is the vapor pressure of the solution (or rather the partial pressure of the solvent in solution), $p°$ is the vapor pressure of the pure solvent, n_2 is the number of moles of solute, n_1 is the number of moles of solvent, and N_1 is the mole fraction of the solvent in the solution. Rearranging terms

$$\frac{p° - p}{p°} = \frac{n_2}{n_1 + n_2} = N_2 \tag{2}$$

where N_2 is the mole fraction of the solute.

Exercise 1. Carry out the algebraic transformations in converting equation 1 into equation 2.

Example 1. The vapor pressures of aqueous solutions of mannitol at 20° have been measured very accurately by Frazer, Lovelace, and Rogers.* They have computed $p°$ from their data with the equation

$$(p° - p)/N_2 = p°$$

The true value of $p°$, the vapor pressure of water at this temperature, is 17.54 mm.

Molal Concentration	$p° - p$, mm	$\dfrac{p° - p}{N_2}$, mm
0.0984	0.0307	17.31
0.2962	0.0922	17.37
0.4938	0.1536	17.42
0.5958	0.1863	17.55
0.7927	0.2478	17.60

This example emphasizes the value of applying calculations to a small correcting term, $p° - p$, as is done in equation 2. Calculations based on measurements of the larger quantity p in $p° = p/N_1$ would have required carrying more figures in the calculation.

The vapor pressure of a solution may be determined by a static method in which the pressure is read directly with a manometer. A differential manometer is convenient for measuring the difference between the vapor pressure of the solution and that of the pure solvent, one arm of the manometer being connected with the solution and the other with the solvent. An oil or other liquid of low density is used as the manometer liquid, and the difference in vapor pressure is read directly on the manometer. Both liquids must be boiled out to remove any dissolved air which might lead to an abnormal pressure.

According to another method, if vessels containing two different solutions are placed side by side in a closed container, vapor will distil from

* Frazer, Lovelace, and Rogers, *J. Am. Chem. Soc.*, *42*, 1793 (1920).

the solution having the higher vapor pressure and condense in the one having the lower vapor pressure. In this process the concentrated solution is diluted and the dilute solution is concentrated until, at equilibrium, the two solutions have the same vapor pressure. This *isopiestic* method is simple but can yield very precise results.*, † It is important that the vessels be in good thermal contact so that both are held at the same temperature until there is no further change in concentration. The attainment of equilibrium is accelerated by the removal of air from the containing vessel. This method depends upon knowing the vapor pressure of one of the solutions from other studies. Thus the reference solution may contain potassium chloride, since the vapor pressures of potassium chloride solutions are accurately known as a function of concentration. At equilibrium the second solution will have exactly the same vapor pressure. A determination of the concentration of potassium chloride permits a calculation of the vapor pressures of both solutions.

The gas-saturation method described on page 160 is suitable also for determining the vapor pressure of a solution. The loss in weight of the solution is determined after bubbling through a known volume of an inert gas, or the vaporized solvent is caught in an absorption tube and weighed or titrated. Again, more accurate results can be obtained with a differential method because errors involving the absolute measurements of volume, temperature, and other variables tend to cancel out. The measurements are made first on the pure solvent and then on the solution. Accurate measurements have been made with this method on the lowering of the vapor pressure of the solvent caused by addition of the solute.‡

Elevation of the Boiling Point. Since the vapor pressure of a solvent is lowered by the addition of a nonvolatile solute, it is obvious that the solution must be heated to a higher temperature than the solvent in order that both may have the same vapor pressure. This fact is shown in *Fig. 10-1*, where the curve for the vapor pressure of the solution is seen to cut the line of barometric pressure at a higher temperature than the curve representing the vapor pressure of the solvent.

As the temperature is raised the solvent or solution will begin to boil when its vapor pressure becomes equal to the pressure of the atmosphere (taken to be 760 mm in this figure). The boiling temperature of the solvent at this pressure is T_l and of the solution T_s. This elevation of the boiling point $T_s - T_l$ or ΔT_b is directly connected with the change in

---

* Robinson and Sinclair, *J. Am. Chem. Soc.*, *56*, 1830 (1934).

† Scatchard, Hamer and Wood, *J. Am. Chem. Soc.*, *60*, 3061 (1938).

‡ Bechtold and Newton, *J. Am. Chem. Soc.*, *62*, 1390 (1940).

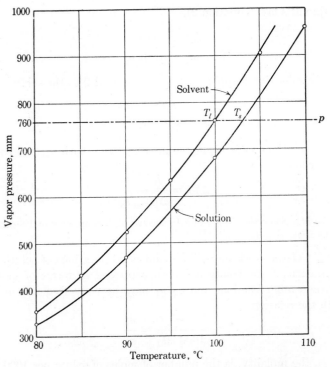

Fig. 10-1.   Elevation of the boiling point of a solvent by the addition of a nonvolatile solute—a 2.56-molal solution of sodium chloride in water.

the vapor pressure p and, accordingly, with the concentration of the solution.

According to the Clausius-Clapeyron equation (page 164)

$$\frac{d \ln p}{dT} = \frac{dp}{p \, dT} = \frac{\Delta H_{\text{vap}}}{RT^2} \tag{3}$$

where p is the vapor pressure of the liquid and ΔH_{vap} is the heat of vaporization per mole.

For small changes such as occur with dilute solutions equation 3 may be written

$$\Delta T_b = \frac{RT^2}{\Delta H_{\text{vap}}} \frac{\Delta p}{p^\circ} \tag{4}$$

where p° is the vapor pressure of the pure solvent.

By Raoult's law (equation 2),

$$\frac{\Delta p}{p^\circ} = \frac{n_2}{n_1 + n_2}$$

where the subscript 1 applies to the solvent and 2 to the solute. Then,

$$\Delta T_b = \frac{RT^2}{\Delta H_{\text{vap}}} \frac{n_2}{n_1 + n_2} \tag{5}$$

In dilute solutions n_2 is negligible in comparison with n_1, and so equation 5 becomes

$$\Delta T_b = \frac{RT^2}{\Delta H_{\text{vap}}} \frac{n_2}{n_1} \tag{6}$$

Exercise II. Show that in a 1-molal aqueous solution an error of 1.8 per cent is caused by neglecting n_2.

In most of the work on boiling-point determinations of solutions the concentration of the solute has been expressed in terms of molalities rather than mole fractions and n_2/n_1 may be converted into molality through the relation

$$\frac{m}{1000/M_1} = \frac{n_2}{n_1}$$

where m, the molality, is the number of moles of solute per 1000 grams of solvent and M_1 is the molecular weight of the solvent. Then equation 6 becomes

$$\Delta T_b = \frac{RT^2 M_1}{1000 \, \Delta H_{\text{vap}}} m \tag{7}$$

The several constants are conveniently replaced by K_b, the boiling-point constant or molal boiling-point elevation.

$$\frac{RT^2 M_1}{1000 \, \Delta H_{\text{vap}}} = K_b \tag{8}$$

Then equation 7 becomes

$$\Delta T_b = K_b m \tag{9}$$

This relation shows that for dilute solutions the elevation of the boiling point is directly proportional to the molality of the solution, a prediction that has been abundantly verified by experiment.

The molal boiling-point constants for several liquids are given in Table I together with the molal freezing-point constants, which will be considered in a later section. The constant K_b is not the actual eleva-

Table I. Molal Boiling-Point Constants and Freezing-Point Constants

Solvent	Boiling Point	K_b	Freezing Point	K_f
Acetic acid	118.1	2.93	17	3.9
Acetone	56.0	1.71	....	......
Benzene	80.2	2.53	5.4	5.12
Chloroform	61.2	3.63	....	......
Ethanol	78.3	1.22	....	......
Ethylene bromide	.....	....	10	12.5
Ethyl ether	34.4	2.02	....	......
Heptachloropropane	.....	....	29.5	12.0
Naphthalene	.....	....	80	6.8
Tribromophenol	.....	....	95	20.4
Water	100	0.51	0	1.860

tion of boiling point for a 1-molal solution, because the assumptions involved in its derivation are not valid in a solution as concentrated as 1 molal. The value of K_b may be determined experimentally by measuring the elevation of the boiling point ΔT_b at a given molality m in a dilute solution, or more accurately by determining the value $\Delta T_b/m$ at several concentrations and extrapolating to zero concentration. As in many other experiments which will be met with later, it is difficult to make accurate measurements in solutions that are dilute enough to give exact values of theoretical significance. The experiments are carried out in several solutions as dilute as convenient for accurate measurements and then the values are graphed and extrapolated to zero concentration.

The molal boiling-point constants can be calculated using equation 8 without making any direct experimental measurements of the boiling points of solutions. These values agree closely with the values obtained by direct experimental measurements on dilute solutions.

Example 2. Calculate the molal boiling-point constant for water, which has a boiling point of 100.00°, a heat of vaporization of 539.7 cal per gram, and a molecular weight of 18.02.

$$K_b = \frac{RT^2M_1}{1000\,\Delta H_{vap}} = \frac{(1.987)(373.1)^2(18.02)}{(1000)(18.02)(539.7)} = 0.513$$

Equation 9 can be used for calculating the boiling point of a dilute solution of known composition.

Example 3. What is the boiling point of a solution containing 5.00 gram of urea in 75.000 grams of water? The molecular weight of urea is 60.06.

$$\Delta T_b = 0.513m = (0.513)\left(\frac{5.00}{60.06}\right)\left(\frac{1000}{75.000}\right) = 0.569°$$

The boiling point of the solution at 1 atm is 100.000° + 0.569° = 100.569°.

In order to determine the molecular weight of a solute it is convenient to rearrange equation 9. If w_2 grams of solute having a molecular weight M_2 is dissolved in w_1 grams of solvent, the number of moles of solute is w_2/M_2 and the molality m is $\dfrac{w_2}{M_2}\dfrac{1000}{w_1}$. Then

$$\Delta T_b = K_b m = K_b \frac{w_2}{M_2}\frac{1000}{w_1} \tag{10}$$

Example 4. What is the molecular weight of dinitrobenzene if the addition of 1.00 gram to 50.00 grams of benzene raises the boiling point of the benzene 0.30°? K_b for benzene = 2.53.

$$M_2 = K_b \frac{w_2}{\Delta T_b}\frac{1000}{w_1} = 2.53 \frac{1.00}{0.30}\frac{1000}{50.00} = 170 \text{ g mole}^{-1}$$

Experimental Determination of Boiling Points.* In determining the boiling point of a solution the thermometer must be placed in the liquid, because if it were placed in the vapor the film of liquid condensing on the thermometer would be pure solvent and the temperature recorded would be that of the solvent rather than the solution. The liquid, however, is likely to become superheated by conduction from the heated walls of the container, and then the temperature recorded by the thermometer will not be the true boiling point of the solution. This difficulty can be overcome by heating the solution with electrical resistance wires immersed in the solution. Small bubbles formed locally on the wires tend to prevent superheating.

In another method the vapor from the boiling liquid pumps a mixture of liquid and vapor into an inverted funnel just below the surface. The mixture then goes upward in a tube which discharges the mixture onto the thermometer bulb, placed above the liquid. During the passage of the vapor and liquid through this tube the two have opportunity to come to equilibrium, and any superheated liquid is cooled by further evaporation to the normal boiling point.

In carrying out the determinations of the boiling points of solutions, a weighed quantity of solute is introduced into a weighed quantity of solvent, or, in a better procedure, samples are withdrawn and analyzed by chemical or physical means after the temperature readings have been taken. Since the boiling point is affected by changes in the atmospheric pressure, the determinations on the solution and solvent should be made simultaneously in two pieces of apparatus, or over such short periods of time that the barometer fluctuations are negligible. In accurate

* Swietoslawski and Anderson, in Weissberger, *Physical Methods of Organic Chemistry*, Part I, Chapter 4, Interscience Publishers, New York, 1949.

work, a barostat may be used to maintain a fixed pressure. By automatic regulation with an electric circuit, compressed air is admitted into a chamber whenever the mercury manometer falls below a predetermined pressure. The need of these precautions is evident from the fact that a change of 0.3 or 0.4 mm changes the boiling point of most solvents by 0.01°.

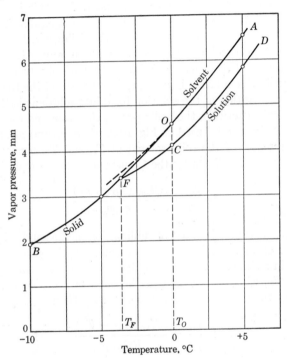

Fig. 10-2. Lowering of the freezing point of a solvent by a solute—a 2.56-molal solution of sodium chloride in water.

Lowering of the Freezing Point. The freezing point of water, or other liquid, is lowered by the addition of a solute, and this lowering is directly proportional to the concentration of the solution for dilute solutions. The reason for the lowering may be understood with the help of *Fig. 10-2.*

At the freezing point of the pure solvent O the liquid and solid solvent have the same vapor pressure and so they continue to exist in equilibrium. The sublimation-pressure curve BFO for the solid solvent (ice) is steeper than the vapor-pressure curve for the liquid solvent OA. At temperatures above the melting point the solid has a higher vapor pressure than the liquid, and so it all changes into the liquid; i.e., the solid solvent melts. At temperatures below the freezing point the liquid has the higher vapor pressure and so it goes over to form solid; i.e., the liquid freezes. When a solute is added to the solvent the vapor pressure of the solvent is lowered as shown by the curve CD, below the curve OA for solvent. The vapor-pressure curve for the solution intersects the vapor-pressure curve for pure solid solvent at point F. This is the freezing point of the solution, where ice and solution are in equilibrium because each has the same vapor pressure. In the following derivation it is assumed that pure solvent freezes out without any solute when the solution freezes. This is generally, but not invariably, true.

The quantitative relation between the depression of the freezing point and the concentration of the solution for dilute solutions is the same as that which exists between the boiling-point elevation and the concentration. The derivation is based on Fig. 10-2, where p_O and p_F are the sublimation pressures of the solid solvent at T_O and T_F corresponding to the points O and F. Then by the Clausius-Clapeyron equation

$$\ln \frac{p_O}{p_F} = \frac{\Delta H_{sub} (T_O - T_F)}{R T_O T_F} \tag{11}$$

where ΔH_{sub} is the molar heat of sublimation of the solid solvent.

The heat of vaporization of the solvent from the solution ΔH_{vap} is calculated in a similar manner by taking the vapor pressures p_C and p_F at T_O and T_F, where the point C is the point on the solution curve directly below the freezing point of the solvent. Then

$$\ln \frac{p_C}{p_F} = \frac{\Delta H_{vap}(T_O - T_F)}{R T_O T_F} \tag{12}$$

Subtracting equation 12 from equation 11,

$$\ln \frac{p_O}{p_F} - \ln \frac{p_C}{p_F} = \frac{(\Delta H_{sub} - \Delta H_{vap})(T_O - T_F)}{R T_O T_F} \tag{13}$$

This equation may be simplified by introducing the relation $\Delta H_{sub} = \Delta H_{vap} + \Delta H_{fus}$.

$$\ln \frac{p_O}{p_C} = \frac{\Delta H_{fus}(T_O - T_F)}{R T_O T_F} \tag{14}$$

If the solvent obeys Raoult's law (page 185), $p_C = N_1 p_O$, and equation 14 may be written

$$- \ln N_1 = \frac{\Delta H_{fus}(T_O - T_F)}{R T_O T_F} \tag{15}$$

This equation gives the relationship between the concentration of the solution and its freezing point, but it may equally well be considered to give the solubility of solid solvent in the solution at temperature T_F. This equation is based upon the assumptions that ΔH_{fus} is independent of temperature and that the solvent separates as a pure solid.

If the freezing-point lowering $\Delta T_f = T_O - T_F$ is small, $T_O T_F$ may be replaced by T^2.

$$- \ln N_1 = \frac{\Delta H_{fus} \, \Delta T_f}{RT^2} \tag{16}$$

In binary solutions which contain only one solute and one solvent $N_1 = 1 - N_2$, where N_2 is the mole fraction of the solute. According to Maclaurin's series,

$$- \ln N_1 = - \ln (1 - N_2) = N_2 + \tfrac{1}{2}N_2{}^2 + \tfrac{1}{3}N_2{}^3 + \cdots$$

For small values of N_2 the higher powers may be neglected.* Then approximately, $- \ln N_1 = N_2$, and equation 16 becomes

$$\Delta T_f = \frac{RT^2}{\Delta H_{fus}} N_2 = \frac{RT^2 n_2}{\Delta H_{fus}(n_1 + n_2)} \tag{17}$$

Equation 17 is of the same form as equation 5 for the elevation of the boiling point and it can be converted into useful forms like those of equations 8, 9, and 10. Thus it can be shown that

$$K_f = \frac{RT^2 M_1}{1000 \, \Delta H_{fus}} \tag{18}$$

and

$$\Delta T_f = K_f m = K_f \frac{w_2}{M_2} \frac{1000}{w_1} \tag{19}$$

where K_f is the molal freezing-point constant, m is the molality of the solution, M_1 is the molecular weight of the solvent and M_2 that of the solute, and w_2 is the weight of solute dissolved in weight w_1 of the solvent to give a freezing-point depression of ΔT_f.

Example 5. For water K_f has the value 1.86°, calculated as follows:

$$K_f = \frac{RT^2 M_1}{1000 \, \Delta H_{fus}} = \frac{(1.987)(273.1)^2(18.02)}{(1000)(18.02)(79.7)} = 1.86$$

According to this equation solute added to 1000 grams of water will lower the freezing point at the rate of 1.86° per mole, but the relation holds only for dilute solutions. Even a 1-molal solution is too concentrated, and the depression will be something less than 1.86°.

* For example, if $N_2 = 0.01$ the expression becomes $0.01 + \tfrac{1}{2}(0.0001) + \tfrac{1}{3}(0.000001)$, which is equal to 0.01 within 0.5 per cent.

Experimental Determination of Freezing Points.   Freezing-point depressions can be determined with great accuracy.   Measurements of moderate accuracy can be made easily with simple apparatus. The freezing points of the pure solvent and the solution are determined with an accurate thermometer.   A tube containing the solution is

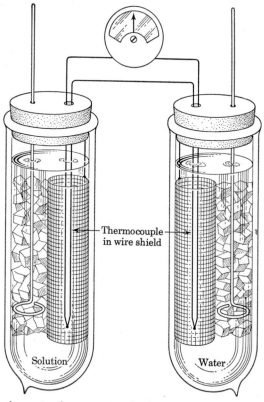

Thermocouple in wire shield

Solution   Water

FIG. 10-3.   Apparatus for measuring the freezing-point lowering by a solute.

jacketed and immersed in a bath of ice and salt.   It is provided with a stopper through which an efficient ring stirrer, encircling the thermometer, is operated with a vertical movement.   The temperature gradually falls until the solid appears, and the first steady temperature is recorded as the freezing point.   The concentration of the solution in equilibrium with the solid solvent is determined by analyzing the solution.

In a less accurate method, the solution is made up to a known concentration by direct weighing of the solute and solvent, but, if much of the solvent freezes out, the concentration will be different at the time the thermometer reading is taken. This difficulty is accentuated by super-cooling, which leads to the freezing out of a considerable quantity of solvent.

The most accurate results are obtained with two vacuum-jacketed vessels placed in an ice bath and partly filled with cracked ice, as shown in *Fig. 10-3*. One vessel contains solvent; the other, solution. The difference in temperature is measured to 0.0001° with a multiple-junction thermoelement and sensitive potentiometer. The two liquids are stirred vigorously, and the concentration of the solution in equilibrium with the ice is determined accurately by chemical analysis or by physical measurements, for example, with a refractometer.

Table II gives the freezing-point lowerings for solutions of urea. The ratio $\Delta T_f/m$ would have the value 1.860 in very dilute solutions. Table

Table II. Lowering of Freezing Point of Water by Urea [1,2]

m, moles per 1000 g H_2O	ΔT_f	$\Delta T_f/m$
0.324_1	0.595_3	1.837
0.431_5	0.789_3	1.829
0.645_8	1.169_8	1.811
1.521_3	2.673_2	1.757
3.360_1	5.489_7	1.635

[1] Caldwell and Politi, *J. Am. Chem. Soc.*, *60*, 1291 (1938).
[2] When the last figure is uncertain it is sometimes set slightly below the line.

II indicates the kind of deviations from ideality that are encountered in more concentrated solutions of nonelectrolytes.

Osmotic Pressure. If two solutions of different concentration, or solution and solvent, are separated by a membrane permeable to solvent but impermeable to solute, the solvent will diffuse into the more concentrated solution. This flow of solvent may be stopped or the direction of the flow reversed by the application of sufficient pressure to the more concentrated solution using a piston, a column of mercury, or a column of solution. The extra pressure that must be applied to a solution in order just to prevent the flow of solvent through the membrane from the pure solvent is known as the *osmotic pressure* of the solution. This pressure is closely related to the lowering of the freezing point, the elevation of the boiling point, and the lowering of the vapor pressure by the non-volatile solute.

The flow of solvent into the more concentrated solution is a spontaneous process because the escaping tendency or chemical potential of the solvent in the more concentrated solution is reduced by the presence of the solute. The effect of applying pressure to the solution is to raise the chemical potential of the solvent molecules. The osmotic pressure is the additional pressure that must be applied to raise the chemical potential of the solvent in the solution until it is equal to the chemical potential of the pure solvent. It may also be considered that this extra applied pressure raises the partial vapor pressure of the solvent in the solution until it is equal to that of the pure solvent.

The phenomenon of osmotic pressure was described by Abbé Nollet in 1748, and Pfeffer, a botanist, made the first direct measurements in 1877. The measurement of osmotic pressure requires the use of a *semipermeable membrane*, that is, one permeable to one component of the solution but not to the other. If the molecules of the solute are very large in comparison with those of the solvent, as in a solution of a high polymer, it is not so difficult to find a membrane in which the holes are large enough to pass molecules of solvent but too small to pass molecules of solute. Cellophane is frequently used as the membrane for high-polymer solutions. If the solute and solvent molecules are of more nearly the same size the membrane may still be semipermeable because the solvent can dissolve in the membrane, but the solute cannot. Thus, a rubber membrane separating pure pyridine from a solution of sugar in pyridine dissolves pyridine and permits its flow from the region where its chemical potential is highest to the region where its chemical potential is lowest. The rate with which equilibrium is reached varies with different membranes, but all semipermeable membranes will give the same osmotic pressure with a given solution.

Using a mercury manometer Pfeffer was able to measure the hydrostatic pressure generated in a solution by the osmotic flow of water through a semipermeable membrane into a solution of sugar. Pfeffer's results are given in Tables III and IV. The volume of solution holding

Table III.   Relation of Osmotic Pressure to Concentration at 287°K

v, ml gram^{-1}	π, atm	πv
100	0.70	70
50	1.34	67
25	2.74	68
16.5	4.10	68

1 gram of cane sugar is given under v, the osmotic pressure in atmospheres under π, and the absolute temperature under T.

The significance of Pfeffer's measurements was first perceived by van't Hoff, who pointed out the existence of a striking parallelism between the properties of gases and the osmotic properties of solutions. As shown in Table III, the product πv is a constant, just as it is for gases according to Boyle's law. As shown in Table IV, the pressure is propor-

Table IV.   Relation of Osmotic Pressure to Temperature

Approximately 1 Gram of Sucrose per 100 Ml of Solution

T, °K	π, atm	π/T
273.0	0.649	0.00238
279.8	0.664	0.00237
286.7	0.691	0.00241
288.5	0.684	0.00237
295.0	0.721	0.00244
305.0	0.716	0.00235
309.0	0.746	0.00241

tional to the absolute temperature just as it is for gases; that is, $\pi/T =$ constant.

Moreover, the two relations may be combined to give the same constant R as is obtained for gases,

$$\pi v = nRT = (g/M)RT \tag{20}$$

where π is osmotic pressure, v is the volume of the solution, and g is the weight of solute having molecular weight M.

Example 6.   From Pfeffer's data in Table IV, it is seen that 1 gram in 100 ml or 1 mole (342 grams) in 34.2 liters gives an osmotic pressure of 0.649 atm at 0°.   Then,

$$R = \frac{\pi v}{T} = \frac{(0.649 \text{ atm})(34.2 \text{ l mole}^{-1})}{273 \text{ deg}} = 0.0813 \text{ l-atm deg}^{-1} \text{ mole}^{-1}$$

Within the limits of the experimental error, this is the same as the gas constant R, namely, 0.08205, and the standard equation used for making calculations on gases can thus be used for calculating approximate osmotic pressures.

Example 7.   If 2.00 grams of sugar having a molecular weight of 342 is dissolved in 50 ml of solution at 25°, what will be the osmotic pressure?

$$\pi = \frac{gRT}{Mv} = \frac{(2.00 \text{ g})(0.08205 \text{ l atm deg}^{-1} \text{ mole}^{-1})(298.1 \text{ deg})}{(342 \text{ g mole}^{-1})(0.0500 \text{ l})}$$

$$= 2.86 \text{ atm}$$

Equation 20 is not an exact law except in the limit of very dilute solutions.   More exact relations are derived in a later section (page 228). In general, somewhat better results can be obtained in calculating osmotic pressures of concentrated solutions if the volume of the solvent alone, rather than that of the solution, is substituted for v.   Thus

Berkeley and Hartley, who measured the osmotic pressures of sugar solutions at 0°, found, for example, that in a solution containing 660.5 grams of sugar per liter (nearly 2 molar) the experimentally determined osmotic pressure at 0° was 100.8 atm, and the value calculated by equation 20 was 51.2 atm. However, if the effective volume is taken as the volume of the solution minus the volume of the sugar, the calculated osmotic pressure is about 75 atm.

Comparison of Experimental Methods. The four properties of solutions which have just been studied, vapor-pressure lowering, boiling-point elevation, freezing-point depression, and osmotic pressure, are closely connected. The freezing-point depression can be measured most accurately and most easily, but the method is limited to low temperatures where the solubility is often small. The boiling-point readings may be seriously affected by fluctuations in the barometric pressure, and, in water, the molal elevation is only about one-third as great as the freezing-point depression. The temperature range is limited in both the boiling-point and the freezing-point method. The vapor-pressure lowering is adaptable to different temperatures and capable of high accuracy, but it requires more elaborate apparatus. Osmotic pressure was extensively used in the early development of the theory of solutions and now finds its greatest application in the measurement of molecular weights of high polymers * (page 498).

Free Energy of Dilution. The properties of a system are conveniently and quantitatively defined in terms of energy. In the study of solutions, for example, the free energy of dilution is a useful thermodynamic quantity. The formulas for the free energy of dilution are based on formula 21, which holds true at constant temperature as shown on page 143.

$$dF = V\,dp \qquad (21)$$

The following three-step derivation leads to useful equations for the free energy of dilution at constant temperature:

I. A reservoir of pure solvent having a vapor pressure $p°$ is placed near a large reservoir of solution which has the vapor pressure p. The pure solvent, of course, has a higher vapor pressure than the solution. One mole of solvent is vaporized from the liquid solvent by keeping the pressure infinitesimally less than $p°$. Since the process is carried out reversibly at constant pressure and temperature

$$\Delta F = 0$$

---

* Wagner, in Weissberger, *Physical Methods of Organic Chemistry*, Interscience Publishers, New York, 1949, Vol. I, Part I, page 487.

II. The mole of vapor at pressure $p°$ is placed in a cylinder with a piston and expanded reversibly (that is, by infinitesimal decreases of pressure) until the pressure is p. For this process

$$F - F° = \Delta F = \int_{p°}^{p} V \, dp = \int_{p°}^{p} \frac{RT}{p} \, dp = RT \ln \frac{p}{p°}$$

where $F°$ is the free energy of 1 mole of the vapor at pressure $p°$, and F is the free energy at pressure p.

III. The mole of solvent vapor at pressure p is then added reversibly to a large reservoir of solution at pressure p by applying an external pressure infinitesimally greater than p. The reservoir is assumed to be so large that the addition of 1 more mole of solvent does not change the concentration of the solution appreciably. The free-energy change for this process is

$$\Delta F = 0$$

All three steps are carried out isothermally and reversibly, and the total change of free energy involved in the transfer of 1 mole of solvent from solvent to solution is

$$\Delta F = RT \ln (p/p°) \tag{22}$$

This value of ΔF for the transfer is applicable, regardless of how the transfer is carried out.

This formula can be used equally well for calculating the free-energy change when a mole of solvent is transferred from a solution of concentration c_1 having a vapor pressure p_1 to another solution of concentration c_2 having a vapor pressure p_2. Thus,

$$\Delta F = RT \ln (p_2/p_1) \tag{23}$$

Moreover, these formulas are not limited to the solvent. They may be applied to any volatile material in the solution, whether called solvent or solute.

In ideal solutions, where the vapor pressure of the volatile component is proportional to the mole fraction N, equation 23 may be written

$$\Delta F = RT \ln (N_2/N_1) \tag{24}$$

In very dilute solutions, the vapor pressures of either solvent or solute are proportional to the concentration; thus,

$$\Delta F = RT \ln (c_2/c_1) \tag{25}$$

Example 8. What is the free-energy change when 1 mole of a solute in a very large volume of 0.01-molal aqueous solution at 25° is transferred to a large volume of a 0.001-molal solution?

$$\Delta F = RT \ln \frac{c_2}{c_1} = (1.987 \text{ cal deg}^{-1} \text{ mole}^{-1})(298.1 \text{ deg})(2.303) \log \frac{0.001}{0.01}$$

$$= -1364 \text{ cal mole}^{-1}$$

The negative sign indicates that the process of dilution is spontaneous. The reverse process in which the solute becomes more concentrated would not occur spontaneously, as explained on page 147. ΔF would have a positive sign.

It has been shown that the four properties, vapor-pressure lowering, boiling-point elevation, freezing-point depression, and osmotic pressure, may be readily calculated for dilute solutions, but that the simple formulas fail when applied to concentrated solutions. It is a necessary consequence of thermodynamics, however, that at a given temperature the deviations from ideal behavior are the same in all the different properties. For example, if the vapor-pressure lowering is known by experimental measurement, the osmotic pressure may be calculated with exactness, even in concentrated solutions where Raoult's law does not hold and where the osmotic pressure cannot be calculated from the gas laws. These relations follow from the fact that the free energy of dilution is the same, whether it is effected by evaporation, by freezing, or by application of pressure through a semipermeable membrane.

The free energy of transfer of a mole of solvent from solvent to solution is given by equation 22. The change in free energy when the solution is compressed to give an excess pressure equal to the osmotic pressure may be calculated by means of equation 21.

$$\Delta F = \int_{F^\circ}^{F} dF = \int_{P}^{P'} \overline{V} \, dp \tag{26}$$

where $\overline{V}$ is the partial molal volume of the solvent, P is the total pressure on the solvent phase, and P' is the total pressure on the solution phase at equilibrium.

If $\overline{V}$ is a constant

$$\Delta F = \overline{V}(P' - P) = \overline{V}\pi \tag{27}$$

where π, the difference between the pressure on the solution (P') and that on the solvent (P), is the osmotic pressure. Since the transfer of solvent from pure solvent to solution, followed by compression of the solution to the osmotic pressure, is equivalent to the transfer of solvent through the membrane at equilibrium, the sum of the ΔF changes must be equal to zero. Thus from equations 22 and 27

$$RT \ln p/p^\circ + \overline{V}\pi = 0$$

$$\pi = (RT/\overline{V}) \ln (p^\circ/p) \tag{28}$$

With this formula it is possible to calculate the osmotic pressure of a solution from the vapor pressures of the solvent and the solution, and the molar volume of the solvent. At high concentrations, where the osmotic pressures calculated by the simple gas law (equation 20) are in error by more than 30 per cent, the values calculated by equation 28 check with the observed values within less than 1 per cent.

Example 9. Calculate the osmotic pressure of a 1-molar sucrose solution in water from the fact that at 30° the vapor pressure of the solution is 31.207 mm. The vapor pressure of water at 30° is 31.824 mm. The density of pure water is 0.99564 g cm^{-3}.

$$\pi = (RT/\overline{V}) \ln (p°/p)$$

$$\overline{V} = \frac{18.02 \text{ g mole}^{-1}}{0.99564 \text{ g cm}^{-3}} = 18.10 \text{ cm}^3 \text{ mole}^{-1} \text{ or } 0.01810 \text{ l mole}^{-1}$$

$$\pi = \frac{(0.08205 \text{ l atm deg}^{-1} \text{ mole}^{-1})(2.303)(303.1 \text{ deg})}{(0.01810 \text{ l mole}^{-1})} \log \frac{31.824}{31.207}$$

$$= 26.9 \text{ atm}$$

This problem may be solved to a sufficiently high degree of accuracy with a slide rule rather than logarithm tables by writing the logarithmic term as a series. For small values of x it may be seen on page 654 of the Appendix that

$$\ln (1 + x) = x$$

Thus, carrying out the division,

$$\ln \frac{31.824}{31.207} = \ln \left(1 + \frac{31.824 - 31.207}{31.207}\right)$$

$$= \ln (1 + 0.0198)$$

$$= 0.0198$$

$$\pi = 27.1 \text{ atm.}$$

Equation 28 can be used also for deriving formula 20. For ideal solutions or dilute solutions, where Raoult's law holds,

$$p = p°N_1$$

where N_1 is the mole fraction of the solvent. Then,

$$\ln (p°/p) = - \ln N_1 \qquad (29)$$

Since N_1 is equal to $1 - N_2$, where N_2 is the mole fraction of the solute,

$$\ln N_1 = \ln (1 - N_2) = - \ln (p°/p) \qquad (30)$$

Then substituting into equation 28 gives

$$\pi = (RT/\overline{V})[- \ln (1 - N_2)] \qquad (31)$$

Expanding in a series, we have

$$\pi = (RT/\overline{V})(N_2 + \tfrac{1}{2}N_2{}^2 + \tfrac{1}{3}N_2{}^3 + \cdots) \tag{32}$$

When N_2 is small, higher powers may be neglected, and

$$\pi\overline{V} = N_2RT \tag{33}$$

But $N_2 = n_2/(n_1 + n_2)$, and in dilute solutions $N_2 = n_2/n_1$, where n_2 is the number of moles of solute and n_1 the number of moles of solvent. Therefore,

$$\pi\overline{V}n_1 = n_2RT \tag{34}$$

Setting v, the volume of the dilute solution containing n_2 moles of solute, equal to the volume of the solvent, $\overline{V}n_1$ (that is, to the volume of 1 mole of solvent times the number of moles of solvent), gives

$$\pi v = n_2RT \tag{35}$$

This is equivalent to equation 20, discovered experimentally, and it is evident from the approximations introduced why it cannot hold for concentrated solutions.

Dissociation of Solutes. If the nonvolatile solute is broken down into smaller nonvolatile units in solution, the effect on the vapor pressure and other related properties will be increased. Van't Hoff pointed out that dilute aqueous solutions of most inorganic acids, bases, and salts give abnormally large osmotic pressures, whereas dilute solutions of sugar and many organic substances give osmotic pressures in close agreement with the values calculated with the simple law $\pi V = RT$. He found that by introducing an additional term i he could obtain agreement with experimental values using the formula:

$$\pi V = iRT \tag{36}$$

At first i was regarded as a constant, but it was soon found that it decreases as concentration of the solute increases. The value of i may be determined for any solution by comparing the osmotic pressure or any of the related properties of the solution with these properties as measured for a nondissociating solute such as sucrose. Thus

$$i = \frac{\pi}{\pi_0} = \frac{\Delta p}{(\Delta p)_0} = \frac{\Delta T_f}{(\Delta T_f)_0} = \frac{\Delta T_b}{(\Delta T_b)_0} \tag{37}$$

where the subscript zero refers to the solution of a normal solute of the same molality. The vapor-pressure lowering Δp is equal to $p_{\text{solvent}} - p_{\text{solution}}$.

The abnormal behavior of salts is easily observed in the depression of the freezing points of solutions. Since for a normal solute in aqueous solution $\Delta T_f/m$ is 1.86, $i = \Delta T_f/1.86m$. Usually the molal freezing-point depressions $\Delta T_f/m$ are considerably greater than 1.86.

The data are shown graphically in *Fig. 10-4*, where it is seen that i approaches the values 2, 3, and 4 at infinite dilution. It is evident that the depressions are considerably greater than those of normal solutes such as sucrose or mannitol. For a given solute i increases as the

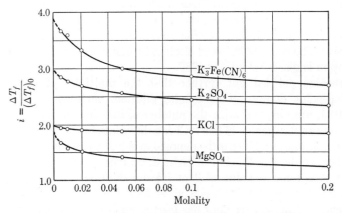

FIG. 10-4. Values of i extrapolated to infinite dilution for electrolytes of different valence types.

concentration is decreased and, at infinite dilution, approaches definite limits which are integers. Thus, with solutions of KCl and $MgSO_4$, the molal depression approaches the value $3.72°$ (or $2 \times 1.86°$) as the solutions are diluted, while the respective limits toward which the molal depressions of solutions of K_2SO_4 and $K_3Fe(CN)_6$ tend are $3 \times 1.86°$ and $4 \times 1.86°$.

These facts, together with numerous other properties of dilute solutions of acids, bases, and salts, find their most satisfactory explanation in the theory of electrolytic dissociation.

Arrhenius's Theory of Electrolytic Dissociation.* In 1887 Arrhenius proposed the theory that aqueous solutions of acids, bases, and salts are dissociated, to a greater or lesser extent, into positively and negatively charged *ions*, and that the increase in the number of dissolved units due to this dissociation is the cause of the increased osmotic pressure. These ions, like the original solutes from which they come, are nonvolatile. Arrhenius strengthened this theory greatly by

* Arrhenius, Z. *physik. Chem.*, *1*, 631 (1887).

pointing out that substances which give abnormal osmotic effects yield solutions which conduct electric current, whereas solutions of such substances as cane sugar, urea, and alcohol, which exert normal osmotic pressures, do not conduct electricity any better than the pure solvent. In other words, only electrolytes * are capable of undergoing ionic dissociation and of exhibiting abnormally large osmotic pressures and related effects; hence Arrhenius termed the hypothesis the *electrolytic dissociation theory*. When electrically charged electrodes are introduced into the solution, the positive ions move toward the negative electrode, and the negative ions move toward the positive electrode, the passage of a current through the solution consisting in the transfer of electric charges. The relation between electrical conductance and the degree of ionization is discussed on page 387.

Arrhenius pointed out further that the multiples of the normal freezing-point depression at infinite dilution, such as are shown in Fig. 10-4, are identical with the number of ions into which a molecule of solute can dissociate. Thus KCl can dissociate into two ions, K^+ and Cl^-, and at infinite dilution the depression is just twice the normal value. In other words, i is 2. For K_2SO_4, three ions are possible, $2K^+$ and $SO_4^=$; thus i has a value of 3 at infinite dilution. Likewise $MgSO_4$ gives two ions, and $K_3Fe(CN)_6$ gives four ions, $3K^+$ and $Fe(CN)_6^\equiv$. This explanation of Arrhenius has been abundantly verified.

Although it was originally Arrhenius's idea that the change of i with concentration was due to the change of the degree of dissociation of the salt, it became apparent later that there is considerable electrostatic interaction between the ions in solution so that the solutions are not ideal except in the limit of infinitely dilute solutions. The application of the Debye-Hückel theory in accounting for this nonideality will be discussed later (page 483).

Example 10. The freezing point of a 0.01-molal solution of barium chloride is $-0.050°$. What is the approximate vapor pressure of the solution at 25° if the vapor pressure of pure water is 23.756 mm?

$$i = \frac{\Delta T_f}{(\Delta T_f)_0} = \frac{0.050}{(0.01)(1.86)} = 2.7$$

$$\Delta p = i \frac{n_2 p°}{n_1} = 2.7 \frac{0.01}{(1000/18.02)} 23.756 = 0.0115 \text{ mm}$$

$$p = 23.756 - 0.0115 = 23.744 \text{ mm}$$

---

* The term *electrolyte* strictly refers to the solution of an ionized substance, although it is often applied to acids, bases, or salts because, when dissolved, they produce electrolytes.

REFERENCES

Hildebrand and Scott, *Solubility of Non-Electrolytes*, Reinhold Publishing Corp., New York, 1950.

Glasstone, *Textbook of Physical Chemistry*, D. Van Nostrand Co., New York, 1946, Chapter IX.

Weissberger, *Physical Methods of Organic Chemistry*, Interscience Publishers, New York, 1949, Chapters 4 and 5, Vol. I, Part I.

PROBLEMS

1. The vapor pressure of a solution containing 13 grams of a nonvolatile solute in 100 grams of H_2O at 28° is 27.371 mm. Calculate the molecular weight of the solute. The vapor pressure of water at this temperature is 28.065 mm. *Ans.* 92.3.

2. Purified nitrogen gas is slowly bubbled through a solution of 3.000 grams of a nonvolatile organic compound dissolved in 200 grams of benzene and then bubbled through pure benzene. The solution is found to be 2.1540 grams lighter, while the pure benzene suffered a loss in weight of 0.0160 gram. What is the apparent molecular weight of the dissolved substance? *Ans.* 157.

3. The boiling point of chloroform can be measured with a particular apparatus with an accuracy of 0.01 °C. Calculate the number of grams of an impurity of $M = 100$ which would be required to raise the boiling point of 50 grams of chloroform by this amount. *Ans.* 0.0138 gram.

4. A hydrocarbon of the type $H(CH_2)_nH$ is dissolved in ethylene bromide, which freezes at 10.00 °C. A solution which contains 0.81 gram of hydrocarbon per 190 grams of ethylene bromide freezes at 9.47 °C. Calculate the value of n. *Ans.* 7.

5. The protein albumin has a molecular weight of 69,000. Calculate the osmotic pressure of a solution of this protein containing 2 grams per 100 ml at 25° in (a) millimeters of mercury and (b) millimeters of water. The experiment is carried out using a salt solution for solvent and a membrane permeable to salt. *Ans.* (a) 5.38 mm Hg. (b) 73.1 mm H_2O.

6. Calculate ΔF for the mixing of 1 mole of benzene and 1 mole of toluene, to give an ideal solution at 25°. (See problem 20.) *Ans.* −822 cal.

7. Ten grams of benzene, 10 grams of toluene, and 10 grams of naphthalene are added together to give a homogeneous solution. If it is assumed that the solution is ideal, how many grams of toluene will be vaporized by passing through 10 liters of air at 30° if the vapor pressure of toluene at this temperature is 36.7 mm, that of benzene is 118.5 mm, and that of naphthalene is negligible? *Ans.* 0.617 g.

8. Solutions of hydrogen chloride in chlorobenzene obey Henry's law. In dilute solutions,

$$K = \frac{p}{m} = 0.438$$

where p is given in atmospheres and m is molality. What is the partial pressure of HCl in millimeters over a 1 per cent by weight solution of HCl in chlorobenzene? *Ans.* 92.1 mm.

9. A certain number of grams of a given substance in 100 grams of benzene lowers the freezing point by 1.28°. The same weight of solute in 100 grams of water gives a freezing point of −1.395°. If the substance has its normal molecular weight in

benzene and is completely dissociated in water, into how many ions does a molecule of this substance dissociate when placed in water?   *Ans.* 3.

10. The vapor pressure of water at 25° (23.756 mm) is lowered 0.071 mm by the addition of 1.53 grams of a nonvolatile substance to 100 grams of water. Calculate the molecular weight of the solute using Raoult's law. (See the discussion in example 1 concerning the most convenient form of Raoult's law for this calculation.)

11. If 68.4 grams of sugar (molecular weight = 342) is dissolved in 1000 grams of water, what are (*a*) the vapor pressure, and (*b*) the osmotic pressure, at 20°? (*c*) What is the freezing point? (*d*) What is the boiling point? The density of the solution at 20° is 1.024 g cm^{-3}. The vapor pressure of water at 20° is 17.363 mm. The heat of vaporization of water is 539 cal per gram, and the heat of fusion is 79.6 cal per gram.

12. Calculate the molal boiling-point constant for chloroform (M = 119.4) from the fact that its boiling point is 61.2° and its heat of vaporization is 59.0 cal g^{-1}.

13. Calculate the freezing-point depression of water produced by dissolved air in equilibrium with air (79 per cent nitrogen, 21 per cent oxygen) at 1 atm. At 0°, 100 grams of water dissolves 4.49 ml of oxygen and 2.35 ml of nitrogen when the pressure of each gas is 1 atm.

14. An aqueous solution of maltose at 25° has a vapor pressure of 23.476 mm whereas pure water has a vapor pressure of 23.756 mm. What is the osmotic pressure of the solution?

15. When cells of the skeletal muscle of a frog were placed in a series of sodium chloride solutions of different concentrations, it was observed microscopically that the cells remained unchanged in 0.7 per cent NaCl solution but shrank in more concentrated solutions and swelled in more dilute solutions. Calculate the osmotic pressure of the cell protoplasm at 25°.

16. When 1.4511 grams of dichloroacetic acid is dissolved in 56.8699 grams of carbon tetrachloride, the boiling point is increased 0.518°. The boiling point of carbon tetrachloride is 76.75°, and its heat of vaporization is 46.5 cal per gram at the boiling point. What is the apparent molecular weight of the acid? How can the discrepancy be explained?

17. Calculate the change in free energy involved when a mole of water is transferred (by isothermal distillation) at 25° from pure water to a large quantity of a 9.9 per cent glycerol solution which has a vapor pressure of water amounting to 23.300 mm. The vapor pressure of pure water at 25° is 23.756 mm.

18. Calculate the vapor pressure at 25° of an aqueous solution of urea (M = 60.06) containing 5 grams of urea per 1000 grams of water. The vapor pressure of water at this temperature is 23.756 mm, and ideal solution behavior may be assumed.

19. Human plasma freezes at −0.56°. (*a*) What is its osmotic pressure at 37°? (*b*) What is the free-energy change when 1 mole of water is evaporated from this plasma?

20. Show that the free energy of mixing of two liquids which form a perfect solution is

$$\Delta F = n_1 RT \ln N_1 + n_2 RT \ln N_2$$

21. Given a 0.01-molal solution of urea (M = 60.06) in water at 25°, calculate: (*a*) the boiling point of the solution; (*b*) the vapor pressure of the solution if the vapor

pressure of pure water is 23.756 mm; (c) the osmotic pressure (assuming that the density of the solution is practically 1.0 g cm^{-3}).

22. By combining Raoult's law, the Clausius-Clapeyron equation, and Trouton's rule, show that the boiling point T_B of a dilute solution of a nonvolatile solute and the mole fraction of *solvent* N_A are related by the approximate equation:

$$N_A T_B{}^{21/R} = \text{constant}$$

23. The vapor pressure of water at 25° is 23.756 mm. Calculate the vapor pressure of solutions containing (a) 6.01 grams of urea, NH_2CONH_2, (b) 9.4 gram of phenol, C_6H_5OH, and (c) 6.01 grams of urea + 9.4 grams of phenol per 1000 grams of water, assuming no chemical action between the two substances. (d) Calculate (c) assuming that a stable compound is formed containing 1 mole of the urea to 1 mole of phenol.

24. (a) How many grams of methanol, CH_3OH, must be added to a 10-liter tank of water to prevent freezing at −5°? (b) How many grams of calcium chloride, $CaCl_2$, assuming complete dissociation and no interaction? (c) How many grams of glycol, $(CH_2OH)_2$?

25. Ten grams of benzene vaporizes isothermally from a solution containing an equimolecular mixture of benzene and diphenyl and condenses in a large amount of solution of benzene and nitrobenzene in which the mole fraction of benzene is 0.1. Calculate the change in free energy at 25°, assuming that both solutions are ideal.

26. (a) What molal concentration of solutes at 20° is required to raise by osmosis a column of solution having a density of approximately 1.0 g cm^{-3} to a height of 100 ft?* (b) What is the vapor pressure of the solution at 20°? The vapor pressure of pure water at 20° is 17.363 mm.

* The rise of the sap in a tall tree is not to be attributed *entirely* to osmosis.

11

Homogeneous Chemical Equilibria

The Law of Mass Action. The idea of the reversibility of chemical reactions was first stated clearly in 1799 by C. Berthollet, while he was acting as scientific adviser to Napoleon in Egypt. He noted the deposits of sodium carbonate in certain salt lakes and concluded that they were produced by the high concentration of sodium chloride and dissolved calcium carbonate, the reverse of the laboratory experiment in which sodium carbonate reacts with calcium chloride to precipitate calcium carbonate.

In 1862 the influence which the concentrations of alcohol and acetic acid have on the amount of ethyl acetate formed was reported by M. Berthelot and St. Gilles.

These investigations and others led Guldberg and Waage in 1863 to state the *mass law*, according to which *the rate of a chemical reaction is directly proportional to the concentrations * of the reacting materials*. They realized clearly that the important factor in determining reaction rate is not the quantity of reactant but the quantity of reactant *per unit of volume*. The use of concentrations, such as moles per liter, does not give accurate calculations unless the gases or solutes are ideal. Accordingly, for accurate work or for gases at high pressures or for solutions of high concentration, the concentrations are replaced by activities, which are defined later.

This chapter will be concerned with equilibria in homogeneous gas or liquid phases. The following chapter on heterogeneous equilibria will deal with equilibria between different phases.

In general, a reversible reaction may be written

$$A + B = G + H \tag{1}$$

and the concentrations c of each constituent in moles per liter may be written c_A, c_B, c_G, c_H. According to the mass law, the speed with which

---

* Guldberg and Waage used the term "active masses."

A and B react is proportional to the concentrations of A and B. Then,

$$\text{Rate}_{\text{forward reaction}} \propto c_A c_B \quad \text{or} \quad \text{Rate}_{\text{forward reaction}} = k_1 c_A c_B$$

where k_1 is the specific rate constant.

The products of the reaction, G and H, can react in the reverse reaction to give A and B, and the rate of this reaction is proportional to the concentrations of G and H. Then,

$$\text{Rate}_{\text{reverse reaction}} = k_2 c_G c_H$$

The concentration of each of the reacting substances is involved. If the reaction requires more moles of one substance than the other, this fact must be incorporated into the rate expression. Thus, if 2 molecules of A react with 1 molecule of B, the reaction is written

$$2A + B \quad \text{or} \quad A + A + B$$

and

$$\text{Rate} = k_1 c_A c_A c_B = k_1 c_A{}^2 c_B$$

In the more general case, each of the substances in the equation has a coefficient, 1, 2, or 3, etc., and equation 1 may be rewritten

$$aA + bB = gG + hH \tag{2}$$

showing that a moles of A and b moles of B react to give g moles of G and h moles of H. At equilibrium, there is no further apparent change, and

$$\text{Rate}_{\text{forward reaction}} = \text{Rate}_{\text{reverse reaction}}$$

$$k_1 c_A{}^a c_B{}^b = k_2 c_G{}^g c_H{}^h$$

and

$$\frac{c_G{}^g c_H{}^h}{c_A{}^a c_B{}^b} = \frac{k_1}{k_2} = K_c \tag{3}$$

where the concentrations c are the concentrations which exist when the system is at equilibrium, and K_c is the equilibrium constant expressed in concentrations. Concentrations are usually given in moles per liter. A more rigorous derivation for the equilibrium constant is given by means of thermodynamics on page 251. It must be emphasized that equations 3 and 4 are strictly true only for ideal dilute solutions, and ideal gases or gases at low pressures.

Equilibrium Constants. In the study of equilibria in solutions K_c is widely used, but in various equilibria of gases the concentrations are frequently given in terms of the partial pressures p of the gases. Since, at any one temperature, the partial pressure p of an ideal gas is proportional to its concentration c in the gas phase, we may write equation 3 in the following manner:

$$K_p = \frac{p_G{}^g p_H{}^h}{p_A{}^a p_B{}^b} \tag{4}$$

where K_p is the equilibrium constant expressed in partial pressures. Unless otherwise specified, the pressures are given in atmospheres.

The values of K_c for gas reactions can be easily converted into K_p because $c = 1/V = p/RT$, where c is expressed in moles per liter (the reciprocal of the number of liters containing 1 mole), and p is expressed in atmospheres. Substituting these values of c into equation 3, we have

$$K_c = \frac{\left(\dfrac{p_G}{RT}\right)^g \left(\dfrac{p_H}{RT}\right)^h}{\left(\dfrac{p_A}{RT}\right)^a \left(\dfrac{p_B}{RT}\right)^b} = \left(\frac{1}{RT}\right)^{(g+h)-(a+b)} \frac{p_G{}^g p_H{}^h}{p_A{}^a p_B{}^b} = \left(\frac{1}{RT}\right)^{\Delta n} K_p$$

where R is given in liter-atmospheres $\deg^{-1}$ mole^{-1} and Δn = the change in the number of moles of gas during the reaction, that is $(g + h) - (a + b)$. Then

$$K_p = K_c(RT)^{\Delta n} \tag{5}$$

In reactions where there is no change in the number of moles of gas, $\Delta n = 0$ and $K_p = K_c$.

Example 1. For the reaction $N_2 + 3H_2 = 2NH_3$, at 400°:

$$K_c = \frac{c_{NH_3}{}^2}{c_{N_2} c_{H_2}{}^3} = 0.500$$

Calculate K_p.

$$K_p = (RT)^{\Delta n} K_c = [(0.08205)(673.1)]^{-2}(0.500) = 1.64 \times 10^{-4}$$

If the reaction is such that it proceeds far to the right as written, the concentrations of the products at equilibrium are much greater than the concentrations of the reactants and K has a large value. On the other hand, a small value of K indicates that equilibrium is reached when there are only small concentrations of the products. The magnitude of the equilibrium constant then is a quantitative measure of the extent to which the reactants react to give the products.

Certain conventions are observed in the use of equilibrium constants. The chemical equation is always written so that the proper exponents can be ascertained, and the concentrations or pressures of the substances at the right of the equation, called the products, are placed in the numerator.

When the equation for the reaction is reversed, the new equilibrium constant becomes the reciprocal of the other. Thus, rewriting Example 1,

$$2NH_3 = N_2 + 3H_2$$

$$K_c = \frac{c_{N_2}c_{H_2}{}^3}{c_{NH_3}{}^2} = \frac{1}{0.500} = 2.00 \tag{6}$$

If the reaction is written

$$NH_3 = \tfrac{1}{2}N_2 + \tfrac{3}{2}H_2$$

$$K_c = \frac{\sqrt{c_{N_2}}\sqrt{c_{H_2}{}^3}}{c_{NH_3}} = \sqrt{2.00} = 1.41$$

These fractional exponents are usually avoided by multiplying through by an appropriate integer.

Determination of Equilibrium Constants. Many chemical and physical measurements can be used in the determination of equilibrium constants. A considerable amount of ingenuity is often needed, not only in devising methods for analyzing the mixture without disturbing the equilibrium but also in calculating the concentrations of all the substances present from an experimental determination of only one or two.

If there is a change of pressure or of volume during the reaction, the composition at equilibrium can be calculated readily, as shown in the following section. Other physical properties, such as absorption of light, refractive index, or electrical conductance, can be used in special cases to determine the concentration of one or more of the substances at equilibrium. Frequently chemical methods can be used, but it is necessary to perform the analysis rapidly enough so that the equilibrium will not shift upon removal of one of the reactants. In some cases it is possible to "freeze" the equilibrium mixture so that the equilibrium attained will not shift during the analysis. Sudden chilling or the addition of an excess of some chemical reagent or the removal of a catalyst may be used to preserve the equilibrium mixture for analysis.

Often it is convenient to calculate the concentrations of some of the reactants and products from a knowledge of the starting concentrations of the reactants. For example, in the reaction

$$A + B = G + H$$

if 1 mole of A and 1 mole of B are mixed in a volume of 1 liter and allowed to come to equilibrium, and if 0.9 mole per liter of G is found by analysis, it follows that the concentration of H must equal that of G, and the concentration of A and of B at equilibrium must be $1 - 0.9$ or 0.1. The equilibrium constant then is written

$$K_c = \frac{c_G c_H}{c_A c_B} = \frac{(0.9)(0.9)}{(0.1)(0.1)} = 81$$

It is essential to know that equilibrium has been reached before the analysis of the mixture can be safely used for calculating the equilibrium constant. Sometimes the reaction is very slow and the mixture may be far from equilibrium even though it does not appear to change. The following may serve as criteria for the attainment of equilibrium.

1. The same equilibrium constant is obtained when the equilibrium is approached from both sides. In the example given, the same value is obtained for K when A and B are mixed as when G and H are mixed.

2. The same equilibrium constant is obtained when the concentrations of reacting materials are varied over a wide range.

Flow methods are sometimes used for determining equilibrium constants. For example, known mixtures of nitrogen and hydrogen are forced through a heated chamber (containing a catalyst), and the issuing gas is passed quickly through a capillary tube to an absorption bottle where the ammonia is titrated. The partial pressures of all three gases can then be calculated. The gas is passed through at various rates of flow, and the equilibrium constant is calculated when the passage through is so slow that making it still slower does not increase the concentration of ammonia. When equilibrium is established, a longer period of time will not produce any further change in the concentrations.

It is frequently found that the equilibrium constant is not exactly constant but depends, for example, upon the total pressure of gas. This is because equation 4 applies with exactness only to ideal gases. Although equations 3 and 4 are adequate for low concentrations and pressures, further concepts will have to be introduced later to make accurate equilibrium calculations for nonideal systems.

Dissociation of Gases. The determination of the density of a gas provides one of the simplest methods for measuring quantitatively the extent to which the gas is dissociated. When a gas dissociates, more molecules are produced, and at constant temperature and pressure the volume increases. The density or the weight per liter at 1 atm pressure then decreases, and the difference between the density of the undissociated gas and the partially dissociated gas permits a calculation of the degree of dissociation.

If we start with 1 mole of gas and let α represent the fraction dissociated, then $1 - \alpha$ will denote the fraction remaining undissociated.

If 1 mole of gas yields ν moles of gaseous products, where $\nu = 1, 2,$ or $3,$ or $1\frac{1}{2}$, etc., the total number of moles present at any time will be

$$(1 - \alpha) + \nu\alpha \qquad \text{or} \qquad 1 + (\nu - 1)\alpha$$

Since the density of a given weight of gas at constant pressure is *inversely* proportional to the number of moles, the ratio of the density d_1 of the undissociated gas to the density d_2 of the partially dissociated gas is given by the expression

$$\frac{d_1}{d_2} = \frac{1 + (\nu - 1)\alpha}{1} \tag{7}$$

$$\alpha = \frac{(d_1/d_2) - 1}{\nu - 1} = \frac{d_1 - d_2}{d_2(\nu - 1)} \tag{8}$$

It is always advantageous to visualize a formula if possible by checking it with some simple calculation. With reference to equation 8, if there is no dissociation, $\alpha = 0$ and $d_1 = d_2$; if dissociation is complete, $\alpha = 1$ and $d_2(\nu - 1) = d_1 - d_2$ and $d_1 = \nu d_2$. Obviously, both these relations are in agreement with the experimental facts.

Molecular weights may be substituted for the densities of gases, giving

$$\alpha = \frac{M_1 - M_2}{M_2(\nu - 1)} \tag{9}$$

where M_1 is the molecular weight of the undissociated gas and M_2 is the average molecular weight of the gases when the gas is partly dissociated. The use of formula 9 is illustrated in Table I with the reaction

$$N_2O_4 = 2NO_2$$

in which $\nu = 2$.

Table I. Average Molecular Weight of Partially Dissociated Nitrogen Tetroxide (N_2O_4) at 1 Atm Pressure

Temperature, °C	Average Molecular Weight Partially Dissociated Gas, M_2	$\alpha = \dfrac{92.02 - M_2}{M_2}$
15	82.00	0.122
25	77.64	0.185
35	72.45	0.270
45	66.80	0.378
55	61.24	0.502
65	56.51	0.628
75	52.85	0.741

The average molecular weight M_2 of the partially dissociated gas is determined experimentally, and M_1 is taken as the theoretical molecular weight of undissociated nitrogen tetroxide (N_2O_4), that is, 92.02. The degree of dissociation of N_2O_4 may be conveniently determined by an independent method, since the NO_2 formed by dissociation is brown and the undissociated N_2O_4 is colorless. It is easily noticed that the color becomes darker brown as the temperature is raised and the density becomes less. The intensity of the brown color may be measured quantitatively with a photoelectric colorimeter or spectrophotometer.

Example 2. If 1.588 grams of nitrogen tetroxide gives a total pressure of 760 mm when partially dissociated in a 500-ml glass vessel at 25°, what is the degree of dissociation α?

$$pv = (g/M)\, RT$$

$$M_2 = \frac{RT}{p}\frac{g}{v} = \frac{(0.08205 \text{ l atm deg}^{-1} \text{ mole}^{-1})(298.1 \text{ deg})(1.588 \text{ g})}{(1 \text{ atm})(0.500 \text{ l})}$$

$$= 77.68 \text{ g mole}^{-1}$$

$$\alpha = \frac{92.02 - 77.68}{77.68} = 0.1846$$

Equilibrium Constants for Gaseous Reactions. The dissociation of nitrogen tetroxide is represented by the equation

$$N_2O_4 = 2NO_2$$

and

$$K_p = p_{NO_2}^2 / p_{N_2O_4} \tag{10}$$

If α represents the degree of dissociation, $(1 - \alpha)$ is proportional to the number of moles of undissociated N_2O_4; 2α is proportional to the number of moles of NO_2; and $(1 - \alpha) + 2\alpha$ or $1 + \alpha$ is proportional to the total number of moles.

If the total pressure is P, the partial pressures are as follows:

$$p_{N_2O_4} = \frac{1 - \alpha}{1 + \alpha} P \qquad \text{and} \qquad p_{NO_2} = \frac{2\alpha}{1 + \alpha} P$$

Then,

$$K_p = \frac{\left(\dfrac{2\alpha}{1 + \alpha} P\right)^2}{\dfrac{1 - \alpha}{1 + \alpha} P} = \frac{4\alpha^2 P}{1 - \alpha^2} \tag{11}$$

In this reaction there is an increase in volume; each mole of gas that dissociates produces 2 moles of gas. According to the principle of Le

Châtelier, it is possible to predict qualitatively that a decrease of pressure will cause the system to shift toward $2NO_2$, which occupies the larger volume. Equation 11 makes it possible to calculate quantitatively the degree of dissociation of N_2O_4 at any pressure if K_p is known.

Example 3. At 25.0° and 1 atm, nitrogen tetroxide has been found by vapor-density measurements to be 18.46 per cent dissociated. Find K_p.

$$K_p = \frac{4\alpha^2 P}{1 - \alpha^2} = \frac{(4)(0.1846)^2}{1 - (0.1846)^2} \times 1 = 0.141$$

Calculate the degree of dissociation of nitrogen tetroxide at 0.5 atm and 25°.

$$K_p = 0.141 = \frac{4\alpha^2(0.5)}{1 - \alpha^2}$$

and

$$0.141(1 - \alpha^2) = 2\alpha^2$$

$$\alpha = 0.257$$

Another gaseous equilibrium only slightly more complicated than the dissociation of nitrogen tetroxide is the dissociation of phosphorus pentachloride. At temperatures above 200°C the following reaction takes place:

$$PCl_5 = PCl_3 + Cl_2$$

When 1 mole of PCl_5 dissociates, there will be at equilibrium $1 - \alpha$ mole of PCl_5, α mole of PCl_3, and α mole of Cl_2, where α is the degree of dissociation. If these gases are contained at equilibrium in a vessel of v liters, the concentrations in moles per liter are

$$c_{PCl_5} = \frac{1 - \alpha}{v} \qquad c_{PCl_3} = \frac{\alpha}{v} \qquad c_{Cl_2} = \frac{\alpha}{v}$$

The total number of moles is

$$[1 - \alpha] + \alpha + \alpha = 1 + \alpha$$

and the mole fractions are

$$N_{PCl_5} = \frac{1 - \alpha}{1 + \alpha} \qquad N_{PCl_3} = \frac{\alpha}{1 + \alpha} \qquad N_{Cl_2} = \frac{\alpha}{1 + \alpha}$$

If P is the total pressure, the partial pressures are

$$p_{PCl_5} = \frac{1 - \alpha}{1 + \alpha} P \qquad p_{PCl_3} = \frac{\alpha}{1 + \alpha} P \qquad p_{Cl_2} = \frac{\alpha}{1 + \alpha} P$$

The equilibrium constant can be expressed in terms of concentrations in moles per liter (K_c), or in partial pressures (K_p), as follows:

$$K_c = \frac{c_{PCl_3} c_{Cl_2}}{c_{PCl_5}} = \frac{(\alpha/v)(\alpha/v)}{(1-\alpha)/v} = \frac{\alpha^2}{(1-\alpha)v} \tag{12}$$

$$K_p = \frac{p_{PCl_3} p_{Cl_2}}{p_{PCl_5}} = \frac{\left(\dfrac{\alpha}{1+\alpha} P\right)\left(\dfrac{\alpha}{1+\alpha} P\right)}{[(1-\alpha)/(1+\alpha)]P} = \frac{\alpha^2 P}{1-\alpha^2} \tag{13}$$

Exercise I. Show that equations 12 and 13 are in agreement with equation 5.

Several examples will be given to illustrate the calculation and use of equilibrium constants.

Example 4. At 250°, 1 liter of partially dissociated phosphorus pentachloride gas, at 1 atm, weighs 2.695 grams. Calculate the degree of dissociation α from the measured density of the gas, and calculate the equilibrium constant K_p.

$$M_1 = 208.3$$

$$M_2 = \frac{gRT}{pV} = \frac{(2.695 \text{ g})(0.08205 \text{ l atm deg}^{-1} \text{ mole}^{-1})(523 \text{ deg})}{(1 \text{ l})(1 \text{ atm})} = 116.0 \text{ g mole}^{-1}$$

$$\alpha = \frac{M_1 - M_2}{M_2} = \frac{208.3 - 116.0}{116.0} = 0.80$$

According to equation 13,

$$K_p = \frac{0.80^2 \times 1}{1 - 0.80^2} = 1.78$$

This reaction is an interesting one to study in more detail. Qualitatively, it can be seen that increasing the total pressure will decrease the amount of dissociation, because the undissociated gas occupies the smaller volume. If chlorine is added, p_{Cl_2} increases and, since K_p remains constant, p_{PCl_3} must diminish and p_{PCl_5} must increase. The degree of dissociation is decreased also by the addition of p_{PCl_3}. In general the dissociation of any substance is repressed by the addition of its dissociation products. The addition of an inert gas at constant volume has no effect on the dissociation because the partial pressures of the gases involved in the reaction remain constant.

Example 5. What will be the degree of dissociation of phosphorus pentachloride when 0.1 mole at 250° is placed in a 3-liter vessel containing chlorine at 0.5 atm pressure? Let x = the number of moles of PCl_3 formed or additional moles of Cl_2 formed by the dissociation of the PCl_5.

$$K_p = 1.78 = \frac{p_{PCl_3}p_{Cl_2}}{p_{PCl_5}} = \frac{\dfrac{xRT}{v}\left(0.5 + \dfrac{xRT}{v}\right)}{[(0.1 - x)RT]/v} = \frac{x\left[0.5 + \dfrac{(0.08205)(523.1)x}{3}\right]}{0.1 - x}$$

$$x = 0.0574 \text{ mole}$$

The degree of dissociation = $0.0574/0.1 = 0.574$.

Example 6. How many moles of PCl_5 must be added to a liter vessel at 250° in order to obtain a concentration of 0.1 mole of chlorine per liter?

$$x = \text{number of moles of } PCl_5 \text{ added to vessel}$$

$$K_p = 1.78 = \frac{p_{PCl_3}p_{Cl_2}}{p_{PCl_5}} = \frac{\left(0.1\dfrac{RT}{v}\right)\left(0.1\dfrac{RT}{v}\right)}{(x - 0.1)(RT/v)} = \frac{0.1^2}{(x - 0.1)}\left(\frac{RT}{v}\right)$$

$$= \frac{(0.01)(0.08205)(523.1)}{(x - 0.1)}$$

$$x = 0.341 \text{ mole}$$

Example 7. Under what total pressure must an equimolar mixture of chlorine and phosphorus trichloride be placed in order to obtain 1 atm of phosphorus penta-chloride at 250°? If we let $x = p_{PCl_3} = p_{Cl_2}$ at equilibrium,

$$K_p = 1.78 = \frac{p_{PCl_3}p_{Cl_2}}{p_{PCl_5}} = \frac{x^2}{1}$$

$$x = 1.33 \text{ atm}$$

The total pressure at equilibrium is the sum of the partial pressures of each of the gases.

$$p_{PCl_3} + p_{Cl_2} + p_{PCl_5} = 1.33 + 1.33 + 1 = 3.66 \text{ atm}$$

Example 8. Under what pressure must an equimolar mixture of chlorine and phosphorus trichloride be placed at 250° in order to obtain an 80 per cent conversion of the phosphorus trichloride into phosphorus pentachloride?

$$K_p = 1.78 = \frac{\alpha^2}{1 - \alpha^2}P = \frac{(0.20)(0.20)}{1 - 0.20^2}P$$

$$P = 42.7 \text{ atm}$$

Another classical example of an equilibrium in gases is the dissociation of hydrogen iodide gas at temperatures above 400°.

Very careful measurements are available * for the equilibrium

$$2HI = H_2 + I_2$$

* Taylor and Crist, *J. Am. Chem. Soc.*, *63*, 1381 (1941).

Quartz vessels of known volume were filled with hydrogen iodide at a measured pressure and heated in an electric thermostat at 425.1° for several hours until equilibrium was established. The vessels were then chilled quickly and analyzed for iodine by titration with sodium thio-sulfate. The concentration of hydrogen at equilibrium is equal to that of the iodine. The concentration of hydrogen iodide at equilibrium was obtained by subtracting twice the iodine concentration from the initial hydrogen iodide concentration. The equilibrium concentrations in moles per liter are shown in Table II. The first three sets of data were

Table II. Equilibrium between Hydrogen, Iodine, and Hydrogen Iodide at 698.2°K

$c_{I_2} \times 10^3$, mole/l	$c_{H_2} \times 10^3$, mole/l	$c_{HI} \times 10^3$, mole/l	$K = \dfrac{c_{H_2} c_{I_2}}{c_{HI}^2}$
0.4789	0.4789	3.531	1.840×10^{-2}
1.1409	1.1409	8.410	1.840
0.4953	0.4953	3.655	1.832
1.7069	2.9070	16.482	1.827
1.2500	3.5600	15.588	1.831
0.7378	4.5647	13.544	1.835
2.3360	2.2523	16.850	1.853
3.1292	1.8313	17.671	1.835

obtained by starting with hydrogen iodide. The last five were obtained by starting from the other side of the equilibrium, weighing the initial quantity of iodine, measuring the pressure of hydrogen, and titrating the iodine after equilibrium was reached. The close check between the two sets of data shows that equilibrium was reached in every case.

When many routine calculations are needed, it is advantageous to express the concentrations with letters and obtain a general formula. Thus, if a moles of hydrogen is mixed with b moles of iodine, and $2x$ moles of hydrogen iodide is formed, when equilibrium is established, $a - x$ is the number of moles of hydrogen, and $b - x$ is the number of moles of iodine present.

Exercise II. Show that for the hydrogen iodide dissociation equilibrium

$$K_c = \frac{(a - x)(b - x)}{4x^2} \qquad \text{and that} \qquad x = \frac{a + b - \sqrt{(a - b)^2 + 16abK_c}}{2(1 - 4K_c)}$$

It is of interest to note that a change in pressure does not alter the equilibrium in this gaseous reaction. Making use of the partial pressures of the components of the gaseous system, instead of the concentrations, we have

$$\frac{p_{H_2}p_{I_2}}{p_{HI}^2} = K_p$$

Now, if the total pressure on the system is increased to n times its original value, all the partial pressures are increased in the same proportion, and

$$\frac{(np_{H_2})(np_{I_2})}{n^2 p_{HI}^2} = K_p$$

which is equivalent to the original expression, since n cancels out. The equilibrium is thus seen to be independent of the pressure. This independence applies only to those systems in which no change in volume occurs during the reaction. It will be remembered also that in this case $K_p = K_c$.

Illustrations of the calculations of more complicated gaseous equilibria will now be given.

Example 9. The reaction $CO_2 + H_2 = CO + H_2O$ was investigated by passing mixtures of CO_2 and H_2 over a catalyst at 900° at 1 atm pressure. The resulting gas was chilled quickly to room temperature by passage through a capillary and was analyzed. In one experiment the partial pressures were as follows: $CO_2 = 0.2142$; $H_2 = 0.2549$; $CO = 0.2654$; $H_2O = 0.2654$ atm. Calculate the number of moles of hydrogen present in another equilibrium mixture containing 22.72 moles of CO, 22.72 moles of H_2O, and 48.50 moles of CO_2.

$$K_p = \frac{p_{CO}p_{H_2O}}{p_{CO_2}p_{H_2}} = \frac{(0.2654)(0.2654)}{(0.2142)(0.2549)} = 1.290$$

$$K_p = 1.290 = \frac{(22.72RT/v)(22.72RT/v)}{(48.50RT/v)(xRT/v)}$$

$$x = \frac{22.72^2}{48.50 \times 1.290} = 8.25 \text{ moles } H_2$$

Example 10. Ammonia is formed from a mixture of 3 moles of hydrogen and 1 mole of nitrogen (page 238). At lower temperatures the yield is higher, but the time required for equilibrium to be reached would be too great to be practical, except for the addition of a catalyst. The pressure is kept as high and the temperature as low as practical.

Under equilibrium conditions at 400° and 10 atm pressure, 3.85 mole per cent of ammonia is obtained.

Calculate K_p for the reaction $N_2 + 3H_2 = 2NH_3$. The ratio of 3 volumes of hydrogen to 1 volume of nitrogen is maintained, regardless of the amount of ammonia formed. Of the 96.15 per cent by volume which is not ammonia, one-fourth is nitrogen and three-fourths is hydrogen.

$$K_p = \frac{p_{NH_3}^2}{p_{N_2}p_{H_2}^3} = \frac{(0.0385 \times 10)^2}{[(\frac{1}{4})(0.9615)(10)][(\frac{3}{4})(0.9615)(10)]^3} = 0.000164$$

Calculate the total pressure P necessary to give a mixture containing 5 per cent ammonia at this temperature.

$$p_{NH_3} = 0.05P \qquad p_{N_2} = \tfrac{1}{4} \times 0.95P \qquad p_{H_2} = \tfrac{3}{4} \times 0.95P$$

$$K_p = 0.000164 = \frac{(0.05P)^2}{(0.2375P)(0.7125P)^3} = \frac{0.0025P^2}{0.0859P^4}$$

$$P^2 = \frac{0.0025}{0.000164 \times 0.0859} = 177.5 \qquad P = 13.3 \text{ atm}$$

Calculate the percentage of ammonia when the mixture is subjected to a pressure of 50 atm.

$$p_{H_2} = 3p_{N_2} \qquad p_{N_2} + p_{H_2} + p_{NH_3} = 50 \text{ atm} \qquad p_{NH_3} = 50 - 4p_{N_2}$$

$$K_p = 0.000164 = \frac{p_{NH_3}^2}{p_{N_2}p_{H_2}^3} = \frac{(50 - 4p_{N_2})^2}{(p_{N_2})(3p_{N_2})^3} = \frac{(50 - 4p_{N_2})^2}{27p_{N_2}^4}$$

$$\frac{50 - 4p_{N_2}}{p_{N_2}^2} = \sqrt{0.000164 \times 27} = 6.65 \times 10^{-2}$$

$$p_{N_2} = 10.62 \qquad p_{H_2} = (3)(10.62) = 31.86$$

$$p_{NH_3} = 50 - (10.62 + 31.86) = 7.52$$

$$\text{Per cent ammonia} = (7.52/50.0)(100) = 15.0$$

Equilibria in Solutions. The following reaction is a classical example of an equilibrium involving liquids:

$$CH_3COOH + C_2H_5OH = CH_3COOC_2H_5 + H_2O$$

The volume of the solution is v liters, and the initial numbers of moles of the four compounds are designated as a, b, c, and d, respectively. The additional number of moles of ester and water formed by the reaction of acetic acid and alcohol is denoted by x. Then, if the slight change in volume of the liquids due to the chemical reaction is neglected, the concentration of each of the compounds at equilibrium is

$$[CH_3CO_2H] * = (a - x)/v \qquad [C_2H_5OH] = (b - x)/v$$

$$[CH_3CO_2C_2H_5] = (c + x)/v \qquad [H_2O] = (d + x)/v$$

Then

$$K_c = \frac{[CH_3COOC_2H_5][H_2O]}{[CH_3COOH][C_2H_5OH]} = \frac{(c + x)(d + x)}{(a - x)(b - x)} \qquad (14)$$

The use of this equation is illustrated in the following example.

* Square brackets are used to indicate the concentrations of solutes in solution. In gases, the concentrations are given in moles per liter c or partial pressures p.

Example 11. One mole of acetic acid is mixed with 1 mole of ethanol at 25°, and after equilibrium is reached a titration with standard alkali solution shows that 0.667 mole of acetic acid has reacted. Calculate K_c.

$$K_c = \frac{[CH_3COOC_2H_5][H_2O]}{[CH_3COOH][C_2H_5OH]} = \frac{(0.667/v)(0.667/v)}{[(1.000 - 0.667)/v][(1.000 - 0.667)/v]} = 4.00$$

When 0.50 mole of ethanol is added to 1.000 mole of acetic acid at 25°, how much ester will be formed at equilibrium?

$$K_c = 4.00 = \frac{x^2}{(1.000 - x)(0.500 - x)} \qquad x = 0.422 \quad \text{or} \quad 1.577$$

In a quadratic equation two solutions are always possible, but usually one may be shown to be wrong and incompatible with the physical-chemical facts. In the present example it is impossible to produce more moles of ester than the original number of moles of ethanol, and so the value 1.577 is ruled out. Actually 0.422 mole of ester and 0.422 mole of water are formed, and (0.500 − 0.422) or 0.078 mole of ethanol and (1.000 − 0.422) or 0.578 mole of acetic acid remain unreacted. An experimental value of 0.414 mole of ester was obtained. Additional calculations are as follows:

Moles ethanol added to 1 mole of acetic acid	0.080	0.280	2.240	8.000
Moles of ethyl acetate calculated	0.078	0.232	0.864	0.945
Moles of ethyl acetate found experimentally	0.078	0.226	0.876	0.966

It may be noted from this example that a large excess of one of the reactants causes the other reactant to undergo nearly complete reaction.

In the equilibrium just studied, the volume terms cancel out, and so the equilibrium constant is not affected by changing the volume. When there is a change in the number of molecules, however, it is necessary to consider the volume of the solution in calculating the equilibrium constant.

Example 12. Amylene C_5H_{10} and acetic acid react to give the ester according to the reaction

$$C_5H_{10} + CH_3COOH = CH_3COOC_5H_{11}$$

What is the value of K_c if 0.00645 mole of amylene and 0.001 mole of acetic acid mixed in 845 ml of a certain inert solvent react to give 0.000784 mole of ester?

$$K_c = \frac{(7.84 \times 10^{-4})/0.845}{\left[\dfrac{(64.5 \times 10^{-4} - 7.84 \times 10^{-4})}{0.845}\right]\left[\dfrac{10 \times 10^{-4} - 7.84 \times 10^{-4}}{0.845}\right]} = 540$$

The equilibrium constants for reactions in solution may be markedly affected by the solvent even if the solvent is not a direct participant in the reaction.

Free-Energy Changes in Chemical Reactions. Thermodynamics is of great help in predicting equilibria in chemical reactions. It is the free energy which is the criterion as to whether or not a chemical reaction will occur at a constant temperature and pressure. There is an important relation between the change in free energy and the equilibrium constant which forms the basis not only of many chemical calculations but also of electrochemical relations which are described in a later chapter.

The following expression is representative of any chemical reaction:

$$aA + bB = gG + hH$$

At constant temperature, the change in free energy produced by a change in pressure was given on page 143.

$$\left(\frac{\partial F}{\partial p}\right)_T = V$$

For ideal gases $pV = RT$ and

$$(\partial F/\partial p)_T = V = RT/p \tag{15}$$

Let F_A = the free energy of 1 mole of substance A at any specified partial pressure p', and $F_A{}^\circ$ = the free energy of A in the reference or standard state, 1 atm pressure in this case. Then integrating equation 15 at constant temperature

$$\int_{F^\circ_A}^{F_A} dF = RT \int_1^{p'} d \ln p \qquad \text{and} \qquad F_A - F_A{}^\circ = RT \ln p' \tag{16}$$

If the reactants in their standard states (at 1 atm) are converted into the products in their standard states, the change in free energy during the reaction is

$$\Delta F^\circ = gF_G{}^\circ + hF_H{}^\circ - aF_A{}^\circ - bF_B{}^\circ$$

and if the reactants and products are at other specified pressures p'

$$\Delta F = gF_G + hF_H - aF_A - bF_B$$

Subtracting,

$$\Delta F - \Delta F^\circ = g(F_G - F_G{}^\circ) + h(F_H - F_H{}^\circ)$$
$$- a(F_A - F_A{}^\circ) - b(F_B - F_B{}^\circ)$$

Substituting relations of the type of equation 16 into this equation

$$\Delta F - \Delta F^\circ = RT \ln \frac{p'_G{}^g p'_H{}^h}{p'_A{}^a p'_B{}^b} \tag{17}$$

The primed pressures p' emphasize the fact that they indicate any specified pressure. In the special case where all the reactants and products are in their standard states, all the p''s become 1, ln $p'_G{}^g p'_H{}^h / p'_A{}^a p'_B{}^b$ becomes zero, and ΔF is equal to $\Delta F°$ according to equation 17. In the special case of an equilibrium condition the pressures are designated as p, instead of p', and, since there is no free-energy change when reactants at their equilibrium pressures go to products at their equilibrium pressures, it follows that $\Delta F = 0$. Then equation 17 becomes

$$\Delta F° = -RT \ln \frac{p_G{}^g p_H{}^h}{p_A{}^a p_B{}^b}$$

$$\Delta F° = -RT \ln K_p \tag{18}$$

Thus, since $\Delta F°$ is a constant, we have proved that at constant temperature K_p is a constant as already indicated on page 237.

Equation 18 states that when reactants in their standard states are converted to the products in their standard states there is a change in free energy equal to $-RT$ times the natural logarithm of the equilibrium constant. This relation has been derived for ideal gases for which the standard states are 1 atm of pressure, but similar expressions can be derived also for other standard states. For example, in the equation

$$\Delta F° = -RT \ln K_c \tag{19}$$

the equilibrium constant K_c expressed in moles per liter will have a different value and $\Delta F°$ will have a correspondingly different value. It refers not to reactants at 1 atm pressure going to products at 1 atm pressure, but to reactants at 1 mole per liter going to products at 1 mole per liter. More frequently for solutions K_c refers to the number of moles per 1000 grams, that is, to molalities. The units used are specified, and they determine the standard states and the numerical values of $\Delta F°$.

Example 13. What is $\Delta F°$ at 25° for the reaction

$$N_2O_4(g) = 2NO_2(g)$$

$$K_p = p_{NO_2}{}^2 / p_{N_2O_4} = 0.141$$

$$\Delta F° = -RT \ln K_p = -(1.987)(298.1)(2.303) \log 0.141 = +1161 \text{ cal}$$

According to this calculation, 1 mole of N_2O_4 at 1 atm can be converted into 2 moles of NO_2 at 1 atm and 25° only with some external aid which increases the free energy of the system by 1161 cal.

Example 14. What is $\Delta F°$ at 25° for the reaction

$$2NO_2(g) = N_2O_4(g)$$

$$K_p = p_{N_2O_4}/p_{NO_2}^2 = 1/0.141 = 7.09$$

$$\Delta F° = -RT \ln K_p = -(1.987)(298.1)(2.303) \log 7.09 = -1161 \text{ cal}$$

It is clear that, if a reaction is reversed, the equilibrium constant becomes the reciprocal of that for the forward reaction, and the free-energy change has the same magnitude but the opposite sign. In this case $\Delta F°$ has a negative sign, and so the reaction is said to be a spontaneous reaction.

Example 15. The equilibrium constant for the association of benzoic acid to a dimer in dilute benzene solutions at 43.9° is 2.7×10^2 in terms of molar concentrations. Calculate $\Delta F°$, and state its meaning.

$$2C_6H_5COOH = (C_6H_5COOH)_2$$

$$K_c = \frac{[(C_6H_5COOH)_2]}{[C_6H_5COOH]^2} = 2.7 \times 10^2$$

$$\Delta F° = -RT \ln K_c = -(1.987)(317.0)(2.303) \log K_c$$

$$= -3530 \text{ cal}$$

Hence, there is a free-energy decrease of 3530 cal when 2 moles of benzoic acid monomer, C_6H_5COOH, at a concentration of 1 mole per liter of solution, is converted to 1 mole of benzoic acid dimer at a concentration of 1 mole per liter, in benzene at 43.9°. The reaction is spontaneous as written.

Free Energy of Formation. The free-energy changes for many reactions have been calculated from experimental measurements of equilibrium constants. The free-energy changes for other reactions which cannot be studied directly may be calculated from heats of formation and absolute entropies as discussed on page 261. By adding and subtracting the reactions for which ΔF is known, the free-energy changes may be obtained for many other reactions, but the most convenient way to tabulate the accumulated data on free-energy changes is by means of the *free energy of formation* $\Delta F_f°$, which is defined similarly to the heat of formation (page 117). The free energy of formation is the free-energy change for the reaction in which a substance in its standard state (at 25°) is formed from its elements in their standard states (at 25°). The superscript indicates that the standard states, gases at 1 atm and 25° and solids in their designated crystalline form at 25°, are referred to. This amounts to taking the free energies of the elements in their standard states as zero.

Table III gives some free energies of formation taken from the larger table of the Bureau of Standards. The free-energy change for any

Table III.[1]   Free Energy of Formation at 25°

$\Delta F_f°$ in kcal mole^{-1}

Elements and Inorganic Compounds

$O_3(g)$	39.06	C(s, diamond)	0.6850
$H_2O(g)$	-54.6357	$CO(g)$	-32.8079
$H_2O(l)$	-56.6902	$CO_2(g)$	-94.2598
$HCl(g)$	-22.769	$PbO_2(s)$	-52.34
$Br_2(g)$	0.751	$PbSO_4(s)$	-193.89
$HBr(g)$	-12.72	$Hg(g)$	7.59
$HI(g)$	0.31	$AgCl(s)$	-26.224
S(monoclinic)	0.023	$Fe_2O_3(s)$	-177.1
$SO_2(g)$	-71.79	$Fe_3O_4(s)$	-242.4
$SO_3(g)$	-88.52	$Al_2O_3(s)$	-376.77
$H_2S(g)$	-7.892	$UF_6(g)$	-485
$NO(g)$	20.719	$UF_6(s)$	-486
$NO_2(g)$	12.390	$CaO(s)$	-144.4
$NH_3(g)$	-3.976	$CaCO_3(s)$	-269.78
$HNO_3(l)$	-19.100	$NaF(s)$	-129.3
$P(g)$	66.77	$NaCl(s)$	-91.785
$PCl_3(g)$	-68.42	$KF(s)$	-127.42
$PCl_5(g)$	-77.59	$KCl(s)$	-97.592

Organic Compounds

Methane, $CH_4(g)$	-12.140	Propylene, $C_3H_6(g)$	14.990
Ethane, $C_2H_6(g)$	-7.860	1-Butene, $C_4H_8(g)$	17.217
Propane, $C_3H_8(g)$	-5.614	Acetylene, $C_2H_2(g)$	50.000
n-Butane, $C_4H_{10}(g)$	-3.754	Formaldehyde, $CH_2O(g)$	-26.3
iso-Butane, $C_4H_{10}(g)$	-4.296	Acetaldehyde, $C_2H_4O(g)$	-31.96
n-Pentane, $C_5H_{12}(g)$	-1.96	Methanol, $CH_3OH(l)$	-39.73
n-Hexane, $C_6H_{14}(g)$	0.05	Ethanol, $C_2H_6O(l)$	-41.77
n-Heptane, $C_7H_{16}(g)$	2.09	Formic acid, $CH_2O_2(l)$	-82.7
n-Octane, $C_8H_{18}(g)$	4.14	Acetic acid, $C_2H_4O_2(l)$	-93.8
Benzene, $C_6H_6(g)$	30.989	Oxalic acid, $C_2H_2O_4(s)$	-166.8
Benzene, $C_6H_6(l)$	29.756	Carbon tetrachloride, $CCl_4(l)$	-16.4
Ethylene, $C_2H_4(g)$	16.282	Glycine, $C_2H_5O_2N(s)$	-88.61

[1] These data have been obtained from Rossini, Wagman, Evans, Levine, and Jaffe, "Selected Values of Chemical Thermodynamic Properties," *Circular of the National Bureau of Standards* 500, U. S. Government Printing Office, Washington, D. C., 1952, and Rossini, Pitzer, Taylor, Ebert, Kilpatrick, Beckett, Williams, and Werner, "Selected Values of Properties of Hydrocarbons," *Circular of the National Bureau of Standards* C461, U. S. Government Printing Office, Washington, D. C., 1947.

reaction involving these substances may be calculated by use of

$$\Delta F° = \Sigma \Delta F°_{f,\text{products}} - \Sigma \Delta F°_{f,\text{reactants}}$$

The equilibrium constant for the reaction may then be calculated by use of equation 18 or 19.

Although it would be possible, it is unnecessary, to construct tables of free energies of formation at other temperatures, and the way in which free-energy changes for reactions at other temperatures may be calculated will be discussed in a later section.

The use of Table III in calculating free-energy changes may be illustrated with the following examples.

Example 16.   Calculate K_p at 25° for

$$CO(g) + H_2O(g) = CO_2(g) + H_2(g)$$

$$\Delta F^\circ = (-94.2598 + 0) - (-32.8079 - 54.6357)$$

$$= -6.8162 \text{ kcal}$$

Thus, the reaction is spontaneous at 25°.

$$\Delta F^\circ = -6816.2 = -(1.987)(298.1)(2.303) \log K_p$$

$$K_p = \frac{p_{H_2} p_{CO_2}}{p_{CO} p_{H_2O}} = 1.02 \times 10^5$$

Example 17.   Calculate the equilibrium constant for the isomerization of *n*-butane to *iso*-butane at 25°.

$$n\text{-Butane}(g) = iso\text{-Butane}(g)$$

$$\Delta F^\circ = -4296 - (-3754) = -542 \text{ cal.}$$

Using $\Delta F^\circ = -RT \ln K_p$,

$$K_p = p_{iso\text{-butane}}/p_{n\text{-butane}} = 2.50$$

Calculations of ΔF.   The last two sections and equation 18 have referred to the special case where the reactants and products are in their standard states.   Equation 17 refers to the general case in which they are not in their standard states.   The quantity $p'_G{}^g p'_H{}^h / p'_A{}^a p'_B{}^b$, which involves pressures which are not equilibrium pressures, but any specified pressures, is easily confused with the equilibrium constant; it is called the pressure quotient and given the symbol Q_p.   Thus, equation 17 becomes

$$\Delta F = \Delta F^\circ + RT \ln Q_p = -RT \ln K_p + RT \ln Q_p \qquad (20)$$

A similar expression for K_c and Q_c refers to moles per liter instead of atmospheres.   This equation is very important for calculating the extent to which chemical substances will react.

If ΔF° has a positive value the reactants in their standard states will not react spontaneously to give products in their standard states. However, by increasing the pressures of the reactants, it may often be possible to make the reaction proceed even if ΔF° has a positive value —as long as ΔF has a negative value.

Example 18.   In the hypothetical reaction $A = B$ at 27°, equilibrium is established when the pressure of the product B is one-tenth that of the reactant A.   Calculate ΔF°, that is, the free-energy change when A at 1 atm is converted to B at 1 atm.

$$K_p = \frac{p_B}{p_A} = \frac{0.1}{1} \qquad \Delta F^\circ = -RT \ln K_p = -(1.987)(300.1)(2.303) \log 0.1$$

$$= -(1.987)(300.1)(2.303)(-1) = +1373 \text{ cal}$$

It is clear from the positive value of ΔF° that A at 1 atm will not react spontaneously to give B at 1 atm. However, it is still possible to make the reaction useful for the production of B. When the pressure of A is 1 atm, B can still be removed in some practical way even though its concentration at equilibrium is only 0.1 atm. Or the product B can be produced at 1 atm if the reactant A is increased in pressure to 10 atm. In neither of these cases are both reactants and products in their standard states. Equation 20 rather than equation 18 is applicable.

Example 19. Referring to Example 18, calculate ΔF at 27° for the production of 1 mole of B at a pressure of 1 atm from A at a pressure of 20 atm.

$$A(p = 20) = B(p = 1)$$

$$\Delta F = -RT \ln K_p + RT \ln Q_p = \Delta F^\circ + (1.987)(300.1)(2.303) \log \tfrac{1}{20}$$

$$= 1373 + (1.987)(300.1)(2.303)(-1.301)$$

$$= 1373 - 1786 = -413 \text{ cal}$$

The negative sign of ΔF shows that the reaction will go spontaneously when A is introduced at a pressure of 20 atm and B is withdrawn at a pressure of 1 atm, in spite of the unfavorable equilibrium constant and the positive value of ΔF°.

Influence of Temperature on Chemical Equilibrium.   The last three sections have referred to ΔF and ΔF° at a single temperature. Tables of ΔF_f° are usually available at 25°. Very frequently, however, we need to know ΔF and ΔF° at other temperatures. According to equation 18 for ideal gas systems,

$$-\Delta F^\circ = RT \ln K_p$$

Differentiating with respect to temperature

$$\frac{-d(\Delta F^\circ)}{dT} = R \ln K_p + RT \frac{d \ln K_p}{dT} \qquad (21)$$

When the reactants and products are in their standard states the Gibbs-Helmholtz equation * (page 144) is

$$\Delta F^\circ - \Delta H^\circ = T \, d(\Delta F^\circ)/dT \qquad (22)$$

* Ordinary differentiation replaces partial differentiation holding p constant, because ΔF° applies to conditions of constant pressure.

Substituting in equation 22 the value of $d(\Delta F^\circ)/dT$ obtained in equation 21,

$$\Delta H^\circ - \Delta F^\circ = RT \ln K_p + RT^2 d \ln K_p/dT \qquad (23)$$

Since, by equation 18, $-\Delta F^\circ = RT \ln K_p$, equation 23 becomes

$$d \ln K_p/dT = \Delta H^\circ/RT^2 \qquad (24)$$

This is a very important equation, which is used for calculating heats of reaction from chemical equilibria and for calculating equilibrium constants at different temperatures. The Clausius-Clapeyron equation, discussed on page 164, is a special case of this general equation. In fact, the equilibrium constant K_p can be extended to include any type of equilibrium such as reactions of gases or solutes, vaporization of liquids, and sublimation or solubility of solids.

Exercise III. Show that for gaseous equilibria where $K_p = K_c(RT)^{\Delta n}$

$$d \ln K_c/dT = \Delta E^\circ/RT^2 \qquad (25)$$

Exercise IV. Show that for solutions where there is no work done against the atmosphere

$$d \ln K_c/dT = \Delta E^\circ/RT^2 = \Delta H^\circ/RT^2 \qquad (26)$$

If the temperature range is small, or if the heat capacities of reactants and products are nearly the same, ΔH° can be assumed to be constant, and integration of equation 24 gives

$$\ln K_p = -\Delta H^\circ/RT + C \qquad (27)$$

Data are given in Table IV for the equilibrium constant at different

Table IV.   Equilibrium Constants for the Reaction $N_2 + O_2 = 2NO$ and Equilibrium Pressures of Nitric Oxide

Partial Pressures of NO in Atmospheres

Temperature, °K	$K_p \times 10^4$	$p_{N_2} = 0.8$ $p_{O_2} = 0.2$	$p_{N_2} = 0.8$ $p_{O_2} = 0.1$	$p_{N_2} = 0.8$ $p_{O_2} = 0.05$
1800	1.21	0.44×10^{-2}	0.31×10^{-2}	0.22×10^{-2}
1900	2.31	0.61	0.43	0.31
2000	4.08	0.81	0.57	0.40
2100	6.86	1.05	0.74	0.53
2200	11.00	1.33	0.94	0.67
2300	16.90	1.64	1.16	0.82
2400	25.10	2.00	1.42	1.00
2500	36.00	2.40	1.70	1.20
2600	50.30	2.84	2.01	1.42
2700	68.70	3.32	2.34	1.66

temperatures for the reaction $N_2 + O_2 = 2NO$. Given also are the partial pressures of nitric oxide in equilibrium with air and with mixtures of nitrogen and varying amounts of oxygen. The equilibrium pressures of nitric oxide are proportional to the square roots of the pressures of oxygen when the pressure of nitrogen is kept constant.

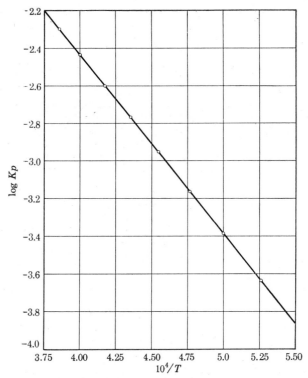

FIG. 11-1. Log K_p plotted against reciprocal absolute temperature for the reaction $N_2 + O_2 = 2NO$. The heat of reaction is calculated from the slope of the straight line.

In *Fig. 11-1* the values of log K_p are plotted against $1/T$, and it is evident that a straight line is produced. Such a result is to be expected from equation 27, and, in fact, the heat of reaction ΔH° can be calculated from the slope of the line, as follows:

$$\Delta H^\circ = -\text{slope} \times 2.303R$$

$$= -(-9510)(2.303)(1.987) = 43{,}520 \text{ cal} \qquad (28)$$

The value of the integration constant C in equation 27 can be determined from experimental values of K_p at definite temperatures, and the practical working equation for this reaction becomes

$$\log K_p = \frac{-43,520}{(2.303)(1.987)T} + 5.365$$

Equation 24 can be solved also by integrating between limits K_{p_2} at T_2 and K_{p_1} at the lower temperature T_1, as was done on page 165.

$$\log \frac{K_{p_2}}{K_{p_1}} = \frac{\Delta H°(T_2 - T_1)}{2.303RT_1T_2} \tag{29}$$

Example 20. Calculate the enthalpy change for the reaction $N_2 + O_2 = 2NO$ from the data at 2000°K and 2500°K given in Table IV.

$$\log \frac{K_{p_2}}{K_{p_1}} = \log \frac{0.00360}{0.000408} = \frac{\Delta H°(2500 - 2000)}{(2.303)(1.987)(2500)(2000)}$$

and

$$\Delta H° = 43,300 \text{ cal}$$

Example 21. The equilibrium constant K_p for the reaction

$$CO + H_2O = CO_2 + H_2$$

is 10.0 at 690°K. The heat of the reaction $\Delta H°$ is $-10,200$ cal. Calculate the partial pressure of each of the gases in an equilibrium mixture prepared by mixing 0.400 mole of CO and 0.200 mole of H_2O in a volume of 5 liters at 500°K.

$$\log \frac{K_{690°K}}{K_{500°K}} = \frac{-10,200(690 - 500)}{(2.303)(1.987)(500)(690)} = -1.228$$

$$\log K_{500°K} = \log 10.0 + 1.228 = 2.228$$

$$K_{500°K} = 169$$

Let x = number of moles of CO_2 and H_2 produced.

$$K_p = 169 = \frac{\left(x\dfrac{RT}{v}\right)\left(x\dfrac{RT}{v}\right)}{\left[(0.4 - x)\dfrac{RT}{v}\right]\left[(0.2 - x)\dfrac{RT}{v}\right]} = \frac{x^2}{(0.4 - x)(0.2 - x)}$$

$$x = 0.199$$

$$p_{CO_2} = p_{H_2} = \frac{nRT}{v} = \frac{(0.199)(0.08205)(500.0)}{5} = 1.63 \text{ atm}$$

$$p_{CO} = \frac{(0.4 - 0.199)(0.08205)(500.0)}{5} = 1.65 \text{ atm}$$

$$p_{H_2O} = \frac{(0.2 - 0.199)(0.08205)(500.0)}{5} = 0.01 \text{ atm}$$

If the heat of reaction at constant pressure is zero, the right-hand side of equation 24 becomes equal to zero. In other words, in such a reaction a change in temperature does not cause a displacement of the equilibrium.

The reaction of acetic acid and ethanol is an example of a reaction in which very little heat is evolved. Accordingly, the equilibrium constant should have practically the same value at all temperatures. Experimental measurements show that this is indeed so.

Influence of Temperature on Free-Energy Changes. We have just seen how to calculate equilibrium constants at a specified temperature if we know the equilibrium constants at two different temperatures or if we know the equilibrium constant at one temperature and the heat of reaction. Another approach to the same problem is through the calculation of the free-energy change for the reaction at a specified temperature. Knowing $\Delta F°$, we can then calculate K from the important relation $\Delta F° = -RT \ln K$.

In the present section we will show how to calculate the change with temperature of $\Delta F°$ from a knowledge of the heat of reaction and the heat capacities of products and reactants. Often the free energies of formation $\Delta F_f°$ and the heats of formation $\Delta H_f°$ are known at 25°, and it is desired to calculate $\Delta F°$ at high temperatures. This can be done if the heat capacities are known over a range of temperatures. In order to obtain a formula for calculating free-energy changes at different temperatures, we first differentiate $\Delta F/T$ with respect to temperature at constant pressure, thus:

$$\frac{\partial\left(\dfrac{\Delta F}{T}\right)}{\partial T} = \frac{T\dfrac{\partial(\Delta F)}{\partial T} - \Delta F \dfrac{\partial T}{\partial T}}{T^2} \tag{30}$$

But, according to the Gibbs-Helmholtz equation derived on page 144, at constant pressure,

$$\frac{\partial(\Delta F)}{\partial T} = \frac{\Delta F}{T} - \frac{\Delta H}{T} \tag{31}$$

Substituting into equation 30, we have

$$\frac{\partial\left(\dfrac{\Delta F}{T}\right)}{\partial T} = \frac{T\left(\dfrac{\Delta F}{T} - \dfrac{\Delta H}{T}\right) - \Delta F}{T^2} = -\frac{\Delta H}{T^2} \tag{32}$$

Exercise V. Remembering (page 125) that $\Delta H_T = \Delta H_0 + \displaystyle\int_0^T \Delta C_p\, dT$, where ΔH_0 is an integration constant (the hypothetical heat of reaction at absolute zero), and remembering that $C_p = a + bT + cT^2 + \cdots$ and that $\Delta C_p = \Delta a + (\Delta b)T + (\Delta c)T^2 + \cdots$, show that

$$\Delta H = \Delta H_0 + (\Delta a)T + \tfrac{1}{2}(\Delta b)T^2 + \tfrac{1}{3}(\Delta c)T^3 + \cdots \tag{33}$$

Substituting this value of ΔH into equation 32 and integrating, show that

$$\Delta F = \Delta H_0 - (\Delta a)T \ln T - \tfrac{1}{2}(\Delta b)T^2 - \tfrac{1}{6}(\Delta c)T^3 + \cdots + IT \tag{34}$$

The free-energy change for a reaction may be calculated from equation 34 if (1) the heat capacity of each reactant and product is known as a function of temperature (that is, the values of the constants a, b, and c have been determined for each reactant and product); (2) the heat of reaction ΔH is known at one temperature so that ΔH_0 may be evaluated; and (3) the value of ΔF is known at one temperature so that the integration constant I may be calculated.

Example 22. Calculate $\Delta F°$ and the equilibrium constant at 1000 °K for the reaction

$$C(\text{graphite}) + H_2O(g) = CO(g) + H_2(g)$$

$$\Delta F°_{298°K} = -32.8079 - (-54.6357)$$

$$= 21.8278 \text{ kcal}$$

From Table II, page 118,

$$\Delta H°_{298°K} = -26.4157 - (-57.7979)$$

$$= 31.3822 \text{ kcal}$$

According to the empirical equations for the heat capacities of gases, Table IV, page 123, and $C_{p,\,\text{graphite}} = 3.81 + 1.56 \times 10^{-3}T$,

$$\Delta C_p = C_{p,H_2} + C_{p,CO} - C_{p,H_2O} - C_{p,\,\text{graphite}}$$

$$= 2.29 - 2.30 \times 10^{-3}T - 0.077 \times 10^{-7}T^2$$

$$\Delta H_0° = \Delta H° - 2.29T - \tfrac{1}{2}(-2.30 \times 10^{-3})T^2 - \tfrac{1}{3}(-0.077 \times 10^{-7})T^3$$

$$= 31{,}382.2 - (2.29)(298.1) + (1.15 \times 10^{-3})(298.1)^2$$

$$+ (0.026 \times 10^{-7})(298.1)^3$$

$$= 30{,}801 \text{ cal}$$

Substituting in equation 34

$$21{,}827.8 = 30{,}801 - (2.29)(298.1)(2.303)(2.474) - \tfrac{1}{2}(-2.30 \times 10^{-3})(298.1)^2$$

$$-\tfrac{1}{6}(-0.077 \times 10^{-7})(298.1)^3 + 298.1 I$$

$$I = -17.4$$

and

$$\Delta F° = 30{,}801 - 5.26T \log T + (1.15 \times 10^{-3})T^2 + (0.013 \times 10^{-7})T^3 - 17.4T$$

This general equation may now be used to calculate the free-energy change for the reaction at any temperature in the range for which the heat capacity equations are valid (300–1500°K). At 1000°K this general equation yields

$$\Delta F°_{1000°K} = -1330 \text{ cal.}$$

It should be noted that the reaction is spontaneous at 1000°K, although it is far from being a spontaneous reaction at room temperature.

The equilibrium constant for the reaction at 1000°K may be calculated from

$$\Delta F°_{1000°K} = -RT \ln K_p = -1330 = -(1.987)(1000)(2.303) \log K_p$$

$$K_p = 1.96$$

Calculations of Equilibrium Constants from Enthalpy and Entropy.

The relation between the entropy change, enthalpy change, and free-energy change in an isothermal reaction was given in equation 20 of Chapter 7:

$$\Delta F = \Delta H - T \Delta S \tag{35}$$

It is evident that, when there is no change in entropy during a reaction, the change in enthalpy is equal to the change in free energy. Usually, however, there is an entropy change during the reaction, and the decrease in free energy is greater or less than the decrease in enthalpy, depending on the sign of ΔS. At very high temperatures the entropy term may become of primary importance because it is multiplied by the absolute temperature. Consequently compounds like AlCl which are unfamiliar at room temperature may be stable at high temperatures.

Since entropies and heats of reaction can be determined from calorimetric measurements alone, it is now possible to calculate free-energy changes and equilibrium constants without involving any chemical measurements. This determination of chemical affinities from thermal data is a goal which was eagerly sought by many early investigators.

The calculation of chemical equilibria from entropy data using equations 14 and 20 of Chapter 7 is particularly valuable in organic chemistry because frequently no other method is available. Often the reaction rates are so very slow that direct measurements of equilibrium are impossible. Methane may be taken as an example. Methane appears to be a stable substance at room temperature, and carbon and hydrogen appear to be unreactive toward each other. It is not possible then to measure the equilibrium among the three at low temperatures, but it may be determined indirectly from the absolute entropies and the heat of reaction.

Example 23. Calculate the equilibrium constant for the following reaction at 25°:

$$C(\text{graphite}) + 2H_2(g) = CH_4(g)$$

From Table II on page 118, $\Delta H° = -17,889$ cal. From Table II on page 141, the entropy change for this reaction is

$$\Delta S^\circ = 44.50 - 2(31.211) - 1.3609$$

$$= -19.28 \text{ cal deg}^{-1}$$

$$\Delta F^\circ = \Delta H^\circ - T \Delta S^\circ = -17,889 - (298.1)(-19.28)$$

$$= -12,140 \text{ cal}$$

The free-energy change obtained in this way is identical with that obtained directly from Table III.

The equilibrium constant may be calculated from

$$-12,140 = -(1.987)(298.1)(2.303) \log K_p$$

$$\log K_p = 8.91$$

$$K_p = 8.1 \times 10^8$$

Although this reaction is thermodynamically feasible at room temperature it is not possible to use it since no catalyst is known. At high temperatures where a catalyst would probably not be required the equilibrium constant for the reaction is unfavorable for the synthesis of methane.

The limiting factor in many calculations of this type is the low accuracy with which the heats of reactions are known. These values are usually obtained from differences between large quantities, and a small error in them makes a large error in the value of ΔH and hence of ΔF. In the calculation of the methanol equilibrium, for example, an error of 0.1 per cent in one of the values for the heat of combustion makes an error of 35 per cent in the equilibrium constant. For a time the validity of the third law itself was questioned because of the large discrepancy between the calculated and observed equilibrium in the methanol synthesis. This discrepancy was finally traced to a considerable error in the heat of combustion of methanol. As a rule, a greater error can be tolerated in the entropy measurements than in the measurements that determine the values of the enthalpy.

Many new measurements of entropies and free energies are being recorded in the current literature, and tables of reliable data will ultimately make possible the calculation of most equilibrium constants.

Tables published by the National Bureau of Standards (see footnote, Table III) have largely superseded the earlier tables of thermochemical data.* Special attention has been paid to hydrocarbons, and much of the work has been supported by the American Petroleum Institute.

* Parks and Huffman, *Free Energies of Some Organic Compounds*, Chemical Catalog Co., New York, 1932.

A very helpful collection of data and techniques for calculating thermodynamic data has been made by Wenner.* Semiempirical and theoretical methods are given for estimating specific heats and other important constants from meager data.

Useful rules for estimating enthalpies, entropies, and free energies are given by Hougen and Watson.†

When data are not available for certain compounds it is still possible to estimate free energies and entropies, using empirical rules based on the molecular structures. For example, when CH_3 is substituted for a hydrogen atom, attached to a chain, the molar free energy of formation at $25°$, $\Delta F°_{298°\,K}$, is increased by about 1900 cal; when C_2H_5 is substituted, it is increased by 3000 cal. In a similar way the substitution of a hydrogen atom by an OH group to form a primary alcohol gives a change in $\Delta F°_{298°\,K}$ of $-34,000$; Cl for H gives a change of -1600; NH_2 for H gives a change of 6000; and NO_2 for H gives a change of 7000. For example, if $\Delta F°_{298°\,K}$ of C_2H_6 is known to be $-10,700$, $\Delta F°_{298°\,K}$ of C_2H_5OH should be about $(-10,700 - 34,000)$, or $-44,700$. Experimental measurements give $-40,200$ cal.

The calculation of free-energy changes and equilibrium constants at high temperatures has been greatly improved by the use of statistical mechanics (page 567). By these methods it is possible to calculate the thermodynamic properties of substances from spectroscopic and other molecular data. Such calculations are of great value in predicting the temperature at which a reaction must be carried out in order for it to be spontaneous (thermodynamically possible).

The amount of "isoöctane" available for aviation fuel has been greatly increased by use of the reaction

$$C_4H_{10}(g, \text{ } iso\text{-butane}) + C_4H_8(g, \text{ } iso\text{-butene}) = C_8H_{18}(g, \text{ "isoöctane"})$$

The variation of log K for this reaction with temperature as calculated from various thermodynamic data by Rossini ‡ is shown with line A in *Fig. 11-2*.

This reaction cannot be carried out at high temperatures because of the unfavorable equilibrium. The use of this reaction at temperatures as low as room temperature where the equilibrium is quite favorable was made possible by the discovery of commercially usable catalysts (sulfuric acid and hydrofluoric acid).

* Wenner, *Thermochemical Calculations*, McGraw-Hill Book Co., New York, 1941.

† Hougen and Watson, *Chemical Process Principles*, Part II, *Thermodynamics*, John Wiley & Sons, New York, 1947.

‡ Rossini, *J. Wash. Acad. Sci.*, *39*, 249 (1949).

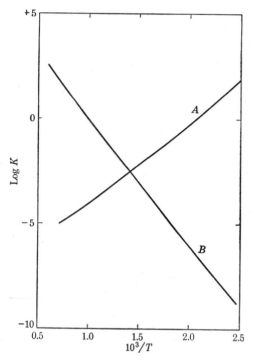

FIG. 11-2.   Influence of temperature on equilibrium constants.

$A.$ $C_4H_{10}(g) + C_4H_8(g) = C_8H_{18}(g)$

$B.$ $C_4H_8(g) = C_4H_6(g) + H_2(g)$

An example of a reaction which can be carried out only at rather high temperatures is the dehydrogenation of 1-butene to yield 1,3-butadiene.

$$\underset{\substack{| \ | \\ H \ H}}{\overset{\substack{H \ H \ H \ H \\ | \ | \ | \ |}}{H-C=C-C-C-H}}(g) = \overset{\substack{H \ H \ H \ H \\ | \ | \ | \ |}}{H-C=C-C=C-H}(g) + H_2(g) \quad (36)$$

The variation of log K for this reaction with temperature as calculated from various thermodynamic data by Rossini * is shown by line B in Fig. 11-2. This reaction must be carried out at high temperatures since the equilibrium constant is unfavorable below 1000°K.

The Free-Energy Function. It was shown in equation 34 how ΔF and the corresponding equilibrium constant can be calculated for

* Rossini, *J. Wash. Acad. Sci., 39,* 249 (1949).

various temperatures from values of $\Delta F°$ and $\Delta H°$ at one temperature, usually 25°, if the heat capacities of the reactants and products are known. It is also possible to compute certain thermodynamic properties of gases at various temperatures from spectroscopic data (see page 567), and Giauque * has pointed out the usefulness of the quantity $(F° - H_0°)$, which is especially easy to compute, in equilibrium calculations.

Various authors †·‡·§ have compiled values for the *free-energy functions* $\left(\dfrac{F° - H_0°}{T}\right)$ or $\left(\dfrac{F° - H°_{298}}{T}\right)$, and the *enthalpy function*, $\left(\dfrac{H° - H_0°}{T}\right)$. The superscripts refer to the chemical compounds in their standard states, which for gases means the ideal gas at 1 atm pressure. The subscript 0 indicates absolute zero.

For gases the free-energy function may be computed directly from spectroscopic data.¶ For solids and liquids, however, which have not been adequately described by any theory, experimental heat capacity data must be used. Remembering that $F° = H° - TS°$, and subtracting the constant $H_0°$, the enthalpy at absolute zero,

$$\frac{F° - H_0°}{T} = \frac{H° - H_0°}{T} - S°$$

Then, for a substance showing no phase changes between 0 and $T°K$,

$$H° - H_0° = \int_0^T C_p \, dT \quad \text{and} \quad S° - S_0° = S° - 0 = S° = \int_0^T \frac{C_p \, dT}{T}$$

and

$$\frac{F° - H_0°}{T} = \frac{1}{T} \int_0^T C_p \, dT - \int_0^T C_p \, d\ln T \tag{37}$$

The values of C_p at various temperatures may be determined experimentally, and if transitions occur any heat of fusion, vaporization or

* Giauque, *J. Am. Chem. Soc.*, *52*, 4808 (1930).

† Rossini et al., "Selected Values of Properties of Hydrocarbons," *Circular of the National Bureau of Standards* C461 (1947); and *Selected Values of Physical and Thermodynamic Properties of Hydrocarbons and Related Compounds*, Carnegie Press, 1953.

‡ *Selected Values of Chemical Thermodynamic Properties*, Series III, National Bureau of Standards, 1947 to 1952.

§ Brewer, Bromley, Gilles, and Lofgren, in Quill, *Chemistry and Metallurgy of Miscellaneous Materials: Thermodynamics*, McGraw-Hill Book Co., New York, 1950, Papers 3, 5, and 6.

¶ Margrave, *J. Chem. Education*, *32*, 520 (1955).

transition is included also in the $H° - H°_0$ values; and these heats of fusion, vaporization, or transition divided by the temperature at which the change occurs are included in the $S°$ values.

Values of $(F° - H_0°)/T$ for many chemical compounds at several temperatures are listed in tables, and so it is easy to calculate $\Delta\left(\dfrac{F° - H_0°}{T}\right)_{\text{reaction}}$ by subtracting $\Sigma\left(\dfrac{F° - H_0°}{T}\right)_{\text{reactants}}$ from $\Sigma\left(\dfrac{F° - H_0°}{T}\right)_{\text{products}}$. Fortunately, the values of this free-energy function do not change much with temperature, and tables giving values every 100° or 500° are sufficient for interpolation and extrapolation. For the difference between the free-energy function of the products and reactants we find

$$\Delta\left(\frac{F° - H_0°}{T}\right) = \frac{\Delta F°}{T} - \frac{\Delta H_0°}{T}$$

Then

$$\frac{\Delta F°}{T} = \frac{\Delta H_0°}{T} + \Delta\left(\frac{F° - H_0°}{T}\right) \tag{38}$$

But, since $\Delta F° = -RT \ln K$,

$$\ln K = -\frac{1}{R}\left[\frac{\Delta H_0°}{T} + \Delta\left(\frac{F° - H_0°}{T}\right)\right] \tag{39}$$

In order to solve equation 39 for the value of an equilibrium constant at a given temperature, it is necessary to know the value of $\Delta H_0°$ as well as the values of the free-energy function. $\Delta H_0°$ is determined from measurements of the heat of reaction at constant pressure at one temperature and the heat capacities at several temperatures. Usually, the heats of reaction are given at 25°, and the relation

$$\Delta H_0° = \Delta H°_{298.16} - \Delta(H°_{298.16} - H_0°)$$

may be used for conversion. Some tables are given in terms of $(F° - H°_{298.16})/T$ so that ΔH_{298} may be used directly in computing $\ln K$.

Another important application of free-energy functions is for evaluating heats of reaction from equilibrium data in a more dependable manner than by taking the slope of a $\log K$ vs. $1/T$ plot. From equation 39 it is easily seen that one $\Delta H_0°$ (or $\Delta H°_{298}$) value can be obtained from each measurement of an equilibrium constant or $\Delta F°$ rather than only one for an entire series of data as when equation 28 is used. The free-energy-function approach often allows accurate evaluation of heats of reactions even for reactions at very high temperatures.

Example 24. Calculate the equilibrium constant for the dissociation of gaseous oxygen at 2000°K.

$$O_2(g) = 2O(g)$$

Then, calculate the degree of dissociation when the total pressure is 1 atm and when it is 10^{-6} atm.

The heat of dissociation of the oxygen molecule into atoms is 117,172 cal mole^{-1}, as given in Table V. The free-energy functions are also from Table V. Thus,

$$\log K = -\frac{1}{2.303R}\left[\frac{\Delta H_0{}^\circ}{T} + \Delta\left(\frac{F^\circ - H_0{}^\circ}{T}\right)\right]$$

$$= -\frac{1}{(2.303)(1.987)}\left[\frac{117,172}{2000} + (2)(-43.00) - (-56.12)\right]$$

$$= -6.26$$

Thus,

$$K = \frac{4\alpha^2 P}{1 - \alpha^2} = 5.50 \times 10^{-7}$$

At 1 atm total pressure,

$$4\alpha^2(1) = (5.50 \times 10^{-7})(1 - \alpha^2)$$

$$\alpha = 3.70 \times 10^{-4}$$

At 10^{-6} atm total pressure,

$$4\alpha^2(10^{-6}) = (5.50 \times 10^{-7})(1 - \alpha^2)$$

$$\alpha = 0.348$$

Table V.   Free-Energy Function and $\Delta H_0{}^\circ$ [1]

$$-(F^\circ - H_0{}^\circ)/T \text{ cal mole}^{-1} \text{ deg}^{-1}$$

	298.16°K	500°K	1000°K	1500°K	2000°K	$\Delta H_0{}^\circ$ kcal mole^{-1}
$H_2(g)$	24.44	27.96	32.75	35.60	37.68	0
$O_2(g)$	42.08	45.69	50.71	53.83	56.12	0
$Cl_2(g)$	45.95	49.86	55.45	58.88	61.36	0
$N_2(g)$	38.83	42.43	47.32	50.30	52.50	0
$HCl(g)$	37.73	41.32	46.17	49.10	51.25	−21.84
$CO(g)$	40.31	43.96	48.89	51.88	54.09	−27.18
$CO_2(g)$	43.57	47.68	54.14	58.51	61.88	−98.95
$H_2O(g)$	37.20	41.32	47.05	50.66	53.41	−57.11
$NH_3(g)$	37.99	42.25	48.63	53.03	56.56	−9.36
$CH_4(g)$	36.46	40.75	47.65	52.84		
$C_2H_6(g)$	45.27	50.77	61.11	69.46		
$C_3H_8(g)$	52.73	59.81	74.10	85.86		
$C_4H_{10}(g)$	58.52	67.93	86.73	102.04		
$C_6H_6(g)$	52.93	60.24	76.57	90.45		
$C_2H_4(g)$	43.98	48.74	57.29	63.94		
$H(g)$	22.42	24.99	28.44	30.45	31.88	51.62
$N(g)$	31.65	34.21	37.66	39.67	41.10	(112.55)[2]
$O(g)$	33.08	35.84	39.46	41.54	43.00	58.586
$Cl(g)$	34.44	37.07	40.69	42.84	44.35	28.45

[1] Data from Brewer in Quill, *Chemistry and Metallurgy of Miscellaneous Materials: Thermodynamics*, McGraw-Hill Book Co., New York, 1950, page 61, and Rossini et al., *Circular of the National Bureau of Standards* C461, Washington, D. C., 1947.

[2] Gaydon, *Dissociation Energies*, Chapman & Hall, London, 1953.

Activities. The formulas for equilibrium constants discussed thus far are strictly true only for ideal gases and ideal solutions, but they are sufficiently accurate for many practical purposes, particularly if the pressure is not greater than 1 atm and the concentration of nonelectrolytes is not greater than 1 molal.

A good illustration of the difficulty of using pressures and concentrations is shown in the determination of the dissociation constant at 25° of N_2O_4, at different concentrations,* as given in *Fig. 11-3*. If N_2O_4 and NO_2 behaved as ideal gases, the values of the dissociation constant, calculated from $K_p = p_{NO_2}^2/p_{N_2O_4}$, should be independent of the pressure. Then, when K_p is plotted against the total pressure, a horizontal line

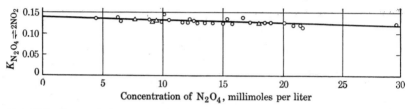

FIG. 11-3. Extrapolation of apparent equilibrium constants K_p to zero concentration.

should be produced. In Fig. 11-3, K_p is plotted against millimoles of gas per liter, calculated as N_2O_4, and it is evident that K_p increases as the total pressure is reduced. In the derivation of the relation $\Delta F° = -RT \ln K_p$ it is assumed that the gases are ideal gases, and, accordingly, the correct value of K_p to use in thermodynamical calculations is the value extrapolated to zero pressure where the gases are strictly ideal. The value of K_p at zero pressure as obtained by this extrapolation is 0.143, which is therefore the thermodynamic value of this equilibrium constant.

To make exact calculations possible, G. N. Lewis introduced the term *activity*. The activity or escaping tendency of a volatile liquid may be visualized as the tendency to pass off into the vapor state as measured approximately by its vapor pressure $p°$. When a solute is added, the vapor pressure of the solvent p is decreased. The ratio $p/p°$ is a measure of the escaping tendency of the solvent as compared to the escaping tendency in the pure liquid. It may be considered as describing approximately the *activity* of the solvent. For example, the vapor pressure of pure water at 25° is 23.7 mm, and the partial pressure of water in a 10 per cent solution of sulfuric acid is 22.4 mm. Then the relative escaping tendency or activity in solution is 22.4/23.7, or 0.95.

The term activity a is defined by the equation

$$\Delta F_A = F_A - F_A° = RT \ln a_A \qquad (40)$$

* Verhoek and Daniels, *J. Am. Chem. Soc.*, *53*, 1250 (1931).

It represents the change in free energy when the substance A goes from its standard state to another state. Thus, in the example given in the preceding paragraph, when a mole of water goes from its standard state as pure water at 23.7 mm to water in a large quantity of 10 per cent sulfuric acid solution where it has a vapor pressure of 22.4 mm,

$$\Delta F_A = F_A - F_A^\circ = RT \ln 22.4 - RT \ln 23.7 = RT \ln \frac{22.4}{23.7} = RT \ln a_A$$

Here the pressures of 22.4 and 23.7 mm are so low that the water vapor behaves as an ideal gas and the equation is exact. Lewis introduced another term, *fugacity*, f, which has the dimensions of pressure and which gives the true thermodynamical value of ΔF even if the gases are not ideal. The fugacities of gases may be calculated from pressures by correcting for the deviations from ideal behavior at several pressures and by other specialized calculations.* They are particularly useful in dealing with gases under high pressures.

As already stated, the standard state of the solvent is taken as the pure liquid solvent, where $N_1 = 1$. The standard state of the solute, however, for practical convenience in many situations is taken as that for which the fugacity is equal to the Henry law constant (p. 199) obtained in dilute solutions.

In Table VI the partial pressures of acetone and ether, as determined by Sameshima † at 30°, are given in millimeters at various mole fractions.

Table VI. Vapor Pressure of Acetone-Ether Solutions at 30°

Mole Fraction Ether, N_1	Vapor Pressure Ether, p_1	Mole Fraction Acetone, N_2	Vapor Pressure Acetone, p_2	K', $\dfrac{N_2}{p_2}$	Total Pressure, $p_1 + p_2$
1.000	646.0	0.000	0	....	646.0
0.961	623.5	0.0387	21.8	0.00177	645.3
0.867	570.8	0.133	66.2	0.00201	637.0
0.749	510.2	0.251	106.7	0.00235	616.9
0.504	390.3	0.496	167.5	0.00291	557.8
0.349	301.5	0.651	201.2		502.7
0.162	166.5	0.838	243.1		409.6
0.047	55.3	0.953	270.7		326.0
0.000	0.0	1.000	282.7		282.7

* Lewis and Randall, *Thermodynamics and the Free Energy of Chemical Substances*, Chapter XVII, McGraw-Hill Book Co., New York, 1923; and Hougen and Watson, *Chemical Process Principles*, Part II, *Thermodynamics*, John Wiley & Sons, New York, 1947.

† Sameshima, *J. Am. Chem. Soc.*, *40*, 1489 (1918).

If ether is considered to be the solvent, its activity at any mole fraction is simply the ratio of the partial pressure to the vapor pressure of pure ether, which is 646.0 mm. For example, the partial pressure of ether at 0.295 mole fraction is 266.0 mm, and the activity of the ether is 266.0/646.0, or 0.412. If the solution were ideal, the activity would be equal to the mole fraction, that is 0.295. The difference between 0.412 and 0.295 shows that the solution is far from ideal, but the activity in this nonideal solution permits exact thermodynamic calculations. Thus, when a mole of pure ether in its standard state is transferred into a large quantity of ether-acetone solution with a mole fraction of 0.295 ether,

$$\Delta F = +RT \ln 0.412 = -524 \text{ cal}$$

If the acetone is considered to be the solute, the standard reference state is taken as a hypothetical acetone with the properties that it possesses as a solute at infinite dilution. Writing the equilibrium constant for the reaction

$$(CH_3)_2CO_{gas} = (CH_3)_2CO_{solution}$$

gives

$$K = a_{solution}/a_{gas} = a_2/p_2 \qquad (41)$$

The gas is sufficiently ideal so that no serious error is introduced by substituting the pressure of the gas for the activity. Since the solution is far from ideal, a considerable error would be introduced by substituting the mole fraction for the activity of acetone in solution, and K would not be the same at different concentrations. However, by writing

$$K' = N_2/p_2 \qquad (42)$$

and calculating the value of K' at several different concentrations, it is possible to extrapolate to infinite dilution where the solution is ideal. This extrapolated value of K' is the true equilibrium constant under conditions where the activity is equal to the mole fraction. This extrapolation is illustrated in *Fig. 11-4*, where values of K' from Table VI are plotted and it is found that K has the value 0.00170.

Since K has been evaluated, it is now possible with the help of equation 41 to determine the activity of acetone at any concentration from its vapor pressure. Thus, at a mole fraction of 0.251, the partial vapor pressure is 106.7, and its activity in solution is given by the relation

$$a_2 = Kp_2$$

$$a_2 = (0.00170)(106.7) = 0.181$$

The fact that the activity of acetone is less than its mole fraction means that its escaping tendency (represented approximately by its vapor pressure) is less than if the acetone retained in this solution the properties it possesses in an extremely dilute solution in ether.

Of course it is quite arbitrary to take ether as the solvent and acetone as the solute; equally useful results would be obtained if ether were considered to be the solute. The standard state adopted should be specified, but in calculations involving only changes in concentration the standard state cancels out.

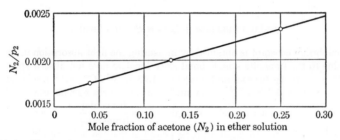

Fig. 11-4. Evaluation of the equilibrium constant for acetone vapor and liquid acetone in infinitely dilute ether solution.

It may be suggested that nothing is gained by the introduction of these arbitrary quantities, fugacity and activity—that the ability thus acquired to express laboratory facts with simple formulas is artificial. However, a great gain is made in a practical way. The relation between activities and concentration may be determined empirically for a given substance by independent experimental measurements, and then many of the useful formulas of thermodynamics may be applied with exactness. Particularly in the study of electrolytes, where the electric charges cause large deviations from ideal behavior, it is necessary to use activities even in fairly dilute solutions.

Methods for determining activities of electrolytes and other solutes are described on pages 444 and 485.

REFERENCES

Rossini, *Chemical Thermodynamics*, John Wiley & Sons, New York, 1950.
Glasstone, *Thermodynamics for Chemists*, D. Van Nostrand Co., New York, 1947.
Lewis and Randall, *Thermodynamics and the Free Energy of Chemical Substances*, McGraw-Hill Book Co., New York, 1923, Chapter XXIV.
Wenner, *Thermochemical Calculations*, McGraw-Hill Book Co., New York, 1941.
Pitzer, *Chem. Revs.*, 27, 39 (1940).

Rossini, Pitzer, Taylor, Ebert, Kilpatrick, Beckett, Williams, and Werner, "Selected Values of Properties of Hydrocarbons," *Circular of the National Bureau of Standards* 461, U. S. Government Printing Office, Washington, D. C., 1947.

Rossini, Wagman, Evans, Levine, and Jaffe, "Selected Values of Chemical Thermodynamic Properties," *Circular of the National Bureau of Standards* 500, U. S. Government Printing Office, Washington, D. C., 1950.

Hougen and Watson, *Chemical Process Principles*, Part II, *Thermodynamics*, John Wiley & Sons, New York, 1947.

PROBLEMS

1. The following equilibrium is attained in the presence of the enzyme fumarase:

$$\text{Sodium fumarate} + H_2O = \text{Sodium } l\text{-malate}$$

The equilibrium constant is obtained by measuring the light absorption in the ultraviolet due to the fumarate double bond since l-malate does not absorb appreciably. At 2500 A where a_M for sodium fumarate is $1.43 \times 10^3 \ M^{-1} \ cm^{-1}$, a solution which originally contained $2 \times 10^{-3} \ M$ sodium fumarate absorbs 69.8 per cent of the light of this wavelength in a 1-cm cell.   Calculate $K = \dfrac{[l\text{-malate}]}{[\text{fumarate}]}$.   *Ans.* $K = 4.5$.

2. Under what pressure must PCl_5 be placed at $250°$ in order to obtain a 30 per cent conversion into PCl_3 and Cl_2?   For the reaction $PCl_5 = PCl_3 + Cl_2$, $K_p = 1.78$.
Ans. 17.9 atm.

3. When sulfur dioxide is oxidized to sulfur trioxide in the presence of a catalyst at $727°$ the following relation holds:

$$K_p = 1.85 = \left(\frac{p_{SO_3}}{p_{SO_2}}\right) \times \frac{1}{\sqrt{p_{O_2}}}$$

(a) What is the ratio of SO_3 to SO_2 when the partial pressure of oxygen at equilibrium is 0.3 atm?   (b) What is the ratio of SO_3 to SO_2 when the partial pressure of oxygen is 0.6 atm at equilibrium?   (c) What is the effect on the ratio SO_3/SO_2 when an equilibrium mixture containing 0.3 atm of oxygen is compressed so that the oxygen pressure is doubled?   (d) What is the effect on the ratio SO_3/SO_2 if the total pressure of the mixture of gases is increased by forcing in nitrogen under pressure?
Ans. (a) 1.01.   (b) 1.42.   (c) 1.42.   (d) No change.

4. What is the free-energy change when 1 mole of N_2O_4 at $25°$ and 2 atm is converted into 2 moles of NO_2 at 0.2 atm?   For the reaction $N_2O_4 = 2NO_2$ at $25°$ $K_p = 0.141$.
Ans. -1160 cal.

5. For the reaction, $A + B = AB$, $\Delta F° = -2000$ cal at $27°$.   Under what total pressure must an equimolecular gaseous mixture be placed in order to produce a 40 per cent conversion into AB?   *Ans.* 0.063 atm.

6. ΔH for the gaseous reaction $C_2H_2 + D_2O = C_2D_2 + H_2O$ is 530 cal.   At $25°$ K_p is 0.82.   How much C_2D_2 is formed if 1 mole of C_2H_2 and 2 moles of D_2O are put together at a total pressure of 1 atm and at $100°$?   Assume that the substitution of deuterium D for hydrogen does not change the heat capacity.   *Ans.* 0.66 mole.

7. The following reaction takes place in the presence of aluminum chloride:

$$\text{Cyclohexane} = \text{Methylcyclopentane}$$

From the following data, calculate: (a) ΔF° at 25°, (b) ΔH° at 25°:

Temperature	K_c
25°	0.143
45	0.193
65	0.272

Ans. (a) 1152, (b) 3200 cal mole^{-1}.

8. The following data apply to the reaction

$$Br_2(g) = 2Br(g)$$

$T, °K$	1123	1173	1223	1273
K_p	0.000403	0.00140	0.00328	0.0071

Determine by graphical means the heat change involved when 1 mole of Br_2 dissociates completely at 1200 °K. *Ans.* 55 kcal mole^{-1}.

9. (a) Calculate the free energy of formation of urea, $CO(NH_2)_2(s)$, from the following data:

$$CO_2(g) + 2NH_3(g) = H_2O(g) + CO(NH_2)_2(s) \qquad \Delta F_{298}^\circ = 456.1 \text{ cal}$$

$$H_2O(g) = H_2(g) + \tfrac{1}{2}O_2(g) \qquad \Delta F_{298}^\circ = 54{,}635.7$$

$$C \text{ (graphite)} + O_2(g) = CO_2(g) \qquad \Delta F_{298}^\circ = -94{,}259.8$$

$$N_2(g) + 3H_2(g) = 2NH_3(g) \qquad \Delta F_{298}^\circ = -7952$$

(b) Calculate ΔF_f° for urea at 298.1 °K from S_f°, which is -109.05 cal deg^{-1} mole^{-1}, and ΔH_f°, which is 79,634 cal mole^{-1}. *Ans.* (a) $-47{,}120$, (b) $-47{,}120$ cal mole^{-1}.

10. Using Table VI calculate the activity of (a) the solute acetone, and (b) ether in a solution in which ether has a mole fraction of 0.504. (c) Calculate the free-energy change when 1 mole of ether is removed from a very large quantity of acetone solution, in which the mole fraction of ether is 0.047, and added to pure ether. *Ans.* (a) 0.284. (b) 0.604. (c) 1480 cal mole^{-1}.

11. If the heat capacities of the reactants and the products are the same in a given reaction, ΔH° is independent of temperature, and log K plotted against $1/T$ gives a straight line. When they are different, the heat of reaction changes with the temperature, and the log K vs. $1/T$ line is curved. Extrapolation of a straight line is much more accurate than extrapolation of a curved line. Develop some function of K which will give a straight line when plotted, so that K_p can be determined by the extrapolation of a straight line, beyond the range of the measurements.

Ans. Plot $\ln K_p$ versus $\left[\dfrac{\Delta H_0^\circ}{RT} + \dfrac{\Delta a}{R} \ln T + \dfrac{\Delta b}{2R} T + \dfrac{\Delta c}{6R} T^2 \right]$.

12. Chlorine gas is dissociated thermally at elevated temperatures. If the heat of the dissociation (ΔH_0°) is 56.9 kcal mole^{-1} and the free-energy functions of Cl atoms have the values -40.69, -42.84, and -44.35 cal mole^{-1} deg^{-1} at 1000°, 1500°, and 2000 °K, respectively, calculate the degree of dissociation of Cl_2 gas at (a) 1250° and (b) 1750 °K when the total pressure is 0.1 atm. *Ans.* (a) 1.33×10^{-2}. (b) 0.379.

13. For the gaseous reaction $COCl_2 = CO + Cl_2$ at 100°, the dissociation constant K_p is 6.7×10^{-9}. Calculate the partial pressure of carbon monoxide in equi-

librium with phosgene at this temperature under a total pressure of 2 atm. The dissociation is so slight that the partial pressure of phosgene may be taken as equal to the total pressure.

14. For the reaction, $N_2O_4 = 2NO_2$, K_p at 25° is 0.141. What pressure would be expected if 1 gram of liquid N_2O_4 is allowed to evaporate into a liter vessel at this temperature? Assume that N_2O_4 and NO_2 are perfect gases.

15. For the reaction $2HI = H_2 + I_2$ at 698.6°K, $K_p = 1.83 \times 10^{-2}$. (a) How many grams of hydrogen iodide will be formed when 10 g of iodine and 0.2 g of hydrogen are heated to this temperature in a 3-liter vessel? (b) What will be the partial pressures of H_2, I_2, and HI?

16. Show that for a reaction of the type

$$AB = A + B$$

at any temperature, the total pressure at which AB is 50 per cent dissociated will be numerically equal to 3 times the equilibrium constant K_p.

17. Calculate the total pressure which must be applied to a mixture of 3 moles of hydrogen and 1 mole of nitrogen to give a mixture containing 10 mole per cent ammonia at 400°. At 400°, $K_p = 1.64 \times 10^{-4}$ for the reaction, $N_2 + 3H_2 = 2NH_3$.

18. Derive an equation for K_p in terms of α and P for the reaction, $2A = 2B + C$, both reactant and products being gaseous. Show that α varies inversely as the cube root of P, when P/K_p is large.

19. When 4.0×10^{-4} mole of amylene and 3.0×10^{-4} mole of acetic acid are mixed in 200 ml of an inert solvent, 1.28×10^{-4} mole of ester is formed according to the reaction $CH_3COOH + C_5H_{10} = CH_3COOC_5H_{11}$. How much ester will be formed when 0.002 mole of amylene and 0.001 mole of acetic acid are mixed in 500 ml?

20. The reaction $A(g) = B(g)$ is at equilibrium at 25° when A has a partial pressure of 6.0 atm and B has a partial pressure of 1.5 atm. Calculate: (a) K_p. (b) $\Delta F°$. (c) A (2 atm) $= B$ (10 atm). Is the reaction spontaneous or not? (d) A (100 atm) $= B$ (5 atm). Is the reaction spontaneous or not?

21. Given the reaction $N_2O_4 = 2NO_2$ at 55°. (a) At 55° and 1 atm pressure the average molecular weight of the partially dissociated gas is 61.2. Calculate α, and calculate K_p. (b) What is the value of α if sufficient nitrogen is introduced into the equilibrium mixture at 55° to bring the pressure up to 2.3 atm keeping the volume constant? (c) Calculate α at 55° if the total pressure is reduced to 0.1 atm. (d) Calculate the free-energy change when 1 mole of N_2O_4 at 1 atm pressure and 55° goes to 2 moles of NO_2 at 1 atm pressure. (e) Calculate the free-energy change when 1 mole of N_2O_4 at 3 atm pressure and 55° goes to 2 moles of NO_2 at $\frac{1}{3}$ atm pressure. (f) How many moles of N_2O_4 must be added to a 10-liter vessel at 55° in order that the concentration of NO_2 will be 0.1 mole per liter? (g) How many moles of N_2O_4 must be added to a previously evacuated 10-liter vessel at 55° in order that the total pressure will be 2 atm?

22. For the gaseous reaction at 200°,

$$A + 2B = AB_2$$

$\Delta F° = 1000$ cal. When 2 moles of B is mixed with 1 mole of A, what total pressure must be applied in order to produce a 60 per cent conversion of A into AB_2?

23. The free energy of the reaction

$$CO(g) + Cl_2(g) = COCl_2(g)$$

can be represented by the equation

$$\Delta F° = -24,100 + 4T \ln T + 3.5T$$

Calculate the partial pressure of chlorine in equilibrium with phosgene at 250°C and a total pressure of 1 atm, assuming that the gases are perfect gases.

24. The average molecular weights M_{avg} of NO_2 and N_2O_4 at 1 atm total pressure are given in the table at three temperatures. The reaction is $N_2O_4 = 2NO_2$. (a) Calculate the degree of dissociation and the equilibrium constant at each of these

$t°$	25°	45°	65°
M_{avg}	77.64	66.80	56.51

temperatures. (b) Plot log K_p against $1/T$, and determine $\Delta H°$ for the dissociation of N_2O_4. (c) Calculate the equilibrium constant at 35°. (d) Calculate the degree of dissociation α for N_2O_4 at 35° when the total pressure is 0.5 atm.

---

25. N_2O_4 dissociates into NO_2 according to the reaction

$$N_2O_4(g) = 2NO_2(g)$$

If the density of the equilibrium gas mixture is 3.174 grams per liter at a total pressure of 1 atm at 24°C, what minimum pressure would be required to keep the degree of dissociation of N_2O_4 below 0.1 at this temperature?

26. The reaction

$$2NOCl = 2NO + Cl_2$$

comes to equilibrium at 1 atm total pressure and 227° when the partial pressure of the nitrosyl chloride NOCl is 0.64 atm. (a) Calculate $\Delta F°$ for this reaction. (b) At what total pressure will the pressure of Cl_2 be 0.1 atm?

27. For the formation of nitric oxide $N_2 + O_2 = 2NO$, K_p at 2126.9° is 0.00251. (a) In an equilibrium mixture containing 0.1 atm partial pressure of nitrogen and 0.1 atm partial pressure of oxygen, what is the partial pressure of nitric oxide? (b) In an equilibrium mixture of N_2, O_2, NO, CO_2, and other inert gases at 2126.9° and 1 atm total pressure, 80 per cent by volume of the gas is nitrogen and 16 per cent is oxygen. What is the per cent by volume of nitric oxide?

28. Adkins and Adams studied the equilibria involved in the formation of acetals by titrating the mixture and determining the aldehyde concentration. At 25°, 1 mole of ethanol was mixed with 0.091 mole of acetaldehyde in a volume of 63.0 ml, and it was found that, when equilibrium was reached, 90.72 per cent of the acetaldehyde had reacted to give acetal. The reaction is

$$2C_2H_5OH + CH_3CHO = CH_3CH(OC_2H_5)_2 + H_2O$$

(a) Calculate the equilibrium constant, assuming an ideal solution. (b) If the mixture is diluted to 100 ml with an inert solvent, what per cent of acetaldehyde will have reacted?

29. In determining equilibrium constants for reactions with large or small constants, the analytical method usually puts a limit on the magnitude of the constant which may be experimentally determined. For a reaction of the type $A = B$ it is found that there is less than 1 part per 1000 of B at equilibrium. Calculate the *minimum* value for $\Delta F°_{298}$ for this reaction.

30. At 227° and 1 atm the gas A_2B is dissociated to the extent of 60 per cent according to the reaction

$$A_2B = 2A + B$$

(a) Calculate K_p. (b) Calculate the free-energy change when A_2B at 1 atm is converted into 2 moles of A at 1 atm and 1 mole of B at 1 atm. (c) What total pressure on the equilibrium mixture will make the partial pressure of B equal to 20 per cent of the total pressure? (d) When 1 mole of B and 2 moles of A_2B are introduced into a 10-liter vessel what will be the concentration of A?

31. For the reactions

$$M(s) = M(g) \qquad \Delta H_1$$

$$M(s) = \tfrac{1}{2} M_2(g) \qquad \Delta H_2$$

$$\tfrac{1}{2} M_2(g) = M(g) \qquad \Delta H_D$$

find the relation between ΔH_1, ΔH_2, and ΔH_D. If $\Delta H_2 > \Delta H_1$, will the pressure of monomer (M) or dimer (M_2) gas molecules above $M(s)$ increase more rapidly as the temperature is increased?

32. The measured density of an equilibrium mixture of N_2O_4 and NO_2 at 15°C and 1 atm is 3.62 g/l, and the density at 75°C and 1 atm is 1.84 g/l. What is the enthalpy change of the reaction $N_2O_4 = 2NO_2$?

33. (a) Calculate the activities of the solute acetone and the solvent ether at 30° in a binary solution which has a mole fraction of 0.25 acetone. (b) Calculate the free-energy change involved when 1 mole of ether is removed from a very large quantity of this solution having a mole fraction of 0.75 ether and condensed in a very large quantity of solution which has a mole fraction of 0.50 ether. Assume that no acetone is evaporated.

34. A certain optically active organic compound slowly racemized in solution, and eventually the solution showed no optical rotation, the d and l forms being in equal concentrations. When the temperature of the solution was varied over wide limits there was no return of optical activity. What facts can be deduced about $\Delta F°$ and $\Delta H°$ for the racemization reaction?

35. What are the possibilities of producing (a) methanol and (b) ethanol by the following reactions:

(a) $$CO(g) + 2H_2(g) = CH_3OH(l)$$

(b) $$C_2H_4(g) + H_2O(g) = C_2H_5OH(l)$$

Details of the thermodynamic calculations are given by Ewell in *Ind. Eng. Chem.*, *32*, 147 (1940).

36. The equilibrium vapor pressure of tantalum has been determined as 6.216×10^{-9} atm at 2624°K, as 9.692×10^{-8} atm at 2839°K, and as 3.655×10^{-7} atm at 2948°K. The free-energy functions for solid and gaseous Ta are:

$T°K$	$-\left(\dfrac{F° - H°_0}{T}\right)_{\text{solid}}$ cal deg^{-1} mole^{-1}	$-\left(\dfrac{F° - H°_0}{T}\right)_{\text{gas}}$ cal deg^{-1} mole^{-1}
2624	18.12	51.38
2839	18.67	51.92
2948	18.94	52.18

Calculate the heat of sublimation of Ta at 0°K. Compare this with the heat obtained from the slope of a log P vs. $1/T$ plot. Why do these heats differ?

Equilibria Involving Gases and Solids. In the preceding chapter equilibrium constants were calculated for homogeneous reactions and emphasis was placed on gaseous reactions. The calculations are simplified when the concentration of one or more of the reactants or products remains fixed because it is present as a solid or liquid. The vapor pressure or solubility is a constant at a given temperature independent of the amount of solid or liquid present. This constant is then incorporated into the equilibrium constant. Thus, for the reaction

$$CaCO_3(s) = CaO(s) + CO_2(g)$$

the equilibrium constant may be written

$$K_p{}' = p_{CaO}p_{CO_2}/p_{CaCO_3}$$

But since p_{CaO} and p_{CaCO_3} are constant at any one temperature, the constant K_p is used where

$$K_p = p_{CO_2} \tag{1}$$

The equilibrium constant, at any one temperature, is determined solely by the pressure of the carbon dioxide evolved. Table I gives the values

Table I. Dissociation Pressures of CaCO₃

Temperature, °C	Pressure, atm	Temperature, °C	Pressure, atm
500	0.000096	897	1.000
600	0.00242	1000	3.871
700	0.0292	1100	11.50
800	0.220	1200	28.68

of the pressure of carbon dioxide corresponding to various temperatures.

When solid ammonium hydrosulfide is heated, it is almost completely dissociated into ammonia and hydrogen sulfide, as shown by the following equation:

$$NH_4HS(s) = NH_3(g) + H_2S(g)$$

This reaction was investigated by Isambert, who found that the total gas pressure at 25.1° is equal to 0.66 atm. The NH_4HS is so completely dissociated in the gaseous state that its partial pressure is negligible and each of the two gases H_2S and NH_3 has a partial pressure of 0.66/2, or 0.33 atm. In calculating an equilibrium constant the partial pressure of NH_4HS is dropped out not because it is low but because it is a constant fixed by the presence of the solid, and

$$K_p = p_{NH_3}p_{H_2S} = (0.33)(0.33) = 0.109$$

The equilibrium constant may be calculated also by mixing various concentrations of ammonia and hydrogen sulfide as shown in Table II.

Table II.   Equilibrium Constants for the Dissociation of NH_4HS at 25.1°

Pressure of Ammonia, atm	Pressure of Hydrogen Sulfide, atm	$p_{NH_3}p_{H_2S} = K_p$
0.33	0.33	0.109
0.274	0.387	0.106
0.182	0.603	0.110
0.549	0.192	0.105
0.596	0.188	0.112

Exercise I.   The dissociation of ammonium carbamate * takes place according to the reaction

$$(NH_2)CO(ONH_4)(s) = 2NH_3(g) + CO_2(g)$$

When an excess of ammonium carbamate is placed in a previously evacuated vessel the partial pressure generated by NH_3 is twice the partial pressure of the CO_2, and the pressure of $(NH_2)CO(ONH_4)$ is negligible in comparison. Moreover, it is a constant at constant temperature. Show that

$$K_p = (p_{NH_3})^2(p_{CO_2}) = (\tfrac{2}{3}P)^2(\tfrac{1}{3}P) = \tfrac{4}{27}P^3$$

where P is the total pressure.

Example 1.   For the reaction $C(s) + 2H_2(g) = CH_4(g)$ at 1000°, $K_p = 0.263$. Calculate the total pressure at equilibrium when 0.100 mole of CH_4 is placed in a volume of 2 liters at 1000°. Let x = the number of moles of CH_4 which dissociate.

* Briggs and Migrdichian, *J. Phys. Chem.*, *28*, 1121 (1924).

$$p_{CH_4} = \frac{nRT}{v} = \frac{(0.1 - x)(0.08205)(1273)}{2} = 5.22 - 52.2x$$

$$p_{H_2} = \frac{nRT}{v} = \frac{2x(0.08205)(1273)}{2} = 104x$$

$$K_p = 0.263 = \frac{p_{CH_4}}{p_{H_2}^2} = \frac{5.22 - 52.2x}{(104x)^2} \qquad x = 0.035$$

$$p_{CH_4} = \frac{(0.1 - 0.035)(0.08205)(1273)}{2} = 3.4$$

$$p_{H_2} = \frac{2(0.035)(0.08205)(1273)}{2} = 3.7$$

Total pressure $= 3.4 + 3.7 = 7.1$ atm

Equilibria of a Solute in Two Immiscible Solvents. If a solid (or liquid) is soluble in two different liquids which do not mix with each other, and an excess of solute is added to the two liquids in contact, each becomes saturated and the concentrations in the two immiscible solutions will be different, depending on the relative solubilities.

In unsaturated solutions there is also a definite equilibrium of solute between the two immiscible solvents. The solute will distribute itself between the two solvents until equilibrium is reached, and the rate of passage of molecules across the surface between the two liquids is the same from the first solvent to the second as it is from the second solvent to the first. This ratio of concentrations in the two solutions is known as the distribution ratio, or

$$K_c = c_2/c_1 \tag{2}$$

where c_2 and c_1 are the concentrations in the two solvents.

This distribution ratio K_c would be the same as the ratio of the solubilities if both the solutions were ideal. However, generally the solvents are not completely immiscible, and so the solubility properties are not identical with those of the pure solvents. When the solubility of the solute is fairly large, the distribution ratio may vary with concentration for the same reason that equilibrium constants, in general, are not perfectly constant. Here again if activities are substituted for concentrations as described on page 268 the "constants" K_c will be true constants over a wide range of concentrations.

Over reasonably small concentration ranges, however, equation 2 is useful for most practical purposes as shown in Table III.

Table III. Distribution of Bromine between Water and Bromoform

Moles per liter in water	0.0075	0.015	0.022	0.029	0.036
Moles per liter in bromoform	0.5	1.0	1.5	2.0	2.5
$K_c = c_{CHBr_3}/c_{H_2O}$	66.7	66.7	68.2	69.0	69.5

If the solute associates or dissociates in one of the solvents but not in the other, a complication is introduced, and K_c as given in equation 2 may change considerably as the concentration is changed. One example is the distribution of electrolytes between water and an insoluble organic liquid such as benzene. Hydrochloric acid dissolves in water to give H^+ and Cl^- ions, but in benzene it is not dissociated into ions. Other solutes, as, for example, benzoic acid associate in nonpolar solvents like benzene to give double molecules as determined by boiling-point or freezing-point measurements, but they do not associate in polar solvents like water or ether.

If a substance is associated to form double molecules in an organic solvent but has its normal molecular weight in water, the equilibrium may be written

$$A_2(\text{organic phase}) = 2A(\text{aqueous phase})$$

and the equilibrium constant is given by

$$K_c = c^2_{A,\text{aq}}/c_{A,\text{org}} \tag{3}$$

The denominator should be written $c_{A_2,\text{org}}$, but, unless it is known in advance that double molecules are formed, it is necessary to express concentrations in both phases on the basis of the unassociated molecular weight.

In the more general case, where

$$A_n(\text{organic phase}) = nA(\text{aqueous phase})$$

$$K_c = c^n_{A,\text{aq}}/c_{A,\text{org}} \tag{4}$$

The value of n may be obtained by plotting $\log c_{A,\text{org}}$ versus $\log c_{A,\text{aq}}$ since the slope of this plot is equal to n.

The properties of mixed solutes are additive in dilute solutions, each solute behaving as if the other were not present. In some cases and particularly in concentrated solutions, however, the presence of other solutes may profoundly affect the distribution ratio either by forming some complex compound with the other solute or by combining with solvent molecules and thus changing the character of the solvent. A common example of the latter is the "salting-out" procedure in solvent extraction. Certain organic substances, for example, can be removed from water by repeated extractions with ether, but the extraction can be improved by saturating the water with sodium chloride or other salt which does not dissolve in the ether. A similar example was discussed on page 201.

Exercise II. Show that in a solvent extraction a given volume of the insoluble solvent will extract more solute from a given volume of water solution if the solvent is divided into several small parts and used in a series of successive extractions. For a given concentration and distribution ratio calculate the amount of solute extracted from 100 ml of aqueous solution by 100 ml of solvent. Repeat the calculation using two extractions with 50 ml each and then with n extractions with $100/n$ ml of solvent in each extraction.

Extraction with immiscible solvents is an important operation which finds many practical applications. Organic compounds are frequently more soluble in organic solvents than in water and can be removed from water by shaking with hydrocarbons or other immiscible organic liquids. Proteins and other compounds in plant and animal products can be separated by a suitable choice of solvent and electrolyte concentration. Several inorganic salts, like ferric chloride or uranyl nitrate, are soluble in organic solvents. A separation can then be effected from salts of metals such as potassium which are not soluble. Choice of solvent, addition of "salting-out" solutes, change of valence, and use of "complexing" agents are some of the variables that can be used to increase the efficiency of the separations.

The greater the surface area exposed between the two liquids, the more rapidly will equilibrium be achieved. Accordingly, it is common practice to shake the two solutions together. The most effective separation involves flowing two different immiscible solvents of different densities in opposite directions through tall towers filled with special packing to give a large surface like the fractionation towers used for separating liquids by vaporization and condensation. These packed towers are equivalent to a large number of batch extractions, and, like any continuous process, they are preferred for industrial or large-scale operations. The number of theoretical plates equivalent to the number of batch operations replaced can be calculated for a solvent-extraction tower in much the same manner that the number of theoretical plates is calculated for a fractionating column.

Solubility of Solids in Liquids. When a solution is in equilibrium at a definite temperature with a solid, or gas, or a second liquid, the solution is said to be *saturated*, and the concentration of the solute in the saturated solution is known as the *solubility*. The saturated solution may be prepared by agitating the solution with an excess of the finely divided solute until there is no change in concentration on further standing. Or a solution may be prepared at a given temperature and the temperature changed to the desired value causing excess solute to be thrown out and leaving a solution saturated with solute at that temperature.

For the equilibrium $A_{\text{solid}} = A_{\text{solution}}$,

$$K_c = c_{\text{sat}} \tag{5}$$

The solubility c_{sat} may be expressed as molality m_{sat} or mole fraction $N_{2\,\text{sat}}$. Then, according to page 256,

$$\frac{d \ln m_{\text{sat}}}{dT} = \frac{\Delta H_{\text{sat}}}{RT^2} \quad \text{or} \quad \frac{d \ln N_{2\,\text{sat}}}{dT} = \frac{\Delta H_{\text{sat}}}{RT^2} \tag{6}$$

Equation 6 is an exact equation for ideal solutions in which ΔH_{sat} is the heat of solution of the solute in the saturated solution. It is clear that for nonideal solutions more complicated equations will be required which allow for the change in activity with the concentration and with the temperature.*

The solubilities of a few typical crystals in water at different temperatures are given in *Fig. 12-1*. They are expressed in grams of solute per 100 grams of solution, that is, in per cent by weight. Solubilities are also often expressed in terms of molality, molarity, or mole fractions as defined on page 183.

The influence of temperature on the solubility depends on the differential heat of solution in the nearly saturated solution, as predicted by the laws of thermodynamics. Generally, heat is absorbed when salts dissolve, and, accordingly, they are more soluble at the higher temperatures. A few salts are known for which the process of solution is exothermic, and, in agreement with the thermodynamic formulas, the solubility then *decreases* as the temperature rises. When a salt exists in different hydrated forms, as is true of sodium sulfate Na_2SO_4, the heat of solution will be different, and the temperature effect will be different for different forms. Thus, the solubility curve for $Na_2SO_4 \cdot 10H_2O$ has a different slope than that for Na_2SO_4. The higher hydrates absorb a larger amount of heat upon solution because heat has been previously evolved in the formation of the hydrate.

Exercise III. The solubility data for $Ba(OH)_2 \cdot 8H_2O$ are as follows: 0.0°, 0.0974 molal; 10°, 0.1447 molal; 20°, 0.227 molal. Calculate the heat of solution of a mole of $Ba(OH)_2 \cdot 8H_2O$ in a saturated aqueous solution, and predict the solubility at 30°. The experimentally determined value at 30° is 0.326 m.

The dissolving of a solid in a liquid involves several factors. When a volatile solid is placed in an evacuated vessel the molecules of the substance escape and fill up the space. The volatilization goes on until the saturation equilibrium is attained and the rate of return of vapor

* Williamson, "The Exact Calculation of Heats of Solution from Solubility Data," *Trans. Faraday Soc.*, *40*, 421 (1944).

molecules to the sublimable solid is equal to the rate of escape of molecules from the solid. Under these conditions the chemical potentials, μ, are the same. The saturation equilibrium in solution, i.e., the solubility, is usually much greater than the vapor equilibrium because many of the solute molecules react with the solvent. In aqueous solutions this interaction with the solvent is called hydration. The general term is solvation.

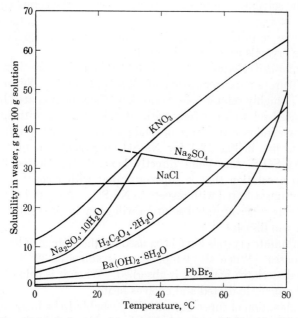

Fig. 12-1. Influence of temperature on the solubility of solids.

If the heat evolved by hydration of the dissolved solute nearly offsets the heat absorbed by pulling the solid crystal apart, the over-all heat of solution is nearly zero. Sodium chloride is an example of a solute which neither evolves nor absorbs much heat when it dissolves in water. Thermodynamical considerations previously discussed predict that the solubility of such a solute is not changed by a change in temperature. Figure 12-1 shows that the solubility of sodium chloride does, indeed, remain nearly constant.

Just as an increase in temperature increases the solubility of a salt that absorbs heat, so an increase in pressure increases the solubility of a salt that dissolves with a shrinkage in volume. The influence of pressure on solubility of a solid or liquid is quite small. It was stated by van't Hoff that the solubility of ammonium chloride, which gives an increased volume on solution, decreased by 1 per cent for 160 atm, whereas the solubility of copper sulfate, which gives a decreased volume on solution, increased by 3.2 per cent for 60 atm. These data are in agreement with the theorem of Le Châtelier. Extensive work on the compressibilities of solutions has been done by Gibson.*

It is well recognized that the rate of solution of solute in a solvent is greatly accelerated by pulverizing the material so as to expose a larger area to the solvent. Quite apart from this effect, the actual equilibrium solubility of very small crystals is greater than that of large crystals.† This increase in solubility with decreasing size is not a significant factor unless the crystals are extremely small.

Supersaturated solutions are solutions that contain more than the equilibrium-saturation concentration of dissolved solute. Supersaturated solutions of highly soluble solutes can sometimes be prepared by cooling the saturated solution carefully without agitation and with special precautions to eliminate any trace of solid particles of the crystalline solute. The dotted line in Fig. 12-1 for Na_2SO_4 represents an unstable solution of Na_2SO_4. Any point directly beneath this dotted line corresponds to a solution that is supersaturated with respect to $Na_2SO_4 \cdot 10H_2O$ but unsaturated with respect to Na_2SO_4. A crystal of the former added to this supersaturated solution will grow in size, but a crystal of the latter will dissolve.

Sodium sulfate crystals have been used for the storage of heat in solar-heated houses. When the temperature is above $32.38°$ the $Na_2SO_4 \cdot 10H_2O$ is dissociated and heat is absorbed. When it is below $32.38°$ the Na_2SO_4 becomes hydrated and evolves heat.

The explanation of supersaturation is probably to be found in the fact that the submicroscopic crystals which would normally be the first to deposit have a higher solubility, and the crystallization process cannot start easily. When an ordinary crystal of the solute is introduced, however, the extra dissolved material crystallizes out immediately. The greater solubility of the very small crystals may be attributed to the existence of some isolated atoms or groups of molecules that can break away from the crystal more easily. This view is strengthened by the fact that, if a mixture of large crystals and very small ones is allowed to stand, the small ones disappear and the larger ones grow larger—a procedure which is followed in the digesting of precipitates in quantitative analysis to render them better suited for filtration.

Extremely small crystalline particles, occurring, for example, as dust in a room, are sometimes sufficient to prevent supersaturation. Super-

* Gibson, *J. Am. Chem. Soc.*, *57*, 284 (1935).
† May and Kolthoff, *J. Phys. & Colloid Chem.*, *52*, 836 (1948).

saturation can sometimes be relieved also by vibrations due to friction on glass or metal surfaces immersed in the solution. Important advances are being made in the study of nucleation which have practical applications in control of crystallization.

The Phase Rule. In preceding sections we have examined the concentrations of solutes in saturated solutions and the pressures of gases in equilibrium with solids and liquids. They have all been simple examples of heterogeneous equilibrium involving the three variables of temperature, pressure, and concentration. Whereas a *homogeneous* system is one in which all parts of the system have the same physical and chemical properties, a *heterogeneous system* is one in which the composition and the physical properties are different in different parts of the system. A system consisting of liquid water, ice, and water vapor is an example of a heterogeneous system containing three phases.

A phase is a definite part of a system which is homogeneous throughout and physically separated from other phases by distinct boundaries. In a heterogeneous system, for example ice, water, and water vapor, the relative amounts of the various phases are not important. The existence or nonexistence of a given phase under specified conditions of temperature and pressure is a matter of practical importance. The conditions under which the different phases can exist are conveniently described by means of phase diagrams, and the total quantities, whether expressed in grams or tons, are not important. Time is not a variable because the phase diagrams are used for systems that are in a state of equilibrium. Many different types of phase diagrams will be illustrated.

The interpretation of phase diagrams was placed on a sound thermodynamic basis by use of an important generalization known as the phase rule discovered in 1876 by Professor J. Willard Gibbs * of Yale University. The phase rule, and his many important generalizations in thermodynamics, have given Gibbs a position as one of the great geniuses of science. Phase diagrams and the phase rule have been of great value in solving practical problems such as the preparation of alloys or salts from complicated mixtures and the adjustment of temperature, pressure, and composition to obtain a desired product. The extraction of potassium chloride from the Stassfurt salt deposits was one of the early examples.

The greater the number of chemical substances in a system, the greater is the number of variables. On the other hand, the greater the number of phases the smaller is the number of variables such as temperature, pressure, and concentration that must be specified. The mere fact

* Gibbs, *Trans. Conn. Acad. Sci.*, 1876–78; *The Collected Works of J. Willard Gibbs*, Vol. 1, Yale University Press, New Haven, Conn., reprinted 1948.

that ice, water, and vapor are existing together limits the temperature to a single value.

The phase rule of Gibbs is concerned with the number of variables involved in any system and with the number of relations between these variables. It deals with the number of variables such as concentration, temperature, and pressure that have to be specified in order to define the system completely, including the concentration in each phase. This number is called the *variance* (or the number of degrees of freedom) and is represented by v. It is equal to the number of independent variables. For example, in a system of two different chemical substances if one has a concentration which gives a mole fraction of 0.3 the concentration of the other is fixed at 0.7 because the sum of the two must be 1.0. The variance in concentration then is 1, not 2.

The number of components c is the smallest number of independently variable chemical compounds that must be specified in order to describe quantitatively the composition of each phase present in the system. In the system $PCl_5(g) = PCl_3(g) + Cl_2(g)$, three chemically individual substances are present but the number of components is only two because the three constituents are connected by an equilibrium and when the concentrations of two are known the third is automatically fixed by the equilibrium. In the system liquid water, ice, and water vapor there is only one chemical individual, H_2O. At very high temperatures there is some dissociation of water vapor into hydrogen and oxygen, but this dissociation is negligible at ordinary temperatures.

Consider a system in equilibrium which consists of p phases and c independent components. If a phase contains c components its composition may be specified by stating $c - 1$ concentrations, one less than the number of components because the concentration of the last component can be obtained from $\sum_i N_i = 1$, where $\sum_i N_i$ represents the sum of the mole fractions of all the i components. Thus the total number of independent variables for the whole system is $(c - 1)$ for each of the p phases plus an additional number, two, to take account of the variables temperature and pressure which can be varied independently of each other and of the concentrations. Thus the total number of independent variables in a system at equilibrium is $p(c - 1) + 2$.

Next we consider the number of relationships which must be satisfied in a state of equilibrium. The chemical potential μ (page 150) is the same in each phase α, β, γ, etc., and $\mu_{i\alpha} = \mu_{i\beta} = \mu_{i\gamma} = \cdots$ for the component i. Altogether there are c components, each one of which can be involved in an equilibrium between phases. There are p phases but only $p - 1$ equilibrium relationships for each component. For example, if there are two phases there is only one equilibrium relationship for each component. There is a total of $c(p - 1)$ equilibrium relations.

The variance v is defined as the number of independent variables in a system at equilibrium. It is equal to the total number of variables minus the number of relations between these variables. Thus

$$v = [p(c - 1) + 2] - [c(p - 1)]$$

or

$$v = c - p + 2 \tag{7}$$

This is the important phase rule of Gibbs. The number 2 comes from the assumption that the state of the system is completely determined at equilibrium by specifying only the temperature and pressure in addition to the composition. In considering systems which contain only solid and liquid phases at pressures sufficiently high to eliminate the vapor phase, the vapor phase is often excluded and then the pressure does not have to be specified. Then the phase rule has the form

$$v = c - p + 1 \tag{8}$$

This form of the phase rule is convenient in studying solid and liquid systems in which temperature is plotted against concentration. If there is a third variable such as a magnetic or electrostatic field or surface tension in addition to temperature and pressure, equation 7 would have to be replaced by $v = c - p + 3$. It should be pointed out that the phase rule applies only to systems that are in a state of equilibrium, that it does not predict new things, but that it is very valuable in correlating data. It may be used to state what type of relations may be expected, but the exact shape of the curves relating different variables must be determined by experiment.

Pressure-Temperature Diagram for Water. The temperature-pressure diagram for water is one of the simplest phase diagrams. The conditions of temperature and pressure under which ice, liquid water, and vapor can exist in a state of equilibrium are given in *Fig. 12-2*, which is not drawn to scale on the vertical axis. The high pressures needed to produce an appreciable temperature change would give too small a pressure range to plot around atmospheric pressure.

Three general areas are labeled in which ice, water, or vapor can exist alone. For example, vapor may exist anywhere in the area labeled "vapor," and it is necessary to specify both the pressure and the temperature in order to define the system completely. The mere statement that water vapor is present at a specified pressure does not describe the system completely because at a given pressure it is possible to have water vapor existing at many different temperatures. Applying the phase rule, there is only one component H_2O and in each area there is only one phase, and so $v = c - p + 2 = 1 - 1 + 2 = 2$. Two variables, temperature and pressure, must be specified in order to define the system completely.

Where two of these areas touch, there is a line, and along each line the two phases exist in equilibrium. The vapor-pressure curve of water is represented by the line OA. Above this line liquid water exists alone;

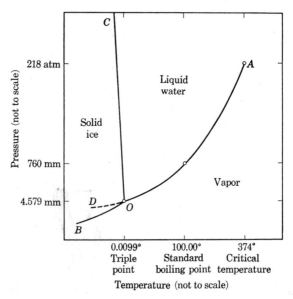

FIG. 12-2. Schematic pressure-temperature diagram of water showing three phases.

and below it water vapor exists alone. Only on the line OA where both regions touch is it possible to have water and its vapor in equilibrium. Thus, if the pressure is reduced to a point below the line OA, all the water will be vaporized; if, on the other hand, the pressure is raised above the line OA, all the vapor will condense to the liquid state.

If it is stated that the system contains *both* liquid water and water vapor at 25°, it is not necessary to specify the pressure, because it has been found by experiment that water and its vapor can exist together at 25° only under a pressure of 23.7 mm. The pressure at any temperature may be read from the vapor-pressure curve. Likewise, if the pressure is stated, the temperature may be determined from the graph. A single variable, either temperature or pressure, is sufficient to describe completely the system along a line since the variance $v = c - p + 2 = 1 - 2 + 2 = 1$.

The line BO is the sublimation curve of ice.   Above it lies ice, and below it lies vapor.   Only along BO can ice and vapor exist together in equilibrium.

The line OC shows how the melting point changes with pressure.   At all points on the line the pressure is greater than the vapor pressure, as given by the line BOA; so it may be concluded that no vapor is present. This line is inclined toward the vertical axis, and the melting point of ice is lowered by increasing the pressure—a fact that can be predicted from the principle of Le Châtelier, since the liquid water occupies a smaller volume than the solid ice.   The exact slope of this line may be calculated from the Clapeyron equation (page 163).   Along OC there are two phases, ice and liquid water, and, again, it is necessary to specify only one variable, either temperature or pressure, to describe the system completely.

Where the three lines, representing pairs of phases, intersect, the three areas touch, and all three phases exist together in equilibrium. Only one such point is possible with three phases, and it is called a *triple point*.   It is not necessary to specify either temperature or pressure under these conditions, for there is only one possible temperature and one possible pressure which will permit all three phases to exist together in equilibrium.   If the temperature is raised at constant pressure, the ice will melt, and the liquid will vaporize, leaving only vapor; if the temperature is lowered, there will be only ice; if the pressure on the vapor is raised at constant temperature, the vapor will condense; and, finally, if the pressure is lowered, the liquid and ice will evaporate. The variance v is zero because there are three phases and $v = 1 - 3 + 2 = 0$.

Ice and water, saturated with air, are in equilibrium with their vapor in air under atmospheric pressure at a temperature of $0°$.   The definition of the centigrade scale depends on this fact.   The situation is somewhat complicated, because the pressure of water vapor is only 4.57 mm, whereas the total pressure on the ice and water is 1 atm.

If ice and water, from which dissolved air has been removed, are allowed to evaporate into a previously evacuated space, the pressure on the ice and water will be 4.57 mm instead of 1 atm, and the melting point will be slightly higher.   The exact temperature of this triple point is $0.0099°$.   This difference from $0°C$ of $0.0099°$ is due to two factors. The solubility of air at atmospheric pressure is sufficient to lower the freezing point by $0.0024°$, and the increase of pressure from 4.57 mm to 1 atm lowers the freezing point $0.0075°$ as shown on page 164.

The dotted curve OD, which is a continuation of OA, represents the vapor pressure of supercooled water.   It may be noticed that there is no break in the vapor-pressure curve so long as the solid phase does not separate, and that the vapor pressure of supercooled water, which is an unstable phase, is greater than that of the stable phase, ice, at the same temperature.   Unstable phases always have higher vapor pressures.

The lower limit of the sublimation curve OB is theoretically determined by the absolute zero; the vaporization curve OA terminates at A,

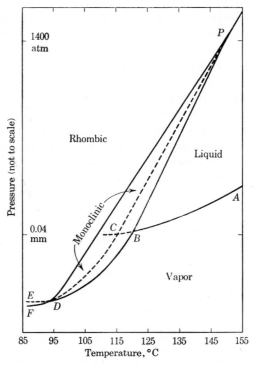

FIG. 12-3.   Pressure-temperature diagram of sulfur which has a transition between two different crystalline forms.

which is the critical temperature 374°, corresponding to a pressure of 218 atm.   Above this critical temperature at A the vapor and liquid phases become indistinguishable.

Investigations conducted by Bridgman with a view to determining the course of the fusion curve OC have revealed the existence of seven different crystalline modifications of ice, all of which, with the exception of ordinary ice, are denser than water.   The first of these new forms of ice makes its appearance at a pressure of 2115 kg per square centimeter, and the last at a pressure of 22,400 kg cm^{-2}.

Exercise IV   The *P-T* diagram for sulfur is shown in *Fig. 12-3*.   The phase diagram is similar to that of water except that there are two solid phases, monoclinic sulfur and rhombic sulfur, with a transition temperature at 95.6°. The rhombic sulfur which is stable at room temperature changes very slowly to the monoclinic form above 95.6°. When liquid sulfur is cooled it slowly crystallizes as monoclinic sulfur at 119°, but if it is cooled quickly, the liquid may go directly to the rhombic at 113°. The dotted lines within the area labeled monoclinic sulfur indicate unstable, nonequilibrium conditions. Write down all the phases that are present for each area, line, and point on the diagram, and show that as always in a diagram of this type $v = 2$ for an area, 1 for a line, and 0 for a point.

Concentration, Temperature, and Pressure. We have just studied simple temperature-pressure diagrams for a one-component system. Earlier in this chapter we considered simple concentration-temperature solubility diagrams for two-component systems. In order to graph completely a system with two components by specifying concentration, temperature, and pressure, it is necessary to go to three dimensions. Concentration may be plotted along one axis and temperature and pressure along two other axes, giving a space model as shown in *Fig. 12-4a* for the system copper sulfate and water.

Temperature is plotted horizontally along the X axis, concentration of water is plotted vertically along the Z axis, and pressure is plotted in the base plane along the Y axis at right angles to both the X and Z axes. The concentrations of water corresponding to the copper sulfate crystals with increasing amounts of water of crystallization are plotted vertically, leading at the higher concentrations of water to a saturated solution and then to unsaturated solutions which become more dilute as the percentage of water increases.

This space model is complete but it is awkward to handle, and it is more common to project lines onto intersecting planes. The projection onto the base plane in Fig. 12-4c gives a T-P diagram with several lines corresponding to the vapor pressures for pure water, a saturated solution of $CuSO_4$, and various pairs of hydrates.

The P-C diagram shown in Fig. 12-4b is actually a cross section of the space model cut at right angles to the temperature axis at a temperature of 50° and intersecting the surface along $LMNOP$ indicated by the horizontal shading. Temperature is not a variable in this diagram. It illustrates the behavior when water is gradually removed from a dilute solution of copper sulfate along the line $LMNOP$. Such a procedure could be carried out by placing the solution in a desiccator at 50°, which is provided with a manometer, and allowing the solution to lose water gradually until only the anhydrous salt $CuSO_4$ remains.

As water is removed from the solution the concentration of copper sulfate increases, and the vapor pressure of the solution decreases along the line LM. When the solution becomes saturated, the pressure remains constant, as shown by the vertical line at M, while the water is removed from the saturated solution. The composition of the whole system changes as water is removed. The relative amounts of saturated

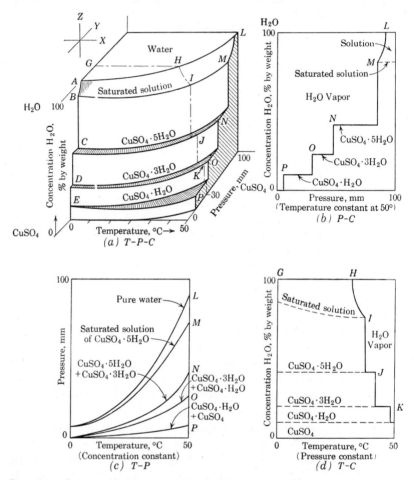

Fig. 12-4. Space model showing concentrations, temperature, and pressure for the system copper sulfate and water.

solution and $CuSO_4 \cdot 5H_2O$ change, but the compositions of the two phases do not change; hence, the vapor pressure remains constant. Finally, when all the solution has disappeared, the pressure drops abruptly to 47 mm at N. The pressure over a mixture of $CuSO_4 \cdot 5H_2O$ and $CuSO_4 \cdot 3H_2O$ remains constant at 47 mm until all the $CuSO_4 \cdot 5H_2O$ has been dehydrated to $CuSO_4 \cdot 3H_2O$, when it drops abruptly to 30 mm

at O and remains constant until 2 more moles of water have been lost
at P. It then drops to 4.5 mm, and remains constant until dehydration
is complete. In practice, the lines are less steep because of the slow diffusion of the water vapor.

The several equilibria are as follows:

$$\text{Saturated solution} = CuSO_4 \cdot 5H_2O + xH_2O$$

$$CuSO_4 \cdot 5H_2O = CuSO_4 \cdot 3H_2O + 2H_2O$$

$$CuSO_4 \cdot 3H_2O = CuSO_4 \cdot H_2O + 2H_2O$$

$$CuSO_4 \cdot H_2O = CuSO_4 + H_2O$$

Since the activities of the solids $CuSO_4 \cdot 5H_2O$ and $CuSO_4 \cdot 3H_2O$ are
constant, an equilibrium constant for the second equilibrium can be
written,

$$K_p = p_{H_2O}^2$$

and similar equilibrium constants can be written for the other reactions.
The vapor pressure is constant only when an equilibrium exists, and an
equilibrium can exist only when two hydrated salts and water vapor (or a
saturated solution and a hydrate) are present together.

The T-C diagram is shown in Fig. 12-4d, which indicates a section
of the space model cut at a constant pressure of 30 mm along $GHIJK$.

Mixtures of two hydrates of a given crystalline salt are useful in establishing definite partial pressures of water. There are many different
hydrated salts to choose from, so that it is possible to obtain nearly
any desired pressure. Sometimes the partial pressures of the anhydrous
salt and the lowest hydrate are so low that they are used for dehydrat-
ing agents. Zinc chloride or calcium chloride is suitable. At 25° the
mixture of $CuSO_4 \cdot H_2O$ and $CuSO_4$ has a partial pressure of 0.8 mm of
water, and, accordingly, anhydrous copper sulfate will not take up any
water at this temperature if the vapor pressure is less than 0.8 mm.

Concentration-Temperature Diagrams. Of the many types of
phase diagrams, the concentration-temperature diagrams are the most
common. The concentrations are usually given in per cent by weight,
or in mole per cent which is equivalent to mole fraction multiplied by 100.

A simple type of concentration-temperature curve is shown in *Fig.
12-5*, where the line ABC indicates the conditions which will produce a
change in the number of phases. For temperatures and compositions
outside of this line ABC there is one homogeneous liquid phase and inside there are two liquid phases, one of which is water saturated with
n-butanol and one of which is n-butanol saturated with water. The
vapor phase is not shown, and the pressure is fixed and not considered

as a variable. Then $v = c - p + 1$. Since there are two components, $v = 2 - p + 1$. Outside of the area enclosed by the line ABC there is one phase and $v = 2 - 1 + 1 = 2$. Both temperature and concentration must be specified in order to define the system completely.

The area inside the line ABC is a two-phase area and $v = 2 - 2 + 1 = 1$. In this area, which has a variance of 1, if the temperature is specified the system is completely defined because the compositions of both liquid phases can be read off from the intersections of the temperature line with the line ABC. Again, if there are two phases in equilib-

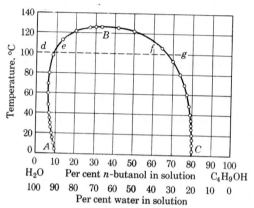

FIG. 12-5   Influence of temperature on the solubility of liquids, n-butanol and water.

rium in the system and if the composition of one of them is specified, the temperature can be determined from the line AB or CB, and the intersection of this temperature line with the other part of the curve gives the composition of the second phase.

The phase diagram of Fig. 12-5 is determined by preparing various mixtures of n-butanol and water, heating till one homogeneous liquid phase is produced, and then cooling till two liquid phases appear. The temperature is recorded at which a slight cloudiness first appears, due to the formation of droplets of liquid with different refractive index. Temperatures for several mixtures are plotted, and the smooth curve ABC is drawn.

The concentration may be changed as well as the temperature. If one starts with pure water and adds increasing quantities of n-butanol, a concentration eventually will be reached at which the solution separates into two layers. This concentration at 0° is represented by the point A. When the temperature is raised, the solubility of butanol in water decreases slightly at first and then increases, as shown by the curve AB. In like manner, if one starts with pure butanol and adds increasing amounts of water at 0°, separation into two layers occurs at a concentration represented by the point C. As the temperature is raised, the solubility of water in butanol increases, as shown by the curve CB. When the temperature is raised above 126°, corresponding to the height of the point B, butanol and water become soluble in all proportions. This temperature, above which there cannot be more than one liquid phase no matter what the composition, is called the *critical solution temperature*.

If one starts with a solution at a temperature and composition represented by the point d, the addition of increasing amounts of butanol at constant temperature is represented by the dotted line $defg$. When the point e is reached, the solution separates into two layers. As more butanol is added, the quantity of the butanol layer saturated with water increases, but the compositions of the two layers remain constant and are given by e and f. Beyond f the solution again becomes homogeneous, and the addition of more butanol increases the concentration of butanol in the solution, as, for example, at g.

Use of Cooling Curves in Studying Solid-Liquid Equilibria. A type of two-component system which is of great interest involves two metals which are completely miscible in the liquid state at a sufficiently high temperature. The details of the phase diagram may be determined by studying the rate of cooling of solutions of various compositions. Known mixtures of the two components are heated to give a single liquid phase. Then the liquid solution is cooled slowly and the temperature is plotted against time. These cooling curves show a change in slope when a solid phase separates out because the heat evolved on crystallization partially offsets the heat being lost by radiation and conduction. A plateau is obtained at the temperature at which the whole liquid phase solidifies. The temperatures at which the change of cooling rate is first noted are then plotted against the composition of the molten solution. An example of the cooling curves and the phase diagram constructed from them is shown in *Fig. 12-6* for bismuth and cadmium.

The cooling curve for pure bismuth indicated by 0 per cent cadmium is shown at the extreme left. The liquid cools off along AB, but, when B is reached, solid bismuth appears, and the temperature remains stationary at 273°, the melting point of bismuth, until the liquid has solidified. The cooling curve of the solid bismuth is shown along the line BC. A similar curve for the freezing of pure cadmium is indicated by the line marked 100 per cent cadmium, which indicates a freezing point at 323°. The cooling curve marked 40 per cent shows a single plateau F which corresponds to the eutectic point at 140° where solid bismuth and solid cadmium come out together. The cooling curve for a solution containing 20 per cent cadmium shows two changes, one when the bismuth first starts to freeze out at D and another one at E where the bismuth also freezes out giving the eutectic at 140°. For the 80 per cent cadmium solution the first change in the slope of the cooling curve at G is due to the freezing-out of some cadmium and the eutectic at F comes as always at 140°.

The temperatures at which new phases appear as indicated by the cooling curves are then transferred to the temperature-composition diagram as shown in Fig. 12-6. In the area above JKL there is one liquid phase and $v = c - p + 1 = 2 - 1 + 1 = 2$. Along JK bismuth

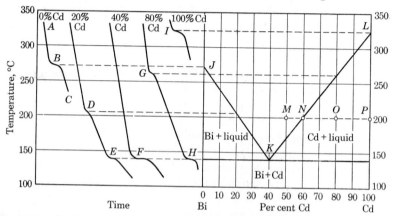

FIG. 12-6. Cooling curves from which the temperature-concentration phase diagram is constructed for the system bismuth and cadmium.

freezes out, and along LK cadmium freezes out. Thus in the area under JK and down to the eutectic temperature K there are two phases, solid bismuth and a solution of definite composition which is determined by the temperature. Since $v = 2 - 2 + 1 = 1$, either the temperature or the composition of the liquid phase is sufficient to describe the system completely.

At K there are three phases—solid bismuth, solid cadmium, and liquid solution containing 40 per cent cadmium. Then $v = 2 - 3 + 1 = 0$. There is only one temperature and one composition of solution where all three phases can exist together at equilibrium.

The area below the eutectic temperature K is a two-phase area in which solid bismuth and solid cadmium are present, and $v = 2 - 2 + 1 = 1$. Only the temperature need be specified. The ratio of bismuth to cadmium may change, but there is only pure bismuth and pure cadmium and there is no need to specify any concentration. The eutectic may appear different on account of fine grain structure, but it is not a phase; it is simply a mixture of bismuth and cadmium as two separate phases.

Looking at the line $MNOP$ it is clear that M represents a 50–50 solution of bismuth and cadmium at 200°. As pure cadmium is added to this solution at 200° it dissolves and increases the concentration of cadmium in the solution until the solution becomes saturated at N. Further addition of pure cadmium will not make any further change in the composition of the liquid, but the ratio of solid cadmium to the solution of composition N continues to increase along the line NOP. There is no change in the number of phases or in the composition. Since there are

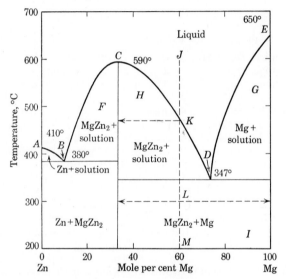

FIG. 12-7.   Temperature-composition phase diagram showing a maximum for the system zinc-magnesium.

two phases, $v = 1$. When either temperature or concentration of the liquid phase is specified the other may be found from the diagram. The ratio of the quantity of cadmium solid to liquid phase is not counted in determining the variance.

Systems Involving Chemical Interaction.   As shown in the concentration-freezing-point diagram of Fig. 12-6 cadmium lowers the freezing point of bismuth, and bismuth lowers the freezing point of cadmium, and the two freezing-point curves meet at the eutectic temperature.   In some freezing-point diagrams there is a maximum in the curve with a eutectic point on each side.   Such a maximum indicates the formation of a chemical compound, and the composition which corresponds to the maximum temperature is the composition of the compound.   On the mole per cent scale these maxima come at ratios of 1 to 1, 2 to 1, 1 to 3, and similar simple ratios.   A freezing-point diagram for the zinc-magnesium system is shown in *Fig. 12-7*.

The maximum falls at a composition corresponding to $MgZn_2$ with a melting point of 590°. When zinc is added to melted $MgZn_2$ the freezing point is lowered along the line CB; and when magnesium is added the freezing point is lowered along CD. The compound $MgZn_2$ freezes out in both cases.

A broad, flat maximum in a temperature-composition diagram shows that the compound dissociates readily, whereas a sharp maximum coming to a narrow peak indicates that the dissociation in solution is slight.

Example 2. State the phases present and the variance at B, F, G, H, J, and L.

	Phases	Variance			Phases	Variance
B	Solution, Zn, $MgZn_2$	0		H	$MgZn_2$, solution	1
F	Solution, $MgZn_2$	1		J	Solution	2
G	Solution, Mg	1		L	$MgZn_2$, Mg	1

In the region H, it is sufficient to fix either temperature or concentration of the liquid phase. The ratio of $MgZn_2$ to liquid is not counted as a variable, because the phase rule does not deal with the relative amounts of various phases.

Example 3. Six-tenths mole of Mg and 0.4 mole of Zn are heated to 600°, giving the point J in Fig. 12-7. Describe what happens when this total mixture is cooled down to 200°, as indicated by the vertical dotted line. (The experiment would have to be done in an inert atmosphere to prevent oxidation by air.) At 470° solid $MgZn_2$ separates out, as indicated by the top arrow; the remaining solution becomes richer in magnesium; the temperature falls still lower; and more solid $MgZn_2$ is thrown out of solution. The freezing point is gradually lowered as the solution becomes richer in Mg. At 400° a considerable amount of $MgZn_2$ has come out of solution, leaving a solution of 0.68 mole fraction Mg and 0.32 mole fraction Zn. Finally, at 347°, when the liquid has become 74 mole per cent Mg and 26 mole per cent Zn, the whole solution freezes, solid $MgZn_2$ and solid Mg coming out together.

From this temperature down to 200° there is no further change in composition or phases. At all temperatures below 347° there are pure solids Mg and $MgZn_2$. Since all of the zinc present is in the form of $MgZn_2$ there is 0.2 mole of this compound and 0.4 mole of Mg in the eutectic mixture. The ratio Mg/Zn is of course $60/(100-60) = 1.5$ for the 60% solution.

Phase diagrams are useful in the study of aqueous solutions as well as metallic solutions. Definite hydrates which produce maxima in phase diagrams are frequently encountered in aqueous solutions. An example is given in *Fig. 12-8* for sulfuric acid and water.

When sulfuric acid is added to water, the freezing point is lowered, as shown by the line along which there is an equilibrium between solid ice and the liquid solution of sulfuric acid in water. This lowering continues until at about 10 mole per cent of sulfuric acid the freezing temperature is about $-70°$. Further addition of sulfuric acid to the solution now leads to the precipitation of a new solid phase $H_2SO_4 \cdot 4H_2O$. At the first eutectic there are two solid phases, ice and $H_2SO_4 \cdot 4H_2O$

and one liquid phase (10 mole per cent sulfuric acid), so that $v = 0$. In aqueous solutions a eutectic point is called a *cryohydric point*, and the eutectic mixture is called a *cryohydrate*. When first discovered, these cryohydrate mixtures were thought to be chemical compounds, but the lack of homogeneity can be detected under the microscope. Furthermore, the constituents are seldom present in simple whole-number ratios which correspond to chemical compounds.

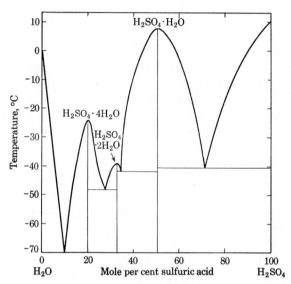

FIG. 12-8.   Temperature-composition phase diagram for the system water-sulfuric acid.

When there are exactly 4 moles of water to 1 of sulfuric acid, the solution freezes sharply at the freezing point of this pure compound. Addition of more sulfuric acid to the solution lowers the freezing point along the line leading to a second eutectic point.

It is found that there are three compounds of sulfuric acid and water and four cryohydrates or eutectic mixtures.

The chemical compound $H_2SO_4 \cdot H_2O$ melts at $8.0°$ above the freezing point of water. It is interesting to consider what happens when water is removed (by evaporation) from dilute sulfuric acid, isothermally at $0°$. The remaining solution becomes more concentrated in sulfuric acid through loss of water, and the concentration moves along a horizontal line to the right until the solubility curve is intersected and crystals are formed. The solution gradually solidifies, but on further removal of water another solubility curve is intersected, and the crystals disappear. This alternate crystallization and melting by removal of water vapor would have been difficult to understand without the phase diagram. Diagrams of this type are of great practical importance for obtaining specified products or properties through the control of concentration and temperature.

Solid Solutions. In aqueous solutions and in most common solutions in the laboratory the solvent freezes out as a pure solid. However, there are many solutions in which the solid solvent which freezes out contains the solid solute dissolved in it. An example is a solution of iodine dissolved in benzene. When the temperature is lowered to about 5°, the crystals of benzene which freeze out are colored with iodine, and the amount of iodine dissolved in the solid is proportional to the amount of iodine dissolved in the liquid solution. There is a distribution of iodine between the liquid and solid phases, just as there is distribution between two immiscible solvents. A homogeneous mixture of two or more crystalline solids in varying proportions is known as a *solid solution*.

The attainment of equilibrium in solid solutions is much slower than the attainment of equilibrium in liquid solutions. It takes a considerable length of time, particularly at low temperatures, for a change in concentration at the surface to affect the concentration at a point in the interior of the solid solution. Slow diffusion does take place, however. For example, when a bar of gold and a bar of lead were placed in contact at room temperature for a period of 4 years, gold was detected at a distance of 7 mm. The way is open now to study diffusions of this type with the merest trace of material, making use of radioactive tracers (page 637).

The existence of these solid solutions causes difficulty in experimental measurements of equilibria, and it introduces complications in phase diagrams.

Solid solutions involve *two* solutions, a liquid phase and a solid phase, in equilibrium with each other, as shown, for example, in *Fig. 12-9* for platinum and gold.

Above the upper line of Fig. 12-9 the two metals exist in liquid solutions; below the lower line the two metals exist in solid solutions. The upper curve is the freezing-point curve, and the lower one is the melting-point curve. The space between the two curves represents *mixtures* of the two solutions—one liquid and one solid solution in equilibrium. For example, a mixture which originally contained 50 mole per cent gold and 50 mole per cent platinum, when brought to equilibrium at 1400°, will consist of two phases, a solid phase containing 70 mole per cent platinum and a liquid phase containing 28 mole per cent platinum.

If the original mixture contained 60 mole per cent platinum, there would
still be the same two phases containing 28 and 70 per cent platinum,
but there would be a relatively greater amount of the solid phase, which
contains 70 mole per cent platinum.

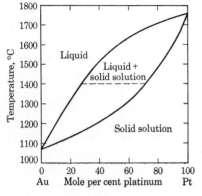

FIG. 12-9. Phase diagram for gold-plat-
inum showing solid solutions.

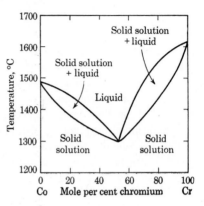

FIG. 12-10. Phase diagram for cobalt-
chromium showing two series of solid
solutions.

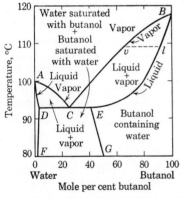

FIG. 12-11. Phase diagram showing the
vapor and liquid compositions of water
and *n*-butanol (1 atm pressure).

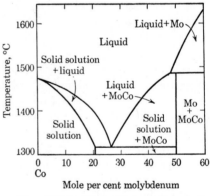

FIG. 12-12. Phase diagram for cobalt-
molybdenum.

The diagrams which describe the melting behavior of solid solutions
are quite like those studied earlier which described the vaporization of
liquids. In both types of diagrams there is equilibrium between two
phases at a given temperature although the composition of the two
phases is different. For the vaporization curves it was helpful to remem-

ber that at a given temperature the vapor is richer in the more volatile component or mixture. In these solid solutions, it is convenient to remember that the liquid phase is richer in that component or mixture which has the lower melting point. In this way it can be determined which is the liquid curve and which is the solid curve.

It is possible to separate materials which form an unbroken series of solid solutions by fractional crystallization just as it was shown to be possible, in Fig. 9-7 on page 191, to separate two compounds by fractional distillation. For example, if it is desired to separate pure gold from an alloy containing 70 per cent platinum, the alloy is melted slightly to give a liquid richer in gold, which is removed and then frozen completely. It is then melted partially to give liquid still richer in gold, and so on until pure gold is obtained.

The fractional crystallization of solid solutions is seriously complicated by the fact that equilibrium is reached very slowly, and it is often impractical to wait long enough to obtain the separations previously predicted on the basis of reaching equilibrium at every stage.

Solid solutions may have minima in the freezing-point curves analogous to the vaporization curves on page 191 which had a minimum boiling point. An example is given for cobalt and chromium, shown in *Fig. 12-10.* Again, the liquid or mixture with the lowest melting point is in excess in the liquid phase. In this case it is the mixture of 56 per cent chromium melting at 1300° which has the lowest melting point. There are two sets of solid solutions with different properties, the solid solutions with less than 56 per cent chromium and the solid solutions with more than 56 per cent chromium. It is theoretically possible to separate pure chromium from solutions having more than 56 per cent chromium and pure cobalt from solutions having less than 56 per cent chromium, but it is not possible to separate pure chromium starting with a solution containing more than 44 per cent cobalt.

Partial Miscibility. Sometimes two different liquids or two different solid solutions are miscible only within certain temperature ranges and immiscible within other temperature ranges. The phase diagrams then become somewhat more complicated.

If we consider the separation of partially miscible liquids by vaporization, *Fig. 12-11,* for water and n-butanol, serves as an illustration.* The lines *AC, AD, BC,* and *BE* give a diagram like that of Fig. 9-9 on page 191 for a pair of liquids which exhibit a minimum boiling point, but it is cut off by a horizontal straight line at about 94°.

If a solution of composition *l* is evaporated, the vapor will contain more water than the solution, the solution will become richer in n-bu-

* Stockhardt and Hull, *Ind. Eng. Chem.*, *23*, 1438 (1931).

tanol, and the temperature will rise until the boiling point of pure butanol is reached. If, however, a mixture lying between D and E is evaporated, the boiling point remains constant as long as the two phases are
present. One is of composition D which is rich in water and the other
of composition E which is less rich in water. The composition of each
phase remains unchanged when the mixture of the two solutions is
evaporated as long as both phases are present, but the relative amounts
of the phases change. The composition of the vapor is given by C,
and it remains constant until one of the phases is evaporated away. If
only the butanol-rich phase remains, the temperature will rise along the
line EB, and the composition of the vapor at any liquid composition
can be determined by drawing a horizontal line similar to vl. At lower
temperatures, as, for example, when distilling under reduced pressure,
the range of immiscibility is wider, and so the line DE of constant composition and boiling temperature would broaden along the lines EG and
DF below D.

In *Fig. 12-12* is shown the system molybdenum and cobalt, which
bears a resemblance to the partially miscible liquids of Fig. 12-11 and
the solid solutions of Fig. 12-10. Solid solutions are observed, but solid
solutions with more than 21 per cent molybdenum do not mix with the
cobalt-molybdenum compound. From this diagram it is possible to
predict what products will be obtained by fractional crystallization,
starting with various composition and temperature ranges.

Under equilibrium conditions the freezing-point curve for the CoMo
compound does not reach the maximum temperature, the melting point
of the pure CoMo, because it is intersected first by the freezing-point
curve of pure molybdenum.

Uses of Temperature-Concentration Phase Diagrams. Phase
diagrams are of great help in understanding the production and behavior
of alloys, ceramics, and complex mixtures of organic and inorganic compounds. The presence of a maximum in the curve shows that a chemical
compound is produced by the combination of two substances and gives
the information regarding temperature and concentrations which is
necessary to produce this compound.

Many desirable properties of alloys, ceramics, and structural materials depend on the components being in the form of solid solutions.
The hardening and tempering of steel involve the existence of solid solutions of carbon in different iron-carbon compounds. The solid solution
stable at the high temperatures is hard, and, in order to retain this
hardness, the proper compositions and temperatures are obtained, as
indicated by the phase diagrams, and then the steel is quenched quickly
in oil or water, so that it does not have time to form the solid solution

which is stable at lower temperatures. By heating up again to a some-what lower temperature, opportunity is given for partial conversion to the softer solid solution which is stable at the lower temperature. In this way the steel may be given different degrees of hardening.

Exercise V. Describe the iron-carbon diagram shown in *Fig. 12-13*, stating the variances for each area, line, and point.

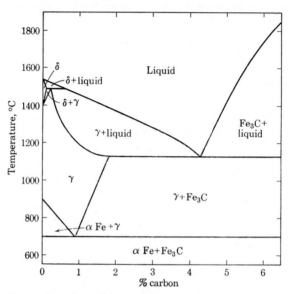

FIG. 12-13. Iron-carbon phase diagram (αFe, ferrite; γ, austenite; Fe$_3$C, cementite).

Three-Component Systems. Whereas the composition of a system of two components can be readily represented with rectangular coordinates, the composition of a three-component system calls for representation with an equilateral triangle. In such a triangle, in which all the angles are 60°, the sum of the distances from any given point to the three sides, along the perpendiculars, is equal to the height of the triangle. The perpendicular height from each apex to the opposite side of the equilateral triangle is divided into 100 parts, corresponding to percentage composition, and the composition corresponding to a given point is readily obtained by measuring the distance along the perpendiculars toward each of the three apices. The three percentages must add up to 100 per cent.

The use of triangular diagrams is illustrated in *Fig. 12-14* for a system consisting of the three liquids, water, acetic acid, and vinyl acetate, at 25° and atmospheric pressure.* For example, the point O represents

* Smith, *J. Phys. Chem.*, *45*, 1301 (1941).

50 per cent of acetic acid, that is, 50 units out of 100 from the base toward the apex A of 100 per cent acetic acid; 10 per cent of vinyl acetate, and 40 per cent of water.

When water is added to pure vinyl acetate along the line BC the water dissolves at first forming a homogeneous solution, but as more water is added saturation is reached at composition x, and there are two liquid phases, vinyl acetate saturated with water and a little water saturated

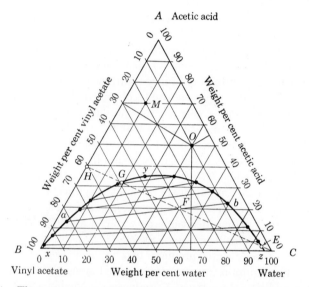

FIG. 12-14.   Three-component phase diagram at 25° showing regions of miscibility and immiscibility plotted on triangular coordinates.

with vinyl acetate, having the composition z. As more water is added the amount of the z phase increases and that of the x phase decreases, but the composition of each phase remains always the same. Finally, when the per cent of water exceeds that given by z, there is only one liquid phase, an unsaturated solution of vinyl acetate in water. At all compositions between x and z there are two liquid phases of compositions x and z.

If acetic acid, which dissolves completely in both liquids, is added, it renders the aqueous phase more soluble in the vinyl acetate phase, and vice versa. Acetic acid distributes itself between the two layers, forming two immiscible ternary solutions of vinyl acetate, water, and acetic acid which are in equilibrium with each other. These solutions are represented by two points such as a and b within the triangular diagram. The line joining a and b is known as a *tie line*. Other tie lines are shown for other compositions; usually they are not parallel to the base BC of the triangle. The compositions of the two phases, which are in equilibrium with each other, corresponding to the intersection of the tie line with the curves xy and zy have to be determined experimentally. As more acid is added, the two phases become more alike, and the tie lines become shorter, and, ultimately, when the compositions of the two solutions become identical, they shrink to the single point y. The point y is a *critical point*, since further addition of acetic acid will result in the formation of a single homogeneous phase. Any point under the curve represents a ternary mixture which will separate into two liquid phases; any point above the curve represents a single homogeneous liquid phase.

A ternary mixture whose over-all composition is represented by the point F will separate into two ternary solutions having the compositions a and b. Significant information can be obtained by drawing a line from C representing pure water, through the specified point F, and extending it to cut the curve at G and the line AB at H. Starting now with a mixture of vinyl acetate and acetic acid at H and adding water, the over-all composition of the system is given by points in succession passing from H to C. Along the line HG, the addition of water gives a single homogeneous liquid phase, in which the ratio of vinyl acetate to acetic acid is always equal to HA/HB. The percentage of vinyl acetate and acetic acid in the total system decreases as water is added, but the ratio of their percentages remains constant at $60/40$. When point G is reached, the addition of more water produces two liquid phases, and two phases persist in equilibrium as more water is added along the line GE. From E to C the addition of more water produces a single homogeneous phase, the water being in such large excess that the vinyl acetate and acetic acid can both dissolve in it. Between G and E the quantity of the phase which is richer in water increases and the phase which has the smaller percentage of water decreases in quantity. Not only do the relative amounts of the two different liquid phases change, but also the composition of each phase changes as indicated by the intersections of the tie lines with the curve xyz. The over-all ratio of vinyl acetate to acetic acid in the two solutions, added together, is still, however, equal to HA/HB.

Vinyl acetate and water become more soluble at higher temperatures, and the region where there are two immiscible phases would become smaller. The line xyz would fall below its present position at higher temperatures.

In applying the phase rule to these triangular diagrams, it must be remembered that the temperature is fixed, and the pressure is fixed at a value high enough to condense the vapor. Then $v = c - p + 0 = 3 - p$.

The percentage compositions X of two of the three components are the only variables, but these may apply to several different liquid phases. When there is but one liquid phase, as in Fig. 12-14 above xyz, the variance is $3 - 1 + 0 = 2$, namely X_A and X_B (or X_B and X_C, or X_A and X_C), where A, B, and C are the components. The composition of the third component is not a variable because it can be determined by subtracting the sum of the other two from 100 per cent.

Where there are two liquid phases, as in the area below the line xyz, $v = 3 - 2 = 1$. Along the line xyz on the triangular diagram, as soon

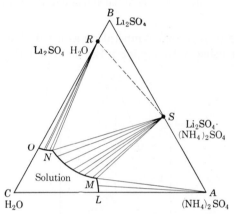

Fig. 12-15. Triangular diagram showing regions of solubility and double salt formation for two salts in water.

as the percentage of one component in one phase is specified, the system is completely described. For example, if on the line xyz the water is specified at 5 per cent giving the point a, the compositions of vinyl acetate and acetic acid in this vinyl acetate layer are easily obtained, as is also the composition of the other liquid phase having the composition b. When a point is chosen below xyz the tie line passing through it will specify the concentration of both liquid phases.

Another type of phase diagram is shown in *Fig. 12-15*. Here two different salts and water are given at the three apices of the equilateral triangle. The area at the left of the curve $ONML$ represents unsaturated solution. The solubility in water of pure $(NH_4)_2SO_4$ in per cent at 30° is given by L; and the solubility of pure Li_2SO_4 is given by O. The line LM shows how the solubility of $(NH_4)_2SO_4$ is decreased by the addition of Li_2SO_4, and the line ON shows how the solubility of Li_2SO_4 is changed by the addition of $(NH_4)_2SO_4$. Along the line MN, a double salt $Li_2SO_4 \cdot (NH_4)_2SO_4$ precipitates out. The tie lines give the composition of the solution that is in equilibrium with the salt for any total composition specified within these areas.

Exercise VI. Show that the phase rule applies in the various areas shown in Fig. 12-15. In area $CONML$ there is one liquid phase and $v = 2$. In the area NMS there are two phases, solid $Li_2SO_4 \cdot (NH_4)_2SO_4$ and saturated solution of the composition given by the intersection of the tie line with the line NM. Then $v = 1$, and the composition of the saturated solution is the only variable. In the area SAM there is solid $Li_2SO_4 \cdot (NH_4)_2SO_4$, solid $(NH_4)_2SO_4$, and saturated solution of composition M. $v = 3 - 3 = 0$. The relative amounts of the three phases change in the different parts of area SAM, but the composition of each phase is always the same. Name the phases and state the variance in the areas AML, RSN, and RSB.

It is possible to represent temperature as a variable in a three-component system using a triangular prism in which the temperature is

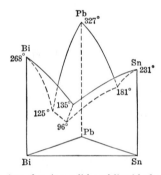

FIG. 12-16.　Triangular prism showing solid and liquid phases for a three-component system at different temperatures.

plotted at right angles to the base of the prism. Such prisms are useful in determining the composition of a three-metal alloy which will give the lowest possible melting point. Low-melting alloys are used, for example, in automatic water sprinklers for fire protection. *Figure 12-16* illustrates the representation of three components and temperature. The front plane gives the freezing-point curves of bismuth and tin with a eutectic at 135°; the plane at the left of the back gives the freezing-point curves for bismuth and lead with a eutectic at 125°; and the remaining plane for lead and tin gives a eutectic at 181°. When these three binary freezing-point curves are placed vertically and joined along the edges, a triangular prism is formed. A pair of freezing-point depression curves extends below the melting point of each pure metal, and these are connected by a surface. The extensions of each of these three surfaces meet in a eutectic point at 96° where all three metals freeze out together. This is the lowest possible melting temperature that can be obtained from any mixture of these three metals, and the exact composition of this ternary alloy is found by projecting a vertical line down from this point until it hits the triangular base. Without the help of such curves and space models a great many more "cut and try"

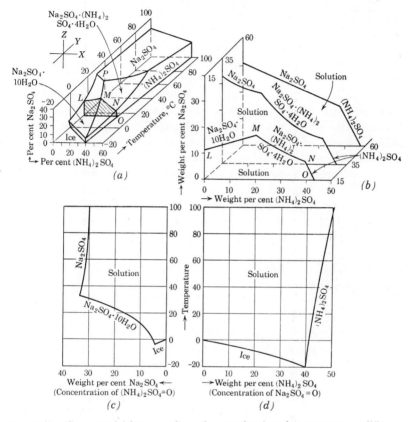

FIG. 12-17. Space model for two salts and water showing phases present at different concentrations of salts and at different temperatures.

experiments would be required to find the composition which has the lowest possible melting point.

Some three-component systems may be represented with rectangular coordinates at various temperatures by space models of the type shown in *Fig. 12-17a*. The per cent by weight of ammonium sulfate in aqueous solution is plotted along the X axis, the percentage of sodium sulfate is plotted along the Z axis, and temperature is plotted along the Y axis at right angles to the two concentration axes. The meaning of this space model is made apparent by the three graphs accompanying the model. The left side of the model is shown at c, where the concentration of ammonium sulfate is zero. The figure gives simply the concentration-temperature graph for sodium sulfate in water. It shows the solubility curve of Na_2SO_4 and of $Na_2SO_4 \cdot 10H_2O$ and the freezing-point curve along which ice separates. The bottom of the model shown at d gives the concentration-temperature graph for ammonium sulfate, and the solubility and freezing-point curves are shown intersecting at the eutectic point or cryohydric point. In Fig. 12-17b three isothermal planes are shown intersecting the space model at 15°, 35°, and 60°. The model is constructed by placing Figs. 12-17c and 12-17d at right angles and spacing the isothermal concentration curves shown in b for the two salts at the proper intervals along the temperature axis. If desired, plaster of paris or other plastic material can be used to construct a space model along the curves given in these three dimensions.

The isothermal section at 15° is labeled $LMNO$ in Figs. 12-17a and b. The solubility of $Na_2SO_4 \cdot 10H_2O$ in pure water at 15° is 11 per cent by weight. As $(NH_4)_2SO_4$ is added to the solution, the solubility of $Na_2SO_4 \cdot 10H_2O$ increases along the line LM. When the solution contains 21 per cent $(NH_4)_2SO_4$, the solubility of $Na_2SO_4 \cdot 10H_2O$ is 16.5 per cent (expressed as per cent of Na_2SO_4). When more ammonium sulfate is added, a double salt makes its appearance along MN, and, the more ammonium sulfate is added, the lower is the solubility of this double salt. The line NO represents the decrease in solubility of $(NH_4)_2SO_4$ at 15° caused by the addition of Na_2SO_4 to the solution. Similar curves are shown for 35° and 60°. In the space model shown in Fig. 12-17a the pressure is fixed, and the vapor is considered to be condensed. All the volume inside the space model refers to unsaturated salt solution. It is the only phase present, and there are three degrees of freedom. Percentages of two components in the solution and temperature must be specified in order to define the system completely. ($v = 3 - 1 + 1 = 3$.)

The various solid phases touching the model are specified on the model. For example, on top of the model there is Na_2SO_4, at the right there is $(NH_4)_2SO_4$, over the curved face is the double salt $Na_2SO_4 \cdot (NH_4)_2SO_4 \cdot 4H_2O$, and in front of the model is ice. At these surfaces there are two phases (solution and a solid phase). Along the lines there are three phases, and at the points of intersection there are four phases. The variances are, respectively, 2, 1, and 0. For example, at the point P there are Na_2SO_4, $Na_2SO_4 \cdot 10H_2O$, $Na_2SO_4 \cdot (NH_4)_2SO_4 \cdot 4H_2O$, and solution; then $v = 3 - 4 + 1 = 0$.

REFERENCES

Findlay, Campbell, and Smith, *The Phase Rule and Its Applications*, Dover Publications, New York, 1951.

Hill in Taylor's *Treatise on Physical Chemistry*, D. Van Nostrand Co., New York, 1931, Chapter IX.

Purdon and Slater, *Aqueous Solutions and Phase Diagrams*, Edward Arnold & Co., London, 1946.

Bowden, *The Phase Rule and Phase Reactions*, The Macmillan Co., New York, 1938.

Blasdale, *Equilibria in Saturated Salt Solutions*, Chemical Catalog Co., New York, 1927.

Hall and Insley, *A Compilation of Phase-Rule Diagrams of Interest to the Ceramicist and Silicate Technologist*, American Ceramic Society, 1933.

Seidell, *Solubility of Organic and Inorganic Compounds*, D. Van Nost·and Co., New York, 1954.

Deming, "An Introduction to the Phase Rule," *J. Chem. Education*, *16*, 215, 260 (1939).

Briggs, "Phase Diagrams and the Mass Law," *J. Chem. Education*, *20*, 484 (1943).

PROBLEMS

1. At $1273°K$ and at a total pressure of 30 atm the equilibrium in the reaction $CO_2(g) + C(s) = 2CO(g)$ is such that 17 molar per cent of the gas is CO_2. (a) What percentage would be CO_2 if the total pressure were 20 atm? (b) What would be the effect on the equilibrium of adding N_2 until the partial pressure of N_2 is 10 atm? (c) At what pressure will 25 per cent of the gas be CO_2?

$Ans.$ (a) 12.5%. (b) No effect. (c) 54 atm.

2. Picric acid distributes itself between the two immiscible solvents, benzene and water, at different concentrations as follows:

Conc. in Water Phase	Conc. in Benzene Phase
0.00208 mole/liter	0.000932 mole/liter
0.00327	0.00225
0.00701	0.0101
0.0101	0.0199

Picric acid exists as nondissociated and nonassociated $C_6H_2(NO_2)_3OH$ in benzene. What conclusions can you draw regarding dissociation or association in the water phase? $Ans.$ Picric acid dissolved in water dissociates into two ions.

3. When platinum is heated in the presence of chlorine gas the following reaction takes place

$$Pt(s) + Cl_2(g) = PtCl_2(g)$$

At $1000°K$, $\Delta F°_{1000°} = 14$ kcal. If the pressure of Cl_2 is 1 atm, what will be the partial pressure of $PtCl_2$? $Ans.$ 8.7×10^{-4} atm

4. For the reaction at $750°C$

$$\tfrac{1}{2}SnO_2(s) + H_2(g) = \tfrac{1}{2}Sn(s) + H_2O(g)$$

the total pressure of the system is 32.0 mm and the partial pressure of water is 23.7 mm. (a) Calculate K_p for this reaction. For the reaction

$$H_2(g) + CO_2(g) = CO(g) + H_2O(g)$$

K_p has a value of 0.771 at 750°C. (b) Calculate K_p for the reaction

$$\tfrac{1}{2}SnO_2(s) + CO(g) = \tfrac{1}{2}Sn(s) + CO_2(g)$$

Ans. (a) 2.85. (b) 3.71.

5. The vapor pressure of water above mixtures of $CuCl_2 \cdot H_2O(s)$ and $CuCl_2 \cdot 2H_2O(s)$ is given as a function of temperature in the following table:

$t°$	17.9	39.8	60.0	80.0
p, atm	0.0049	0.0247	0.120	0.322

(a) Calculate $\Delta H°$ for the reaction $CuCl_2 \cdot 2H_2O(s) = CuCl_2 \cdot H_2O(s) + H_2O(g)$. (b) Calculate $\Delta F°$ for the reaction at 60.0°. (c) Calculate $\Delta S°$ for the reaction at 60.0°.
Ans. (a) 13,700 cal mole^{-1}. (b) 1410 cal mole^{-1}. (c) 36.9 cal deg^{-1} mole^{-1}.

6. Mercuric oxide dissociates according to the reaction, $2HgO(s) = 2Hg(g) + O_2(g)$. At 420° the dissociation pressure is 387 mm, and at 450° it is 810 mm. Calculate (a) the dissociation constants, and (b) the heat of dissociation per mole.
Ans. (a) 0.0196; 0.1794 atm^3, (b) 36,750 cal mole^{-1}.

✓ 7. For UF_6 the vapor pressures (in millimeters) for the solid and liquid are given by

$$\log p_s = 10.648 - 2{,}559.5/T$$

$$\log p_l = 7.540 - 1{,}511.3/T$$

Calculate the temperature and pressure of the triple point.   Ans. 64°, 1142 mm.

8. Calculate the solubility of monoclinic sulfur in CCl_4 at 25°. That of rhombic sulfur is 0.84 grams per 100 grams of CCl_4. Sulfur exists in both solutions as S_8. The free energy of formation of monoclinic sulfur is 23 cal per mole greater than that of rhombic sulfur at 25°.   Ans. 1.14 gram per 100 grams CCl_4.

9. Construct and interpret the phase diagram based on the following data where N_{PbI_2} is the mole fraction of lead iodide and t is the freezing point of the solution in degrees centigrade for the system KI-PbI_2:

N_{PbI_2}	1.00	0.90	0.80	0.70	0.60	0.50	0.40	0.30	0.20	0.10	0.0
$t°$	412	395	367	324	337	349	422	504	585	641	686

Assume that all compositions below 0.5 N_{PbI_2} give a final solidification temperature of 346°.
Ans. Compound $KI \cdot PbI_2$ melting at 349°.
Eutectics at 0.47 N_{PbI_2} and 346° and 0.7 N_{PbI_2} and 324°.

10. (a) Under what conditions of temperature and composition is it possible to produce crystals of $H_2SO_4 \cdot H_2O$? (b) How would you try to prepare the compound $MoCo$?   Ans. (a) 50 mole per cent H_2SO_4 below 8°C.
(b) 50 mole per cent Mo below 1480°C.

11. Interpret the phase diagram for CaO and ZrO_2, Fig. 12-18, stating the phases and the variance at each area, line, and point.

PROBLEMS 313

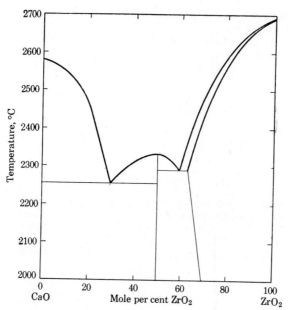

FIG. 12-18. Phase diagram for calcium oxide-zirconium oxide.

12. The following tie line data have been obtained for the ternary system benzene-isobutanol-water at 25°.

Compositions of Phases in Equilibrium

Water-Rich Phase		Benzene-Rich Phase	
Isobutanol, weight %	Water, weight %	Isobutanol, weight %	Benzene, weight %
2.33	97.39	3.61	96.20
4.30	95.44	19.87	79.07
5.23	94.59	39.57	57.09
6.04	93.83	59.48	33.98
7.32	92.64	76.51	11.39

Plot these data on a triangular graph, indicating the tie lines. (a) Estimate the compositions of the phases which will be produced from a mixture of 20 per cent isobutanol, 55 per cent water, and 25 per cent benzene. (b) What will be the composition of the first drop of the second phase which separates when water is added to a solution of 80 per cent isobutyl alcohol in benzene?

Ans. (a) H_2O layer: 5.23% isobutanol, 94.5% H_2O.

Benzene layer: 39.57% isobutanol, 57.09% benzene.

(b) 10% H_2O; 72% isobutanol; 18% benzene.

13. Ten grams of calcium carbonate is placed in a container of 1-liter capacity and heated to 800°. (a) How many grams of calcium carbonate remain undecom-

posed? (*b*) If the amount of $CaCO_3$ were 20 grams, how much would remain undecomposed?

14. The equilibrium pressure of solid NH_4HS is 500 mm at 25°. Assuming that the vapor is completely decomposed into NH_3 and H_2S, calculate the maximum pressure of H_2S which can be added to a system containing NH_3 at 50 mm without precipitating NH_4HS.

15. Calculate $\Delta H°$ for the reaction

$$CaCO_3(s) = CaO(s) + CO_2(g)$$

in the range 1000–1200° from the data of Table I, page 277.

16. For the reaction $Fe_2O_3(s) + 3CO(g) = 2Fe(s) + 3CO_2(g)$ the following values of K_p are known:

t°C	100	250	1000
K_p	1100	100	0.0721

At 1120° for the reaction $2CO_2(g) = 2CO(g) + O_2(g)$, $K_p = 1.4 \times 10^{-12}$ atm. What equilibrium partial pressure of O_2 would have to be supplied to a vessel at 1120° containing 1 mole of solid Fe_2O_3 in order just to prevent the formation of Fe?

17. The distribution coefficient at 25° of lactic acid between water and chloroform c_{CHCl_3}/c_{H_2O} is 0.0203 when concentrations are expressed in moles per liter. (*a*) How much lactic acid will be extracted from 100 ml of a 0.8 molar solution of lactic acid in chloroform by shaking with 100 ml of water? (*b*) How much will be extracted if the 100 ml of chloroform is shaken first with 50 ml of water and later with another 50 ml of water?

18. For the reaction $2NaHCO_3(s) = Na_2CO_3(s) + CO_2(g) + H_2O(g)$, $K_p = 0.23$ at 100°. On a day when the barometric pressure was 740 mm, the room temperature 27°, and the relative humidity 0.70, 20 grams of solid sodium bicarbonate was placed in a 5-liter flask and sealed with the air from the room. It was then brought up to 100°. (*a*) What was the partial pressure of CO_2 at equilibrium in the flask (if the carbon dioxide of the air is neglected)? The vapor pressure of water at 27° is 26.8 mm. (*b*) What was the pressure in the flask?

19. The following cooling curves have been found for the system antimony-cadmium.

Per cent cadmium by weight	0	20	37.5	47.5	50	58	70	93	100
First break in curve, °C	...	550	461	....	419	...	400	...	...
Continuing constant temp., °C	630	410	410	410	410	439	295	295	321

Construct a phase diagram assuming that no other breaks than these actually occur in any cooling curve. Label the diagram completely, and give the formula of any compound formed.

20. Sketch a phase diagram for thallium and mercury with freezing points plotted against per cent by weight. Use the following facts: mercury melts at $-39°$; the compound Tl_2Hg_5 melts at 15°; thallium melts at 303°; thallium lowers the freezing point of mercury down to a minimum of $-60°$ at a composition of 8 per cent thallium; the eutectic point for Tl and Tl_2Hg_5 is 0.4° at a composition corresponding to 41 per cent thallium. Label the phases present at each area, line, and point.

21. (*a*) Referring to Fig. 12-8 choose two areas, two lines, and two points, and state what components and what phases are present. (*b*) State how many degrees of freedom there are at each of these areas, lines, and points. (*c*) Name the solid and liquid phases which appear in succession as water vapor is pumped away from a dilute solution of sulfuric acid which is maintained at $-30°C$.

22. The following data are available for the system $NiSO_4$-H_2SO_4-H_2O at 25°. Sketch the phase diagram on triangular coordinate paper, and draw appropriate tie lines.

Liquid Phase

Wt. % $NiSO_4$	Wt. % H_2SO_4	Composition of Solid Phase
28.13	0	$NiSO_4 \cdot 7H_2O$
27.34	1.79	"
27.16	3.86	"
26.15	4.92	$NiSO_4 \cdot 6H_2O$
22.26	7.93	"
15.64	19.34	·
10.56	44.68	"
9.65	48.46	$NiSO_4 \cdot H_2O$
2.67	63.73	"
0.23	72.38	"
0.12	91.38	"
0.11	93.74	$NiSO_4$
0.08	96.80	"

23. The following are the data for the system methylcyclohexane-aniline-n-heptane at 1 atm and 25°. Draw a triangular diagram for the system, including tie lines, and compute the exact composition of the first drop of the new liquid phase to form when a sufficient quantity of pure aniline is added to a 40 per cent solution of methylcyclohexane in n-heptane to give separation into two phases.

Hydrocarbon Layer		Aniline Layer	
Wt. % Methylcyclohexane	Wt. % n-Heptane	Wt. % Methylcyclohexane	Wt. % n-Heptane
0.0	92.0	0.0	6.2
9.2	83.0	0.8	6.0
18.6	73.4	2.7	5.3
33.8	57.6	4.6	4.5
46.0	45.0	7.4	3.6
59.7	30.7	9.2	2.8
73.6	16.0	13.1	1.4
83.3	5.4	15.6	0.6
88.1	0.0	16.9	0.0

24. For the reaction:

$$PtCl(s) = Pt(s) + \tfrac{1}{2}Cl_2(g) \qquad \Delta F°_{500°K} = 6000 \text{ cal}$$

calculate the equilibrium pressure of chlorine at 500°K.

25. In the formation of 1 mole of $AgI(s)$ from solid silver and solid iodine 14,815 cal are evolved at 25°. From specific heat measurements at low temperatures the molal entropy of $AgI(s)$ at 25° has been found to be 27.6 cal per degree, whereas the

atomic entropy of silver at 25° is 10.2 and that of iodine is 13.3 cal per degree. Calculate the standard molal free energy of $AgI(s)$ at 25°.

26. From the entropy values and the heats of formation given in Chapters 6 and 7, together with the value 29.09 cal $degree^{-1}$ $mole^{-1}$ for the entropy of Ag_2O at 25°, calculate $\Delta F°$ and K for the reaction,

$$2Ag_2O(s) = 4Ag(s) + O_2(g)$$

at 25°. What is the dissociation pressure of Ag_2O at 25°?

27. The data for the solubility of urea in water are given below. Calculate the heat of solution of urea in H_2O at 100°C.

N_{urea}	1.000	0.9004	0.8190	0.7217	0.5680	0.4741
$t°$	132.6	123.2	115.3	104.4	84.4	68.5

28. The following data for isobutene may be found in the literature. Using these data, calculate the free energy of formation of gaseous isobutene at 25° (Todd and Parks, *J. Am. Chem. Soc.*, *58*, 134 (1936)).

$$S_{90°K} = 10.81 \text{ cal } deg^{-1} \text{ } mole^{-1}$$
$$\text{F.P.} = -140.7°$$
$$\text{Heat of fusion} = 25.22 \text{ cal per gram}$$
$$\text{B.P.} = -7.1°$$
$$\text{Heat of vaporization} = 96.5 \text{ cal per gram}$$
$$\Delta H \text{ of formation } (25°) = -4060 \text{ cal}$$
$$C_p \text{ (gas) in range } 226\text{--}298°K = 20 \text{ cal } deg^{-1} \text{ } mole^{-1}$$

Specific Heat

°K	93.3	105.5	118.9	139.2	166.1	179.8	210.2	253.1
C_p	0.2498	0.2749	0.3056	0.4547	0.4621	0.4681	0.4860	0.5173

29. Ammonium hydroselenide dissociates (Mikus and Poss, *J. Am. Chem. Soc.*, *71*, 429 (1949)) as follows:

$$NH_4HSe(s) = NH_3(g) + H_2Se(g)$$

(a) Express K_p in terms of total pressure. K_p increases with temperature as follows:

Temperature, °C	15	18	21	24.8	29.3
$K_p \times 10^4$	0.20	0.31	0.45	0.85	1.9

(b) What is the value of ΔH for this reaction at 18°C?

30. The heat of vaporization of water at 0° is 10,720 cal $mole^{-1}$, and the heat of sublimation of ice is 12,120 cal $mole^{-1}$. Given the fact that the triple point is at 0.0099° and a pressure of 4.57 mm of mercury, calculate the vapor pressure of water at 15° and of ice at −15° using the Clausius-Clapeyron equation. These three points are used to construct a plot of log p versus $1/T$. The fusion curve may be drawn in as a vertical line above the triple point since the effect of pressures in this range is negligible. The regions in the diagram are then labeled.

31. Which process will be most important in the vaporization of $NiCl_2$: (a) vaporization of gaseous nickel chloride molecules or (b) decomposition to $Ni(s)$ and $Cl_2(g)$? The equilibrium gas pressure over $NiCl_2(s)$ is 10^{-3} atm at 934°K. Use these data:

	$-(F° - H°_{298})/T$ cal deg^{-1} mole^{-1}			$\Delta H°_{298}$
	298.1°K	500°K	1000°K	kcal mole^{-1}
$NiCl_2(s)$	25.6	27.1	34.5	−73
$Ni(s)$	7.12	7.82	10.68	0
$Cl_2(g)$	53.31	54.25	57.65	0
$Ni(g)$	43.53	44.17	46.46	101.75

32. Given the following freezing points at several compositions of magnesium and bismuth:

Per cent by weight Mg	0	10	15	20	30	40	70	100
Temperature at which freezing occurs	271°	640°	710°	670°	600°	560°	610°	652°
Eutectic temperature	—	271°	553°	553°	553°	553°	553°	—

Plot temperature versus mole per cent magnesium, and calculate the composition of the compound formed.

33. Given the system water, KNO_3, and $NaNO_3$ at 25°. Sketch this system on a triangular diagram, labeling the areas in which you would expect to find (a) only solution; (b) a mixture of solution and solid KNO_3; (c) a mixture of solution and solid $NaNO_3$; (d) a mixture of solid KNO_3, $NaNO_3$, and solution. The solubility of KNO_3 in pure water is 46.2 per cent, the solubility of $NaNO_3$ in pure water is 52.2 per cent, and all three of these phases are in equilibrium when the composition is as follows: water 31.3 per cent, KNO_3 28.9 per cent, and $NaNO_3$ 39.8 per cent. No crystalline hydrates or double salts are formed.

34. The following data are available for the system Na_2SO_4-$Al_2(SO_4)_3$-H_2O at 42°. Draw the phase diagram on triangular coordinate paper, and draw in some appropriate tie lines.

Liquid Phase		Composition of
Wt. % Na_2SO_4	Wt. % $Al_2(SO_4)_3$	Solid Phase
33.20	0	Na_2SO_4
32.00	1.52	Na_2SO_4
31.79	1.87	Na_2SO_4
28.75	1.71	$Na_2SO_4 \cdot Al_2(SO_4)_3 \cdot 14H_2O$
24.47	2.84	$Na_2SO_4 \cdot Al_2(SO_4)_3 \cdot 14H_2O$
16.81	5.63	$Na_2SO_4 \cdot Al_2(SO_4)_3 \cdot 14H_2O$
10.93	10.49	$Na_2SO_4 \cdot Al_2(SO_4)_3 \cdot 14H_2O$
4.72	17.11	$Na_2SO_4 \cdot Al_2(SO_4)_3 \cdot 14H_2O$
1.75	18.59	$Al_2(SO_4)_3$
0	16.45	$Al_2(SO_4)_3$

13

Chemical Kinetics

The aim of chemical kinetics is to predict the rates of chemical reactions and to understand the mechanisms of reaction. It is more difficult than the prediction of chemical equilibria, which are concerned only with the initial and final states and not with time or intermediate states. Science has not progressed very far in the prediction of reaction rates, but the mere fact that the study of kinetics is a pioneer field adds interest to the subject. Many chemical changes involve two or more reactions which are going on simultaneously in a very complicated manner. Impurities and traces of catalysts are likely to change the velocities, so that it is often difficult to obtain reproducible results.

Most ionic reactions of inorganic chemistry take place so fast that their rates cannot be measured, but in many of the reactions of organic chemistry the study of chemical kinetics is particularly important. Most reactions of organic chemistry are slow, and the relative rates of competing reactions are often more important considerations than is the extent to which the reactions are completed at equilibrium. If two organic substances are mixed together, there may be many different products which are all possible according to thermodynamics. By altering the concentrations and the temperature and by using specific catalysts, it is possible to bring about a desired reaction. If there are many competing reactions which use up the reacting material there will be many different products. Only if one of the reactions goes much faster than all the others is it possible to obtain a high yield of a single product.

Experimental Measurements of Reaction Rates. Usually, reaction rates are studied under conditions of constant temperature, preferably at two or more temperatures. A well-regulated thermostat is thus necessary in most kinetic studies. The rate of a chemical reaction may be followed in many different ways. Samples may be removed from the thermostated reaction vessel at intervals, chilled rapidly, and analyzed by titration or other analytical methods. Again, several bulbs of reacting material may be started out together, and each may be chilled quickly at different time intervals and analyzed. The chill-

318

ing must be so rapid that the concentration does not change appreciably during the sampling operation.

Physical means of analysis which do not disturb the system are convenient. For example, the concentration of one of the materials may be determined by measuring the absorption of light at a given wavelength and applying Beer's law. The use of ultraviolet and infrared light makes possible wider applications of this method. If one of the reactants or products rotates the plane of polarized light, its concentration may be determined during the course of the reaction with the help of a polarimeter.

An increase in volume of a solution during the course of the reaction may be followed with a dilatometer which has a large bulb and capillary with a scale, like a thermometer. Again, the volume of gas evolved by certain reactions in a liquid solution may be taken as a measure of the extent of the reaction. The volume V_0 is measured at the beginning and the volume V_∞ when the reaction has been completed. Measurements of volume V_t are taken at various times t during the reaction. Then $V_\infty - V_0$ is a measure of the total amount of material that can react, and $V_\infty - V_t$ is the measure of the amount of material that still remains unreacted at time t. Then, the fraction of the material remaining unreacted at time t is given by the expression $(V_\infty - V_t)/(V_\infty - V_0)$.

Example 1. When nitrogen pentoxide decomposes in carbon tetrachloride solution, oxygen gas is evolved. In one experiment 23.95 ml of gas was evolved during 1 hour's time, and, after standing till no more gas was given off, the total volume of the gas was 34.75 ml. What fraction of nitrogen pentoxide remained unreacted after 1 hour?

Fraction unreacted = $(34.75 - 23.95)/34.75 = 0.311$

Electrical conductivity of a solution and total pressure of a gas are other physical properties that may be used in a similar manner to follow the rate of a chemical reaction. In complicated reactions, however, it is unwise to use total pressure as a measure of the extent of decomposition unless the measurements are accompanied by chemical or physical analyses which are specific for one or more of the reacting substances.

Example 2. In the gaseous reaction $C_2H_5Br \rightarrow C_2H_4 + HBr$, the pressure increased from 200 mm at the beginning to 390 mm at the end. After 500 seconds the pressure was 300 mm. What fraction remained undecomposed? If it is assumed that the pressure should double to 400 mm at the end, as indicated by the equation, half of the material would be left, that is, $(400 - 300)/(400 - 200) = 0.50$. However, the fact that the final pressure was 10 mm less than 400 mm indicates that some complication is involved, and the calculation is not entirely safe. Obviously, some other reaction in addition to the one written on paper is involved. In this example the polymerization of ethylene on the walls accounts for part of the pressure change.

The rate of a reaction may be determined by measuring either the rate of decrease of the concentrations of the reactants or the rate of increase of the concentrations of the products. The rate of increase of concentration is represented by dc/dt, and the rate of decrease of concentration is represented by $-dc/dt$.

The flow method, as distinguished from a closed-vessel method, is often useful especially for gas reactions. The volume of the vessel divided by the volume of the gases passing through the vessel in 1 second gives a measure of the time in seconds during which the gases are in the vessel. The reaction vessel or tube may be filled with a solid catalyst or the temperature may be raised so as to accelerate the reaction, while the inlet and outlet tubes are small so that the gases will enter and leave the reaction zone quickly and thus be exposed to regions of uncertain temperature gradients for only negligible periods of time. The exact time of residence in the reaction tube is difficult to determine, particularly if there is a change in the number of gaseous molecules during the reaction. Nevertheless the flow method has the advantages * that it makes possible the use of large quantities of materials for analysis and that it simulates the flow processes of industrial chemistry.

Example 3. A volume of 1200 ml of gas is passed through a 100-ml heated tube in 300 seconds. The volume is the calculated volume of the gas at the temperature of the furnace. How long is each moelcule at this higher temperature, assuming no change in the number of molecules due to chemical reaction?

The flow of gas is 1200/300, or 4 ml per second. The time t of residence of the gas in the tube is given by the calculation:

$$t = (100 \text{ ml})/(4 \text{ ml sec}^{-1}) = 25 \text{ sec}$$

First-Order Reactions. The first consideration in chemical kinetics is the influence of concentration on the reaction rate. The simplest case is the *first-order reaction*, in which the rate of reaction is found by experiment to be directly proportional to the concentration of the reacting substance. The situation is described mathematically as follows:

$$-dc/dt = kc \tag{1}$$

where c is the concentration of reacting material, t is the time, $-dc/dt$ is the rate at which the concentration decreases, and k is the constant known as the specific reaction-rate constant or velocity constant.

Integrating, we have

$$- \ln c = kt + \text{constant}$$

$$\log c = - \frac{k}{2.303} t - \frac{\text{constant}}{2.303} \tag{2}$$

* Hougen and Watson, *Chemical Process Principles*, Part III, *Kinetics and Catalysis*, John Wiley & Sons, New York, 1947, page 832.

Thus in a first-order reaction a straight line is produced when the logarithm of the concentration is plotted against time. The velocity constant k can be evaluated by multiplying the slope of the line by -2.303.

Integrating equation 1 between the limits, concentration c_1 at time t_1, and c_2 at a later time t_2, we have

$$-\int_{c_1}^{c_2} \frac{dc}{c} = k \int_{t_1}^{t_2} dt$$

$$- \ln c_2 - (- \ln c_1) = k(t_2 - t_1)$$

$$k = \frac{2.303}{t_2 - t_1} \log \frac{c_1}{c_2} \tag{3}$$

This equation may be modified to give the following equation:

$$k = \frac{2.303}{t} \log \frac{c_0}{c} \tag{4}$$

where c_0 is the concentration at the beginning of the reaction when the time is zero and c is the concentration after time t has elapsed.

This equation is often written in the exponential form:

$$c = c_0 e^{-kt} \tag{5}$$

Still another modification is used, in which a is the initial quantity of reacting material in a given volume, x is the amount reacting in time t, and $a - x$ is the amount remaining after time t. Then,

$$-\frac{dc}{dt} = -\frac{d(a - x)}{dt} = dx/dt = k(a - x) \tag{6}$$

and

$$k = \frac{2.303}{t} \log \frac{a}{a - x} \tag{7}$$

The *specific reaction-rate constant* or the *velocity constant*, k, for a first-order reaction is a number per unit of time and may be expressed in reciprocal seconds (or in other units of time). When, for example, k has a value of 0.001 sec^{-1} the material is decomposing at the rate of 0.1 per cent per second.

Reaction rates may be described by giving the numerical value of k, or sometimes by giving the *period of half-life*, $t_{1/2}$, that is, the time necessary for half a given quantity of material to decompose. It is meaningless to speak of the time necessary for all the material to decompose, because, theoretically, an infinite time is required. For a first-order reaction,

$$k = \frac{2.303}{t_{\frac{1}{2}}} \log \frac{1}{\frac{1}{2}} = \frac{0.693}{t_{\frac{1}{2}}}$$

The period of half-life in a first-order equation then is

$$t_{\frac{1}{2}} = 0.693/k \qquad (8)$$

The determination of the specific rate constant makes possible a calculation of the amount of material which will react in a given time, or the time required for any specified portion of the material to react.

The calculation of first-order reaction rates may be illustrated by the decomposition of nitrogen pentoxide.* Nitrogen pentoxide, the anhydride of nitric acid, is a crystalline solid which gives a gaseous pressure of 1 atm at about 30°. It decomposes completely in the gas phase, or when dissolved in inert solvents, at a rate which is conveniently measured at room temperature. The reaction is strictly first order, and the end products are oxygen and a mixture of N_2O_4 and NO_2. The following equation represents the over-all reaction,

$$N_2O_5 \rightarrow N_2O_4 + \tfrac{1}{2}O_2$$
$$\Updownarrow$$
$$2NO_2$$

For every molecule of oxygen produced, 2 molecules of nitrogen pentoxide have decomposed. It will be shown later, however, that this reaction is much more complicated than this, with intermediate steps, some of which happen to cancel out. It may be suggested that in chemical kinetics the only simple reactions are the ones that have not been studied very thoroughly.

When a solution of nitrogen pentoxide in carbon tetrachloride decomposes, the N_2O_4 and NO_2 remain in solution while the oxygen escapes and is measured in a gas buret. The reaction vessel is carefully thermostated, and it is agitated to prevent supersaturation of the oxygen.

Experimental data for the decomposition of nitrogen pentoxide dissolved in carbon tetrachloride at 45° were interpreted as illustrated in Example 1. They are given in Table I and plotted in the accompanying figures.

* Daniels and Johnston, *J. Am. Chem. Soc.*, *43*, 53 (1921); Eyring and Daniels, *ibid.*, *52*, 1472 (1930).

Table I. Decomposition of N_2O_5 in CCl_4 Solution at 45°

t, seconds	c, moles/liter	$\log c$	$\dfrac{\Delta c}{\Delta t}$	Average c	$k \times 10^4$ equation 4
0	2.33	0.367	.....	....	....
184	2.08	0.318	0.00136	2.20	6.14
319	1.91	0.281	0.00126	2.00	6.23
526	1.67	0.223	0.00116	1.79	6.32
867	1.36	0.133	0.00090	1.51	6.23
1198	1.11	0.045	0.00075	1.23	6.20
1877	0.72	1.857	0.00057	0.92	6.27
2315	0.55	1.740	0.00039	0.64	6.25
3144	0.34	1.531	0.00028	0.44	6.14

In *Fig. 13-1a* the concentration is plotted against time, where it is seen that the concentration decreases with time, rapidly at first, then more slowly, and finally approaches zero.

In Fig. 13-1b the straight line produced by plotting the logarithm of the concentration against time shows that the reaction is first order and follows strictly the relation given by equation 2.

In Fig. 13-1c the values of $-\Delta c / \Delta t$ obtained by taking increments of concentration and time between successive observations are plotted against the average concentration. The increments are sufficiently small so that the graph constitutes a confirmation of equation 1 and gives a straight line which runs into the origin. It shows that the rate of decrease in concentration with time is proportional to the concentration.

The value of the specific reaction rate, as given in the last column of Table I, ranges around 0.00062. The best value is 0.000622 as obtained by multiplying the slope of the line in Fig. 13-1b by 2.303, in agreement with equation 2. The slope of the straight line in Fig. 13-1c, which is k in agreement with equation 1, has a value of 0.00062.

Sometimes it is inconvenient and unnecessary to determine so many points on the curve. If the reaction is first order, it will take twice as long for three-fourths of the material to decompose as it takes for half of it to decompose. This single criterion is sometimes useful.

After proving with a sufficient number of properly spaced measurements that the reaction is strictly first order, the best value of the constant k can be determined from the slope of the straight line as in Fig. 13-1b or by substituting two widely separated readings into formula 3. The best results are obtained when the first reading is chosen near the beginning of the experiment, as soon as the reaction vessel has reached the temperature of the thermostat, and the second one when

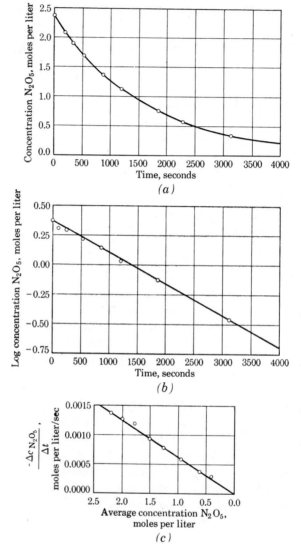

Fig. 13-1. Three different ways of plotting experimental data for a first-order reaction.

the reaction is about two-thirds completed. In this way the errors of experimental measurement are reduced to a minimum. Two other independent readings over about the same range may be used as a check.*

* Mathematical methods for calculating rate constants are discussed critically by Roseveare, *J. Am. Chem. Soc.*, **53**, 1651 (1931); and by Reed and Theriault, *J. Phys. Chem.*, **35**, 673 (1931).

Exercise I. Show that it is not satisfactory to average all the constants obtained in successive time intervals using formula 3. If the time intervals are all the same, an average of the k's would exclude all the intermediate measurements and base the value only on the first and last, which might well be the least accurate. Thus,

$$k = \frac{2.303}{t_2 - t_1} \log \frac{c_1}{c_2} \qquad k = \frac{2.303}{t_3 - t_2} \log \frac{c_2}{c_3} \qquad \text{and} \qquad k = \frac{2.303}{t_4 - t_3} \log \frac{c_3}{c_4}$$

$$k_{avg} = \frac{2.303}{3(t' - t)} [\log c_1 - \log c_2 + \log c_2 - \log c_3 + \log c_3 - \log c_4]$$

$$= \frac{2.303}{3(t' - t)} \log \frac{c_1}{c_4}$$

Exercise II. In first-order reactions the units of concentration measurement cancel out and simplify the calculations. For example, the reaction $A \rightarrow B$, where A absorbs light of a given wavelength and B does not, may be studied spectrophotometrically. At time 0, $A_{s,0} = a_s c_{A,0}$; and, at time t, $A_{s,t} = a_s c_{A,t}$, where A_s is the absorbancy and a_s is the absorbancy index. Show that $k = \frac{2.303}{t} \log \frac{A_{s,0}}{A_{s,t}}$ so that it is not necessary to determine the value of a_s.

Second-Order Reactions. When the rate of a reaction as determined in the laboratory is proportional to the concentration of each of two reacting substances, the reaction is of the second order. Thus, in the reaction $A + B \rightarrow AB$, if

$$-dc_A/dt = -dc_B/dt = kc_A c_B \tag{9}$$

the reaction is said to be of the second order. Also, if

$$-dc_A/dt = kc_A{}^2$$

the reaction is second order.

If a and b represent the initial molar concentrations of the two reacting substances A and B, and if x denotes the number of moles per liter which react in the interval of time t, then the velocity of the reaction is expressed by the equation

$$dx/dt = k(a - x)(b - x) \tag{10}$$

In the simplest case the two substances (A and B) are present in equal concentrations, and $a = b$. Under these conditions, the rate equation becomes

$$dx/dt = k(a - x)^2 \tag{11}$$

Integrating equation 11,

$$1/(a - x) = kt + C \tag{12}$$

Evaluating the integration constant C by setting $x = 0$ when $t = 0$, we have

$$k = \frac{1}{t} \cdot \frac{x}{a(a - x)} \tag{13}$$

If the reacting substances are not present in equivalent amounts, then equation 10 must be employed. On integrating * and evaluating the integration constant, this becomes

$$kt = \frac{1}{a - b} \ln \frac{b(a - x)}{a(b - x)}$$

or

$$k = \frac{2.303}{t(a - b)} \log \frac{b(a - x)}{a(b - x)} \tag{14}$$

The graphical method for obtaining the best value of k is convenient and adequate unless the data are extremely accurate. When $\log [b(a - x)/a(b - x)]$ † is plotted as ordinate against t, a straight line is obtained if the reaction is second order. Its slope is $k(a - b)/2.303$, and k is then obtained by multiplying the slope of the line by $2.303/(a - b)$.

The value of k in a second-order reaction depends on the units in which the concentration is expressed, since the magnitude of the term $(a - b)$ depends on the units used. For the sake of uniformity it is customary to express concentrations in moles per liter. The constant k has the dimensions liters mole^{-1} sec^{-1}. In a first-order reaction the form of the equation is such that the units of concentration cancel out.

The hydrolysis of an ester by an alkali may be taken as an illustration of a second-order reaction. The reaction

$$CH_3COOC_2H_5 + OH^- \rightleftharpoons CH_3COO^- + C_2H_5OH$$

has been studied by several investigators. Reactions of this type may be followed in a number of different ways. Solutions of ester and alkali are placed in separate flasks in a thermostat and then mixed. At frequent intervals, a portion of the reaction mixture is removed, discharged into a measured volume of standard acid, and back-titrated with standard alkali. The decrease in concentration of OH^- ions is a measure of the extent of the reaction. A final titration, after the reaction is completed, is necessary in order to determine how many OH^-

* Daniels, *Mathematical Preparation for Physical Chemistry*, McGraw-Hill Book Co., New York, 1928, page 189.

† This may be replaced for purposes of graphing by its equivalent $\log [(a - x)/(b - x)] +$ constant.

ions have reacted with ethyl acetate molecules and thus determine the number of moles per liter of ethyl acetate and hydroxyl ions which were present at the beginning of the experiment. The reaction may be followed also by measuring the change in the electrical conductance of the system or by measuring the slight increase in volume of the liquid as the reaction proceeds.

Experimental data obtained by titration are recorded in the first three columns of Table II, and the specific rate constant k is given in the last column, as calculated by equation 14.

Table II. Hydrolysis of Ethyl Acetate at 25°

a = initial concentration of NaOH $\doteq$ 0.00980 mole per liter.

b = initial concentration of $CH_3COOC_2H_5$ = 0.00486 mole per liter.

Time, seconds	$[x]^1$ mole l^{-1}	$[a - x]$ mole l^{-1}	$[b - x]$ mole l^{-1}	$\log \dfrac{b\,[a - x]}{a\,[b - x]}$	$k = \dfrac{2.303}{t[a - b]} \log \dfrac{b\,[a - x]}{a\,[b - x]}$
0	0.00000	0.00980	0.00486	.....	.....
178	0.00088	0.00892	0.00398	0.0412	0.108
273	0.00116	0.00864	0.00370	0.0640	0.109
531	0.00188	0.00792	0.00297	0.1208	0.106
866	0.00256	0.00724	0.00230	0.1936	0.104
1510	0.00335	0.00645	0.00151	0.3266	0.101
1918	0.00377	0.00603	0.00109	0.4390	0.106
2401	0.00406	0.00574	0.00080	0.5518	0.107

^{1} Square brackets are used in solutions to indicate concentrations in moles per liter.

The specific rate constant k can be determined easily and with greater accuracy by a graphical method.

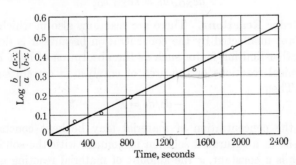

FIG. 13-2. A straight-line graph for a second-order reaction; the hydrolysis of ethyl acetate at 25°.

Example 4. Calculate k from the data of Table II as shown in *Fig. 13-2.* The slope of the line is $0.550/2400 = 0.000229$. It is equal to

$$k(a - b)/2.3$$

Then, since $a - b = 0.00980 - 0.00486 = 0.00494$,

$$k = \frac{(2.303)}{(0.00494)} (0.000229) = 0.107 \text{ l mole}^{-1} \text{ sec}^{-1}$$

Third-Order Reactions. If in a reaction involving three substances, A, B, and C, it is found that

$$-\frac{dc_A}{dt} = -\frac{dc_B}{dt} = -\frac{dc_C}{dt} = kc_A c_B c_C \qquad (15)$$

the reaction is called a third-order reaction. Also a third-order reaction may be given by $-dc_A/dt = kc_A{}^2 c_B$ or by $kc_A{}^3$.

Equation 15 may be written

$$dx/dt = k(a - x)(b - x)(c - x) \qquad (16)$$

and, in the special case where $a = b = c$,

$$dx/dt = k(a - x)^3$$

Integrating,

$$\frac{1}{2(a - x)^2} = kt + \text{constant} = kt + \frac{1}{2a^2} \qquad (17)$$

The oxidation of nitric oxide to nitrogen dioxide

$$2NO + O_2 \rightarrow 2NO_2$$

is a third-order reaction,[*] because the rate equation is found to be

$$dc_{NO_2}/dt = kc_{NO}{}^2 c_{O_2}$$

Zero-Order Reactions. There are reactions also in which the rate is a constant unaffected by the concentration because it is determined by some other limiting factor such as the absorption of light in certain photochemical reactions or the area of catalyst in certain surface reactions. Then

$$-dc/dt = k' \qquad (18)$$

Again, the concentration of material may be kept constant automatically as in a saturated solution in contact with the solid. Then, although c is a constant, x the amount of material reacting as defined in equation 6 is given by the expression

$$dx/dt = k' \qquad (19)$$

$$x = k't + \text{constant} \qquad (20)$$

[*] Hasche and Patrick, *J. Am. Chem. Soc.*, *47*, 1207 (1925); Treacy and Daniels, *ibid.*, *77* (1955).

The value of k' calculated in this way may include arbitrary constants corresponding to the intensity of light or the concentration in a saturated solution or vapor.

Determination of the Order of a Reaction. Simple examples have been given of clean-cut first-, second-, third-, and zero-order equations, but it must not be supposed that all observed chemical reactions fit these types. The order of a reaction is determined by the exponents of concentration terms which determine the rate of the reaction. For example, in the reaction $A + B \rightarrow X$, the rate expression may be

$$dc_X/dt = kc_A{}^m c_B{}^n \tag{21}$$

This reaction is mth order with respect to A, nth order with respect to B, and $(m + n)$th order for the over-all reaction.

The rate of production of X (or the rate of consumption of A and of B) depends on the concentration c of each of the materials taking part in the reaction, each raised to an exponent which is determined empirically by experiment. Sometimes the exponents such as m and n are whole numbers, 1, 2, 3, etc., and they may represent the number of moles of the material taking part stoichiometrically in the reaction or may not. It is just as likely, however, that the experimental data will show that the rate of formation of X or the disappearance of A is given by an expression with fractional exponents such, for example, as

$$-dc_A/dt = kc_A{}^{1.3} c_B{}^{0.9} \tag{22}$$

This situation emphasizes the fact that frequently there is little relation between the stoichiometrical reaction as written on paper and the order of the reaction as determined in the laboratory. In fact, most chemical reactions are complex, involving two or more reaction steps going on simultaneously.

The sum of all the exponents of the concentration terms involved in the rate equation is taken as the order of the reaction. Thus, in equation 9 it is second order, in equation 15 it is third order, and in equation 22 it is 2.2 order. There are several different ways in which the order of a reaction may be determined.

Substitution into Formulas. If a reaction is of first, second, third, or zero order, a constant value of k will be obtained throughout the course of the reaction when the data are substituted into the proper formula. If none of the formulas can be made to fit, the reaction is complicated, and probably two or more reactions are going on simultaneously.

Graphing. The order may sometimes be determined by plotting different functions of the concentration c against the time. If a straight line is obtained when $\log c$ is plotted against time, the reaction is first order as shown in equation 2.

In the special case where all the reactants have the same initial concentration, the reaction is second order if a straight line is obtained when $1/c$ is plotted against time, as shown in equation 12, and third order if a straight line is obtained when $1/c^2$ is plotted against time as shown in equation 17.

In a zero-order reaction a straight line is obtained when x is plotted against time as is evident from equation 20.

Half-Life Periods. In a first-order reaction the period of half-life (or in fact the time required for any given fraction to react) is independent of the initial concentration as shown in equation 8.

In a second-order reaction in which $a = b$, the time required for half to react is inversely proportional to the initial concentration, and $t_{\frac{1}{2}} = 1/ka$, as can be derived from equation 13.

Variation in Ratio of Reactants. When different molecules are involved, the course of the reaction may be studied by altering the ratio of the reacting materials. For example, the oxidation of nitric oxide,

$$2NO + O_2 \rightarrow 2NO_2$$

is accelerated more by increasing the concentration of nitric oxide than by increasing the concentration of oxygen. This fact is in accord with the equation

$$\frac{dc_{NO_2}}{dt} = kc_{NO}{}^2c_{O_2}$$

Much information can be gained in a complex reaction by increasing greatly the concentration of the reactants, one at a time, and observing the change in the reaction rate over a short period of time (for example, a period in which the change in composition is not over 10 per cent). Since

$$dx/dt = kc_A{}^m c_B{}^n c_C{}^j$$

where A, B, and C represent the different molecules reacting and m, n, j are the corresponding exponents in the rate equation, it is seen that m can be evaluated by doubling c_A, keeping c_B and c_C constant, and determining $\Delta x/\Delta t$ experimentally in the two cases. Thus, for short intervals where $(\Delta x/\Delta t)_{2c_A}$ is the observed rate when the concentration of A is doubled, and $(\Delta x/\Delta t)_{c_A}$ is the observed rate before doubling the concentration of A, the ratio of the two is

$$\frac{(\Delta x/\Delta t)_{2c_A}}{(\Delta x/\Delta t)_{c_A}} = \frac{k2^m c_A{}^m c_B{}^n c_C{}^j}{kc_A{}^m c_B{}^n c_C{}^j} = 2^m$$

Example 5. The chemical equation for the reaction between potassium oxalate and mercuric chloride is

$$2HgCl_2 + K_2C_2O_4 \rightarrow 2KCl + 2CO_2 + Hg_2Cl_2$$

The weight of Hg_2Cl_2 precipitated from different solutions in a given time, at $100°$, was as follows:

	$HgCl_2$, moles per liter	$K_2C_2O_4$, moles per liter	Time, minutes	Hg_2Cl_2 Precipitated, moles
(1)	0.0836	0.404	65	0.0068
(2)	0.0836	0.202	120	0.0031
(3)	0.0418	0.404	60	0.0032

Write the differential equation for the reaction rate, evaluating the exponents of the concentrations.

$$dx/dt = k[HgCl_2]^m[K_2C_2O_4]^n$$

From 1 and 2,

$$\frac{\left(\dfrac{\Delta x}{\Delta t}\right)_{2[K_2C_2O_4]}}{\left(\dfrac{\Delta x}{\Delta t}\right)_{[K_2C_2O_4]}} = \frac{\dfrac{0.0068}{65}}{\dfrac{0.0031}{120}} = 4 = \frac{k[HgCl_2]^m[2K_2C_2O_4]^n}{k[HgCl_2]^m[K_2C_2O_4]^n} = 2^n$$

Since $2^n = 4$, $n = 2$. From 1 and 3,

$$\frac{\left(\dfrac{\Delta x}{\Delta t}\right)_{2[HgCl_2]}}{\left(\dfrac{\Delta x}{\Delta t}\right)_{[HgCl_2]}} = \frac{\dfrac{0.0068}{65}}{\dfrac{0.0032}{60}} = 2 = \frac{k[2HgCl_2]^m[K_2C_2O_4]^n}{k[HgCl_2]^m[K_2C_2O_4]^n} = 2^m$$

Since $2^m = 2$, $m = 1$. Then, substituting the experimentally determined exponents into the original rate expression,

$$dx/dt = k[HgCl_2][K_2C_2O_4]^2$$

It may be noted that the rate depends on the square of the potassium oxalate concentration, although the stoichiometric equation indicates that only 1 molecule is involved. Again, the reaction as written involves 2 molecules of mercuric chloride, but the experimental facts show that it is first order with respect to the concentration of mercuric chloride. These differences show that the reaction is complex and that the equation as written does not represent the full course of the reaction with its rate-determining intermediate steps.

Addition of Excess of Reactant. Often a complex reaction may be simplified and studied by adding a large excess of one or more of the reactants so that they do not undergo appreciable change during the reaction. If all but one of the reacting substances are present in large excess, a variation of the concentration of this one reactant permits a direct determination of the exponent to which the concentration of the reactant is raised in the rate equation.

Exercise III. Explain how the value of m in the concentration term $c_A{}^m$ can be determined by changing c_A and measuring the rate of the reaction, and then determining the slope of the line obtained by plotting log reaction rate against log c_A.

Example 6. Three substances A, B, and C are added to a liter of solvent so that $c_A = c_B = c_C$. At the end of 1000 seconds half of A is still left. What will be the concentration of A after 2000 seconds?

If the reaction is first order with respect to A and unaffected by the concentrations of B and C, one-half will remain after 1000 seconds and one-half of the one-half, or 25 per cent, will remain after the second 1000-second period. If the reaction is first order with respect to A and first order with respect to B but independent of the concentration of C, equation 13 shows that 33 per cent will be left. If the reaction is first order with respect to A, B, and C, that is, third order for the over-all reaction, 38 per cent will be left after 2000 seconds according to equation 17. If the reaction is zero order and independent of the concentration one-half is gone in the first 1000 seconds and all of it will be gone at the end of 2000 seconds.

Molecularity of Reactions. We have seen that reactions can be classed as first, second, or nth order, depending on the influence exerted by concentration on the rate of the reaction. They can be classed also as unimolecular, bimolecular, or trimolecular, depending on the number of molecules involved in the reaction.

A *unimolecular* reaction is one in which 1 molecule breaks up into smaller parts, as in

$$Br_2 \rightarrow 2Br$$

or undergoes internal rearrangement, as when maleic acid is converted into fumaric acid on heating, thus

$$
\begin{array}{ccc}
\text{H—C—COOH} & & \text{H—C—COOH} \\
\| & \rightarrow & \| \\
\text{H—C—COOH} & & \text{HOOC—C—H}
\end{array}
$$

A *bimolecular* reaction is one in which 2 molecules must come together before a reaction can take place, as for example in the reaction

$$H_2 + I_2 \rightarrow 2HI$$

A *trimolecular* reaction is one in which 3 molecules must collide simultaneously in order to make possible a reaction. Most reactions involving three molecules consist of two successive bimolecular reactions.

Often a unimolecular reaction will also be first order and a bimolecular reaction second order, but there is no necessary correlation between the molecularity and the order. For instance, in Example 5 it was seen that the reaction between mercuric chloride and potassium oxalate is second order with respect to potassium oxalate although only 1 molecule is involved in the balanced chemical equation as written. The decomposition of nitrogen pentoxide is a beautiful first-order reaction, but the primary unimolecular decomposition, $N_2O_5 \rightarrow NO_2 + NO_3$, is not the rate-determining step and the over-all reaction involves several steps which happen to give a first-order reaction rate.

Sometimes a reaction may take place by either a unimolecular or a bimolecular process but the energy requirements may be quite different. Thus in the unimolecular decomposition of hydrogen iodide

$$HI \rightarrow H + I$$

more energy is required to produce atoms than is required in the bimolecular decomposition

$$HI + HI \rightarrow H_2 + I_2$$

It will be seen later that usually the reaction requiring the least amount of energy is the one that will predominate.

A special case arises in a bimolecular combination of atoms to give very simple molecules. For example, in the reaction

$$H + H \rightarrow H_2$$

the heat of combination of 2 hydrogen atoms to give a molecule is large (103 kcal mole^{-1}), and if this heat is generated within an isolated, newly formed molecule there is no way of dissipating the large amount of energy except by the dissociation of the molecule. In other words, a stable molecule of H_2 can be formed only if there is some way of stabilizing the molecule by taking away energy, such as in the increase of kinetic or translational energy given to a colliding molecule. The reaction then is written

$$H + H + M \rightarrow H_2 + M$$

where M represents a third body, a colliding molecule or a wall surface. Triple collisions are very rare, and so the reaction given above between H, H, and M is slow. This is the principle of the atomic hydrogen torch invented by Langmuir, in which pure hydrogen gas is passed through an electrical discharge. The issuing gas contains a considerable quantity of hydrogen atoms, which persist for a few seconds because of the infrequency of triple collisions and evolve 103 kcal per mole at a convenient rate for welding and other operations. The fact that no oxygen is involved makes this type of welding useful under special conditions where oxidation is a problem.

The recombination of iodine atoms, and hydrogen atoms, requires triple collisions. When the molecule formed has more than 2 atoms there is a chance for the molecule to consume energy by vibration of the atoms within the molecule so that the molecule can be stabilized without the requirement for a triple collision.

Although most chemical reactions are complicated and involve several different steps, it is fortunate that all these individual steps are themselves simple unimolecular, bimolecular, or trimolecular reactions which we can hope to understand.

The over-all reaction as written on paper usually has little significance in chemical kinetics. A determination of the order of the reaction is useful in predicting the rate of the reaction at various times; it is helpful also in understanding the mechanism of the reaction and the ways in which unimolecular and bimolecular reactions go together to give complex reactions as indicated in the following section.

Complex Reactions. The mathematical description of reaction rates thus far has been confined to a few standard types, but it must not be imagined that most chemical reactions are amenable to such simple mathematical treatment. In fact, very few chemical reactions follow first-, second-, or third-order equations throughout their whole course. More often two or more different reactions are taking place at the same time so that the mathematical description of the over-all reaction is the resultant of several different rate expressions. Important among the complications are *consecutive reactions*, *reverse reactions*, and *competing reactions*, some types of which are illustrated here.

Consecutive reactions: $A \rightarrow B \rightarrow C$

Reverse reactions: $A + B \rightleftharpoons AB$

Competing reactions: $A \underset{+C}{\overset{+B}{\big\langle}} \begin{matrix} AB \\ AC \end{matrix}$

Although complex reactions are made up of simple steps it may be exceedingly difficult to describe the over-all reaction mathematically. Accordingly, the chemical reactions chosen for laboratory study are usually ones in which all but one of the reactions are negligible, because they are either too fast or too slow to be of significance in comparison with the one reaction. In general, the accuracy of rate measurement is not high, and it is safe to ignore those reaction steps which do not contribute more than about 1 per cent to the over-all concentration.

For example, in consecutive reactions $A \rightarrow B \rightarrow C$, if the reaction $B \rightarrow C$ is 100 times or more as fast as the reaction $A \rightarrow B$, the latter will be the rate-determining step in the production of C.

Many excellent examples of consecutive first-order reactions are found among the nuclear reactions of the radioactive elements (page 609). These radioactive reactions are unaffected by temperature, pressure, catalysts, or other factors, and they can be expressed with exactness by simple first-order equations. The rates of the nuclear reactions are proportional to the number of atoms present in a given sample, whereas the rates of first-order chemical reactions are proportional to the concentrations of reactants.

Complex reactions are very common. In fact, the equations as ordinarily written give little idea of the intermediate steps, and yet one of these intermediate steps may be the slowest reaction, that is, the rate-determining reaction. Kinetic measurements offer one of the best methods for studying intermediate steps in a reaction. Reactions like the oxidation of hydrocarbons to give carbon dioxide and water really pass through a series of intermediate stages involving the production of peroxides, alcohols, ketones, and acids.

Theoretically, all reactions are reversible, but, usually, the reverse reaction can be ignored because it does not affect the concentration appreciably. An example of a reversible reaction is

$$CH_3COOH + C_2H_5OH \rightleftharpoons CH_3COOC_2H_5 + H_2O$$

At first, the reverse reaction can be ignored, but, after appreciable amounts of ethyl acetate and water have accumulated, both reactions must be included in the rate expression.

Competing reactions are very common, particularly in organic chemistry. When two compounds are mixed, there may be dozens of products all of which are possible according to the laws of thermodynamics. Of the several possible products, that product which is formed by the fastest reaction will consume most of the reacting materials and be the predominating material. In studying chemical kinetics those reactions are usually chosen in which one reaction predominates and all other reactions (consecutive, reverse, or competing) are relatively much slower. In synthesizing compounds the organic chemist chooses reactions in which he can suppress all the competing reactions and leave only the one reaction that gives the desired product. An example of competing reactions is the nitration of bromobenzene to give *ortho-*, *meta-*, and *para*-nitrobromobenzene, which, under certain conditions, gives the yields indicated.

ortho	*meta*	*para*
13.5 per cent	0.3 per cent	86.2 per cent

Obviously, a high conversion of bromobenzene to *para*-nitrobromobenzene can be obtained only if the production of the *meta* and *ortho* forms is small.

Again, the reaction of chlorine with methane might give

$$x\text{Cl}_2 + \text{CH}_4 \left\langle \begin{array}{l} \text{CH}_3\text{Cl} \\ \text{CH}_2\text{Cl}_2 \\ \text{CHCl}_3 \\ \text{CCl}_4 \end{array} \right.$$

The study of kinetics should help to show which product will predominate and suggest means by which the conditions can be controlled to favor the production of one of these specified products at the expense of the others.

The mechanism of many reactions is more complicated than appears from the simple rate equation. For example, the inversion of cane sugar in aqueous solution proceeds according to the following bimolecular equation when hydrogen ions are present:

$$\underset{\text{Sucrose}}{\text{C}_{12}\text{H}_{22}\text{O}_{11}} + \text{H}_2\text{O} \rightarrow \underset{\text{Fructose}}{\text{C}_6\text{H}_{12}\text{O}_6} + \underset{\text{Glucose}}{\text{C}_6\text{H}_{12}\text{O}_6}$$

The rate of the reaction is followed by measuring the rotation of polarized light. Although water (and hydrogen ions) plays an active part in this reaction, its concentration does not appear to change, because the water is present in large excess. For example, in a 0.5-molal solution there are 111 molecules of water to every molecule of sugar, and when the sugar has completely reacted, the water concentration will be reduced by less than 1 per cent. The second-order equation reduces to the simple first-order equation since the concentration of one of the reactants is essentially constant. If 0.5 mole of sucrose and 0.5 mole of water are dissolved in a liter of a nonaqueous solvent it is to be expected that the reaction will be first order with respect to each and hence second order in the over-all reaction.

The decomposition of hydrogen peroxide represents another type of complex reaction. Hydrogen peroxide is fairly stable in the absence of catalysts, but, when it combines with a substance such as ferric chloride, the decomposition is rapid. Although the reaction involves two reacting substances, the ferric chloride is released unchanged after the reaction, and the over-all reaction may be represented by

$$H_2O_2 + FeCl_3 \rightarrow H_2O_2 \cdot FeCl_3 \rightarrow H_2O + \tfrac{1}{2}O_2 + FeCl_3$$

Only the concentration of the H_2O_2 appears to change, and so the reaction is first order although it is a bimolecular reaction. The concentration of the ferric chloride remains constant, and equation 9 reduces to equation 1 since c_B is constant.

Mathematical Analysis of Complex Reactions.   The mathematical treatment of complex reactions will be illustrated with simple examples of consecutive first-order reactions, the rate equations of which can be integrated by standard methods.   For example,

	A $\xrightarrow{k_1=0.1}$	B $\xrightarrow{k_2=0.05}$	C
Initial concentration	1	0	0
Concentration at time t	$1 - x$	$x - y$	y

For these consecutive reactions, the specific reaction rates are 0.1 and 0.05 per hour, respectively. At the beginning of the reactions, it is imagined that there is 1 mole of A and none of B or C. After a time t, x moles of A have decomposed at the rate of 10 per cent per hour, leaving $1 - x$ moles of A. But B also decomposes and does so at the rate of 5 per cent per hour. After time t, y moles of C have been produced. The amount of B is the result of a balance between formation and decomposition, and at any time t it is represented by $x - y$.

The decomposition rate of A is given by the equation:

$$\frac{-d(1 - x)}{dt} = k_1(1 - x) \tag{23}$$

The rate of formation of C is given by the equation:

$$dy/dt = k_2(x - y) \tag{24}$$

The amount of A at any time is obtained by integrating the first equation to give $(1 - x) = e^{-k_1 t} = e^{-0.1t}$, and the amount of C is obtained by substituting this value of x into equation 24 and solving the differential equation * to give $y = 2(1 - e^{-0.05t}) - (1 - e^{-0.1t})$. The amount of B at any time is merely the difference between x and y.

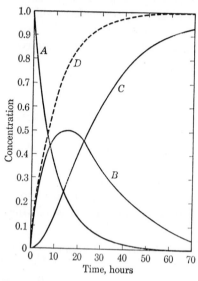

The amounts of A, B, and C as calculated from these formulas are recorded at various times in Table III and *Fig. 13-3*.

Exercise IV. Calculate the quantities of A, B, and C present after 35 hours.

If the course of the reaction were followed by analyzing for A, curve A would be obtained; if it were followed by measuring the quantity of the end product C, curve C would result; and, finally, if only the intermediate product B were determined, it would be found that its concentration would rise to a maximum and then fall off, as shown by curve B. The

FIG. 13-3. Consecutive first-order reactions $A \xrightarrow{k_1} B \xrightarrow{k_2} C$; $k_1 = 0.1$, $k_2 = 0.05$.

broken line D gives the rate at which the decomposition product of A would be formed if it did not undergo further decomposition. The actual rate of production of C is seen to be quite complicated, and the existence of a slow induction period or time lag at the beginning of the reaction is evident.

This mechanism is presented in some detail because it is a comparatively simple example of a complicated reaction. When the rate of each of the steps is known, the over-all reaction rate can be built up as shown, provided that it is possible or practical to carry out the operations of integration. In laboratory practice the situation is usually much more difficult, for the over-all reaction is known, and the problem is to determine the rates of the intermediate steps. Not only is it difficult to solve the resulting differential equations, but it is even more difficult to be sure that the set of reactions thus determined is the only

* The equation is $\quad \dfrac{dy}{dt} + k_2 y = k_2 x = k_2(1 - e^{-k_1 t})$

$$y = \frac{k_2(1 - e^{-k_1 t}) - k_1(1 - e^{-k_2 t})}{k_2 - k_1} = \frac{0.05(1 - e^{-0.1t}) - 0.1(1 - e^{0.05t})}{0.05 - 0.1}$$

$$y = 2(1 - e^{-0.05t}) - (1 - e^{-0.1t})$$

Table III. Consecutive Reactions

$$A \xrightarrow{k=0.1} B \xrightarrow{k=0.05} C$$

Amounts of A, B, and C at various times starting with 1 mole of A

Time, t	Quantity A, $(1-x) = e^{-0.1t}$	$e^{-0.05t}$	Quantity C, y	Quantity B, $x-y$
0	1	1	0	0
10	0.368	0.606	0.156	0.476
20	0.135	0.368	0.399	0.466
30	0.0498	0.223	0.604	0.346
40	0.0183	0.135	0.748	0.234
50	0.00674	0.0821	0.842	0.151
60	0.00248	0.0498	0.903	0.095

set that will be in accord with the observed facts, that is, that the solution is unique.

Reversible as well as consecutive reactions may be treated mathematically if the equilibrium constant is known, allowance being made for the reverse reaction. Starting with a moles of acetic acid and a moles of alcohol in the reaction $CH_3COOH + C_2H_5OH \rightleftarrows CH_3COOC_2H_5 + H_2O$, the rate of the forward reaction is given by the expression $k_1[a-x]^2$, where x represents the amount of acid and alcohol reacted, or the amount of ester and water formed at the time t, and k_1 is the specific reaction rate of the forward reaction.

The rate of the reverse reaction is given by the expression $k_2[x]^2$, where k_2 is the specific reaction rate at which the concentrations of the products, ester and water, *decrease*.

The actually observed rate, including both forward and reverse reactions, is

$$dx/dt = k_1(a-x)^2 - k_2x^2 \tag{25}$$

When equilibrium is reached the rates of the forward and reverse reactions are equal and there is no apparent change in x. Then $dx/dt = 0$, and

$$\frac{x^2}{(a-x)^2} = \frac{k_1}{k_2} = K \tag{26}$$

where K is the equilibrium constant. Then

$$k_2 = k_1/K \tag{27}$$

and

$$dx/dt = k_1(a-x)^2 - (k_1/K)x^2 \tag{28}$$

In the reaction between acetic acid and ethyl alcohol, at room temperature, K has the value 4.0, and equation 28 may be integrated and solved for k_1.

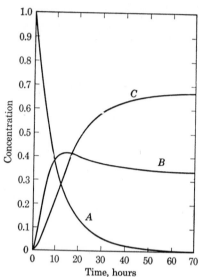

One more example of a complex reaction is cited in *Fig. 13-4*, in which a first-order reaction is followed by another first-order reaction which, however, is accompanied by a reverse reaction as follows:

$$A \xrightarrow{k_1} B \underset{k_3}{\overset{k_2}{\rightleftharpoons}} C$$

where $k_1 = 0.10$, $k_2 = 0.10$, and $k_3 = 0.05$. All the reactions are first-order reactions.

FIG. 13-4. Consecutive first-order reactions with reverse reaction $A \xrightarrow{k_1} B \underset{k_3}{\overset{k_2}{\rightleftharpoons}} C$; $k_1 = 0.10$, $k_2 = 0.10$, $k_3 = 0.05$.

There are many other kinetic expressions which combine competing, consecutive, or reverse reactions, each of which may involve either a first-order or a second-order equation. In only about a dozen general types of these complex reactions is it possible to solve the differential equations by integration.

Exercise V. In addition to the types already illustrated in this chapter equations for the following reactions can be integrated:

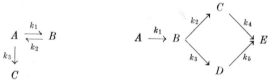

A simple reaction of the type $A \xrightarrow{k_1} B$; $A + B \xrightarrow{k_2} C$ cannot readily be integrated. More details of these integrations are available.[*][†] The development of mechanical and electronic calculators and differential analyzers has opened up important new possibilities in the solution of these differential equations of chemical kinetics.

[*] Moelwyn-Hughes, *Physical Chemistry*, Oxford University Press, 1941, Appendix 9.

[†] R. W. Evans, "Integrated Forms for Certain Differential Rate Expressions in Chemical Kinetics," M.S. Thesis, University of Wisconsin, Madison, Wisconsin, 1950.

Valuable information can be obtained by writing down the differential rate equations in a complex reaction even if they cannot be solved. Through them it is often possible to understand why there are sometimes induction periods in which the reaction proceeds very slowly at first, why complex reactions may approach a first order or a second order or a fractional order, and how these apparent orders can change during the course of the reaction.

In these complex reactions all the possible unimolecular and bimolecular reactions which involve a given substance are considered, and the rates of increase or decrease, dc/dt or $-dc/dt$, for each reactant are written down.

In many reactions it is satisfactory to assume that after a short induction period a steady state is reached in which intermediate compounds are formed as fast as they decompose and that their concentration remains constant; that is, $dc/dt = 0$. When this approximation is made it is frequently possible to simplify the rate equations and estimate the concentrations of the intermediate compounds.

Example 7. Set up the differential rate equations for the following complex reaction, and derive an expression for c_{AB}.

$$A + B \underset{k_2}{\overset{k_1}{\rightleftharpoons}} AB$$

$$AB \overset{k_3}{\longrightarrow} C$$

$$dc_A/dt = -k_1 c_A c_B + k_2 c_{AB}$$

$$dc_{AB}/dt = k_1 c_A c_B - k_2 c_{AB} - k_3 c_{AB}$$

For the stationary state when $dc_{AB}/dt = 0$

$$k_1 c_A c_B = k_2 c_{AB} + k_3 c_{AB} \qquad \text{and} \qquad c_{AB} = k_1 c_A c_B/(k_2 + k_3)$$

Influence of Temperature. It has long been known as an empirical fact that many reactions in the neighborhood of room temperature approximately double or treble their velocity for a 10° rise in temperature.

A more quantitative relation, proposed by Arrhenius, is given in the following equation,

$$k = se^{-\Delta H_a/RT} \tag{29}$$

where s is a constant and ΔH_a is another constant, which is now interpreted as the heat of activation as explained on page 352. Set in logarithmic form,

$$\log k = \frac{-\Delta H_a}{2.303R} \frac{1}{T} + \log s \tag{30}$$

Differentiating equation 30

$$\frac{d \ln k}{dT} = \frac{\Delta H_a}{RT^2} \tag{31}$$

and integrating between limits

$$\log \frac{k_2}{k_1} = \frac{\Delta H_a}{2.303 R} \left(\frac{T_2 - T_1}{T_2 T_1} \right) \tag{32}$$

It may be noted that these equations are similar to those for equilibrium constants studied on page 256. According to equation 30, a straight line is produced when the logarithm of the specific reaction rate is plotted against the reciprocal of the absolute temperature. The specific decomposition rates of gaseous nitrogen pentoxide * at different temperatures are given in the third column of Table IV in sec.

Table IV. Decomposition of Nitrogen Pentoxide at Different Temperatures

$t°$	$1/T$	$k_{obs} \times 10^5$	$\log k$	$k_{calc} \times 10^5$	Half-Life
65	0.002959	487	−2.313	477	2.38 min
55	0.003048	150	−2.824	155	7.72 min
45	0.003145	49.8	−3.303	47.2	21.8 min
35	0.003247	13.5	−3.871	13.2	85.9 min
25	0.003357	3.46	−4.471	3.46	5.71 hours
0	0.003663	0.0787	−6.104	0.0733	10.2 days

The values of $\log k$ are plotted against $1/T$ in *Fig. 13-5*.

The slope of the line in Fig. 13-5 is −5400, and ΔH_a has the value of 24,700 cal mole^{-1}. Equation 30 becomes

$$\log k = - \frac{24,700}{2.303 \times 1.987} \frac{1}{T} + 13.638 \tag{33}$$

and equation 29

$$k = 4.3 \times 10^{13} e^{-24,700/1.987 T}$$

The values of the specific rate constants k in reciprocal seconds, as calculated with this formula, are given in the fifth column of Table IV, and the periods of half-life are given in the last column. Extrapolated values of the half-life period are given in Table V, assuming that the rate expression still holds. Considering the complicated mechanism of the decomposition of nitrogen pentoxide it is unlikely that such extrapolation is safe.

* Daniels and Johnston, *J. Am. Chem. Soc.*, *43*, 53 (1921).

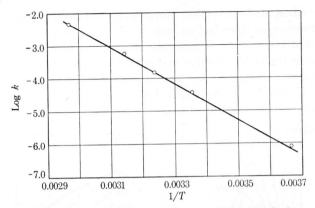

FIG. 13-5. Graph of log k vs. $1/T$ for the decomposition of N_2O_5 from which the activation energy may be calculated.

Table V. Extrapolated Values of Half-Life

$t°$	Half-Life	$t°$	Half-Life
200	0.0039 sec	25	5.7 hours
150	0.088	0	11 days
125	0.56	−25	3 years
100	4.6	−50	830 years
75	51	−75	940,000 years

A few other gas reactions together with the Arrhenius constants are given in Table VI.

Table VI. Gas Phase Reactions

First-Order

$N_2O_5 \rightarrow (N_2O_4 \rightleftharpoons 2NO_2) + \frac{1}{2}O_2$	$k = 4.3 \times 10^{13} e^{-24,700/RT} \text{ sec}^{-1}$
$N_2O_5 \rightarrow NO_3 + NO_2$	$k = 6 \times 10^{12} e^{-18,500/RT} \text{ sec}^{-1}$
$SiH_4 \rightarrow Si + 2H_2$	$k = 2 \times 10^{13} e^{-51,700/RT} \text{ sec}^{-1}$
$C_2H_5Br \rightarrow C_2H_4 + HBr$	$k = 3.8 \times 10^{14} e^{-55,000/RT} \text{ sec}^{-1}$
$CH_3COCH_3 \rightarrow CH_4 + CH_2CO$	$k = 8 \times 10^{14} e^{-68,000/RT} \text{ sec}^{-1}$

Second-Order

$HI + HI \rightarrow H_2 + I_2$	$k = 2.4 \times 10^{14} e^{-45,900/RT} \text{ mole}^{-1} \text{ liter sec}^{-1}$
$NO + NO \rightarrow N_2 + O_2$	$k = 1 \times 10^{9} e^{-70,000/RT} \text{ atm}^{-1} \text{ sec}^{-1}$
$C_2H_4 + H_2 \rightarrow C_2H_6$	$k = 1.24 \times 10^{6} e^{-43,100/RT} \text{ mole}^{-1} \text{ liter sec}^{-1}$
$NO_2 + NO_2 \rightarrow 2NO + O_2$	$k = 6.9 \times 10^{9} e^{-26,600/RT} \text{ mole}^{-1} \text{ liter sec}^{-1}$

Kinetic Theory of Gases. Information concerning the distribution of energy among molecules and the frequency of collisions may be obtained from the kinetic theory of gases. This, in turn, is valuable in the study of reaction rates.

The random motion of colloid particles can be directly observed under the microscope, as described on page 502, and we have every reason to believe that the motions of molecules in a gas are similar. A series of collisions in the right direction may give to a molecule an abnormally high velocity, and on the other hand a head-on collision may completely stop a molecule for a brief interval of time. Since the velocities are determined by chance, and since a very large number of molecules are

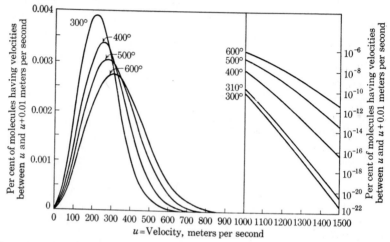

FIG. 13-6. Maxwell-Boltzmann distribution of velocities in N_2O_5. The curves at the right are plotted on a much-magnified logarithmic scale to show the velocities of the very rapidly moving molecules, which are the only ones of significance for chemical reactions.

involved in any measurement, the laws of probability may be applied with exactness.

The distribution of velocities is calculated from the Maxwell-Boltzmann distribution law. It is illustrated * in *Fig. 13-6* for gaseous nitrogen pentoxide.

The per cent of molecules having velocities within a narrow range, between u and $u + 0.01$ meters per second is given at each value of the velocity u. It is evident that there is one velocity which is more likely

* Calculated from the formula

$$dn/n = 4\pi (M/2\pi RT)^{3/2} e^{-(Mu^2/2RT)} u^2 \, du \qquad (34)$$

where M is the molecular weight (108 for nitrogen pentoxide), u is the velocity, n is the total number of molecules, and dn/n is the fraction of molecules having velocities between u and $u + du$.

A derivation is given in Glasstone, *Textbook of Physical Chemistry*, D. Van Nostrand Co., New York, 1946, page 267.

than any other velocity, and that very few molecules have very high or very low velocities. This most likely velocity increases as the temperature increases.

It is only the molecules which possess extremely high velocities that are of any interest in chemical reactions. For example, in nitrogen pentoxide an energy of 24,700 cal per mole, equivalent to a velocity of nearly 1400 meters per second, is required for decomposition.

In other words, those molecules with velocities of about 1400 meters per second or more have sufficient energy to undergo chemical reaction. The relative number of these "activated" molecules is exceedingly small at room temperature, and, hence, the reaction is slow. As shown by the exaggerated scale at the right, the number of these rapidly moving molecules is greatly increased by an increase in temperature.

It is useful to calculate the fraction of molecules which have sufficient energy from collisions to undergo chemical reactions. An approximate form of the Maxwell-Boltzmann law for the distribution of velocities among molecules can be derived by calculating the probability that molecules will move with specified velocities in specified directions in a two-dimensional plane. Under these conditions it can be shown that

$$\frac{dn_E}{n} = \frac{1}{RT} e^{-E/RT} dE \qquad (35)$$

where n is the total number of molecules and dn_E is the number of molecules having kinetic energy of translation between E and $E + dE$. Integrating from E to infinity to determine the number of molecules with energies greater than E yields

$$\frac{1}{n} \int_E^\infty dn_E = \frac{1}{RT} \int_E^\infty e^{-E/RT} dE$$

$$n_E/n = e^{-E/RT} \qquad (36)$$

where n_E/n is the fraction of the molecules having energies greater than E.

Exercise VI. A more exact formula than equation 36 may be derived on the basis of three axes in space instead of two axes. It is

$$\frac{n_E}{n} = \frac{2}{\sqrt{\pi}} e^{-E/RT} \left(\frac{E}{RT}\right)^{\frac{1}{2}} \qquad (37)$$

In deriving this formula from the distribution of velocities given in equation 34, the kinetic energy of the molecules E is set equal to $\frac{1}{2}Mu^2$, and thus $dE = Mu\,du$. Then

$$\frac{dn}{n} = \frac{2}{\sqrt{\pi}}\left(\frac{1}{RT}\right)^{\frac{3}{2}} e^{-E/RT} E^{\frac{1}{2}}\,dE$$

Integrating between E and infinity and neglecting RT in comparison with E gives equation 37.

Example 8. Calculate the fraction of nitrogen pentoxide molecules having at 25° and at 35° a kinetic energy equal to or greater than 24,700 cal per mole and the effect of a 10° rise in temperature on this fraction.

At 25° $\quad \dfrac{n_E}{n} = \dfrac{2}{\sqrt{\pi}} e^{-E/RT} \sqrt{\dfrac{E}{RT}} = \dfrac{2}{\sqrt{\pi}} e^{-24,700/(1.987)(298.1)} \sqrt{\dfrac{24,700}{(1.987)(298.1)}}$

$$= 5.69 \times 10^{-18}$$

At 35° $\quad \dfrac{n_E}{n} = \dfrac{2}{\sqrt{\pi}} e^{-24,700/(1.987)(308.1)} \sqrt{\dfrac{24,700}{(1.987)(308.1)}} = 2.17 \times 10^{-17}$

$$\frac{(n_E/n)_{35°}}{(n_E/n)_{25°}} = \frac{2.17 \times 10^{-17}}{5.69 \times 10^{-18}} = 3.81$$

This calculation brings out the fact that the number of energy-rich molecules is increased greatly by an increase in temperature, whereas the average energy $\frac{3}{2}RT$ is increased only 10/298 or 3.35 per cent in going from 298 to 308°. Most of the molecules have too low a kinetic energy to do anything chemically. Only kinetic energy of 24,700 cal per mole or greater is effective in bringing about this reaction, and this high-intensity energy is increased greatly by a 10° rise, as shown.

Molecular Collisions in Gases. Four quantities of use in chemical kinetics may be calculated from the kinetic theory of gases introduced in Chapter 2. They are: (1) the number of molecules striking a surface, (2) the number of collisions per second between molecules in a gas, (3) the molecular diameters, and (4) the distance a molecule travels before colliding with another molecule.

1. *Number of Molecules Striking a Surface.* If n molecules are contained in a cube 1 cm on an edge, it may be assumed that one-sixth of them are moving toward one wall. The root-mean-square velocity is u centimeters per second, and the number of molecules hitting the wall in a second will be equal to one-sixth of the number which are within a distance of u centimeters from it. Even if one of these molecules is prevented from hitting the wall by colliding with another molecule, the second molecule will be deflected back so that the number of hits is the same. If there are n molecules in the 1-cm cube, the number hitting one wall (1 sq cm) is $\frac{1}{6}nu$. A closer analysis which allows for unequal

speeds and collisions at oblique angles gives $1/\sqrt{6\pi}$ or 0.230.   Then,

Collisions per square centimeter of wall per second $= 0.230nu$ (38)

It was shown on page 29 that

$$u = \sqrt{3RT/M} \qquad (39)$$

Since u, the root-mean-square velocity, is expressed in centimeters per second, R must be expressed in ergs to keep both in cgs units. The average velocities and the probable velocities vary slightly from the root-mean-square velocities.

2. *Frequency of Collisions.* A rough idea of the number of collisions between molecules may be obtained from the following considerations. If the diameter of a molecule is σ, and two molecules are just touching, the distance separating their centers is also σ.   If the position of the center of the molecule is taken as its location, a molecule will collide with any other molecule which comes within the distance σ from its center. A molecule moving with a velocity of u centimeters per second will sweep out during a second a cylindrical space u centimeters long with an *effective* cross section $\pi\sigma^2$. The cylindrical space of $\pi\sigma^2 u$ cubic centimeters may be zigzag in shape on account of deflections suffered during collisions.   If there are n molecules per cubic centimeter, this molecule will collide with $(\pi\sigma^2 u)n$ other molecules. Each of the n molecules will sweep out this effective volume and undergo the same number of collisions. The total number of molecules undergoing collisions is therefore $(\pi u\sigma^2 n)n$.   Certain approximations are involved in this derivation, and, when corrections are made for the distribution of velocities and other factors,[*] the number of molecules colliding is given more exactly by the expression:

$$\tfrac{4}{3}\sqrt{(3\pi)}u\sigma^2 n^2 \quad \text{or} \quad 4.09u\sigma^2 n^2$$

The number of collisions is one-half the number of molecules colliding, because two molecules are necessary for a collision. The number of collisions z per second per cubic centimeter is given by the equation:

$$z = 2.05u\sigma^2 n^2 \qquad (40)$$

By substituting for u its equivalent given in equation 39 and combining and rounding off numbers, the following approximate equation is obtained:

$$z = 3.54\sigma^2 n^2 \sqrt{RT/M} \qquad (41)$$

[*] Glasstone, *Textbook of Physical Chemistry*, D. Van Nostrand Co., New York, 1946.

3. *Molecular Diameters.* All the quantities necessary for calculating the frequency of collisions are readily obtainable except the molecular diameter σ. This quantity can be calculated from viscosity measurements in long capillary tubes similar to those described for liquids on page 176. A few values are given in Table VII.

Table VII. Molecular Diameters (σ)

Gas	σ	Gas	σ
Helium	2.18×10^{-8} cm	Hydrogen chloride	2.86×10^{-8} cm
Argon	3.36	Hydrogen bromide	3.16
Chlorine	4.96	Hydrogen iodide	3.50
Bromine	3.42	Carbon dioxide	4.18
Iodine	3.96	Hydrogen	2.47
Oxygen	3.39	Nitrogen pentoxide	8.53
Nitrogen	3.50		

Many of the diameters calculated from viscosity measurements are in close agreement with the diameters as calculated from X-ray and electron diffraction measurements.

When no data are available, it may be assumed for the purpose of estimating the number of collisions that the molecular diameter is about 5×10^{-8} cm. In certain phenomena involving radiation, however, molecules appear to have much larger effective diameters.

4. *Mean Free Path.* If a molecule travels u centimeters in a second and collides with $\pi u \sigma^2 n$ molecules per second, as shown before, the average distance l, between encounters called the mean free path, is given by the equation:

$$l = \frac{u}{\pi\sigma^2 un} = \frac{1}{\pi\sigma^2 n}$$

Closer analysis shows that

$$l = \frac{1}{\sqrt{2}\pi\sigma^2 n} \qquad (42)$$

A knowledge of the mean free path is useful in calculations involving collisions in chemical reactions and rates of diffusion of gases. In all these formulas, 38, 39, 40, and 42, the velocities u are given as the root-mean-square velocities.

Example 9. Nitrogen is contained in a vessel at 1 atm pressure at 25°. Calculate: (a) the number of collisions on the walls per second per square centimeter; (b) the number of collisions between molecules per second per cubic centimeter; (c) the mean free path.

It is necessary first to calculate the number of molecules n per cubic centimeter and the velocity of the molecules u,

$$n = \frac{(6.02 \times 10^{23})}{(22,400 \times 298.1/273.1)} = 2.46 \times 10^{19}$$

$$u = \sqrt{\frac{3RT}{M}} = \left(\frac{3 \times 8.314 \times 10^7 \times 298.1}{28}\right)^{\frac{1}{2}} = \sqrt{26.56 \times 10^8}$$

$$= 5.15 \times 10^4 \text{ cm sec}^{-1}$$

(a) $$0.230nu = (0.230)(2.46 \times 10^{19})(5.15 \times 10^4)$$

$$= 2.92 \times 10^{23} \text{ collisions cm}^{-2} \text{ sec}^{-1}$$

(b) $$2.05u\sigma^2n^2 = (2.05)(5.15 \times 10^4)(3.50 \times 10^{-8})^2(2.46 \times 10^{19})^2$$

$$= 7.83 \times 10^{28} \text{ collisions between molecules cm}^{-3} \text{ sec}^{-1}$$

(c) $$l = \frac{1}{\sqrt{2}\pi\sigma^2n} = \frac{1}{(1.41)(3.14)(3.50 \times 10^{-8})^2(2.46 \times 10^{19})}$$

$$= 7.47 \times 10^{-6} \text{ cm} = \text{ the mean free path}$$

Activation Energies. According to present theories, it is necessary for molecules to become activated before they can react. If all molecules were equally reactive, it would be difficult to account for the very existence of slow reactions. Since the number of collisions per second is enormous, it might be expected that all reactions would be instantaneous. Ionic reactions, such as neutralizations and precipitations, are, in fact, immeasurably fast, but the energy of activation required for ions to react is usually very small.

Chemical equilibria and thermodynamics involve only the initial and final states, and they are not concerned with the mechanisms of the reaction or with the intermediate steps. In chemical kinetics, however, we are interested in the reaction steps which lead to the final products, and we try to apply our thermodynamical calculations not to the whole reaction but to the activation process.

Thus, in the over-all reaction,

$$\text{Reactants} \rightarrow \text{Products}$$
$$A \quad \rightarrow \quad C$$

we are concerned with ΔH, which is equal to $H_{\text{products}} - H_{\text{reactants}}$, but, in chemical kinetics, the same reaction is written

$$\text{Reactants} \xrightarrow[\text{slow}]{} \text{Activated molecules} \xrightarrow[\text{fast}]{} \text{Products}$$
$$A \quad \longrightarrow \quad B \quad \longrightarrow \quad C$$

and we are concerned with the slow or rate-determining step which requires an activation energy of ΔH_a, given by

$$\Delta H_a = H_{\text{activated molecules, } B} - H_A$$

For the reverse process $C \rightarrow B$,

$$\Delta H_a' = H_{\text{activated molecules, } B} - H_C$$

The relation between the heat of reaction and the heats of activation is shown in *Fig. 13-7*.

The initial molecules A require the absorption of a definite amount of heat ΔH_a in order to put them in an activated state B from which they can give the products C. In order to reverse the reaction, the molecules C must be supplied with the heat of activation $\Delta H_a'$, and, therefore, in passing from the activated state B, to C, an amount of heat equal to $\Delta H_a'$ is evolved. The heat of reaction measured in a calorimeter at constant pressure is equal to the difference between the heats of activation in the two directions.

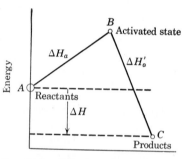

Fig. 13-7. Relation between the activation energies of the forward and reverse reactions and the heat of reaction.

$$\Delta H = \Delta H_a - \Delta H_a' \qquad (43)$$

Usually the heat evolved in the step BC is greater than the heat absorbed in the step AB, and the over-all reaction in going from A to C results in an evolution of heat. If ΔH_a happens to be greater than $\Delta H_a'$, the reaction $A \rightarrow C$ is endothermic.

It may be remembered that, if the reaction is carried out at constant volume instead of constant pressure, the heat of reaction is ΔE rather than ΔH. The two are practically the same in solutions, where there is but little change in volume, and even in gaseous reactions involving a change in volume the difference between ΔH and ΔE is usually small in comparison with the value of ΔH.

The energy required for the activated state is the chief factor in determining the speed of the reaction. It was shown that, the greater the energy required for activation, the fewer are the molecules possessing this energy at a given temperature and the longer is the time necessary to supply a certain number of effective, fast-moving molecules and the slower is the reaction. The heat evolved in a given reaction is of no significance for calculating reaction rates. As Hinshelwood has suggested, there is no more connection between the heat of reaction and the energy of activation than there is between the difference in levels of two valleys and the height of a mountain pass which separates them.

One very useful generalization can be made, however. In endothermic reactions, the energy required for activation must be at least as great as the endothermic heat of reaction. This is equivalent to saying that in going from a lower to a higher valley the route must traverse an elevation at least as high as the upper valley. Often it is difficult to calculate the energy of activation, but, if the reaction is endothermic, the heat of reaction may be used as a *minimum* value.

Example 10. The heat of combustion of a carbohydrate is 112,000 cal per g atom of carbon. To effect the reverse reaction, namely, the combination of carbon dioxide and water to form a carbohydrate and oxygen what is the minimum activation energy required?

Since this reverse reaction is endothermic by 112,000 cal, an activation energy of at least 112,000 cal must be supplied. It is quite likely that more than 112,000 cal will be necessary.

In the special case of an endothermic reaction to give atoms or free radicals like CH_3 (page 359) the heat of reaction is actually close to the energy of activation because the activation energy of the reverse reaction, the recombination of atoms, is nearly zero.

The heat of activation ΔH_a cannot be measured calorimetrically, because the activated molecules have only a brief existence. It is determined indirectly by plotting $\log k$ against $1/T$ and multiplying the slope by $-2.303R$ just as heat of reaction is determined by plotting $\log K$ against $1/T$, where K is the equilibrium constant (page 257). In this way the heat of activation was found, on page 342, to be 24,700 cal per mole for the decomposition of nitrogen pentoxide.

Example 11. Combining equations 31 and 43, show that the Arrhenius equation can be used to derive the known relation between equilibrium constants and heat of reaction.

$$\frac{d \ln k}{dT} = \frac{\Delta H_a}{RT^2} \quad \text{and} \quad \frac{d \ln k'}{dT} = \frac{\Delta H_a'}{RT^2}$$

where k and ΔH_a refer to the forward reaction and k' and $\Delta H_a'$ refer to the reverse reaction.

Subtracting gives

$$\frac{d(\ln k - \ln k')}{dT} = \frac{\Delta H_a - \Delta H_a'}{RT^2}$$

$\Delta H = \Delta H_a - \Delta H_a'$, and, from page 237, $k/k' = K$. Then,

$$\frac{d \ln K}{dT} = \frac{\Delta H}{RT^2}$$

This relation was proved by thermodynamics on page 256, thus lending support to the validity of the Arrhenius equation on which the above derivation is based.

Calculation of Rate Constants. It is now worth while to examine more fully the Arrhenius equation,

$$k = se^{-\Delta H_a/RT}$$

and to interpret the constants in terms of physical-chemical concepts. Since $e^{-\Delta H_a/RT}$ is dimensionless, s has the same dimensions as k, and, for first-order reactions, it has the dimensions of time^{-1}.

The rate of the over-all reaction depends on the concentration of the activated molecules, and this concentration may be calculated with the help of thermodynamical relations. There is an equilibrium between reacting and activated molecules, and

$$K_a = c_{\text{activated}}/c_{\text{reactant}}$$

It will be remembered (pages 142 and 251) that

$$\Delta F = \Delta H - T \Delta S$$

and that

$$\Delta F^\circ = -RT \ln K$$

Then,

$$K_a = e^{-\Delta F_a°/RT} = e^{\Delta S_a/R}e^{-\Delta H_a/RT} \tag{44}$$

where the subscript a refers to the activation process. There are complications involved in calculating the concentration of the activated molecules from this equilibrium constant and the concentration of the reactants; and further calculations are necessary to obtain the rate constant k. The more complete rate equation is derived in part in the Appendix on page 647. It is

$$k = (RT/Nh)e^{\Delta S_a/R}e^{-\Delta H_a/RT} \tag{45}$$

where N is Avogadro's constant and h is Planck's constant, 6.62×10^{-27} (page 655). This fundamental equation is from Eyring's theory of absolute rates. For a complete interpretation the literature must be consulted.*

This equation constitutes the proof, promised earlier, that the constant ΔH_a in the Arrhenius equation is related to the *heat of activation*. The factor s in the Arrhenius equation, known as the *frequency factor*, has the following significance:

$$s = (RT/Nh)e^{\Delta S_a/R} \tag{46}$$

The term $e^{\Delta S_a/R}$ is an entropy term, and for many unimolecular, bond-breaking gas reactions it may often be taken as approximately unity, be-

* Eyring, *J. Chem. Phys.*, *3*, 107 (1935); Glasstone, Laidler, and Eyring, *The Theory of Rate Processes*, McGraw-Hill Book Co., New York, 1941.

cause the activated complex is so much like the original reactants that the entropy change is very small. If $\Delta S_a = 0$, $e^{\Delta S_a/R} = 1$. At ordinary temperatures the term RT/Nh is about

$$(8.3 \times 10^7)(300)/(6.0 \times 10^{23})(6.6 \times 10^{-27})$$

or about 5×10^{13} sec^{-1}. This is the same order of magnitude as the frequency in many infrared spectra (page 74), which is due to the natural vibration period of atoms within the molecule.

According to an oversimplifield, mechanical view the molecule which has acquired sufficient energy will break at a bond, but the rupture cannot occur in less time than is required for a normal vibration period.

In many bimolecular reactions the frequency factor s turns out to be approximately equal to the number of molecules colliding, per unit volume and time, when at unit concentration. As a first approximation in the case of simple, small molecules, it may be supposed that the rate of reaction is determined by the rate at which *activated* molecules collide and give the products of the bimolecular reaction. On this hypothesis it is proportional to the number of molecules colliding multiplied by $e^{-\Delta H_a/RT}$, which by equation 36 is approximately equal to the fraction of molecules in the activated state. But there are many bimolecular reactions, particularly in the case of large or complicated molecules in solution, in which the reaction goes much more slowly than predicted by this formula. It has been customary to assume that a certain orientation at the time of collision, a type of lock-and-key effect, is necessary for complete reaction. The more exact statistical development for the frequency factor leads to terms which are approximately equivalent to the collision frequency in a gas consisting of simple molecules.

Example 12. In the second-order decomposition of gaseous hydrogen iodide the heat of activation has been found by equation 29 to be 45,600 cal. Then, at 393.7°, from equation 37,

$$\frac{n'}{n} = \frac{2}{\sqrt{\pi}} e^{-\Delta H_a/RT} \sqrt{\frac{\Delta H_a}{RT}} = 7.3 \times 10^{-15}$$

If the concentration of hydrogen iodide is 1 mole per liter, the number of molecules colliding per milliliter per second is given by the expression

$$2z = 2 \times 3.54\sigma^2 n^2 \sqrt{RT/M}$$

$$= (2)(3.54)(3.5 \times 10^{-8})^2 \left(\frac{6.02 \times 10^{23}}{1000}\right)^2 \sqrt{\frac{(8.3 \times 10^7)(666.8)}{127.9}}$$

$$= 6.6 \times 10^{31}$$

Expressed in terms of moles colliding per second per liter,

$$2z = \frac{(6.6 \times 10^{31})(1000)}{6.02 \times 10^{23}} = 1.1 \times 10^{11}$$

Then calculating the number of moles per liter reacting per second at 393.7°, we have

$$k = 2z \, (n'/n) = (1.1 \times 10^{11})(7.3 \times 10^{-15}) = 8.0 \times 10^{-4}$$

The experimentally determined value is 2.6×10^{-4} $mole^{-1}$ liter sec^{-1}. This fair agreement shows that there is no large orientation effect in this simple reaction.

The Prediction of Reaction Rates. The Arrhenius equation is found to fit the rate measurements surprisingly well in many chemical reactions over a wide range of temperatures.

It has been shown that all chemical reactions, complex though they may be, can in principle be split up into a number of reverse, successive, or competing reactions, and that each of these is usually a unimolecular or bimolecular reaction. Furthermore, one can estimate the frequency factors, s, and activation energies, ΔH_a, of each of these, and thus make a rough estimate of the rates of the fundamental, primary reactions. These can then, for some reactions, be put together with the help of integration or calculating machines to give the over-all reaction rate.

For unimolecular reactions which produce atoms by an endothermic process ΔH_a is the heat of the endothermic reaction, as determined calorimetrically or from the energy required to break the bonds. In endothermic reactions which do not produce atoms or free radicals the activation energy is greater than the heat of reaction.

In simple bond-breaking unimolecular reactions it was shown on page 353 that the frequency factor is about 10^{13} sec^{-1}. Many unimolecular gas-phase reactions are described by the rate expression

$$k = 10^{13} e^{-\Delta H_a/RT}$$

On the basis of these facts the chart of *Fig. 13-8* is useful in predicting reaction rates for many gas-phase unimolecular decompositions.

The values of k in sec^{-1} on the slanting lines are recorded at the right. It is a simple matter to obtain a rough estimate of k by graphical interpolation. The situation is simplified by the fact that very rapid or very slow reactions are of no practical concern, the ordinary time of observation of the course of a reaction being not less than a few seconds or more than a few months. The values of k falling within this time range are roughly from 10^{-1} to 10^{-7} sec^{-1}.

The prediction of reaction rates is simplified also by the fact that the range of activation energies is limited very roughly to the range 10,000 to 100,000 cal per mole. Very few chemical reactions require more than 100,000 cal per mole of activation energy, and the ones with less than 10,000 cal are usually too fast to measure. A very large number of activation energies range from 15,000 to 60,000 cal.

If the energy of activation for a first-order reaction is 25,000 cal per mole and the temperature is 300°K (a little above room temperature),

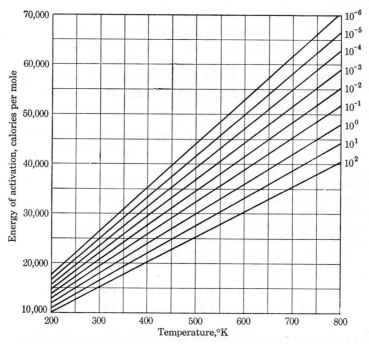

FIG. 13-8.   Graph for prediction of specific reaction rate constants for various activation energies at several temperatures, assuming a frequency factor of 10^{13}.

k has a value of 10^{-5} if it is assumed that s has a value of 10^{13}. When k is 10^{-5}, the period of half-life is about 19 hours. These calculations fit the data for nitrogen pentoxide fairly well.

Again, the energy of activation for the first-order decomposition of ethyl bromide is about 55,000 cal per mole, and it is evident that the temperature must be above 650°K to give appreciable decomposition. As another illustration, it may be concluded that at 500°K one is concerned in unimolecular reactions only with those reactions that have values of ΔH_a between 25,000 and 45,000 cal per mole. With larger values of ΔH_a the reaction is too slow to measure; with smaller values it is too fast.

The graphs may be used as a rough estimate in many simple unimolecular reactions, but large errors may be involved, particularly for
first-order reactions in solutions.

If the activation of the molecule involves a rearrangement of atoms
or a change in configuration, there will be a change in entropy and
$e^{\Delta S_a/R}$ cannot be neglected, as in a bond-breaking unimolecular reaction.
The values of ΔS_a are rarely large enough to give a value of more than
10^2 or less than 10^{-2} to the term $e^{\Delta S_a/R}$, and so frequency factors
$(RT/Nh)e^{\Delta S_a/R}$ may range from about 10^{11} to 10^{15}. If the spatial arrangements in the activated molecule are more probable than in the un-
activated molecule, ΔS_a will have a positive sign; if less probable, it will
have a negative value. If the frequency factor is very large (over
10^{15} or so) a chain reaction is indicated (page 358).

Example 13. The unimolecular rearrangement reaction

$$CH_2{=}CH{-}O{-}CH_2{-}CH{=}CH_2 \ \rightarrow \ CH_2{=}CH{-}CH_2{-}CH_2{-}CHO$$

Vinyl allyl ether   Allyl acetaldehyde

is a very good first-order reaction.*

The rate was followed by passing ultraviolet light of 3130 A through the vapor and
measuring with a photocell the light transmission as a function of time. The vinyl
allyl ether absorbs this light, but the allyl acetaldehyde does not. The partial pressures of the vinyl allyl ether may be calculated from the per cent transmission with
the help of a previous calibration in which the logarithm of the per cent of light
transmitted is plotted against the partial pressures of the pure ether. The experimental data give the following first-order specific rate constants in sec^{-1}:

Temperature, °C	154	167	178	196
$k \times 10^4$	1.2	3.4	7.9	28.7

From a plot of $\log k$ vs. $1/T$ one finds that the activation energy is 30,600 cal per
mole and

$$k = 5 \times 10^{11} e^{-30,600/RT}$$

Also, since

$$k = (RT/Nh)e^{\Delta S_a/R}e^{-\Delta H_a/RT}$$

ΔS_a, the entropy of activation, becomes -7.7 cal deg^{-1} mole^{-1}.† This value of
-7.7 indicates that the molecule must acquire an improbable shape (probably a type
of ring structure) in order to become activated so that it can rearrange to give the allyl
acetaldehyde. In the simple unimolecular, bond-breaking reactions there is no
change in shape and no entropy of activation.

* Schuler and Murphy, *J. Am. Chem. Soc.*, **72**, 3155 (1950).
† In this calculation ΔH_a is obtained from the Arrhenius equation by a $\log k$ vs. $1/T$
graph. The Eyring equation has an extra T term in it, and differentiation does not
give the same value. Accordingly, in calculating ΔS_a the frequency factor is set
equal to $(e)(RT/Nh)e^{\Delta S_a/R}$. The extra factor e is included because the Arrhenius
plot is applied to the Eyring equation.

In *bimolecular* reactions the frequency factor is roughly equal to the number of molecules colliding as shown on page 347, if the molecules are simple and there is no orientation requirement at the time of collision. The frequency factor in a second-order reaction depends on the units in which the concentrations are expressed. When they are expressed in moles per liter, the frequency factor at room temperature is about 10^{10} and the specific rate constant is

$$k = 10^{10}e^{-\Delta H_a/RT}$$

A graph similar to that of Fig. 13-8 could be prepared, but the predictions are not very satisfactory.

An upper limit of the activation energy might be taken as the energy required to pull the reactants completely apart to give isolated atoms, as calculated by adding the heats of dissociation of all the bonds broken (page 122). Certainly, the atoms would then be in an activated state ready to react, but usually the activation can be accomplished with a lesser expenditure of energy. If there is only an instantaneous collision and separation, the energy evolved by the formation of the new bonds is dissipated by collision to the surrounding molecules and cannot be used to activate the reacting molecules. However, some of the energy of new bond formation can be used if a complex is formed and the reactants and products are held together for even a very brief time. Thus,

The energy of activation must be somewhere between the heat of reaction and the energy required to produce separated atoms. According to another very simple approach, the activation energy for a bimolecular reaction is taken as 28 per cent of the energy required to dissociate the molecules into atoms or groups of atoms, that is, the sum of the dissociation energies of the bonds broken. Hirschfelder * arrived at this empirical rule by finding that, in the decomposition of hydrogen iodide gas, which is one of the most accurately known reactions, the experimentally determined activation energy is 28 per cent of the energy required to dissociate HI into hydrogen and iodine atoms. He then assumed that this 28 per cent is a general constant applicable to other

* Hirschfelder, *J. Chem. Phys.*, *9*, 645 (1941).

bimolecular reactions. The rule seems to hold fairly well, but the number of reactions where experimental checks are possible is quite limited.

Example 14. Estimate the activation energy for the reaction:

$$2ICl(g) + H_2(g) \rightarrow 2HCl(g) + I_2(g)$$

For $ICl \rightarrow I + Cl$, $\Delta H = 49,600$; and for $H_2 \rightarrow 2H$, $\Delta H = 103,200$.

Then $\Delta H_a = 0.28 \ (49,600 + 103,200) = 42,800$. The experimentally determined value of ΔH_a calculated from kinetic data is 34,000 cal per mole.

Chain Reactions. We have seen that although the unimolecular and bimolecular steps are reasonably simple the over-all kinetics of most chemical reactions is very complicated. An important type of complex reaction is the chain reaction in which many molecules react for every molecule that is activated.

The theory of chain reactions was first proposed by Bodenstein and by Nernst to account for the large yield obtained in the photochemical combination of chlorine and hydrogen to give hydrochloric acid. The reaction is

$$:\overset{..}{\underset{..}{Cl}}:\overset{..}{\underset{..}{Cl}}: + \text{ Light} \rightarrow :\overset{..}{\underset{..}{Cl}}\cdot + :\overset{..}{\underset{..}{Cl}}\cdot$$

$$:\overset{..}{\underset{..}{Cl}}\cdot + H:H \rightarrow H:\overset{..}{\underset{..}{Cl}}: + H\cdot$$

$$H\cdot + :\overset{..}{\underset{..}{Cl}}:\overset{..}{\underset{..}{Cl}}: \rightarrow H:\overset{..}{\underset{..}{Cl}}: + :\overset{..}{\underset{..}{Cl}}\cdot \quad \text{etc.}$$

Sometimes this cycle continues until over a million molecules have reacted. The chains can be started by other means than light, for example, by bombardment with alpha particles from radium, or by reaction with traces of sodium vapor, or by a spark.

One may ask why such a reaction ever stops. At times, as a matter of fact, the chain reaction does not stop until all the material is consumed. At other times, however, the chain is broken when one of the activated molecules in the chain collides with the wall of the containing vessel or with foreign material that may be present as an impurity. There is a chance, too, that two of the chain carriers such as Cl or H atoms will combine with each other and prevent further reaction involving these atoms. The length of the chain, that is, the number of molecules reacting per molecule activated, is determined by the relative rates of the chain-propagating and the chain-stopping reactions.

Certain oxidations in the gas phase have been explained successfully on the basis of chain reactions.* The specific velocity of the reaction depends among other things on the size of the vessel, the pressure of the

* Semenoff, *Chem. Revs.*, *6*, **347** (1929).

gases, and the temperature, because these factors affect the frequency with which the chain-propagating molecules hit the wall.

It is often difficult to distinguish a chain reaction from an ordinary reaction. Sometimes the presence of a chain mechanism can be established by determining that the number of molecules reacting is much larger than the number of molecules which are activated by the addition of a measured quantity of energy in a photochemical reaction. Again the presence of a chain may sometimes be revealed by the addition of retarding material called an inhibitor. Nitric oxide is an inhibitor for certain reactions in the gas phase.

If each molecule of the inhibitor stops a chain and each chain contains a great many molecules, it is obvious that mere traces of inhibitors are sufficient. For example, the oxidation of sodium sulfite by atmospheric oxygen is inhibited markedly by the addition of traces of alcohols. Lead tetraethyl in gasoline is another example of an inhibitor. Under certain conditions the chain reactions become too violent in a combustion engine, and a "carbon knock" is produced. A trace of the lead compound is sufficient to stop the chains and prevent the knock.

Still another example of the use of inhibitors is found in the preservation of gasoline. Certain unsaturated compounds in the gasoline tend to polymerize and form gums in the presence of air and light. Indophenol, α-naphthol, and certain other oxidizable substances containing phenolic and aromatic amine groups are effective in inhibiting this reaction. Antioxidants are important also in preserving foods.

Free Radical Chains. In the decomposition of organic substances at high temperatures free radicals such as CH_3, C_2H_5, OH, H, and Br are formed, and they may propagate chain reactions. There is adequate evidence in band spectra for the existence of these free radicals which violate the rules of classical valence theories. Again their presence is revealed by the chemical removal of thin metallic mirrors. They are short-lived not because they are unstable but because they are extremely reactive. With these free radicals it is possible to set up a series of chain reactions in such a way that the over-all reaction is first order or second order or fractional order; and they play an important part in the mechanism of many reactions, particularly at high temperatures.

For example, the thermal decomposition of a hydrocarbon, such as propane, may involve the initial breakdown into free radicals, thus:

$$C_3H_8 \xrightarrow{k_1} CH_3 + C_2H_5$$

$$CH_3 + C_3H_8 \xrightarrow{k_2} CH_4 + C_3H_7$$

$$C_3H_7 \xrightarrow{k_3} CH_3 + C_2H_4$$

The CH_3 then continues as before:

$$CH_3 + C_3H_8 \xrightarrow{k_2} CH_4 + C_3H_7 \quad \text{etc.}$$

and the chain is propagated through a great many cycles until it is ended by a collision on the wall or by a combination of free radicals:

$$CH_3 + C_3H_7 \xrightarrow{k_4} C_4H_{10}$$

Other reactions go on also, but these will illustrate the possibilities and explain how methane, ethylene, and butane can be obtained from the decomposition of propane.

Exercise VII. What is the relationship between the concentration of free radicals and the rate constants in the above mechanism? Differential rate equations may be written for these reactions. Thus,

$$dc_{CH_3}/dt = k_1 c_{C_3H_8} - k_2 c_{CH_3} c_{C_3H_8} + k_3 c_{C_3H_7} - k_4 c_{CH_3} c_{C_3H_7}$$

$$dc_{C_3H_7}/dt = k_2 c_{CH_3} c_{C_3H_8} - k_3 c_{C_3H_7} - k_4 c_{CH_3} c_{C_3H_7}$$

Assuming that, at the steady state, $dc_{CH_3}/dt = 0$, and that k_1 is very small, it can be shown that *

$$c_{CH_3} = \sqrt{\frac{k_1 k_3}{2 k_2 k_4}} \quad \text{and that} \quad c_{C_3H_7} = c_{C_3H_8} \sqrt{\frac{k_1 k_2}{2 k_3 k_4}}$$

Thus, it is possible to make a rough calculation of the concentration of free radicals from an estimation of the specific rate constants.

Catalysis. A substance that increases the rate of a chemical reaction without being used up in the reaction is called a *catalyst*. There are many different kinds of catalysts and many different mechanisms by which catalysts operate.

The function of the catalyst is to bring about the desired reaction with a smaller heat of activation. A lower heat of activation gives a more rapid reaction at a given temperature because more molecules have the required amount of energy to react. The high energy requirement is avoided by some by-pass. Usually the by-passing consists in the formation of a new compound with less energy consumption and then the decomposition of this intermediate compound in such a way as to regenerate the catalyst. In this way the catalyst is used over and over again.

The catalytic action of nitrogen dioxide in the oxidation of sulfur dioxide offers a good example. The reaction represented by the equation

$$2SO_2 + O_2 \rightarrow 2SO_3$$

* Daniels, *Chemical Kinetics*, Cornell University Press, Ithaca, N. Y., 1938, p. 52.

is very slow. The accelerating action of nitric oxide on the reaction as used industrially in the old chamber process for the manufacture of sulfuric acid may be represented in the following simplified manner:

$$2NO + O_2 \rightarrow 2NO_2$$

$$2SO_2 + 2NO_2 \rightarrow 2SO_3 + 2NO$$

$$2NO + O_2 \rightarrow 2NO_2 \quad \text{etc.}$$

There are many examples in organic chemistry in which the catalyst accelerates the reaction by forming an intermediate compound which reacts faster than the original reactants. One of the earliest examples was discovered when ethyl sulfate was detected in the reaction of alcohol to give ether, using sulfuric acid as a catalyst. Another important example is the catalytic action of aluminum chloride in the well-known Friedel-Crafts synthesis of organic compounds which has been shown to involve the formation of an addition compound.

The catalyst accelerates the reverse reaction as well as the forward reaction so that the equilibrium constant is unaffected.

Sometimes the catalyst may *appear* to change the equilibrium, but in such cases large quantities of the catalyst are usually required and the material not only accelerates the reaction but also changes the effective concentrations of the reacting materials. Changing the solvent, for example, may accelerate a reaction, and it may also change the equilibrium, but the two effects are entirely independent. The catalytic effect is not responsible for the equilibrium shift.

Sometimes one of the products of reaction functions as a catalyst. Such a substance is called an autocatalyst. Normally, of course, the reaction rate decreases continually, but in autocatalytic reactions the rate increases to a maximum and then decreases.

Many catalytic reactions are effected through a catalytic pair which is alternately oxidized and reduced. An example is the bromide-hypobromous acid catalysis of the hydrogen peroxide decomposition.* In acid solutions bromide ion is oxidized to hypobromous acid by hydrogen peroxide according to the equation

$$H_2O_2 + Br^- + H^+ \rightarrow HBrO + H_2O$$

and the hypobromous acid, in turn, is reduced by hydrogen peroxide according to the equation

$$H_2O_2 + HBrO \rightarrow H_2O + Br^- + H^+ + O_2$$

* Bray and Livingston, *J. Am. Chem. Soc.*, *45*, 1251 (1923).

The second reaction is faster than the first, but eventually a *steady state* is reached in which the concentrations of bromide ion, hypobromous acid, and hydrogen ion are constant, and the only apparent change is

$$2H_2O_2 \rightarrow 2H_2O + O_2$$

and the reaction is first order.

Contact Catalysis. The phenomenon of adsorption is discussed on page 522, where it is seen that in many cases the surface of a solid may be regarded as a checkerboard of atoms on which molecules from the gas phase, or from solution, become attached. When molecules are adsorbed at a surface, the energy content is altered, and there is opportunity for forming new products. Adsorption does not necessarily produce catalytic reactions, but catalytic reactions at surfaces generally involve adsorption. Apparently some atoms at the surface are in better position to bring about reaction than others. Moreover, the exact spacing between atoms in the lattice of the catalyst is important, and this distance can be altered by changing the method of preparation and by addition of extra substances.

The rate of a reaction catalyzed by a surface depends to a large extent on the fraction of the surface that is covered with adsorbed gas. When the surface is nearly bare the limiting step in the rate of the whole reaction is the frequency with which molecules strike the surface. The pressure of the gas determines the extent of adsorption, and this, in turn, determines the rate of the reaction. Since the reaction rate is proportional to the concentration of the gas, the reaction follows the first-order equation. When the surface becomes saturated, on the other hand, most of the molecules hitting the surface do not reach the catalyst but are stopped by the layer of molecules already adsorbed there. The pressure of the gas then has no influence on the reaction rate, and the reaction is of the zero order. When ammonia is decomposed on a tungsten filament, for example, the rate of decomposition is independent of the pressure, over a wide range of pressure.

The activity of a catalyst is altered appreciably by extremely minute amounts of foreign substances. Foreign substances that tend to inhibit catalytic activity are known as *poisons;* substances that tend to enhance the activity are known as *promoters.* It is easy to see how a small number of molecules can react permanently with the atoms exposed at the surface and thus destroy the catalytic properties. For example, in the manufacture of sulfuric acid by the contact process, the presence of a very minute amount of arsenic completely destroys the catalytic activity of the platinum catalyst by forming platinum arsenide at the surface. Certain metals and metallic oxides act as promoters of some catalysts by rendering them less susceptible to poisoning, but in many cases the promotor acts by changing the atomic lattice spacing, or by increasing the number of interfaces at which loose adsorption compounds can be formed, with just the right degree of stability to produce a rapid catalytic reaction.

The catalytic activity of the walls of the containing vessel is a factor in many gaseous reactions. The thermal decomposition of organic materials frequently occurs on the walls. For such reactions the temperature coefficient is usually small, because the slowest process is the diffusion of the products away from the walls, and a diffusion process is subject only to the simple laws of the kinetic theory of gases. A 10° rise at about 300°K increases the diffusion rate by only about 3 per cent, whereas the rate of a chemical reaction is normally increased about 300 per cent, as already explained.

A wall effect may be distinguished from a homogeneous gas reaction by (1) the temperature coefficient, (2) increasing the area greatly, as by adding powdered glass to a glass vessel, (3) changing the nature of the vessel walls. Quartz may be used instead of glass, for example, or the walls may be coated. The reaction between bromine and ethylene is a wall effect, as shown by the fact that the reaction is stopped when the glass walls are covered with paraffin. When glass vessels are coated with fused halides or with nonpolar fluorocarbons or silicones, the characteristics of some gaseous reactions are changed.

Enzyme Catalysis. Many chemical reactions in living organisms are catalyzed by complex organic substances called enzymes produced by the living cell. They are proteins having molecular weights of more than 10,000, and many of them have been isolated in crystalline form. When isolated, they can carry on the same specific reactions in the laboratory (in vitro) as in the living organism (in vivo). *Catalase* exists in plant juice and in blood. It brings about the rapid decomposition of hydrogen peroxide. Dextrose is fermented to give ethanol and carbon dioxide by the enzyme *zymase*, which is present in yeast. The enzyme *urease* catalyzes the hydrolysis of urea, to give ammonium carbonate.

According to thermodynamics most organic compounds may be converted into a number of products of lower free energy. The enzymes present in the cell determine which of these reactions actually occur. The function of the enzyme is to lower the activation energy for a reaction. Many enzymes are such specific catalysts that they act on only one substance.

Many enzyme-catalyzed reactions may be represented by a mechanism which was originally suggested by Michaelis and Menten.*

* Michaelis and Menten, *Biochem. Z.*, *49*, 333 (1913).

$$E + S \underset{k_2}{\overset{k_1}{\rightleftharpoons}} ES \tag{47}$$

$$ES \xrightarrow{k_3} E + P \tag{48}$$

Here the enzyme is represented by E and the reactant, referred to as a substrate by enzyme chemists, is represented by S. The complex ES may dissociate either into E and S or E and product P. The rate equations for reactions 47 and 48 are

$$d[ES]/dt = k_1[E][S] - (k_2 + k_3)[ES] \tag{49}$$

$$d[P]/dt = k_3[ES] \tag{50}$$

Since the molar concentration of the enzyme is generally very small and the reaction rate may be measured before there is an appreciable change in the concentration of S, equation 49 may be written

$$d[ES]/dt = k_1([E]_0 - [ES])[S] - (k_2 + k_3)[ES] \tag{51}$$

where $[E]_0 = [E] + [ES]$ and is the total molar concentration of the enzyme. Once the reaction is under way, $d[ES]/dt$ will be very small and may be taken as zero since ES is being formed at the same time it is decomposing. This approximation is frequently used in the study of kinetics and is referred to as the *steady-state* approximation. If the resulting relationship for the concentration of the intermediate complex is substituted into equation 50

$$\frac{d[P]}{dt} = \frac{k_3[E]_0}{1 + \dfrac{(k_2 + k_3)}{k_1[S]}} \tag{52}$$

The quantity $(k_2 + k_3)/k_1$ is referred to as the Michaelis constant, which may be seen to be equal to the concentration of S at which the rate of formation of the product is half the maximum rate obtained at high concentrations of S, namely $k_3[E]_0$.

This equation is in agreement with the fact that many enzyme-catalyzed reactions are found to be first order with respect to S if the concentration of S is very low, and zero order with respect to S if the concentration of S is sufficiently high. In both cases the reaction is first order with respect to the concentration of the enzyme.

Important advances have been made in biochemistry through a better understanding of enzyme kinetics. In some cases the intermediate reactions, such as those illustrated, have been followed by measuring the amount of light transmitted at a wavelength which corresponds to the absorption band of the intermediate *ES*. Fast enzyme reactions have been followed in this way with a photomultiplier cell and oscillograph.*

Examples of Industrial Catalysis. *Haber Process for Ammonia.* The synthesis of ammonia from purified hydrogen and nitrogen is one of the large chemical industries of the world. The production in 1952 was 2 million tons. Oxidation of ammonia gives nitric acid, which is the basis of most explosives. Much of the world's nitrogen fertilizer is made from ammonia prepared by the Haber process. The reaction is

$$N_2 + 3H_2 \rightleftharpoons 2NH_3$$

The free energy is favorable (ΔF has a negative value), but the reaction at room temperature is slow. When the temperature is raised to produce a faster reaction the equilibrium constant becomes less favorable. Increasing the pressure, however, throws the reaction to the right, because according to Le Châtelier's principle pressure tends to shift an equilibrium in the direction of the smaller volume. Even at high pressures, the temperature must be kept down to give a satisfactory yield, and thus it is necessary to use a catalyst to make the reaction proceed rapidly enough to obtain economical production.

Special iron catalysts are used with additions of vanadium and other metals to make the catalyst more effective and to protect it from too rapid inactivation by traces of impurities in the gases.

In order to obtain high yields of ammonia, the pressure is kept as high as is technically feasible, and the temperature is kept as low as possible. At 550° under a pressure of 200 atm nearly 12 per cent of ammonia is formed. The ammonia is removed and the remaining hydrogen and nitrogen are recirculated through the catalyst chamber.

Hydrogenation. Nickel catalysts and metallic oxide catalysts are used extensively for hydrogenating various liquids and dissolved substances with hydrogen under pressure. An important industrial application of the hydrogenation process is the conversion of unsaturated aliphatic acids, such as oleic acid, into saturated acids, such as stearic acid.

By substituting various groups into a molecule it is possible to add hydrogen to different parts of a molecule. In the same way by adding certain hydrogen acceptors, that is, substances which are capable of taking up hydrogen, it is possible to remove hydrogen from different parts of a molecule with the help of a catalyst.†

* Chance in Friess and Weissberger, *Technique of Organic Chemistry*, Vol. VII, *Investigation of Rates and Mechanisms of Reactions*, Interscience Publishers, New York, 1953.

† Adkins, *The Reactions of Hydrogen*, University of Wisconsin Press, Madison, 1937.

Synthesis of Methanol. One of the outstanding developments in industrial chemistry has been the large-scale production of methyl alcohol from carbon monoxide and hydrogen using a zinc oxide-chromium oxide mixture as a catalyst. The reaction is easily controlled, and the catalyst is not easily poisoned. Pressures up to 200 atm and temperatures between 200° and 400° are ordinarily used. Some of the higher alcohols have been synthesized in a similar manner, but it becomes increasingly difficult to suppress side reactions with the more complex molecules.

Petroleum Products. Striking developments in catalysis have been made in the field of petroleum chemistry. Large-scale plants are now producing from ordinary petroleum a wide variety of products including toluene, butadiene for artificial rubber, and isoöctane and other compounds with high antiknock properties. Moreover, through this catalytic cracking it has been possible to increase greatly the amount of gasoline obtainable from the petroleum.

One of the chief difficulties in these catalytic operations has been the removal of the large amounts of heat formed by the chemical reactions. Fluidized catalysts are now used on a large scale, the catalyst in fine particles being suspended or transported in the gas stream. Intimate contact between catalyst and gas is thus assured, and supporting structures and expensive heat-transfer equipment are greatly reduced. Some of these large catalytic cracking towers are over 100 ft in height.

Fischer-Tropsch Synthesis of Hydrocarbons. Liquid fuel can be made from coal, methane, cellulose, or other carbonaceous material.

Gas of the composition $nCO + 2nH_2$ is converted at comparatively low pressures into long-chain paraffin hydrocarbons using catalysts of cobalt, or of iron or nickel, at about 200°. The catalysts can be made by coprecipitating cobalt and iron hydroxides on a silicious material and reducing to the metals. The carbon monoxide and hydrogen mixture called "synthesis gas" can be made from the partial combustion of methane, by the action of steam on coke, or by heating carbonaceous material. A large supply of cheap oxygen is needed because the use of air leaves an excess of nitrogen which then prevents proper operation of the process.

REFERENCES

Hinshelwood, *Kinetics of Chemical Change*, Oxford University Press, Oxford, 1941.
Glasstone, Laidler, and Eyring, *The Theory of Rate Processes*, McGraw-Hill Book Co., New York, 1940.
Steacie, *Free Radicals*, Rheinhold Publishing Corp., New York, 1954.
Daniels, *Chemical Kinetics*, Cornell University Press, Ithaca, New York, 1938.

Amis, *Kinetics of Chemical Change in Solution,* The Macmillan Co., New York, 1949.
Laidler, *Chemical Kinetics,* McGraw-Hill Book Co., New York, 1950.
Frost and Pearson, *Kinetics and Mechanism,* John Wiley & Sons, New York, 1953.
Hougen and Watson, *Chemical Process Principles,* Part III, *Kinetics and Catalysis,* John Wiley & Sons, New York, 1947.
Friess and Weissberger, *Technique of Organic Chemistry,* Vol. VII, *Investigation of Rates and Mechanisms of Reactions,* Interscience Publishers, New York, 1953.
"Tables of Chemical Kinetics," *Circular of the National Bureau of Standards* 510, U. S. Government Printing Office, Washington, D. C., 1951.

PROBLEMS

1. A stream of air at 10 liters per minute, measured at 25° and 1 atm pressure, is passing through a catalyst tube which is 4 cm in diameter and 100 cm long, maintained throughout at 800°. Half the volume of the chamber is occupied by solid material. Approximately how many seconds does a given molecule remain in the catalyst chamber, if it is assumed that the gas reaches the temperature of the chamber 800° instantly? *Ans.* 1.05 sec.

2. Methyl acetate is hydrolyzed in approximately 1 N HCl at 25°. Aliquots of 5 ml each are removed at intervals and titrated with 0.1852 N NaOH. Calculate the first-order rate constant from the following experimental data.

t, sec	339	1242	2745	4546	∞
v, ml	26.34	27.80	29.70	31.81	39.81

Ans. 1.26×10^{-4} sec^{-1}.

3. From the following data on the rate of the rearrangement of 1-cyclohexenyl allylmalonitrile at 135.7°, determine graphically the first-order reaction-rate constant in reciprocal minutes. Check the graphical evaluation by calculating k from two different times.

Time, min	0	5	10	20	30	45
Per cent rearranged	19.8	34.2	46.7	64.7	77.0	86.3

Ans. 4.03×10^{-2} min^{-1}.

4. Prove that in a first-order reaction, where $dn/dt = -kn$, the average life, that is, the average life expectancy of the molecules, is equal to $1/k$.

Ans. $\dfrac{1}{n_0} \displaystyle\int_0^\infty n \, dt = 1/k$.

5. The reaction $CH_3CH_2NO_2 + OH^- \rightarrow H_2O + CH_3CH\!\!=\!\!NO_2^-$ is of second order, and k at 0° is 39.1 (mole/liter)$^{-1}$ minute^{-1}. An aqueous solution is made 0.004 molar in nitroethane and 0.005 molar in NaOH. How long will it take for 90 per cent of the nitroethane to react? *Ans.* 26.3 min.

6. Isopropyl ether in the vapor state isomerizes to allyl acetone according to a first-order rate equation. The following formula gives the influence of temperature on the specific reaction rate (in sec^{-1}).

$$k = 5.4 \times 10^{11} e^{-29,300/RT}$$

At 150°C how long will it take to build up a partial pressure of 300 mm of allyl acetone starting with 760 mm of isopropyl ether? [Stein and Murphy, *J. Am. Chem. Soc.*, *74*, 1041 (1952).]   *Ans.* 1220 sec.

7. A certain substance A is mixed with an equal quantity of a substance B. At the end of 1 hour A is 75% reacted. How much will be left unreacted at the end of 2 hours if the reaction is (*a*) first order in A and independent of B; (*b*) first order in A and first order in B; (*c*) zero order in A and independent of B?

Ans. (*a*) 6.25, (*b*) 14.3, (*c*) 0%.

8. If a first order reaction has an activation energy of 25,000 cal per mole and, in the equation $k = se^{-\Delta H_a/RT}$, s has a value of 5×10^{13} sec^{-1}, at what temperature will the reaction have a half-life of (*a*) 1 minute; (*b*) 1 month of 30 days?

Ans. (*a*) 76°. (*b*) −4°.

9. The hydrolysis of $(CH_2)_6\,C\underset{\diagdown CH_3}{\overset{\diagup Cl}{}}$ in 80 per cent ethanol follows the first-order rate equation. The values of the specific reaction rate constants as determined by Brown and Borkowski, *J. Am. Chem. Soc.*, *74*, 1896 (1952), are as follows:

Temperature	0°	25°	35°	45°
k	1.06×10^{-5}	3.19×10^{-4}	9.86×10^{-4}	2.92×10^{-3} sec^{-1}

(*a*) Plot log k against $1/T$; (*b*) calculate the activation energy; (*c*) calculate the frequency factor.   *Ans.* (*b*) 21,500 cal mole^{-1}. (*c*) 1.8×10^{12} sec^{-1}.

10. Calculate (*a*) the mean free path and (*b*) the number of collisions with the wall when 1 gram of iodine is placed in a previously evacuated 2-liter spherical flask and heated to 100°.   *Ans.* (*a*) 1.22×10^{-4} cm. (*b*) 3.99×10^{24} collisions sec^{-1}.

11. The thermal decomposition of gaseous acetaldehyde is a second-order reaction. The value of ΔH_a is 45,500 cal per mole, and the molecular diameter of the acetaldehyde molecule is 5×10^{-8} cm. (*a*) Calculate the number of molecules reacting per milliliter per second at 800°K and 760 mm pressure. (*b*) Calculate k in 1 mole^{-1} sec^{-1} [$k = -(1/c^2)(dc/dt)$].

Ans. (*a*) 5.1×10^{16} molecules ml^{-1} sec^{-1}. (*b*) 0.36 l mole^{-1} sec^{-1}.

12. The reaction $2NO + O_2 \rightarrow 2NO_2$ follows the third-order law. Assuming that a small amount of NO_3 exists in rapid reversible equilibrium with NO and O_2 and that the rate-determining step is the slow bimolecular reaction $NO_3 + NO \rightarrow 2NO_2$, show that the reaction will nevertheless appear to be third order.

Ans. $d(NO_2)/dt = k(NO)^2(O_2)$.

---

13. The rate of hydrolysis of 17 per cent sucrose in 0.099 N HCl aqueous solution at 35° was measured by Pennycuick as follows:

Time, min	9.82	59.60	93.18	142.9	294.8	589.4
Sucrose remaining, %	96.5	80.3	71.0	59.1	32.8	11.1

What is the value of the specific reaction rate constant k in reciprocal seconds?

14. A solution of ethyl acetate and sodium hydroxide was prepared which contained (at $t = 0$) 5×10^{-3} M ethyl acetate and 8×10^{-3} M base. After 400 sec at 25° a 25-ml aliquot was found to consume 33.3 ml of 5×10^{-3} M hydrochloric acid. (*a*) Calculate the rate constant for this second-order reaction. (*b*) At what time would you expect 20.0 ml of hydrochloric acid to be required?

15. The specific reaction rate k for the reaction

$$2NO + O_2 \rightarrow 2NO_2$$

has a value of 7.1×10^9 mole^{-2} ml^2 sec^{-1} at $25°$ in $dc_{NO_2}/dt = kc_{NO}{}^2 c_{O_2}$. Air blown through a certain hot chamber and cooled quickly to $25°$ and 760 mm contains 1 per cent by volume of nitric oxide and 20 per cent of oxygen. (a) How long will it take for 90 per cent of this nitric oxide NO to be converted into nitrogen dioxide NO_2 (or N_2O_4)? (b) If the gases are blown through at the rate of 5000 cu ft per minute, how large a chamber must be constructed in order to obtain this 90 per cent conversion?

16. Equal quantities of A and B are added to a liter of a suitable solvent. At the end of 500 seconds half of A has reacted. How much of A will be reacted at the end of 800 seconds if the reaction with respect to A is (a) zero order; (b) first order; (c) second order in which equal parts of A and B react?

17. Hydrogen peroxide reacts with thiosulfate ion in slightly acid solution as follows:

$$H_2O_2 + 2S_2O_3{}^= + 2H^+ \rightarrow 2H_2O + S_4O_6{}^=$$

This reaction rate is independent of the hydrogen-ion concentration in the pH range 4–6. The following data were obtained at $25°C$ and pH 5.0:

Initial concentrations: $[H_2O_2] = 0.03680\ M$; $[S_2O_3{}^=] = 0.02040\ M$

t_{min}	16	36	43	52
$[S_2O_3{}^=] \times 10^3$	10.30	5.18	4.16	3.13

(a) What is the order of the reaction? (b) What is the specific reaction rate?

18. If k_2 is twice as large as k_3 in the reactions $A \xrightarrow{k_1} B \underset{k_3}{\overset{k_2}{\rightleftharpoons}} C$, prove mathematically that, regardless of the value of k_1, c_B and c_C will have the values $\frac{1}{3}$ and $\frac{2}{3}$ when the reaction is completed, as shown in Fig. 13-4.

19. Although the thermal decomposition of ethyl bromide is complex, the over-all rate appears to be first order and the specific reaction rate is given by the expression $k = 3.8 \times 10^{14} e^{-54,800/RT}$. Estimate the temperature at which (a) ethyl bromide decomposes at the rate of 1 per cent per second and (b) the decomposition is 70 per cent complete in 1 hour.

20. The following specific reaction rates were obtained by Wiig for the first-order decomposition of acetone dicarboxylic acid in aqueous solution:

$t°$	0	20	40	60
$k \times 10^5$	2.46	47.5	576	5480 sec^{-1}

(a) Plot $\log k$ against $1/T$, and determine the energy of activation. (b) Evaluate the constant s in the equation, $k = se^{-\Delta H_a/RT}$. (c) What is the period of half-life of this reaction at $80°$?

21. Two different equations have been proposed for the second-order decomposition rate of nitric oxide (expressed in atm^{-1} sec^{-1}):

$$k = 1 \times 10^7 e^{-50,000/RT}$$

in which the frequency factor is based on a statistical mechanical calculation involving the formation of a rigid four-atom activated complex; and

$$k = 1 \times 10^9 e^{-70,000/RT}$$

in which the activation energy is calculated by the Hirschfelder rule. Calculate the values of k at 1800°K and at 2100°K using both formulas.

22. Oxygen is contained in a vessel at 2 mm pressure and 25°. Calculate (a) the number of collisions on the walls per second per square centimeter; (b) the number of collisions between molecules per second per cubic centimeter; (c) the mean free path.

23. The rate of the rearrangement of 1-ethyl propenyl allyl malonitrile to 1-ethyl-2-methyl-4-pentenylidene malonitrile, can be followed by measuring the refractive index. The reaction is

The following first-order constants were obtained:

Temperature	120.0°	130.0°	140.0°
$k \times 10^4$, sec^{-1}	4.02	9.12	19.83

(a) What is the energy of activation? (b) What is the frequency factor?

24. Set up all the differential rate expressions, such as dc_A/dt, for the following complex reaction:

$$A + B \xrightarrow{k_1} AB \xrightarrow{k_2} BA \qquad AB \xrightarrow{k_3} A + B \qquad A + C \xrightarrow{k_4} AC$$

25. The initial rate (v) of oxidation of sodium succinate to form sodium fumarate by dissolved oxygen in the presence of the enzyme succinoxidase may be represented by

$$v = \frac{V}{1 + K_S/(S)}$$

where V is the maximum initial velocity obtainable with a given amount of enzyme, K_S is the Michaelis constant, and (S) is the concentration of sodium succinate. Calculate V and K_S from the following data. (For this calculation it is convenient to plot v^{-1} versus $(S)^{-1}$.)

$(S) \times 10^3$ (M)	10	2	1	0.5	0.33
$v \times 10^6$ (M/sec)	1.17	0.99	0.79	0.62	0.50

---

26. The hydrolysis of 1-chloro-1-methyl-cycloundecane in 80 per cent ethanol has been studied by Brown and Borkowski [*J. Am. Chem. Soc.*, 74, 1894 (1952)] at 25°.

The extent of hydrolysis was measured by titrating the acid formed after measured intervals of time   The data are as follows:

Time, hours	0	1.0	3.0	5.0	9.0	12	∞
x, ml (NaOH solution)	0.035	0.295	0.715	1.055	1.505	1.725	2.197

(a) Plot log $(a - x)$ versus time, where $a = 2.197$ and $a - x$ is proportional to the unhydrolyzed material.   (b) Calculate k in sec^{-1}.   (c) What fraction of the 1-chloro-1 methyl-cycloundecane will be left unhydrolyzed after 8 hours?

27. The reaction between propionaldehyde and hydrocyanic acid has been studied at 25° by Svirbley and Roth [*J. Am. Chem. Soc.*, *75*, 3106 (1953)].   In a certain aqueous solution at 25° the concentrations at various times were as follows:

Time, min	2.78	5.33	8.17	15.23	19.80	∞
HCN, mole l^{-1}	0.0990	0.0906	0.0830	0.0706	0.0653	0.0424
C_2H_5CHO, mole l^{-1}	0.0566	0.0482	0.0406	0.0282	0.0229	0.00

What is the specific reaction-rate constant k?

28. A second-order reaction where $a = b$ is 20 per cent completed in 500 seconds. How long will it take for the reaction to go to 60 per cent completion?

29. The reaction between selenious acid and iodide ion in acid solution is:

$$H_2SeO_3 + 6I^- + 4H^+ \rightarrow Se(s) + 2I_3^- + 3H_2O$$

The initial reaction rates were measured at 0° under a variety of concentrations as indicated in the table in moles per liter.   These initial rates were evaluated from plots

$[H_2SeO_3] \times 10^4$	$[H^+] \times 10^2$	$[I^-] \times 10^2$	Initial Rate $\times 10^7$
0.712	2.06	3.0	4.05
2.40	2.06	3.0	14.6
7.20	2.06	3.0	44.6
0.712	2.06	1.8	0.93
0.712	2.06	3.0	4.05
0.712	2.06	9.0	102
0.712	2.06	15.0	508
0.712	2.06	3.0	4.05
0.712	5.18	3.0	28.0
0.712	12.5	3.0	173.0

of H_2SeO_3 vs. time.   Determine the form of the rate law.   (Note: This rate law holds only as long as insignificant quantities of I_3^- are present.)

30. Given that the specific reaction rate for the over-all decomposition of N_2O_5 is $k = 4.3 \times 10^{13} e^{-24,700/1.987T}$, calculate (a) the half-life at −10°; (b) the time required for 90 per cent reaction at 50°.

31. The trichloroacetate ion in hydrogen-containing ionizing solvents decomposes into carbon dioxide and chloroform according to the reaction

$$H^+ + CCl_3COO^- \rightarrow CO_2 + CHCl_3$$

The unimolecular breaking of the carbon-carbon bond in the trichloroacetate ion is probably the rate-determining step. The reaction is first order, and the specific rate constants are $k_{90°} = 3.11 \times 10^{-4}$, $k_{80°} = 7.62 \times 10^{-5}$, and $k_{70°} = 1.71 \times 10^{-5}$ sec^{-1}. (a) Calculate the activation energy and (b) the specific rate constant at 60°. The experimentally determined value of k at 60° is 3.48×10^{-6} sec^{-1}.

32. One gram of carbon dioxide is introduced into a previously evacuated 10-liter flask at 100°. Calculate (a) the number of collisions on the walls per second per square centimeter; (b) the number of collisions between molecules per second per cubic centimeter; (c) the mean free path; (d) the mean free path when carbon dioxide is pumped out sufficiently to give a pressure of 1 mm.

33. Set up the rate expressions for the following complex reaction:

$$A \underset{k_2}{\overset{k_1}{\rightleftarrows}} B \qquad B + C \overset{k_3}{\longrightarrow} D$$

Show that this reaction may follow the first-order equation at high pressures and second-order equation at low pressures.

34. The energy of activation for the reaction, $C_2H_5Br \rightarrow C_2H_4 + HBr$, is 55,000 cal per mole. From this fact and Table III on page 122 show that the primary step in the dissociation cannot be the splitting off of a hydrogen atom or a CH_3 group but that it can involve the splitting off of an HBr molecule, or (considering the inaccuracy of the data) that it can involve the splitting off of a bromine atom.

35. Which of these two reactions is the more likely with chlorine atoms, (a) giving a free radical or (b) giving a hydrogen atom?

(a)
$$\overset{R}{\underset{R}{RC}}{-}H + Cl \rightarrow \overset{R}{\underset{R}{RC}} + HCl$$

(b)
$$\overset{R}{\underset{R}{RC}}{-}H + Cl \rightarrow \overset{R}{\underset{R}{RCCl}} + H$$

From a knowledge of the energies of dissociation or formation of the C-H, H-Cl and C-Cl bonds one can estimate the heat of reaction. As a rough approximation the entropy change may be disregarded and the sign and magnitude of the heat of reaction taken approximately as an indication of the free-energy change in the reactions. Those reactions which are highly endothermic will probably have a positive value of ΔF and will not be possible from a thermodynamic standpoint. They can then be ruled out in favor of a reaction which is highly exothermic and, therefore, likely to have a negative value of ΔF.

36. Solve the following differential equation for k:

$$dx/dt = k(a - x)(b - x)(c - x)$$

37. For the consecutive first-order reactions

$$A \xrightarrow[k=0.15]{} B \xrightarrow[k=0.1]{} C$$

plot curves which give the concentrations of A, B, and C as a function of time.

38. Carry out the integrations, and calculate the concentrations of A, B, and C shown in Fig. 13-4 for the three first-order reactions given by $A \xrightarrow{k_1} B \underset{k_3}{\overset{k_2}{\rightleftarrows}} C$.

39. A 3-liter container is filled with air at atmospheric pressure. In order to replace the air with carbon dioxide, the carbon dioxide is forced to enter one end of

the container at a rate of 2 liters a minute, and gas is allowed to escape from the other end at the same rate. If instant mixing of the gases is assumed, when will the partial pressure of oxygen be reduced to 0.01 mm?

40. In the reaction

$$N_2 + O_2 \underset{k_2}{\overset{k_1}{\rightleftharpoons}} 2NO$$

$$\frac{dx}{dt} = k_1 \left(p'_{N_2} - \frac{p_{NO}}{2} \right) \left(p'_{O_2} - \frac{p_{NO}}{2} \right) - k_2 p_{NO_2}$$

where p'_{N_2} is the original pressure of N_2, p'_{O_2} is the original pressure of O_2, and p_{NO} is the pressure of NO formed. Values of the equilibrium constant K are given in Table IV on page 256. The rate constant for the reverse reaction is given in $atm^{-1}\ sec^{-1}$ by

$$k_2 = 1 \times 10^9 e^{-70,000/RT}\ atm^{-1}\ sec^{-1}$$

(a) Calculate k_1 at 2400°K and 1900°K. (b) Calculate the time required for nitric oxide at 0.02 atm to undergo 10 per cent decomposition at 2400°K and at 1900°K, using k_2 and neglecting k_1.

14

Electric Conductance

Historical Introduction. Since only small quantities of electricity are ordinarily associated with the phenomena of "static" electricity it was not until the discovery of the battery by Volta in 1796 that it became possible to study the chemical changes produced by electric current. Volta's batteries consisted of a series of zinc or silver disks, arranged alternately with paper soaked in salt water between them. In 1800 Nicholson and Carlisle decomposed water into oxygen and hydrogen by electrolysis, and Davy isolated alkali metals from their hydroxides by electrolysis. Faraday, who had been an assistant to Davy, made great contributions to electrochemistry and introduced many of the terms which are used today: ion, cation, anion, electrode, and electrolyte.

The importance of electric charges in inorganic compounds and in solutions of electrolytes has been fully recognized since physical chemistry became a separate branch of chemistry in the late 1880's. The important part played by electric interaction among neutral molecules in organic chemistry has been realized, however, only since the 1920's. The dipole moment, the concept of paired electrons, the electron theory of valence, and the explanation of electrolysis and oxidation and reduction in terms of the transfer of electrons are all comparatively recent developments which have contributed much to the advancement of science. The quantitative relations between electricity and chemical change are discussed in the three chapters that follow.

Electrolysis. The electric current in an electrolytic solution consists of a flow of ions; in a metal, it consists of a flow of electrons. Thus when an electric current passes from a metallic conductor to a solution electrons must be gained or lost by ions or atoms in the solution next to the surface of the electrode. Thus chemical reactions must accompany the passage of electric current from one type of conductor to the other. In order to complete the circuit there must be two electrodes, one of which may be considered to be positively charged and the other negatively charged. Electrons are drawn by the dynamo from one electrode

374

and fed into the other. If a battery is used, the chemical reactions of the battery remove electrons from one electrode and supply them to the other electrode. The electrode to which the extra electrons are fed becomes negatively charged and attracts the positive ions. This negative electrode through which negative electrons are fed into the electrolytic solution is called the *cathode*, and the positive ions which migrate to it are called *cations*. The other electrode is positively charged, and it attracts the negative ions and removes electrons. It is called the *anode*, and the ions which move toward it are called *anions*. At the anode a stream of electrons is transferred from the negative ions in the solution to the electrode and, thence, into the electric circuit.

The removal or addition of electrons is a matter of the utmost importance, not only in electrolysis but also in many chemical reactions.

The removal of electrons is oxidation. It occurs at the anode.
The addition of electrons is reduction. It occurs at the cathode.

Thus, in electrolysis, ferric ions are reduced to ferrous ions at the cathode:

$$Fe^{+++} + e = Fe^{++}$$

and ferrous ions are oxidized to ferric ions at the anode:

$$Fe^{++} = Fe^{+++} + e$$

Usually there are several different kinds of ions around each electrode competing for electrons at the cathode and competing for an opportunity to give up electrons at the anode. Furthermore, it is quite likely that one or more secondary reactions will follow the primary electrode reaction in which there is a transfer of an electron. Some chemical experience is necessary in order to predict what will happen. For example, if chlorine is liberated in an alkaline solution, hypochlorite or chlorate may be formed. If chlorine is liberated on a silver anode, silver chloride is formed.

If a copper anode is used in the electrolysis of a solution of cupric chloride, the copper will simply go into solution and take the place of the copper which goes out of solution at the cathode. If a platinum anode is used, the platinum cannot go into solution, and oxygen or chlorine is liberated. When several different ions are competing for the transfer of an electron, several possibilities exist, depending on the concentration and on the energies involved. If there are no easily reducible cations around the cathode, hydrogen will be produced from the hydrogen ions of water, and, if there are no easily oxidizable anions around the anode, the hydroxyl ions will be removed with the formation of oxygen. Under certain conditions these reactions lead to an alkaline reaction at the cathode and an acid reaction at the anode, thus explaining the common litmus-paper test used to determine whether a given electrode is positive or negative. Litmus turns blue at the cathode, owing to the alkaline reaction, and it turns red at the anode.

In Table I are listed several reactions typical of those which take place during electrolysis. The electron is designated by e.

Table I. Typical Electrolysis Reactions

Electro-lyte	Elec-trodes	Cathode Reaction		Anode Reaction
H_2O	Platinum	$H^+ + e = \frac{1}{2}H_2$	OH^-	$= \frac{1}{4}O_2 + \frac{1}{2}H_2O + e$
$AgNO_3$	Silver	$Ag^+ + e = Ag$	Ag	$= Ag^+ + e$
$AgNO_3$	Platinum	$Ag^+ + e = Ag$	OH^-	$= \frac{1}{4}O_2 + \frac{1}{2}H_2O + e$
$Fe_2(SO_4)_3$	Platinum	$Fe^{+++} + e = Fe^{++}$	OH^-	$= \frac{1}{4}O_2 + \frac{1}{2}H_2O + e$
$FeSO_4$	Platinum	$H^+ + e = \frac{1}{2}H_2$	Fe^{++}	$= Fe^{+++} + e$
NaI	Platinum	$H^+ + e = \frac{1}{2}H_2$	I^-	$= \frac{1}{2}I_2 + e$
NaI	Silver	$H^+ + e = \frac{1}{2}H_2$	$Ag + I^-$	$= AgI + e$
$CuCl_2$	Platinum	$\frac{1}{2}Cu^{++} + e = \frac{1}{2}Cu$	$\begin{cases} Cl^- \\ OH^- \end{cases}$	$\begin{aligned} &= \frac{1}{2}Cl_2 + e \\ &= \frac{1}{4}O_2 + \frac{1}{2}H_2O + e \end{aligned}$
$CuCl_2$	Copper	$\frac{1}{2}Cu^{++} + e = \frac{1}{2}Cu$	$\frac{1}{2}Cu$	$= \frac{1}{2}Cu^{++} + e$

These changes occur when direct current is passed in the same direction from one electrode to the other through the cell. When the direction of the current is reversed rapidly, that is, 60 times per second, the products given by these reactions do not have a chance to accumulate before they are removed again. In experiments dealing with the conductance of the solution, alternating current is generally used in order to eliminate chemical reactions at the electrodes which change the resistance of the cell as a whole.

Faraday's Law. Faraday studied these phenomena of electrolysis with clear insight and announced in 1834 that for the same electrolyte the weight of material reacting in electrolysis is proportional to the quantity of electricity flowing, and that for a given quantity of electricity the weights of different substances liberated are proportional to the weights of their chemical equivalents.

Faraday's law may now be stated as follows:

In electrolysis, 96,500 coulombs of electricity produce a chemical change of 1 gram-equivalent. For example, 96,500 coulombs (or ampere-seconds) will liberate 1.0080 grams of hydrogen, and it will deposit from solution 107.88 grams of silver, 63.54/2 grams of copper from cupric salts, and 197.2/3 grams of gold from auric solutions. The name *faraday* and the symbol F are given to this important quantity of electricity.

This law is one of the most exact laws in physical chemistry; it has been found to hold at low and high temperatures, in dilute and concentrated solutions, at various pressures, and in different solvents. When the law does not appear to hold, it can usually be shown that secondary chemical reactions are obscuring the primary electron-transferring reaction at the electrode.

Faraday's law can be clearly understood with the help of the hypothesis that atoms are composed of positive nuclei surrounded by negative electrons. When an electron is removed from an atom, the remaining ion is positively charged. When an extra electron becomes attached to an atom, a negative ion is produced. If the ions are bivalent, two electrons are involved.

In the electrolysis of cupric chloride, every time two electrons are supplied to the cathode they become attached to one of the cupric ions which happens to be in contact with the metallic conductor and an atom of copper is deposited on the electrode. For every electron supplied to the cathode, one electron is withdrawn from the anode, and so it is obvious that the same amount of electrochemical reaction must occur at each electrode. At the anode the electrons are taken from ions in contact with the anode or from atoms of the anode, which then become positive ions.

Electrolysis involves, then, a transfer of electrons between the electrodes and the surrounding ions, and Faraday's law is simply the result of counting off one electron for each univalent atom, or two electrons for each divalent ion, etc. Thus, the faraday of electricity should be equal to the magnitude of the charge of the electron e (1.6020×10^{-19} coulomb; see Chapter 20) times the number of atoms in a gram atom ($N = 6.0235 \times 10^{23}$).

$$F = Ne \tag{1}$$

96,496 coulombs equiv^{-1} =

(6.0235×10^{23} electrons equiv^{-1})(1.6020×10^{-19} coulomb electron^{-1})

This number is in agreement with the value already given. As a matter of fact, the experimental determination of the value of the faraday and the charge of the electron provide one of our best means for determining the value for the Avogadro number, 6.0235×10^{23}.

Since Faraday's law involves only a counting process, it is evident why the law is so exact. Its accuracy is limited only by the accuracy of measuring the chemical change and the quantity of electricity.

Faraday's law provides a means not only for calculating the amount of electrochemical reaction during electrolysis but also for determining the quantity of electricity which has passed through a circuit from a measurement of the amount of electrochemical reaction. Even though the current may fluctuate over wide ranges, the total quantity of electricity in coulombs or ampere-seconds which has passed can be determined chemically in a coulometer. The silver coulometer, in which silver is deposited from a solution of silver nitrate and weighed on a platinum cathode, has been used. Usually a weighed platinum dish holds the solution and serves as the cathode. Other types of coulometers depend on the weight of copper deposited, the amount of oxygen and hydrogen liberated, or the quantity of iodine liberated at the anode as determined by titration.

Example 1. A current of 0.1000 ampere is passed through a copper sulfate solution for 10 minutes using platinum electrodes.

(*a*) Calculate the number of grams of copper deposited at the cathode.

$$\frac{(10 \text{ min})(60 \text{ sec min}^{-1})(0.1000 \text{ ampere})(63.54 \text{ g mole}^{-1})}{(96,500 \text{ ampere-sec equiv}^{-1})(2 \text{ equiv mole}^{-1})} = 0.01975 \text{ gram}$$

(*b*) Calculate the number of atoms deposited.

$$\frac{(0.01975 \text{ g})(6.02 \times 10^{23} \text{ atoms mole}^{-1})}{(63.54 \text{ g mole}^{-1})} = 1.872 \times 10^{20} \text{ atoms}$$

(*c*) Calculate the volume of oxygen liberated at the anode at 25° and 740 mm.

$$\frac{(10 \text{ min})(60 \text{ sec min}^{-1})(0.100 \text{ ampere})(32 \text{ g mole}^{-1})}{(96,500 \text{ ampere-sec equiv}^{-1})(4 \text{ equiv mole}^{-1})} = 4.98 \times 10^{-3} \text{ gram}$$

$$\frac{(4.98 \times 10^{-3} \text{ g})(0.08205 \text{ l atm deg}^{-1} \text{ mole}^{-1})(298 \text{ deg})}{(32 \text{ g mole}^{-1})(\frac{740}{760} \text{ atm})} = 0.00392 \text{ liter}$$

Electrical Units. According to Ohm's law, discovered in 1827,

$$I = E/R \tag{2}$$

where I is the current in amperes, E is the difference in potential applied, or the voltage, and R is the resistance in ohms.

The absolute values of the ampere, volt, and ohm are based upon the fundamental mechanical units: the standard meter, the standard kilogram, and the mean solar second. Batteries and resistances of certain constructions will be calibrated by the Bureau of Standards in terms of these absolute units. Before 1948 the legal standards were the older international units which were defined in terms of certain experiments.

The international ohm was defined as the electrical resistance equal to that of a column of pure mercury, at 0°, 106.300 cm in length, and of such constant cross section that the column contains 14.4521 grams of mercury.

The international ampere was defined as that current which under specified standard conditions will deposit 0.001118 gram of silver per second from a solution of silver nitrate.

The relationships between the absolute units and the older international units are indicated by the tabulated conversion factors.

International Standards	Absolute Values
1 ohm	1.000495 absolute ohms
1 volt	1.000330 absolute volts
1 ampere	0.999835 absolute ampere
1 coulomb	0.999835 absolute coulomb
1 joule	1.000165 absolute joules

Electric energy is the product of an intensity factor, voltage, and a quantity factor, coulombs, as pointed out on page 93. Thus

$$\text{Electric energy in joules} = \text{Volts} \times \text{Coulombs}$$

Electric energy may also be divided into a power factor, the *watt*, or *volt-ampere*, and a time factor, the second. One watt-second is 1 volt $\times$ 1 ampere $\times$ 1 second, or 1 joule. One kilowatt-hour is equal to 3,600,000 joules. The "defined calorie" is now defined in physical chemistry as 4.1840 absolute joules.*

In addition to these practical units there are the electrostatic units, esu, and the electromagnetic units, emu. If two equal charges 1 cm apart in a vacuum repel each other with a force of 1 dyne, each charge is equivalent to 1 electrostatic unit. The electromagnetic unit of current is a current such that, when it flows through a conductor 1 cm long bent in an arc of 1-cm radius, the force on a unit magnetic pole at the center of the circle will be 1 dyne.

Electric Conductance. There are two different types of electric conductance: metallic conductance as, for example, in a copper wire, and electrolytic conductance as, for example, in a solution of salt in water. Both types of electric conductance involve the generation of heat, which depends upon the electric resistance of the system. As a general rule the metallic conductors become less conducting at high temperatures, whereas the electrolytic conductors become more conducting. In metallic conductors, the electrons find it more difficult to pass through the crystal lattice when the units of the lattice are in thermal agitation; in electrolytic conductors, the ions can move through the solution more readily, because the viscosity is less, and the solvation of the ions is less.

Electricity may be carried by electrons across an evacuated space as in an ordinary radio tube. The electrons are emitted by a heated wire

* Formerly it was defined as 4.1833 international joules, which is equal to 4.1840 absolute joules.

and drawn to a positively charged plate. Electricity may be carried also by means of gas ions, as in an electrical discharge. The gas ions are charged positively or negatively, and they move in a manner somewhat analogous to the movement of electrolytic ions. There are several points of difference, however. The gas ions may have several different charges, and there is little connection between the valence and the charge, whereas in electrolytic ions the charge is closely connected with the valence. The electrolytic ions are present before the electrodes are charged, the large energy required for ionization being supplied from the solvation of the ions. Most of the gas ions, however, are produced only after the electrodes are charged, the energy required for ionization being supplied by collisions of ions with molecules in the electric field.

The resistance R of a uniform conductor is directly proportional to its length d and inversely proportional to its cross-sectional area A.

$$R = rd/A \quad \text{and} \quad r = RA/d \tag{3}$$

The proportionality constant r is called the *specific resistance* and is the resistance of a cube 1 cm on an edge. The values of the specific resistance are given for various materials in Table II. In the neighborhood of

Table II. Electrical Resistance of Typical Conductors

Material	Temperature, °C	Specific Resistance, ohm cm
Silver	0	1.468×10^{-6}
Copper	0	1.561×10^{-6}
Aluminum	0	2.564×10^{-6}
Iron	0	9.070×10^{-6}
Lead	0	20.480×10^{-6}
Mercury	0	$95.85 \ \times 10^{-6}$
Fused $NaNO_3$	500	0.568
Fused $ZnCl_2$	500	11.93
1 M KCl	25	8.93
0.001 M KCl	25	6,810
1 M acetic acid	18	757.5
0.001 M acetic acid	18	24,400
Water	18	$2.5 \ \times 10^7$
Xylene	25	$7 \ \times 10^{18}$

absolute zero the resistance of metals becomes extremely low. The specific resistance of mercury at 3°K, for example, is less than 10^{-8} ohm cm.

In dealing with solutions of electrolytes the *specific conductance L*, i.e., the reciprocal of the specific resistance, is generally used. Then

$$L = 1/r = d/RA \tag{4}$$

Measurement of the Conductance of Solutions. In the Wheatstone bridge shown in *Fig. 14-1*, R_b is the resistance of the cell containing an electrolytic solution which is to be measured. The resistance R_a is the resistance of the resistance box which may be varied by turning dials to change the number of coils of resistance wire in the circuit. The ratio R_c/R_d may be changed by multiples of 10 by moving a contact.

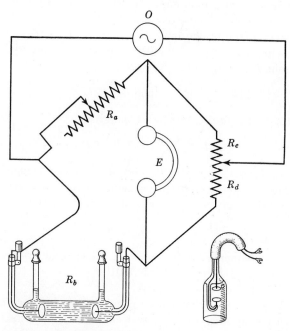

FIG. 14-1. Wheatstone bridge and cell for determining the electric conductance of a solution.

Alternating current of about 1000 cycles per second, which gives a mosquito-like noise in the earphones, is generated by the oscillator at O. A dipping cell is shown in the lower right-hand corner. Cells with long paths are used for concentrated solutions, and cells with short paths and large electrodes are used for dilute solutions so that the resistances to be measured will be of a convenient magnitude.

Alternating current is necessary to prevent complications at the electrodes. Direct current produces gas bubbles on the electrodes which greatly increase the resistance, and the current changes the concentration of electrolytes in the neighborhood of the electrodes. When alternating current is used the electrolysis that occurs when the current passes in one direction is reversed when the current is reversed. The platinum electrodes are covered with a coating of platinum black, produced by electrolytic deposition, to adsorb gases and catalyze their reaction. In this way the formation of a nonconducting gas film is prevented.

In making a measurement of the unknown resistance R_b, the known resistance R_a and the resistance ratio R_d/R_c are adjusted until the sound in the earphones is at a minimum. Then the two terminals of the earphones are at the same potential, and the potential drop E across the different parts of the bridge must be such that $E_b = E_a$ and $E_d = E_c$. Moreover, since according to Ohm's law the drop in potential E is equal to the current I multiplied by the resistance,

$$I_b R_b = I_a R_a \quad \text{and} \quad I_d R_d = I_c R_c$$

Dividing the first equation by the second gives

$$I_b R_b / I_d R_d = I_a R_a / I_c R_c$$

Furthermore, $I_a = I_c$ and $I_b = I_d$, since the current flowing through the two resistances in series must be the same in each resistance when no current flows through the earphones. Thus the equation reduces to

$$R_b = R_d R_a / R_c \tag{5}$$

which is the fundamental equation for the Wheatstone bridge. In many bridges the ratio R_d/R_c may be only 0.01, 0.1, 1, 10, or 100, so that no numerical calculations are necessary.

It would be extremely difficult to make a conductance cell having electrodes 1 cm^2 in area and exactly 1 cm apart and enclosed by plane parallel walls. However, it is not necessary to do this, because it is possible to determine a factor k, called the cell constant, for any conductance cell, which may be used to calculate the specific conductance with the relation

$$L = k/R \tag{6}$$

where R is the measured resistance for the cell. The cell constant k is determined experimentally with a standard solution of known specific conductance.* Measurements on any other solution may then be converted directly into specific conductances. A 0.0200-molar solution of

---

* The data of Jones and Bradshaw, *J. Am. Chem. Soc.*, 55, 1780 (1933), are generally taken as the standard for exact work in electrolytic conductance. When 0.745263 gram of pure potassium chloride is weighed out into pure water to give 1000 grams of solution (corrected to vacuum), the specific conductances are as follows: 0°, 0.0007736; 18°, 0.0012205; 25°, 0.0014087 ohm^{-1} cm^{-1}. This solution contains 0.01 mole per cubic decimeter (which differs very slightly from a liter).

potassium chloride is generally used for the determination of the cell constant. It has the following specific conductances:

$$L_{18°} = 0.002394 \quad \text{and} \quad L_{25°} = 0.002768 \text{ ohm}^{-1} \text{ cm}^{-1}$$

If R is the resistance of the cell, when filled with 0.0200-molar solution of potassium chloride at 25°

$$k = 0.002768R$$

Example 2. When a certain conductance cell was filled with 0.0200 M KCl, it had a resistance of 82.4 ohms at 25° as measured with a Wheatstone bridge; and, when filled with 0.0050 N K_2SO_4, it had a resistance of 326 ohms.

(*a*) What is the cell constant?

$$k = (0.002768 \text{ ohm}^{-1} \text{ cm}^{-1})(82.4 \text{ ohms}) = 0.2281 \text{ cm}^{-1}$$

(*b*) What is the specific conductance L of the potassium sulfate solution?

$$L = \frac{k}{R} = \frac{0.2281 \text{ cm}^{-1}}{326 \text{ ohm}} = 6.997 \times 10^{-4} \text{ ohm}^{-1} \text{ cm}^{-1}$$

Equivalent Conductance. In order to represent the conductance of an equivalent weight of an electrolyte it is convenient to introduce the term equivalent conductance.

The *equivalent conductance* Λ is obtained by multiplying the specific conductance L by the volume V in milliliters * which contains 1 gram equivalent of solute, that is, by $1000/c$, where c is the number of gram equivalents per liter.

$$\Lambda = VL = 1000L/c \tag{7}$$

Since $1000/c$ has the units of cm^3 $equiv^{-1}$ and L has the units of ohm^{-1} cm^{-1}, the equivalent conductance has the units of cm^2 $equiv^{-1}$ ohm^{-1}.

The concept of equivalent conductance may be illustrated by imagining a cell 1 cm square and indefinitely high. Two opposite walls are of metal and act as electrodes. When the cell is filled to a height of 1 cm, the conductance measured is the specific conductance. When the cell is filled with a given volume V of solution which contains 1 gram equivalent of a dissolved electrolyte, the solution will stand V centimeters high in the cell, and the conductance measured under these conditions will be the equivalent conductance.

Example 3. Calculate the equivalent conductance of 0.005 N K_2SO_4 from the data of the preceding example.

$$\Lambda = \frac{1000L}{c} = \frac{(1000 \text{ cm}^3 \text{ l}^{-1})(6.997 \times 10^{-4} \text{ ohm}^{-1} \text{ cm}^{-1})}{(0.005 \text{ equiv l}^{-1})}$$

$$= 139.9 \text{ cm}^2 \text{ equiv}^{-1} \text{ ohm}^{-1}$$

* There is a slight inconsistency here involving the small difference between milliliters and cubic centimeters.

Conductance of Different Electrolytes. Table III gives the specific and equivalent conductances of aqueous solutions of potassium chloride at 25°.

It may be observed that, when the volume is increased tenfold and the number of equivalents per milliliter is decreased to one-tenth, the

Table III. Conductance of Potassium Chloride at 25°

Equivalents per liter, c	Dilution, ml per Equivalent, V	Specific Conductance, L	Equivalent Conductance, Λ
1	1,000	0.1119	111.9
0.1	10,000	0.01289	128.9
0.01	100,000	0.001413	141.3
0.001	10^6	0.0001469	146.9
0.0001	10^7	0.00001489	148.9

specific conductance decreases nearly but not quite to one-tenth its value. The equivalent conductance, on the other hand, changes only slightly but does increase and approach a limiting value at greater dilutions.

In very dilute solutions of potassium chloride there is no appreciable change in equivalent conductance when the solution is diluted. Although the volume is doubled and the number of ions per milliliter is halved, the *total* number of ion carriers between the tall electrodes is still the same. In more concentrated solutions of potassium chloride, however, the equivalent conductance increases on dilution, because the ions move faster when they are farther apart and are not held back by the ions of opposite charge which they tend to drag along.

The equivalent conductance of potassium chloride and other electrolytes at 25° is plotted versus the square root of concentration in *Fig. 14-2*. Extrapolation of this plot to infinite dilution gives an accurate value of Λ_0, the so-called limiting value of the equivalent conductance. This is the value of the conductance when the ions are so far apart that they do not interact and retard each other. It is important to bear in mind that, although Λ_0 is frequently referred to as the conductance at infinite dilution, it is by no means identical with the conductance of the pure solvent. In fact it is necessary in accurate work, particularly at low concentrations, to subtract the conductance of the solvent from that of the solution in order to obtain the conductance due to the electrolyte. Thus,

$$L_{\text{solute}} = L_{\text{solution}} - L_{\text{solvent}} \tag{8}$$

The purest water has a specific resistance of about 20 million ohms, but it is difficult to obtain water with much over a million ohms specific resistance because of the absorption of carbon dioxide and other gases from the atmosphere and of alkali and other electrolytes from the glass containing vessel. Ordinary distilled water in equilibrium with air has a specific resistance of only about 100,000 ohms.

The reason for plotting Λ versus $\sqrt{c}$ rather than c would be made evident by making a Λ-c plot for the KCl data. It would be found that the

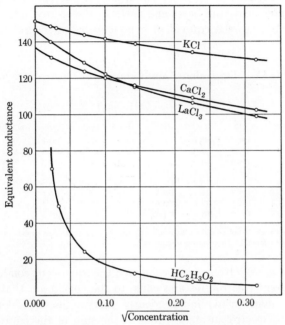

FIG. 14-2. Equivalent conductances of typical electrolytes plotted against the square roots of the concentrations.

slope of the plot increases rapidly as zero concentration is approached so that it would be extremely difficult to extrapolate to Λ_0.

In solutions of acetic acid the situation is quite different, and the equivalent conductance increases markedly on dilution as shown in Fig. 14-2, because the solute dissociates more at the greater dilution, giving a considerable increase in the total number of ions. In the case of substances like acetic acid it is not possible to extrapolate to infinite dilution to obtain the equivalent conductance of completely dissociated acetic acid. However, the value of Λ_0 for acetic acid may be determined indirectly as shown on page 387. The equivalent conductance at infinite dilution is useful in calculating the degree of dissociation of acetic acid as shown on page 388.

Electrolytes may be divided into two general classes: the *strong electrolytes*, such as potassium chloride, with high conductances and slight increases on dilution; and *weak electrolytes*, such as acetic acid, with low conductances and larger increases in conductance on dilution. In general, the strong electrolytes include many inorganic acids such as hydrochloric and sulfuric acid, most salts, and the alkali hydroxides. The weak electrolytes, on the other hand, include the carboxylic acids and many organic acids and bases and partially dissociated salts.

Table IV gives the equivalent conductances of several typical electrolytes.

Table IV.   Equivalent Conductances of Electrolytes at 25°

Equivalents per Liter, N	NaCl	KCl	NaI	KI	HCl	AgNO$_3$	CaCl$_2$	NaC$_2$H$_3$O$_2$	HC$_2$H$_3$O$_2$[1]
0.0000	126.5	149.9	126.9	150.3	426.1	133.4	135.8	91.0	(390.6)
0.0005	124.5	147.8	125.4	.....	422.7	131.4	131.9	89.2	67.7
0.001	123.7	146.9	124.3		421.4	130.5	130.4	88.5	49.2
0.005	120.6	143.5	121.3	144.4	415.8	127.2	124.2	85.7	22.9
0.01	118.5	141.3	119.2	142.2	412.0	124.8	120.4	83.8	16.3
0.02	115.8	138.3	116.7	139.5	407.2	121.4	115.6	81.2	11.6
0.05	111.1	133.4	112.8	135.0	399.1	115.2	108.5	76.9	7.4
0.10	106.7	129.0	108.8	131.1	391.3	109.1	102.5	72.8	5.2

[1] Acetic acid is a weak electrolyte, and the conductance at infinite dilution is obtained by indirect methods. All the other electrolytes given in the table are strong electrolytes.

As early as 1875 Kohlrausch examined the equivalent conductances of many different electrolytes and came to the conclusion that *at infinite dilution* the ions behave independently, so that the equivalent conductance of the electrolyte Λ_0 is equal to the sum of the equivalent conductances of the cations $l_{0,c}$ and anions $l_{0,a}$, thus:

$$\Lambda_0 = l_{0,c} + l_{0,a} \tag{9}$$

This law of Kohlrausch is supported, for example, by the fact that

$$\Lambda_{0,KCl} - \Lambda_{0,NaCl} = 149.9 - 126.5 = 23.4 \text{ cm}^2 \text{ equiv}^{-1} \text{ ohm}^{-1}$$

$$\Lambda_{0,KI} - \Lambda_{0,NaI} = 150.3 - 126.9 = 23.4 \text{ cm}^2 \text{ equiv}^{-1} \text{ ohm}^{-1}$$

This constant difference of about 23.4 is always found between a potassium and a sodium salt of the same acid at infinite dilution. It is easily explained on the basis that the conductance of the potassium ion is 23.4 more than that of the sodium ion, since the anion is the same.

Kohlrausch's law is useful in calculating the equivalent conductance at infinite dilution of a weak electrolyte which cannot be determined by direct extrapolation.

Example 4. Calculate the equivalent conductance of acetic acid at infinite dilution at 25°. Extrapolation gives the following values at infinite dilution:

$$\Lambda_{0,HCl} = 426.1 \qquad \Lambda_{0,NaC_2H_3O_2} = 91.0 \qquad \Lambda_{0,NaCl} = 126.5$$

$$(l_{0,H^+} + l_{0,Cl^-}) + (l_{0,Na^+} + l_{0,C_2H_3O_2^-}) - (l_{0,Na^+} + l_{0,Cl^-})$$

$$= l_{0,H^+} + l_{0,C_2H_3O_2^-}$$

$$\Lambda_{0,HCl} + \Lambda_{0,NaC_2H_3O_2} - \Lambda_{0,NaCl} = \Lambda_{0,HC_2H_3O_2}$$

$$\Lambda_{0,HC_2H_3O_2} = 426.1 + 91.0 - 126.5 = 390.6 \text{ cm}^2 \text{ equiv}^{-1} \text{ ohm}^{-1}$$

Ionization of Weak Acids. Arrhenius suggested that the degree of dissociation of a weak electrolyte, such as acetic acid, could be calculated from the measured conductance of the electrolyte and the equivalent conductance at infinite dilution. It has been shown in equation 9 that at infinite dilution the equivalent conductance Λ_0 is equal to the sum of the ionic conductances $l_{0,c}$ and $l_{0,a}$ of the cation and anion.

If the change in velocity of the ions with concentration is neglected and it is assumed that the only influence of dilution on the equivalent conductance of a weak electrolyte is the production of more ions, it may also be assumed that, for an electrolyte dissociating into two ions,

$$\Lambda = \alpha l_{0,c} + \alpha l_{0,a} = \alpha(l_{0,c} + l_{0,a}) \qquad (10)$$

where Λ is the measured equivalent conductance and α is the degree of dissociation of the electrolyte. If one equivalent of electrolyte is present in solution, there will be α equivalents of each ion.

Dividing equation 10 by equation 9 gives

$$\alpha = \Lambda / \Lambda_0 \qquad (11)$$

Although satisfactory for weak electrolytes, this equation cannot be applied to strong electrolytes in which dissociation is practically complete. The change of equivalent conductance of strong electrolytes with concentration is due to a change in velocity of the ions, as described later in this chapter.

Acetic acid is a good example of a weak electrolyte. When dissolved in water, it dissociates according to the reaction

$$CH_3COOH = CH_3COO^- + H^+$$

If c moles of acetic acid are dissolved in a liter of water and the degree of dissociation of the acid is α, then the concentration of hydrogen ions is $c\alpha$, the concentration of acetate ions is $c\alpha$, and the concentration of un-ionized acetic acid molecules is $c(1 - \alpha)$. The equilibrium or ionization constant K is given by the expression:

$$K = \frac{[H^+][CH_3COO^-]}{[CH_3COOH]} = \frac{c\alpha c\alpha}{c(1 - \alpha)} = \frac{\alpha^2 c}{1 - \alpha} \qquad (12)$$

If more than two ions are formed, the ionization constant will have a different form which may be easily derived.

Example 5. The equivalent conductance of a 0.001028 N acetic acid solution is found to be 48.15 at 25°. The equivalent conductance at infinite dilution is 390.6. Calculate the degree of dissociation of acetic acid at this concentration, and calculate the ionization constant.

$$\alpha = \Lambda/\Lambda_0 = 48.15/390.6 = 0.1232$$

$$K = \frac{\alpha^2 c}{1 - \alpha} = \frac{(0.1232)^2(0.001028)}{0.8768} = 1.781 \times 10^{-5}$$

From calculations like this, Table V is obtained by using the data of MacInnes and Shedlovsky.*

Table V.   Ionization Constant of Acetic Acid at 25°

$(\Lambda_0 = 390.6)$

Concentration, equivalents/liter	Equivalent Conductance	Degree of Dissociation	$K \times 10^5$ Dissociation Constant
0.00002801	210.4	0.5385	1.760
0.0001532	112.0	0.2867	1.767
0.001028	48.15	0.1232	1.781
0.002414	32.22	0.08247	1.789
0.005912	20.96	0.05365	1.798
0.01283	14.37	0.03678	1.803
0.05000	7.36	0.01884	1.808

The value of K calculated in this way is reasonably constant, and it is satisfactory for most practical work. However, unsatisfactory assumptions are involved in this calculation which are partly compensating. Making a correction for the fact that the ionic conductances are not quite the same as they are at infinite dilution and estimating the activity coefficients of the ions from the Debye-Hückel theory (page 483), MacInnes shows that these dissociation constants have values ranging from 1.752×10^{-5} at 0.00002801 N to 1.721×10^{-5} at 0.05000 N. In this revised calculation Λ_0 for acetic acid is not used, but a value of the

* MacInnes and Shedlovsky, *J. Am. Chem. Soc.*, *54*, 1429 (1932); MacInnes, ⁿhe *Principles of Electrochemistry*, Reinhold Publishing Corp., New York, 1939, ᴣe 56.

equivalent conductance for complete dissociation is obtained at the given concentration by subtracting Λ_{NaCl} from the sum of Λ_{HCl} and $\Lambda_{NaC_2H_3O_2}$ at these concentrations, it being assumed that these electrolytes are completely dissociated.

With the help of equation 12 it is possible to calculate at any concentration c the degree of dissociation of acetic acid or any other weak electrolyte which dissociates into two ions.

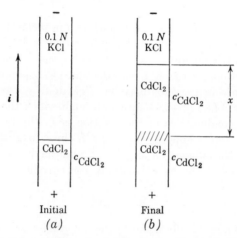

FIG. 14-3. Determining mobility of potassium ion by the moving-boundary method.

Migration of Ions. The velocities of ions vary considerably because of differences in size, hydration, and charge. The velocity of an ion in a unit electric field, i.e., one in which the potential changes 1 volt per centimeter of distance in the direction of the field, is called the *ionic mobility, u.* The most direct method for determining ionic mobilities is to measure the velocity of a boundary between two electrolytic solutions in a tube of uniform cross section through which a current is flowing. For example, if a 0.1 N solution of KCl is layered over a solution of CdCl₂ in a tube as illustrated in *Fig. 14-3a,* and a current i is caused to flow through the tube in the indicated direction,* the potassium ions will move upward away from the position of the initial boundary. They will be followed by cadmium ions, so that there will be no gap in the column of electrolyte. Since the concentration of CdCl₂ above the initial boundary position (c'_{CdCl_2}) will in general be different from that initially placed below the KCl solution, there will be a change in CdCl₂

_____

* By convention the "current" through the solution is considered to flow from + to − like the cations, although part of the electricity is carried in the opposite direction by anions.

concentration at the initial boundary position which is represented by
///////.

The boundary between the solutions moves with the velocity of the
potassium ions in the potassium chloride solution, and so the mobility
u of potassium ions may be calculated from the distance x moved by
the boundary in time t in an electric field of strength E.

$$u = x/tE \qquad (13)$$

It is customary to measure x in centimeters, t in seconds, and E in volts
cm^{-1}, so that the units of the mobility u are cm^2 volt^{-1} sec^{-1}.

If a current of i amperes is passed through a tube of electrolyte which
has a cross-sectional area of A cm^2 the change in potential per centimeter of distance in the tube may be calculated by use of Ohm's law.
Imagine a 1-cm cube of the solution through which the current flows.
If the specific conductance of the solution is L, the resistance of this
cube measured across opposite faces is $1/L$ ohms (page 380). The current density in the cube is i/A amp cm^{-2}, and the difference in potential
of the two faces of the cube is simply the current density times the
resistance

$$E = i/AL \qquad (14)$$

This voltage is numerically equal to the potential gradient (volts cm^{-1})
since the cube is 1 cm thick.

Example 6. In the experiment with 0.1 N KCl illustrated in Fig. 14-3 the boundary
moved 4.64 cm during 67 minutes when a current of 5.21 milliamperes was used.
The cross-sectional area of the tube was 0.230 cm^2, and $L = 0.0129$ ohm^{-1} cm^{-1}
at 25°.

$$E = \frac{(0.00521 \text{ ampere})}{(0.230 \text{ cm}^2)(0.0129 \text{ ohm}^{-1} \text{ cm}^{-1})} = 1.76 \text{ volt cm}^{-1}$$

$$u_{K^+} = \frac{(4.64 \text{ cm})}{(67 \times 60 \text{ sec})(1.76 \text{ volt cm}^{-1})} = 65.5 \times 10^{-5} \text{ cm}^2 \text{ volt}^{-1} \text{ sec}^{-1}$$

This calculation may be simplified somewhat by combining equations
13 and 14

$$u = xAL/ti = vL \qquad (15)$$

where v is the volume moved through by the boundary per coulomb
(xA/it).

Example 7. In the experiment illustrated in Fig. 14-3 the boundary moved through
$(0.230)(4.64)/(67)(60)(0.00521) = 0.0508$ cm^3/coulomb. Thus the potassium-ion mobility is

$$u_{K^+} = (0.0508 \text{ cm}^3 \text{ coulomb}^{-1})(0.0129 \text{ ohm}^{-1} \text{ cm}^{-1})$$

$$= 65.5 \times 10^{-5} \text{ cm}^2 \text{ volt}^{-1} \text{ sec}^{-1}$$

In order to obtain a sharp boundary in an experiment such as that illustrated in Fig. 14-3 it is necessary that the leading ion (in this case, potassium) have a higher mobility than the indicator ion (in this case, cadmium). The cadmium chloride solution below the moving boundary (c'_{CdCl_2}) has a lower specific conductance than the potassium chloride solution above the boundary. By reference to equation 14 it may be seen that the electric field strength is therefore greater in the $CdCl_2$ solution below the moving boundary than in the potassium chloride solution. Therefore, if potassium ions diffuse down into the $CdCl_2$ solution, they will be in a higher electric field strength and will catch up with the boundary. On the other hand, if cadmium ions diffuse ahead of the boundary, they will have a lower velocity than the potassium ions because of their lower mobility and will soon be overtaken by the boundary. This so-called "adjusting effect" keeps the boundary sharp.

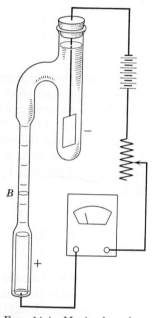

Moving-Boundary Apparatus.* The moving-boundary apparatus illustrated in *Fig. 14-4* is of the so-called autogenic type in which the anode is made of cadmium metal. The upper electrode is of silver coated with silver chloride, and the tube is filled with hydrochloric acid and an indicator so that the moving boundary *B* may be seen easily. In precise experiments a potentiometer and a standard resistance

Fig. 14-4. Moving-boundary apparatus for determining transference numbers.

would be used to measure the current flowing through the cell rather than an ammeter, and the current would be kept constant with an automatic current controller. During the experiment cadmium chloride solution is produced by electrolysis at the anode.

Since the leading solution (HCl) is acidic in this case while the following solution ($CdCl_2$) is nearly neutral, the indicator sharply marks the boundary between the two solutions. In the example illustrated in Fig. 14-3 this experimental trick cannot be used but the boundary between the two electrolyte solutions may be detected with a simple optical system (page 504) since there is a change of refractive index at the boundary.

---

* MacInnes and Longsworth, *J. Am. Chem. Soc.*, **60**, 3070 (1938); Longsworth, *J. Chem. Education*, *11*, 420 (1934).

Ion Mobilities. The mobilities of a number of familiar ions at infinite dilution are given in Table VI.

Table VI.   Limiting Ion Mobilities at 25°

(in cm^2 volt^{-1} sec^{-1})

Ion	$u \times 10^5$	Ion	$u \times 10^5$	Ion	$u \times 10^5$
Li$^+$	40.1	Cl$^-$	79.0	Ca^{++}	61.6
Na$^+$	52.0	Br$^-$	81.2	Ba^{++}	66.0
K$^+$	76.2	I$^-$	79.6	SO$_4^=$	82.7
H$^+$	363	OH$^-$	205	NO$_3^-$	74.0

It is noted that hydrogen and hydroxyl ions have much higher mobilities in water than other ions, and this is believed to be a result of the fact that a positive charge may be transferred along a chain of adjacent water molecules without the actual transport of a hydrogen ion. This is illustrated in the following figure, which represents (a) the approach of a hydrogen ion to a group of oriented water molecules and (b) the departure of a different hydrogen ion from the water molecule on the right.

It is also interesting that in the alkali metal and halogen families of the periodic table the heavier ions have higher mobilities. This is a result of the stronger electric field in the neighborhood of the ions with smaller radius which causes them to be more highly hydrated than the heavier ions. An ion which is hydrated must drag along a shell of water when it moves along in a solution between two electrodes, and so it moves more slowly than the unhydrated ion.

Relation between Ion Mobilities and Conductance. The resistance of a 1-cm cube of electrolyte is $1/L$ ohms. Therefore, if a difference in potential of 1 volt is applied to two opposite faces the current will be, according to Ohm's law,

$$I = E/R = 1/(1/L) = L$$

Thus the specific conductance L is numerically equal to the current in amperes which will flow through a unit cube of solution across which there is a difference in potential of 1 volt.

The total current carried by a solution of a simple electrolyte is equal to the sum of the current carried by the anion a and the cation c. There are $c_a/1000$ equiv per cm^3 of ion a which has mobility u_a, and each ion in the unit cube will move u_a cm in 1 sec if a field of 1 volt cm^{-1} is applied. Therefore, $c_a u_a/1000$ equivalents of ion a will be transported out of the cube per sec, and $c_c u_c/1000$ equivalents of ion c will be transported out of the cube in the opposite direction. To convert equivalents per second to amperes the sum of the currents is multiplied by the faraday F.

$$L = F(c_a u_a + c_c u_c)/1000$$

$$= Fc(u_a + u_c)/1000 \tag{16}$$

where c is the equivalent concentration of the electrolyte and is equal to the equivalent concentrations of the anion c_a and cation c_c($c = c_a = c_c$).

Example 8. Calculate the specific conductance of 0.100 N sodium chloride at 25° from the mobilities of sodium and chloride ions at this concentration, which are $u_c = 42.6 \times 10^{-5}$ and $u_a = 68.0 \times 10^{-5}$ cm^2 $volt^{-1}$ sec^{-1}.

$$L = \frac{(96,500 \text{ coul equiv}^{-1})(0.100 \text{ equiv}/l)}{(1000 \text{ cm}^3 \text{ l}^{-1})} (110.6 \times 10^{-5} \text{ cm}^2 \text{ volt}^{-1} \text{ sec}^{-1})$$

$$= 0.01067 \text{ ohm}^{-1} \text{ cm}^{-1}$$

The relationship between the equivalent conductance and mobilities may be obtained by substitution of equation 16 into equation 7.

$$\Lambda = F(u_a + u_c) = l_a + l_c \tag{17}$$

Thus $u_a = l_a/F$ and $u_c = l_c/F$.

Transference Number. Another quantity which is frequently used in discussing electrolytic solutions is the transference number. With strong electrolytes the *transference number* is the fraction of the current carried by a given ion. The fraction of the current carried through the solution is a function of the relative velocities with which the cation and the anion move. The ions that move faster carry the larger quantity of electricity through the solution in a given time; that is, they carry the larger fraction of the current. If u_c is the mobility of the cation and u_a is the mobility of the anion, then the transference number n_c of the cation is the fraction of the current carried by the cation as given by the following equation:

$$n_c = \frac{\text{Current carried by cation}}{\text{Total current}} = \frac{u_c}{u_c + u_a} \tag{18}$$

Likewise, the transference number of the anion n_a is equal to $u_a/(u_c + u_a)$. It is obvious that

$$n_c + n_a = 1$$

In a moving-boundary experiment the transference number may be calculated from the volume V in liters moved through by the boundary per faraday. If the concentration of the leading ion (i.e., K^+ in Fig. 14-3) is c equivalents per liter, Vc equivalents move through a fixed plane ahead of the moving boundary per faraday, and so

$$n_c = Vc = vFc/1000 \qquad (19)$$

where v is the number of cubic centimeters moved through by the boundary per coulomb.

Example 9. Calculate the transference number of potassium ion in 0.1 N potassium chloride. According to the data given in example **7**, the boundary moves through 0.0508 ml coul^{-1} or $(0.0508$ ml coul$^{-1})(96,500$ coul faraday$^{-1})/(1000$ ml l$^{-1}) = 4.90$ l faraday^{-1}.

$$n_{K^+} = Vc = (4.90 \text{ l faraday}^{-1})(0.1 \text{ equiv l}^{-1}) = 0.490$$

$$n_{Cl^-} = 1 - n_{K^+} = 0.510$$

Table VII gives the transference numbers of the cations of several typical electrolytes as determined by the moving boundary method.

Table VII. Cation Transference Numbers at 25° Determined by the Moving-Boundary Method [1]

Electrolyte	0.01 N	0.1 N	Electrolyte	0.01 N	0.1 N
HCl	0.8251	0.8314	AgNO₃	0.4648	0.4682
LiCl	0.3289	0.3168	NaC₂H₃O₂	0.5537	0.5594
NaCl	0.3918	0.3854	CaCl₂	0.4264	0.4060
KCl	0.4902	0.4898	K₂SO₄	0.4829	0.4890
KBr	0.4833	0.4833	LaCl₃	0.4625	0.4375
KNO₃	0.5084	0.5103	K₃Fe(CN)₆	0.4315	0.4410

[1] MacInnes, *The Principles of Electrochemistry*, Reinhold, New York, 1939.

The transference numbers of the corresponding anions can be found by subtracting the transference numbers of the cations from unity. Transference numbers ordinarily vary slightly with concentration and temperature.

Hittorf Method. Transference numbers were first determined by Hittorf in 1853 by studying the concentration changes which occurred in the anode and cathode compartments during an electrolysis experiment. If the cation moves faster than the anion, more cations will enter the cathode chamber during an experiment than anions enter the anode chamber. The concentration changes in the anode and cathode chambers must be corrected for electrolysis. As an example, the cation transference number of silver nitrate may be determined by carrying out the electrolysis of silver nitrate in an apparatus having three chambers: cathode chamber, anode chamber, and connecting chamber. During an experiment the number of equivalents of silver ion formed at the silver anode $(+)$ is equal to the number of gram atoms of metallic silver formed at the cathode $(-)$. However, the concentration of silver ions in the regions surrounding the two electrodes depends not only upon the duration of the electrolysis and the current used but also upon the velocities of the silver and nitrate ions.

If x faradays of current pass between the electrodes, x equivalents of silver will deposit on the cathode, and x equivalents of silver ion would disappear in the cathode chamber if there were no migration of silver ion. However, the number of equivalents of silver ions y which actually do disappear from the cathode chamber is less than this because silver ions migrate toward the negative electrode. The difference $x - y$ is the number of equivalents of silver ion which have migrated into the cathode chamber during the passage of x faradays of current. The transference number of the silver ion is therefore

$$n_c = (x - y)/x \qquad (20)$$

The transference number of the silver ion may also be calculated from the change in concentration in the anode chamber. Here x equivalents of silver ion are formed by the electrode reaction, but the increase in the number of equivalents of silver ion in this compartment is less than x because of the migration of silver ions away from the positive electrode. If z is the number of equivalents increase found in the anode chamber, then $x - z$ is the number of equivalents of silver ion which have migrated out of the anode chamber. The silver-ion transference number calculated from the data on the anode chamber is thus

$$n_c = (x - z)/x \qquad (21)$$

Example 10. An aqueous solution of copper sulfate was electrolyzed between copper electrodes. On the cathode 0.3000 gram of copper was deposited. The solution in the anode compartment contained 1.4300 grams of copper after electrolysis, and the same weight of water contained 1.2140 grams before electrolysis. Calculate the copper transference number. For Cu^{++} the equivalent weight is $63.54/2 = 31.77$.

$$n_c = \frac{x - z}{x} = \frac{\dfrac{0.300}{31.77} - \dfrac{(1.4300 - 1.2140)}{31.77}}{0.300/31.77}$$

$$= (0.300 - 0.216)/0.300 = 0.28$$

$$n_a = 1 - n_c = 1 - 0.28 = 0.72$$

It is difficult to obtain accurate results by this method because the concentration changes are small. More accurate results may be obtained by the moving-boundary method. The moving-boundary method is also more rapid and may be used for the study of mixtures of ions, which may be colloidal ions such as proteins. The study of colloids by this method is referred to as electrophoresis (see page 513).

In the case of partially dissociated electrolytes (weak electrolytes) the transference number may not be interpreted as simply the fraction of the current carried by a given ion constituent. For example, the cation transference numbers for cadmium iodide solutions at 18°C are given in Table VIII. The negative transference number for cadmium

Table VIII. Cation Transference Numbers for CdI₂ Solutions

$[CdI_2]$ (equiv/l)	0.01	0.05	0.1	0.2	0.5	1.0
n_c	0.444	0.396	0.296	0.127	−0.003	−0.120

in concentrated solutions, which means that cadmium migrates to the anode rather than the cathode, indicates the presence of ions such as CdI_3^- or $CdI_4^=$. In very dilute solutions the salt is apparently completely ionized and behaves normally.

Relation between Transference Numbers and Ionic Conductances. Individual ionic conductances may be calculated from values of the transference number and equivalent conductance. Since the transference number is the fraction of the current carried by a given ion it must be equal to the ratio of the ionic conductance of that ion to the equivalent conductance of the salt.

$$n_c = l_c / \Lambda \qquad (22)$$

If Λ_0 and the value of the transference number extrapolated to zero concentration are determined, the value of the ionic conductance at infinite dilution may be calculated. The equivalent conductance of a weak electrolyte, such as acetic acid, at infinite dilution may be obtained in this way as well as by the method described on page 387.

Example 11. Calculate Λ_0 for acetic acid at 25°, using the data of Tables IV and VII.

$$l_{0,H^+} = n_{0,H^+} \times \Lambda_{0,HCl} = 0.82^* \times 426.1 = 349.4$$

$$l_{0,C_2H_3O_2^-} = n_{0,C_2H_3O_2^-} \times \Lambda_{0,NaC_2H_3O_2} = 0.45^* \times 91.0 = 40.9$$

$$\Lambda_{0,HC_2H_3O_2} = l_{0,H^+} + l_{0,C_2H_3O_2^-} = 390.3$$

When the conductance of one ion at infinite dilution is determined, others may be obtained from the equivalent conductances of the elec-

* Extrapolated values.

trolytes by simple subtraction, using equation 9. An average of several chlorides gives l_{0,Cl^-} as 76.3 cm^2 ohm^{-1} equiv^{-1}. Then, for example,

$$l_{0,K^+} = \Lambda_{0,KCl} - l_{0,Cl^-} = 149.9 - 76.3 = 73.6$$

In this way Table IX has been constructed. With this table it is easy to calculate equivalent conductances of many different electrolytes at infinite dilution, or to calculate transference numbers.

Table IX. Ionic Conductances at Infinite Dilution at 25°

Cations	l_c	a	Anions	l_a	a
H$^+$	349.8	0.014	OH$^-$	198	0.016
K$^+$	73.6	0.019	$\frac{1}{3}$Fe(CN)$_6$$^{\equiv}$	101.0	.....
NH$_4$$^+$	73.4	0.019	$\frac{1}{2}$SO$_4$$^=$	79.8	0.020
$\frac{1}{3}$La^{+++}	69.6	.....	Br$^-$	78.4	0.019
$\frac{1}{2}$Ba^{++}	63.6	0.020	I$^-$	76.8	0.019
Ag$^+$	61.9	0.020	Cl$^-$	76.3	0.019
$\frac{1}{2}$Ca^{++}	59.5	0.021	NO$_3$$^-$	71.4	0.018
$\frac{1}{2}$Mg^{++}	53.1	0.022	HCO$_3$$^-$	44.5	.....
Na$^+$	50.1	0.021	C$_2$H$_3$O$_2$$^-$	40.9	.....
Li$^+$	38.7	0.023			

The temperature coefficient is given under the columns a, where a is defined by the equation

$$l_{0,t} = l_{0,25}[1 + a(t - 25)]$$

for the ionic conductance at temperatures t not far removed from 25°. It may be noted that most of these values give a change of about 2 per cent per degree, which is about the same as the temperature coefficient of the viscosity of water. This relationship is explained by the theory that the frictional resistance offered to the motion of the ion is proportional to the viscosity of water.

Exercise I. Show that transference numbers and mobilities are related by

$$n = Fuc/1000L$$

Conductance of Nonaqueous Solutions. When electrolytes which are completely dissociated in water are dissolved in solvents of low dielectric constant, the simple coulombic forces are sufficient to cause ionic association at extremely low ionic concentrations. Thus all electrolytes are "weak electrolytes" in solvents of low dielectric constant. Solvents such as benzene and carbon tetrachloride which have extremely low dielectric constants do not interact with the solutes sufficiently to produce ionization. Among the solvents that have been important in studies of nonaqueous solutions of electrolytes are alcohols, liquid ammonia, dioxane, acetone and other ketones, anhydrous formic acid and acetic acid, pyridine, and several amines and nitro compounds.

A few miscellaneous examples of conductances in nonaqueous solutions are given in Table X.

Table X. Conductance of Nonaqueous Solutions

Solvent	Temperature, °C	Electrolyte	Concentration, Equivalents per liter	Specific Conductance	Equivalent Conductance
Ammonia	−33	NaI	1.14	0.28	245
Ethanol	18	NaI	1.00	0.035	35.2
Acetone	25	NaI	1.0		26.4
			0.1		64.1
			0.01		109.7
			0.0		(176.2)
Isoamyl alcohol	25	NaI	0.1		1.29
			0.01		2.02
			0.00		(7.79)
Methyl amine	−33	KI	9.3	0.17	17.7
Ethyl amine	−33	AgNO₃	8.0	0.0083	1.04
Nitromethane	25	KI	10.0	0.88	88.1
Ammonia	−33	Na	0.8	1.27	2017

In general, the properties of an electrolytic solution depend on the solvating power and the dielectric constant of the solvent and on the size, configuration, and space distribution of the ions. In water, which has a dielectric constant of 78 and a marked tendency to combine with ions, there is no detectable difference in the ionization of potassium chloride, potassium bromide, and potassium iodide, but there is a marked difference in liquid ammonia, which has a dielectric constant of 22 and a lesser tendency to solvate. At −34° in ammonia, the dissociation constants for potassium iodide and chloride are, respectively, 0.0042 and 0.00087.

The degree of dissociation of electrolytes in solvents of low dielectric constant may be calculated from conductance measurements. However, this is much more difficult than for water since Λ_0 must be determined indirectly by methods described by Fuoss.*

The conductance of metallic sodium in liquid ammonia is interesting. Apparently, the neutral sodium atoms dissociate into positive Na^+ ions and negative electrons.

The conductance in mixtures of solvents can be predicted in some cases by assuming that the effects are additive. In other cases the conductance becomes quite complicated. For example, both pure water

* Fuoss, "Properties of Electrolytic Solutions," *Chem. Revs.*, 17, 27 (1935).

and pure sulfuric acid have extremely low conductances, but mixtures of the two are conducting. As the sulfuric acid concentration increases, the specific conductance increases until a maximum of about 0.72 is attained at about 33 per cent H_2SO_4, after which the conductance decreases until a minimum is reached at 85 per cent, corresponding to the compound $H_2SO_4 \cdot H_2O$. Further increase in concentration of H_2SO_4 causes an increase in conductance to a slight maximum and then a decrease to a very low value at 100 per cent H_2SO_4. Addition of SO_3 to the H_2SO_4 again gives an increase in conductance. These conductance changes provide the basis for automatic recording instruments reading directly in concentration used in industrial processes involving sulfuric acid.

Crystalline salts have very low conductances because the ions are held in fixed positions, but the fused salts are excellent conductors. Even in the crystal form the conductance becomes appreciable at temperatures just below the melting point, a fact which shows that there is some mobility of the ions. Impurities in the salt sometimes give an abnormally large conductance. The specific conductance of many fused salts is large, sometimes exceeding the conductance of the most concentrated aqueous solutions, but the equivalent conductance is comparatively small on account of the high concentration of the electrolyte. The electrolysis of fused salts finds important technical applications in such operations as the production of sodium from fused sodium hydroxide, the production of magnesium from fused magnesium chloride, and the production of aluminum on an enormous scale by the electrolysis of fused aluminum hydroxide dissolved in molten sodium aluminum fluoride. Electrolysis in fused salts and nonaqueous solutions makes possible the production of certain metals which cannot be deposited in the presence of water.

Table XI lists a few examples of the conductance of fused salts.

Table XI. Conductance of Fused Salts

Salt	Temperature, °C	Specific Conductance	Equivalent Conductance
AgCl	600	4.16	111
AgBr	600	3.08	51.9
AgI	600	2.43	64.6
AgNO₃	250	0.83	36.1
	350	1.25	55.4
NaNO₃	350	1.17	52.9
	450	1.56	73.1
KNO₃	350	0.67	36.5

The Interionic Attraction Theory of Conductance. *   Whereas
the decrease in equivalent conductance with increasing concentration of
a weak electrolyte is largely due to the decrease in the degree of ionization, the small decrease in equivalent conductance of strong electrolytes results from interionic attractions.   According to the Debye-
Hückel theory (page 483), interionic attractions lead to the formation
of a diffuse atmosphere of oppositely charged ions around every ion in
solution.   This ion atmosphere has two effects, both of which tend to
retard the motion of the central ion when an electric field is applied to
the solution.   When an ion moves in a field it tends to move out of its
atmosphere, but the atmosphere re-forms.   However, since the atmosphere requires a finite time for its formation, the atmosphere is no longer
symmetrical about the ion and tends to hold it back by electrostatic
attraction.   This retarding effect is called the *relaxation effect*.

The second effect, the *electrophoretic effect*, results from the fact that
the ion atmosphere tends to move in the direction opposite to that of
the central ion.   Since the ions of the atmosphere tend to carry along
water molecules, the central ion has to move upstream against this
counterflow.   These effects have been treated in detail by Onsager,† who
showed theoretically that the equivalent conductance of a strong electrolyte should vary with the concentration according to

$$\Lambda = \Lambda_0 - [\theta \Lambda_0 + \sigma]\sqrt{c}$$

in dilute solution and was able to calculate the values of the constants
θ and σ, which involve the dielectric constant of water, the absolute
temperature, the viscosity of water, and the valences of the ions.   For a
uniunivalent electrolyte such as KCl in water at 25° the constants have
the values $\theta = 0.2273$ and $\sigma = 59.78$.   Careful tests of this equation
have shown that it gives accurately the correct limiting slope of a plot
of Λ versus $\sqrt{c}$ such as Fig. 14-2.

In an alternating field each ion in solution will acquire a periodic
motion.   If the frequency is increased to a point where the period of
oscillation of the ion becomes comparable with the time of relaxation,
the dissymmetry in the ionic atmosphere will decrease, the relaxation
effect will diminish, and the equivalent conductance will increase.
Also, by the application of very high voltages, the ion may be forced to
move fast enough to escape completely from its atmosphere, and increases in equivalent conductance of 10 per cent may be obtained at
200 kilovolts/cm.

* Harned and Owen, *The Physical Chemistry of Electrolytic Solutions*, Reinhold
Publishing Corp., New York, 1950.
† Onsager, *Physik. Z.*, *28*, 277 (1927).

Conductimetric Titrations. The electrical conductance of a solution serves as a means for determining the end point in chemical reactions, such as titrations of acids and bases, or precipitations.

For example, when a strong acid is added to a strong base, the conductance decreases to a minimum, at which the base is completely neutralized, and then it increases, owing to the excess of acid, as shown in *Fig. 14-5* for sodium hydroxide and hydrochloric acid. The two lines

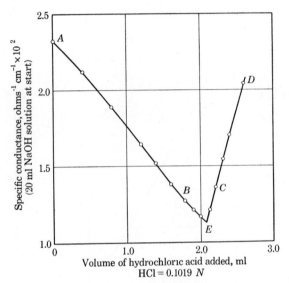

Fig. 14-5. Electric conductance in the titration of a strong base NaOH by a strong acid HCl.

AB and CD intersect at the point E, which is the end point. The OH^- ions of the base and the H^+ ions of the acid have much greater mobilities than the sodium and chloride ions, and so the conductance is least at the end point E where the acid and base are present in exactly equivalent portions, and there is no excess of either OH^- ions or H^+ ions. In order that the lines AB and CD shall be straight and thus permit calculations from sets of only two points, it is desirable to keep the volume constant throughout the titration. In order to approach this condition, the added reagent must be concentrated, whereas the solution which is being titrated must be dilute.

If the same titration is carried out with a weak acid, acetic acid, instead of a strong acid, as shown in *Fig. 14-6*, the excess acid beyond the end point will not cause such a sharp increase in conductance. In fact, with acetic acid a horizontal line is obtained after all the sodium hydroxide has been neutralized, because the number of ions being added in the excess of acetic acid is small, particularly in the presence of the sodium acetate (as explained on page 466). The sharp change in the slope of the line is useful, however, in determining end points. In colored or turbid solutions, where a colored indicator cannot be used, this determination of end points by means of conductance measurements is

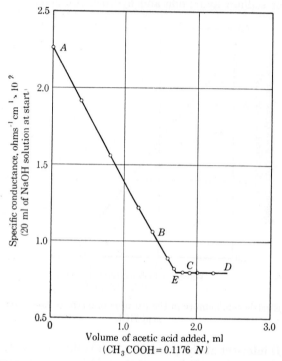

Fig. 14-6.   Electric conductance in the titration of a strong base NaOH by a weak acid CH₃COOH.

particularly useful. In practical work it is often convenient to plot resistance or merely bridge readings instead of specific conductances.

End points in precipitations can be determined by conductance measurements, because the ions left in solution will have ionic conductances somewhat different from the ions which are removed from solution in the precipitation. One of the best reactions for this method is the precipitation of a salt like magnesium sulfate with barium hydroxide, where both products $BaSO_4$ and $Mg(OH)_2$ are insoluble, and the conductance at the end point is very low.

Conductance measurements are used for a variety of testing and control operations, such, for example, as concentration of acids or salts by evaporation, leakage of salt solutions, hardness of water, moisture content of soil or wood, and rates of chemical reaction in which the products have a different conductance from that of the reactants.

Decomposition Voltage. When two platinum electrodes are placed in a solution of an electrolyte and a low voltage is applied, practically no current flows through the circuit. As the voltage is gradually increased, there may be a temporary flow of current until the products accumulate and produce an opposing voltage and cause the current to diminish. However, for each electrolyte there is a voltage above which a large current continues to flow. This voltage is called the *decomposition voltage*. At voltages above the decomposition voltage the current is a linear function of applied voltage. When the current flowing is plotted against the applied voltage, the extrapolation of the steep line to cut the horizontal axis gives a measure of the decomposition voltage. In another method the applied voltage is increased until bubbles of gas or deposits of metal on an electrode can be detected with a microscope. Decomposition voltages vary with the conditions but are characteristic of definite electrolytes. Thus the decomposition voltage of copper sulfate is 1.6, of lead nitrate 1.8, and of cadmium nitrate 2.3 volts. It is a striking fact that most strong acids and bases have decomposition potentials of 1.7 volts. They all behave alike in that at 1.7 volts or above they give off hydrogen and oxygen at the electrodes. Acids such as concentrated hydrochloric acid, which give products other than hydrogen and oxygen, have decomposition potentials below 1.7 volts.

The decomposition potentials play a role in the controlled deposition of metals or other electrolytic products when a potential difference is applied to the electrodes of an electrolytic cell containing several different electrolytes; the one with the lowest decomposition potential is electrolyzed first, and, as the voltage is increased, other salts are electrolyzed and other metals deposited in turn as their decomposition potentials are exceeded.

For example, in a mixture of cadmium, lead, and silver which is subjected to electrolysis, the decomposition potentials of the salts are as follows: $Cd(NO_3)_2 = 2.3$ volts, $Pb(NO_3)_2 = 1.8$ volts, and $AgNO_3 = 0.9$ volt. If the applied electromotive force is made a little less than 1 volt, the silver will be deposited; then, if the electromotive force is raised to about 1.9 volts, the lead will be deposited; and finally, if the electromotive force is raised above 2.3 volts, the cadmium will be deposited.

If a platinum anode is surrounded by a solution containing chloride ions, both Cl^- ions and OH^- ions will be colliding with the electrode and competing for the removal of the electron. Less energy is required to discharge the hydroxyl ion. Therefore, when Cl^- and OH^- ions are in nearly the same concentration, practically pure oxygen will be evolved, but, when the chloride ion is in large excess, chlorine gas will be produced at the anode. In 2 M hydrochloric acid chlorine is evolved, but in 0.02 M solution oxygen is evolved, whereas at intermediate concentrations a mixture of chlorine and oxygen is obtained. Thus, it is seen that the products of electrolysis can be controlled not only by changing the applied voltage but also by changing the concentrations. When different kinds of ions are competing at an electrode for the loss or gain of electrons, two factors are involved—the decomposition potential, which is a measure of the energy requirement, and the concentration, which is a measure of the frequency of collision with the electrode surface.

If a solution of potassium sulfate is electrolyzed, hydrogen and oxygen are evolved because the hydrogen and hydroxyl ions are discharged at a lower voltage than the potassium ions and sulfate ions, as indicated by the normal electrode potentials. However, with very large current densities it is possible to deplete the hydrogen ions in the immediate neighborhood of the cathode to such an extent that some potassium will then deposit in a mercury cathode.

The control of concentration as well as voltage is important in practical electroplating. In nickel plating, for example, if the acidity of the plating baths exceeds a certain limit, hydrogen will be liberated, and the deposit will not be firm and smooth. The electroplating of a mixture of copper and zinc (brass) is another example. Ordinarily, when a mixture of zinc and copper salts is electrolyzed, copper is plated exclusively, because its decomposition potential is much less. However, the concentration of copper ions can be decreased enormously by adding potassium cyanide and locking up most of the copper in complex ions; under these conditions, when the zinc is very concentrated, both metals will be deposited together at the cathode.

Important changes in the electrodeposition of metals can be made through the use of rapidly rotating electrodes. When the solution in the neighborhood of the electrode is changed rapidly, there is less chance for a change in concentration due to electrolysis. Smooth deposits can then be formed even with high current densities. If the solution is not agitated, the current must often be kept so low as to require long times for deposition. Sometimes the introduction of a colloid like gelatin into the solution produces smaller crystals and a smoother deposit on the electrode.

Polarography. * The polarographic method of analysis developed by Heyrovsky is based upon the determination of current flow when a solution containing oxidizable or reducible substances is electrolyzed in a cell in which one electrode consists of mercury falling dropwise from

* Kolthoff and Lingane, *Polarography*, Interscience Publishers, New York, 1952; Müller, *J. Chem. Education*, *18*, 65, 111, 172, 227 (1941).

ı fine-bore capillary glass tube. The apparatus which automatically records the plot of current versus voltage is called a *polarograph*. Both a qualitative and quantitative analysis of a small volume of solution may be obtained by this method.

As the applied potential is increased from 0, the current flowing is small and remains so until one of the components of the solution begins

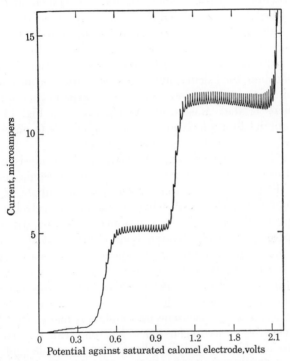

Fig. 14-7. Polarogram of a solution containing 9×10^{-4} M Zn^{++} and 10×10^{-4} M Tl^{+} in 0.2 M KCl. Courtesy Dr. Irving Shain, University of Wisconsin.

to be reduced at the mercury cathode. The rapid rise in current with applied potential is called a wave, and the potential at the midpoint of the wave, the *half-wave potential*, is characteristic of the substance being reduced. It is independent of the concentration of the reducible or oxidizable substance but may be altered by pH changes or the formation of complex ions. It is necessary to remove dissolved oxygen before an experiment by sweeping out the solution with an inert gas since the reduction of oxygen gas leads to the passage of a current which masks the current of most other substances.

As an illustration, the polarogram of a solution containing two reducible species, Tl^{+} and Zn^{++}, is given in *Fig. 14-7*. As may be seen, the half-wave potentials for Tl^+ and Zn^{++} are -0.53 volt and -1.06 volts against the saturated calomel electrode. The wave heights are proportional to the concentrations of the respective ions. The oscillations about a mean current are due to the formation and polarization of mercury droplets. Since a fresh surface is continually exposed by the growing drops the current is solely a function of the applied potential.

As the potential is increased above the half-wave potential a maximum value is reached which is referred to as the *diffusion current*. The diffusion current depends upon the rate with which the reducible substance diffuses to the mercury droplet, and it is proportional to the concentration of the reducible substance in the body of the solution. The proportionality constant for calculating the concentration of an ion from its diffusion current must be determined from experiments with known concentrations of that substance. As illustrated in Fig. 14-7 several waves are obtained for a mixture, and so it is possible to obtain a quantitative analysis of a mixture of several components.

Electrolytic Reduction and Oxidation. Electrolysis provides a simple and effective means for the reduction of inorganic and organic materials. Electrolytic reduction depends on the supply of electrons produced at the cathode. Either hydrogenation or electrolysis or both may take place, depending on the conditions. Likewise, oxidation may be produced electrolytically by removing electrons at the anode; and sometimes the oxygen liberated at the anode can be used to advantage.

The current density, the cathode potential, the acidity of the solution, and the nature of the electrode surface affect the electrolytic hydrogenation and reduction at the cathode.

The conversion of nitrobenzene into aniline is one of the classic examples of electrolytic hydrogenation. Not only can the reduction to aniline be accomplished effectively, but also, by suitable control of the potential and the acidity of the solution, together with proper choice of electrodes, it is possible to obtain large yields of any one of the intermediate products, azoxybenzene, azobenzene, and hydrazobenzene, each representing a step in the reduction of nitrobenzene. Electrolytic oxidations at the anode are also important.

REFERENCES

Harned and Owen, *The Physical Chemistry of Electrolytic Solutions*, Reinhold Publishing Corp., New York, 1950.

MacInnes, *The Principles of Electrochemistry*, Reinhold Publishing Corp., New York, 1939.

Glasstone, *Introduction to Electrochemistry*, D. Van Nostrand Co., New York, 1942.

Dole, *Experimental and Theoretical Electrochemistry*, McGraw-Hill Book Co., New York, 1935.

Creighton and Koehler, *Principles and Applications of Electrochemistry*, John Wiley & Sons, New York, 1935.

PROBLEMS

1. Ten amperes of current flowed for 1 hour through water containing a little sulfuric acid. How many liters of gas were formed at both electrodes at 27° and 740 mm pressure? *Ans.* 7.08 l.

2. It is desired to use a conductance apparatus to measure the concentration of dilute solutions of sodium chloride. If the electrodes in the cell are each 1 cm^2 in area and are 0.2 cm apart, calculate the resistance which will be obtained for 1, 10, and 100 ppm sodium chloride at 25°C. *Ans.* 92,700, 9320, and 950 ohms.

3. Determine the value of Λ_0 for lithium chloride from the following data at 25°:

Equivalents per liter	0.05	0.01	0.005	0.001	0.0005
Equivalent conductance	100.11	107.32	109.40	112.40	113.15

Ans. 114.3 cm^2 equiv^{-1} ohm^{-1}.

4. At 25° the equivalent conductance of propionic acid at infinite dilution is 385.6 cm^2 equiv^{-1} ohm^{-1}, and the ionization constant is 1.34×10^{-5}. Calculate the equivalent conductance of a 0.05 N solution of propionic acid at 25°.
Ans. 6.32 cm^2 equiv^{-1} ohm^{-1}.

5. A moving-boundary experiment is carried out with a 0.1 N solution of hydrochloric acid at 25° ($L = 0.0424$ ohm^{-1} cm^{-1}). Sodium ions are caused to follow the hydrogen ions. Three milliamperes is passed through the tube of 0.3 cm^2 cross-sectional area, and it is observed that the boundary moves 3.08 cm in 1 hour. Calculate (a) the hydrogen-ion mobility, (b) the hydrogen-ion transference number, and (c) the chloride-ion mobility.
Ans. (a) 363×10^{-5} cm^2 volt^{-1} sec^{-1}.
(b) 0.826. (c) 76.6×10^{-5} cm^2 volt^{-1} sec^{-1}.

6. A solution of hydrochloric acid was electrolyzed in a transference cell between platinum electrodes. The cathode compartment contained 0.177 gram of chloride ions before the electrolysis and 0.163 gram afterwards. A silver coulometer in series had a deposit of silver equivalent to 0.0825 gram of chloride ions. What are the transference numbers of H^+ and Cl^-? *Ans.* 0.830 and 0.170.

7. At 25° the equivalent conductance at infinite dilution Λ_0 of sodium monochloro-acetate is 89.8 cm^2 equiv^{-1} ohm^{-1}. Calculate Λ_0 at 25° for monochloroacetic acid.
Ans. 389.4 cm^2 equiv^{-1} ohm^{-1}.

8. The following table gives the specific conductance of a solution of hydrochloric acid, to 100 ml of which have been added various amounts of an 8 N solution of sodium hydroxide. If the dilution effect of the small amount of hydroxide solution added is neglected, what is the normality of the hydrochloric acid solution?

NaOH, ml	0.32	0.92	1.56	2.34
Conductance, L	0.0322	0.0186	0.0164	0.0296

Ans. 0.1 N.

---

9. (a) How many ampere-hours of electricity are required to refine by electrolysis 453 grams (1 lb) of copper, removing it from the impure anode and depositing it in

a pure state on the cathode? (b) If the potential drop across the electrolytic cell is 5 volts, how much will the electricity cost at 1 cent per kilowatt-hour?

10. A conductance cell was calibrated by filling it with a 0.02 N solution of potassium chloride ($L = 0.002768$ ohm^{-1} cm^{-1}) and measuring the resistance at 25°C, which was found to be 457.3 ohms. The cell was then filled with a calcium chloride solution containing 0.555 gram of $CaCl_2$ per liter. The measured resistance was 1050 ohms. Calculate (a) the cell constant for the cell, (b) the specific conductance of the $CaCl_2$ solution, and (c) the equivalent conductance of $CaCl_2$ at this concentration.

11. One hundred grams of sodium chloride is dissolved in 10,000 liters of water at 25°, giving a solution which may be regarded in these calculations as infinitely dilute. (a) What is the equivalent conductance of the solution? (b) What is the specific conductance of the solution? (c) This dilute solution is placed in a glass tube of 4-cm diameter provided with electrodes filling the tube and placed 20 cm apart. How much current will flow if the potential drop between the electrodes is 80 volts?

12. The specific conductance at 25° of a saturated solution of barium sulfate was 4.58×10^{-6} ohm^{-1} cm^{-1}, and that of the water used was 1.52×10^{-6}. The equivalent conductance at infinite dilution of barium sulfate is 143 cm^2 equiv^{-1} ohm^{-1}. What is the solubility of $BaSO_4$ at 25° in (a) gram equivalents per liter, (b) moles per liter, and (c) grams per liter?

13. In 0.1 N HCl at 0°C the mobilities of hydrogen and chloride ions are 365×10^{-5} and 79×10^{-5} cm^2 volt^{-1} sec^{-1}, respectively. (a) Calculate the specific conductance for this solution at 0°C. (b) A moving-boundary experiment is carried out in a tube with a uniform cross-sectional area of 0.200 cm^2, and sodium ions are caused to follow the hydrogen ions. If a current of 5 milliamperes is passed for 1 hour, how far will the hydrogen ions move?

14. A glass tube provided with electrodes at each end has a resistance of 100 ohms when filled with 0.01 N KCl. Estimate, with the help of graphical interpolation, how many grams of NaCl should be weighed out in a liter of solution to give a resistance of 500 ohms in the same tube.

15. From the values of the equivalent conductance at different concentrations for aqueous nitric acid at 18°, determine the equivalent conductance of an infinitely dilute solution at 18°.

Concentration, milliequivalents per liter	Equivalent Conductance
2.0	371.2
10.0	365.0
50.0	353.7
100.0	346.4

16. The equivalent conductance of an infinitely dilute solution of ammonium chloride is 149.7, and the ionic conductances of the ions OH$^-$ and Cl$^-$ are 198.0 and 76.3, respectively. Calculate the equivalent conductance of ammonium hydroxide at infinite dilution.

17. In the titration of 100 ml of a dilute solution of acetic acid with 0.500 N ammonium hydroxide, the following conductance data are obtained.

Volume of NH$_4$OH, ml	8.0	9.0	10.0	11.0	12.0	13.0	15.0	17.0
Resistance of cell, ohms	75.0	68.0	62.0	57.0	53.0	50.8	51.5	52.1

What is the normality of the acetic acid solution?

18. MacInnes and Dole electrolyzed 1.0 N potassium chloride at 25° between a silver anode and a silver chloride cathode and found that 121.41 grams of solution from the anode portion contained 7.9039 grams of potassium chloride. The anode reaction is $Ag + Cl^- = AgCl + e$; the cathode reaction is $AgCl + e = Ag + Cl^-$. The middle portion, unchanged by the electrolysis, contained 7.1479 per cent by weight of potassium chloride. Calculate the number of equivalents of potassium ion which have migrated away from the solution surrounding the anode. The coulometer in the circuit gained 2.4835 grams of silver from the deposition of silver. Calculate the transference number of potassium ion in 1.0 N KCl.

---

19. A glass tube 4 cm in diameter and 30 cm long is closed at each end with a sheet silver electrode and filled with 0.01 N silver nitrate. Sixty volts are applied. (*a*) How much current flows? (*b*) How many degrees will the temperature of the solution rise in 10 minutes, if it is assumed that the heat capacity of the solution is nearly 1 cal deg^{-1} ml^{-1} and that all the heat is taken up by the solution?

20. (*a*) What is the resistance of a glass cell, 5 cm in diameter with electrodes 10 cm apart, when filled with 0.01 N CuSO$_4$ having an equivalent conductance of 83.1 cm^2 equiv^{-1} ohm^{-1}? (*b*) What is the resistance of the same cell when filled with water which contains 0.1 gram of CuSO$_4$ per liter?

21. Estimate the specific conductance at 25° of water which contains 70 parts per million by weight of magnesium sulfate.

22. The specific conductance of a saturated solution of thallous bromide at 20° is 2.158×10^{-4} and the specific conductance of water at the same temperature is 0.044×10^{-6} ohm^{-1} cm^{-1}. The equivalent conductance at infinite dilution is 138.3. Calculate the solubility of thallous bromide in grams per liter.

23. State quantitatively what the chemical changes will be at the cathode and the anode when a current of 1 ampere is passed for 20 minutes through the following solutions:

	(*a*)	(*b*)	(*c*)
Cathode	Graphite	Mercury	Silver
Solution	H$_2$SO$_4$	ZnCl$_2$	FeCl$_3$
Anode	Platinum	Zinc	Silver

24. A 6-volt storage battery operates two 4-ampere lamps in parallel for 5 hours. The reaction is $Pb + PbO_2 + 2H^+ + 2HSO_4^- = 2PbSO_4 + 2H_2O$ (p. 414). How many grams of lead are oxidized? If 5 per cent of the energy goes into light and 95 per cent into heat, how many calories of light are given off by the lamps?

25. One milligram of potassium chloride is dissolved in 1 liter of water at 25°, giving a solution which may be regarded as infinitely dilute. (*a*) What is the equivalent conductance? (*b*) What is the specific conductance? (*c*) This solution is placed in a glass tube of 2-cm diameter provided with electrodes, which fill the tube and are placed 10 cm apart. How much current will flow if the potential drop between the electrodes is 50 volts?

26. A sample of water from a large pool had a resistance at 25° of 9200 ohms when placed in a certain conductance cell. When filled with 0.020 M KCl the cell had a resistance at 25° of 85 ohms. Five hundred grams of sodium chloride was dissolved in the pool, which was then thoroughly stirred. A sample of this solution gave a resistance of 7600 ohms. With the help of graphical interpolation calculate the number of liters of water in the pool.

27. What are the probable products of electrolysis at each electrode when a cur rent of electricity is passed through the following cells? (*a*) An aqueous solution of copper sulfate with copper electrodes. (*b*) An aqueous solution of ferrous sulfate with graphite electrodes. (*c*) An aqueous solution of lithium iodide with mercury electrodes. (*d*) A solution of sodium iodide in acetone with platinum electrodes.

28. An electrolytic cell containing a cadmium sulfate solution was subjected to various applied potentials, and the corresponding currents were measured. The results were as follows:

E, volts	0.5	1.0	1.5	1.8	2.0	2.2	2.4	2.6	3.0
I, amperes	0.002	0.004	0.006	0.007	0.008	0.028	0.069	0.110	0.192

What is the decomposition potential of cadmium sulfate?

29. The silver nitrate solution from the central compartment of a transference cell weighed 36.5 grams and was titrated with 32.7 ml of ammonium thiocyanate solution, 1 ml of which was equivalent to 0.0085 gram of silver nitrate. The solution from the cathode compartment weighed 43.17 grams and required 29.4 ml of ammonium thiocyanate solution. A silver coulometer in series with the transference cell had a deposit of 0.0994 gram of silver. What are the transference numbers of the silver ion and the nitrate ion?

30. In determining the transference numbers of $Ba(HSO_4)_2$ in concentrated H_2SO_4 using platinum electrodes, the following are the analyses for a typical measurement expressed in grams of $BaSO_4$ per gram of solution:

Original	Anode Compartment	Cathode Compartment
0.02503	0.02411	0.02621

The solution had an average density of 1.90 g ml^{-1}; the cathode compartment held 39 ml; and the anode compartment held 41 ml. During the experiment 4956 coulombs were transferred. What is the apparent transference number of Ba^{++} ion in the solution?

31. Outline methods by means of which the formation of a complex ion, such as $Cu(CN)_2{}^-$, might be determined in a solution containing both CuCl and KCN, using (*a*) conductance measurements, (*b*) measurements of transference numbers.

15

Electromotive Force

The behavior of electrolytes during the passage of an electric current was studied in the preceding chapter. We observed that electrons are supplied to the cathode by means of a dynamo or external battery and then transferred to the positive ions which come in contact with it, thus neutralizing positive charges on the ions and frequently causing the deposition of neutral atoms. In a similar manner electrons are removed from the anode by a dynamo or external battery, and oxidation results since the number of valence electrons on the negative ions coming in contact with the anode is decreased.

In the present chapter we will study the electromotive force produced by an excess of electrons at the anode and a deficiency at the cathode caused by the contact with ions which surround the electrodes. Usually a reaction may be divided into two parts: one an oxidation process involving a release of electrons, and the other a reduction process involving an absorption of electrons. The tendency of certain ions to release electrons at the anode feeds electrons into an electrically conducting electrode which is placed in the solution; and the tendency of certain ions to absorb electrons causes electrons to be withdrawn from the cathode placed in the solution. The electrons which are fed in at the anode move along the wire in the external circuit to the cathode, just as in electrolysis they were moved with a dynamo from anode to cathode. A measurement of the voltage between the two electrodes makes it possible to determine the relative tendency of two reactions to release electrons, to calculate the equilibrium constant of the over-all chemical reaction, or to calculate the activities or effective concentrations of the electrolytes surrounding the electrodes.

Galvanic Cells. Electrochemical cells for the production of electricity from chemical reactions have been known since 1800, when Volta described his electric pile of zinc and silver disks separated by paper moistened with salt water. This new source of electricity gave currents of sufficient magnitude to carry out significant experiments in electrochemistry.

One of the oldest and simplest cells consists of a zinc electrode immersed in a solution of zinc sulfate and a copper electrode immersed in a solution of copper sulfate, the two solutions being separated from each other with a porous cup or plate to minimize diffusion of one into the other. The voltage or electromotive force of such a cell is about 1 volt.

The operation of the cell can be understood with the help of *Fig. 15-1*. Each electrode is surrounded by a solution of its ions, and there is an

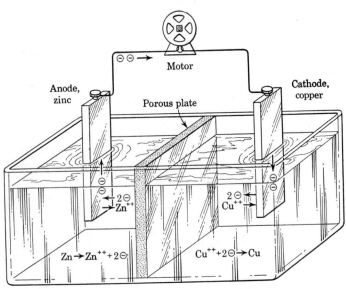

FIG. 15-1. Zinc-copper galvanic cell showing the oxidation reaction which feeds electrons into the zinc anode and the reduction reaction which removes electrons from the copper cathode.

equilibrium at each as indicated by the reactions

$$Zn = Zn^{++} + 2e$$

$$Cu = Cu^{++} + 2e$$

If both metals had the same tendency to ionize and give up electrons each electrode would have the same number of free electrons and there would be no difference in potential, that is no voltage and no flow of electrons or current, when the two electrodes are connected with a wire. However, zinc has a greater tendency to ionize than copper, and so the zinc will go into solution and give up its electrons to the zinc metal in a process of oxidation. Accordingly, in this cell the zinc is the anode. The electrons released by the zinc atoms pass through the wire to the copper electrode, where they are given up to the surrounding copper ions and thus deposit copper atoms. This process of adding electrons to copper ions is reduction, and the electrode at which reduction occurs is called the cathode. This nomenclature is consistent with that of the preceding chapter, in which the electrons were fed in at the cathode in electrolysis, thus causing the positive ions in contact with the electrode to take up electrons and deposit as atoms.

Although several reactions are possible at the electrodes, the two which will take place are

$$\text{Zn} = \text{Zn}^{++} + 2e \quad \text{and} \quad \text{Cu}^{++} + 2e = \text{Cu}$$

The galvanic cell operates spontaneously, and the following phenomena take place:

1. 1 gram equivalent of zinc goes into solution at the anode as 1 gram equivalent of zinc ions.

2. 6.02×10^{23} electrons, equivalent to 96,500 coulombs or 96,500 ampere-seconds, travel along the wire from the zinc anode to the copper cathode.

3. 1 gram equivalent of copper ions is deposited on the copper cathode because the 6.02×10^{23} electrons combine with 3.01×10^{23} copper ions from among those which collide with the copper cathode.

As long as the circuit is closed, these reactions go on, consuming zinc and depositing copper until either the zinc or the supply of copper ions is exhausted. If the circuit is left open, the chemical action ceases, except for diffusion of the ions and local action, which is due to impurities in the zinc acting to give tiny local cells. This action which consumes the zinc on open circuit can be greatly reduced by using very pure zinc or by coating or amalgamating the surface of the zinc with mercury. This procedure gives a coating over the impurities and does not change the voltage appreciably because a saturated solution of zinc in mercury possesses practically the same potential as pure zinc.

Many other galvanic cells have been devised, but the zinc and copper cell serves to illustrate the general principle by which electricity can be furnished from chemical reactions. Several cells of the same kind can be arranged in series with the anode of one cell connected to the cathode of the next to give a *battery* of higher voltage, which is equal to the sum of the voltages of the individual cells. Although electricity can be produced much more cheaply by operating a dynamo with mechanical power, the batteries have the advantage of portability, and two types have survived severe economic competition, the lead storage battery and the Leclanché dry cell of zinc and ammonium chloride.

The lead storage battery consists of an electrode of lead and an electrode of lead oxide immersed in sulfuric acid. Each plate has a rough surface exposing a large area, and the two are held close together in rigid frames. The cell reaction is

$$Pb + HSO_4^- = PbSO_4(s) + H^+ + 2e$$

$$PbO_2 + 3H^+ + HSO_4^- + 2e = PbSO_4(s) + 2H_2O$$

$$Pb + PbO_2 + 2H^+ + 2HSO_4^- \underset{\text{Charge}}{\overset{\text{Discharge}}{\rightleftarrows}} 2PbSO_4(s) + 2H_2O$$

The important thing about this cell reaction is the fact that it is reversible, and if electrons from a dynamo are put into one electrode, additional spongy lead is deposited from the lead ions in the saturated solution of lead sulfate. According to a hypothetical mechanism, the removal of electrons from the other electrode converts Pb^{++} from the lead sulfate into Pb^{++++}, which in turn deposits as PbO_2 according to the reaction

$$Pb^{++++} + 4OH^- = PbO_2 + 2H_2O$$

These electrically replenished electrodes are then ready to follow again the original cell reaction with the flow of electrons from lead electrode to lead oxide electrode, thus generating useful electricity.

When the battery is discharged, the sulfuric acid is converted into lead sulfate and water; the sulfuric acid is regenerated on charging. In a fully charged lead storage battery the voltage is about 2 volts and the specific gravity is 1.215. If the battery is allowed to stand for a while in a discharged condition, the lead sulfate becomes less soluble and crystallizes out on the electrodes, thus tending to cover up the electrode and decrease the current attainable. In cold weather the dilute sulfuric acid may freeze, damaging the electrodes and their retaining structures.

The Leclanché dry cell with a voltage of about 1.6 volts consists of a zinc can containing a carbon electrode surrounded by manganese dioxide and graphite immersed in a starch paste containing zinc chloride and an excess of solid ammonium chloride. When the electrodes are connected through an electrical circuit the zinc goes into solution and the NH_4^+ ion is discharged, giving ammonia and hydrogen. The hydrogen is oxidized to water by the manganese oxide, which in turn is reduced to Mn_2O_3. The NH_3 reacts with the zinc chloride to form insoluble complexes, thus preventing the solution from becoming strongly alkaline. The graphite-manganese dioxide electrode has a lower voltage in alkaline solution.

Voltage Measurements of Cells. In physical chemistry electro-chemical cells are used to obtain information concerning the free energy and equilibria in electrolytic solutions and to determine the activities of the electrolytes. A simple voltmeter cannot be used alone for measur-

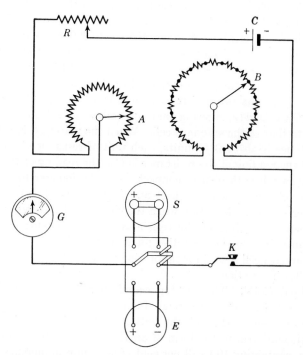

FIG. 15-2. Circuit diagram for a potentiometer, in which the voltage of an unknown cell E is compared with that of a standard cell S by balancing the resistances of the circuit in each case until no current flows as indicated by a zero reading on the galvanometer G.

ing the electromotive force of a small cell, because the operation of the voltmeter causes some current to flow, thus initiating chemical changes at the electrodes and producing a different voltage. Furthermore, if any appreciable current is drawn, the internal resistance of the cell be-comes a complicating factor.

To avoid these difficulties the electromotive force is measured by balancing against the cell a known voltage under conditions such that practically no current flows. For this purpose a potentiometer of the type illustrated in *Fig. 15-2* is convenient. In a potentiometer the po-tential to be measured is opposed by an equal and opposite potential which is provided by a battery C in series with several resistances. A galvanometer G is used to determine the setting at which no current flows. The magnitude of the potential provided by the potentiometer may be varied by adjusting the sliding contacts A and B on the two circular resistances. The larger resistance is usually divided into 15 equal parts, each having the same resistance as the circular slide wire on the left which provides the fine adjustment. The potential drop opposing cell E can be adjusted to less than 1/10,000 of the total.

In practice the double-throw switch is first connected to the standard cell S of known voltage, usually a Weston cell of 1.0186 volts. The sliding contacts A and B are rotated to read 1.0186, and the key K is tapped momentarily as the external resistance R is adjusted, until the galvanometer G reads zero, showing that the voltage at 1.0186 is equal and opposite to that of the standard cell. When the voltage S is 1.0186 and the resistance is also 1.0186 units, each unit of resistance is equal to 1 volt, and the reading of the resistance is also the reading of the voltage. Then the switch is thrown to connect the potentiometer to a cell E of unknown voltage. The contacts A and B are adjusted so that the galvanometer shows no deflection when the circuit is closed by tapping the key. Then the reading of the resistances on the potentiometer gives directly in volts the electromotive force of the cell E.

The standard cell S used for calibrating the potentiometer is described in the following section.

Standard Cells. The Weston cadmium cell, shown in *Fig. 15-3*, is the accepted standard reference for measuring voltages. Platinum electrodes are sealed through the bottom of two glass tubes connected by a horizontal arm in the form of an H. One tube holds a cadmium amalgam, containing 10 to 13 per cent of cadmium in mercury, and the other contains pure mercury on which floats a paste of mercury and mercurous sulfate. The cell is then filled with a concentrated solution of cadmium sulfate or a saturated solution containing an excess of solid crystals of $CdSO_4 \cdot \frac{8}{3}H_2O$. The latter is the accepted standard, but the former has a lower temperature coefficient which renders it more convenient for laboratory use.

This cell is reversible, and, unless abnormally large currents are drawn, the voltage remains constant. When it operates spontaneously, cadmium goes into solution as cadmium ions, and the electrons produced by this reaction pass through the wire to the positive electrode, where mercurous ions take them up and deposit as mercury atoms. When the cell is opposed by a larger electromotive force, the current flows in the opposite direction with the result that cadmium is deposited, and mercury converted into mercurous ions. If the solution is saturated with respect to both cadmium sulfate and mercurous sulfate, a fixed concentration is maintained in spite of additions from the electrode or deposition on the electrode. In the cell which uses an unsaturated solution of cadmium sulfate the concentration is so large that a small gain or loss of cadmium ions does not change the concentration appreciably.

If the materials are carefully prepared and the cell made up according to specific directions,* the voltage will be 1.0186 at 20°, and this voltage will remain unchanged for years. For accurate work in electrochemistry, however, it is well to have the voltage checked occasionally against standard cells maintained at the National Bureau of Standards in Wash-

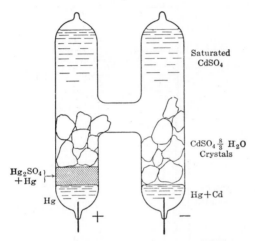

FIG. 15-3. Weston cadmium cell, which is used as a reference cell for measuring voltage.

ington or against secondary standards which, in turn, are calibrated at the Bureau of Standards. The voltage E of the saturated standard cadmium cell is 1.0186 absolute volts † at 20° and decreases 0.0000406 volt for each degree rise in temperature above 20°.

Reference Electrodes. The electromotive force or voltage of a cell is equal to the sum of the potentials of its two electrodes. The *potential* of an electrode is the difference in potential between the electrode and the surrounding solution. The potential of an electrode is determined by combining it with a *reference electrode* which has an arbitrarily assigned potential and measuring the total voltage between the two electrodes. All electrode potentials are assigned numerical values on the assumption that the potential of the standard hydrogen electrode is zero since it is impossible to measure the potential of a single electrode.

* Wolff and Waters, *Bur. Standards Bull.*, *3*, 623 (1907); *4*, 1 (1907); Vosburgh and Derr, *J. Chem. Education*, *18*, 87 (1941).

† The same cells calibrated before Jan. 1, 1948, read 1.0183 international volts.

One type of hydrogen electrode is shown at the right in *Fig. 15-4.*

Hydrogen gas does not conduct the electric current, and it cannot be used alone as an electrode, but, when adsorbed on the surface of platinum, it behaves just as if it were a metallic electrode, and the reaction

$$\tfrac{1}{2}H_2 = H^+ + e$$

is completely reversible, as shown by laboratory tests and by thermo-

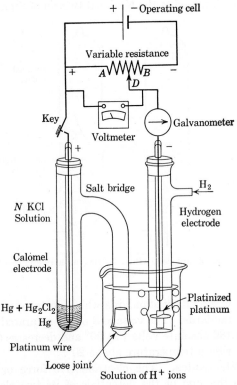

FIG. 15-4. Hydrogen-electrode and normal calomel reference electrode.

dynamic criteria. Hydrogen ions apparently can break away from the hydrogen atoms adsorbed on the surface; and the platinum acts as an inert electric conductor without entering the reaction of the electrode. To act efficiently, the electrode must be covered with platinum black to give a large surface area for adsorption. A coating of platinum black is readily deposited by electroplating from a solution of platinic chloride. The platinized electrode is arranged so that hydrogen bubbles up rapidly around the platinum so that the electrode is immersed partly in solution and partly in the hydrogen. The level of the liquid is changed as the gas bubbles out from a glass hood which surrounds the electrode, and, thus, the electrode is bathed alternately with hydrogen and with the solution.

Many different forms of hydrogen electrodes have been devised, but the one shown in Fig. 15-4 is satisfactory. In accurate work the hydrogen must be at a definite known pressure, and it must contain no oxygen. Corrections are made for the vapor pressure of water. Several solutes may interfere with the proper operation of the hydrogen electrode, particularly oxidizing agents or platinum poisons.

Any oxidizing substances such as ferric, nitrate, or chromate ions, or unsaturated organic compounds which can be reduced by hydrogen in the presence of platinum, must be avoided. Traces of arsenic and sulfur compounds may react with active platinum atoms at the surface, thus diminishing the adsorptive properties for hydrogen and giving erroneous potentials. If a hydrogen electrode does not respond properly and quickly to a change in adjustment of the pressure or if it does not give the correct voltage in a standard solution the difficulty can usually be remedied by electroplating a fresh surface of platinum black.

When the hydrogen ions surrounding the hydrogen electrode have an effective concentration or activity of unity as explained later in this chapter and the hydrogen gas has a pressure of 1.00 atm the hydrogen electrode is arbitrarily assigned a potential of 0.000 volt and used as a standard to which all other potentials are referred. The standard hydrogen electrode is rather difficult to prepare and maintain for high-precision work, and so it is usually replaced by the calomel electrode which is shown at the left in Fig. 15-4. The potential of the calomel electrode with respect to the hydrogen electrode is accurately known. The half cell consists of mercury in the bottom of a vessel with a paste of mercury and mercurous chloride (calomel) over it. A solution of potassium chloride saturated with mercurous chloride makes electric contact, through a side arm provided with a porous plug or a loosely fitting ground-glass joint, with any solution in which the electrode is placed. Such a connecting solution is called a *salt bridge*. Sometimes a beaker of potassium chloride solution is placed between the calomel electrode and the electrode being measured, in order to minimize diffusion of mercurous ions into the solution. Electric connection with the mercury of the calomel electrode is made through a platinum wire fused to a copper wire and sealed through a central glass tube.

The normal calomel electrode contains a molar solution of potassium chloride and has a voltage of -0.2802 at $25°$ with reference to the standard hydrogen electrode. The saturated calomel cell contains saturated potassium chloride and has a potential of -0.2415 with reference to the standard hydrogen electrode. It is used sometimes in special cases where it is desired to minimize the effect of other electrolytes, but it is inconvenient on account of the deposition of salts and because of a larger temperature effect.

Another reference electrode is the silver-silver chloride electrode. A silver wire or a deposit of silver plated on a platinum wire is covered with a thin coating of silver chloride, by making it the anode in a chloride solution. The concentration of silver ions and chloride ions is fixed by the solubility of the silver chloride and maintained constant. The electrode is reversible with respect to chloride ions; that is, chloride ions can be deposited on or produced from the electrode by reversing the current. This electrode is more difficult to prepare, but it is especially valuable for certain measurements.

Reversible Cells. The cadmium-mercury cell, the hydrogen electrode, and the calomel electrode are examples of reversible electrodes which can be brought back to their original state and previous voltage even if a current of some magnitude has been passed through them. In irreversible cells the original conditions cannot be restored by reversing the current, because some of the material involved has been removed, as, for example, when a gas is evolved or a precipitate formed. If more than an infinitesimal quantity of current is passed through the cell, some of the electric energy will be converted into heat and lost, so that the cell cannot be completely reversed unless extra external energy is applied. Under these conditions the work done will not be the maximum work that might have been obtained. The maximum electrical work is definite, and it is of great value in thermodynamic calculations. The measurements of irreversible cells are not significant in theoretical calculations, but they may be of value in practical measurements. Sometimes it is possible to determine from the experimental behavior of a cell whether or not it is reversible. For example, if mechanical agitation produces marked unsteadiness in voltage, or if the cell does not return to the same voltage after a larger current is allowed to pass momentarily, the cell probably is not reversible.

In the electrochemical studies of this chapter we are interested only in reversible cells, because they permit theoretical calculations. The work done in the operation of a reversible cell is maximum work (if it were not maximum there would not be enough work stored up to reverse the cell), and maximum work can be equated to other thermodynamic quantities.

When an electrochemical cell operates reversibly at constant temperature and pressure the electrical work done is nFE, where n is the number of electrons transferred in the reaction, F is the faraday (96,500 coulombs), and E is the voltage or electromotive force of the cell. The voltage E is the intensity factor of energy and nF is the capacity factor. The product of the two gives energy. In order to be sure that the voltage E corresponds to maximum work, it is measured with a potentiometer which allows only an infinitesimal amount of current to flow. The maximum electrical work in joules, nFE, may be converted into calories by dividing by 4.1840. Then F corresponds to 23,060 calories per volt.

When the cell operates it may do some pressure-volume work in addition to the electrical work, as for example in the evolution of hydrogen gas against the atmosphere, but this pressure-volume work is not measured by the potentiometer and is not included in the term nFE. It will be remembered from page 142 that in a chemical reaction at constant temperature and pressure the maximum work done by a reversible process, minus the pressure-volume work, is equal to $-\Delta F$. Then,

$$\Delta F = -nFE \tag{1}$$

According to this important equation the electrical work done in a reversible cell at constant temperature and pressure is equal to the decrease in free energy of the chemical reaction.

Example 1. What is the free-energy change involved when the zinc-copper cell consumes a mole of zinc in the reaction $Zn + Cu^{++} = Zn^{++} + Cu$? The voltage of the cell is 1.107 volts.

$$\Delta F = -nFE = -(2 \text{ equiv mole}^{-1})(96,500 \text{ coulombs equiv}^{-1})(1.107 \text{ volts})$$

$$= -213,650 \text{ joules mole}^{-1} = -\frac{213,650 \text{ joules mole}^{-1}}{4.184 \text{ joules cal}^{-1}}$$

$$= -51,063 \text{ cal mole}^{-1}$$

Many different types of electrochemical cells are available. There are always two electrodes which may be connected through external conducting wires to a potentiometer. A metal may be immersed in a solution of its ions, as in the zinc electrode $Zn; Zn^{++}$. Again an inert electrode such as platinum or gold may be immersed in a solution of oxidizing and reducing ions, as in the ferrous-ferric electrode $Pt; Fe^{++}$, Fe^{+++}.

The semicolon indicates a contact between two phases such as exists between a metal and a solution, or contact between two unmixed liquid solutions such as a solution of zinc sulfate touching a solution of copper sulfate. A comma is used to separate different ions or molecules which exist in the same phase. At the contact between two different electrolytic solutions the small junction potential can be rendered negligible for certain purposes by interposing a salt bridge, usually of potassium chloride, between the two solutions. The salt bridge is useful also if there is a possibility of precipitation when the two solutions are mixed.

Cells may be classified as follows:

A. Cells with liquid junctions:

    Different electrodes   Zn; Zn^{++}; Cu^{++}; Cu

    Concentration cells   Pt, H_2; H^+, $Cl^-(a = 1.0)$; H^+, Cl^-
        $(a = 0.1)$; H_2, Pt

The activities or effective concentrations of the ions are given in parentheses.

B. Cells in which the junction potential is practically eliminated by means of a salt bridge represented by $\parallel$:

    Different electrodes Zn; Zn^{++} $\parallel$ Cu^{++}; Cu

    Concentration cells Pt, H_2; $H^+(a = 0.1)$ $\parallel$ $H^+(a = 0.01)$; H_2, Pt

C. Cells without liquid junction:

    Different electrodes   Pt, H_2; H^+, Cl^-; Cl_2, Pt

    Concentration cell of metal (Hg + 10%Cd); Cd^{++}; (Hg + 1%
        Cd)

Cells without liquid junctions are required for exact thermodynamic treatment. However, cells in which the liquid-junction potentials have been practically eliminated by a salt bridge are used widely in practical work.

The voltages of these reversible cells can be correlated with the free-energy changes in the corresponding chemical reactions, but it is necessary to agree on arbitrary rules so that the calculations can be made without ambiguity.

Relative Oxidation Potentials. When electrons are released in a chemical change, the reaction is oxidation and the electrode in contact with the reacting materials that supply the electrons is called the anode. Examples of oxidation reactions are

$$Zn = Zn^{++} + 2e \qquad Fe^{++} = Fe^{+++} + e \qquad \text{and} \qquad Cl^- = \tfrac{1}{2}Cl_2 + e$$

Reduction reactions which take up electrons occur at the cathode, thus

$$Zn^{++} + 2e = Zn \qquad Fe^{+++} + e = Fe^{++} \qquad \text{and} \qquad \tfrac{1}{2}Cl_2 + e = Cl^-$$

The relative tendency of different elements to lose electrons varies with their position in the periodic table as determined by the number of electrons in the outer shell and by the size of the atom. Thus potassium loses its outer, valence electron more easily than sodium does, because it is farther away from the positive nucleus. Again sodium releases its electron more easily than zinc, and zinc more easily than hydrogen. The hydrogen atom loses its electron to form a hydrogen ion more easily than the chloride ion loses its extra electron to form a chlorine atom. Accordingly, we can arrange the elements in descending order, as shown in Table I, with the elements that lose electrons most easily at the top.

Table I.   Oxidation Potentials [1]

All ions are at unit activity and all gases at 1 atm. The potentials are designated by $E°$ in absolute volts. The values given are for 25°.

Electrode (Anode)	$E°_{electrode;\ electrolyte}$ (Standard hydrogen electrode = 0)	Electrode Reaction (Anode Reaction)
Li; Li$^+$	3.045	Li = Li$^+$ + e
K; K$^+$	2.925	K = K$^+$ + e
Na; Na$^+$	2.714	Na = Na$^+$ + e
Zn; Zn^{++}	0.763	$\frac{1}{2}$Zn = $\frac{1}{2}$Zn^{++} + e
Fe; Fe^{++}	0.440	$\frac{1}{2}$Fe = $\frac{1}{2}$Fe^{++} + e
Pt; Cr^{++}, Cr^{+++}	0.41	Cr^{++} = Cr^{+++} + e
Cd; Cd^{++}	0.403	$\frac{1}{2}$Cd = $\frac{1}{2}$Cd^{++} + e
Tl; Tl$^+$	0.3363	Tl = Tl$^+$ + e
Pb, PbBr$_2$(s); Br$^-$	0.280	$\frac{1}{2}$Pb + Br$^-$ = $\frac{1}{2}$PbBr$_2$ + e
Co; Co^{++}	0.277	$\frac{1}{2}$Co = $\frac{1}{2}$Co^{++} + e
Ni; Ni^{++}	0.250	$\frac{1}{2}$Ni = $\frac{1}{2}$Ni^{++} + e
Ag, AgI(s); I$^-$	0.151	Ag + I$^-$ = AgI + e
Sn; Sn^{++}	0.140	$\frac{1}{2}$Sn = $\frac{1}{2}$Sn^{++} + e
Pb; Pb^{++}	0.126	$\frac{1}{2}$Pb = $\frac{1}{2}$Pb^{++} + e
Pt, D$_2$; D$^+$	0.0034	$\frac{1}{2}$D$_2$ = D$^+$ + e
Pt, H$_2$; H$^+$	0.0000	$\frac{1}{2}$H$_2$ = H$^+$ + e
Pt; Ti^{+++}, Ti^{++++}	−0.04	Ti^{+++} = Ti^{++++} + e
Ag, AgBr(s); Br$^-$	−0.095	Ag + Br$^-$ = AgBr + e
Pt; Sn^{++}, Sn^{++++}	−0.15	$\frac{1}{2}$Sn^{++} = $\frac{1}{2}$Sn^{++++} + e
Pt; Cu$^+$, Cu^{++}	−0.153	Cu$^+$ = Cu^{++} + e
Ag, AgCl(s); Cl$^-$	−0.2224	Ag + Cl$^-$ = AgCl + e
Normal calomel electrode [2]	−0.2802	Hg + Cl$^-$ = $\frac{1}{2}$Hg$_2$Cl$_2$ + e
Cu; Cu^{++}	−0.337	$\frac{1}{2}$Cu = $\frac{1}{2}$Cu^{++} + e
Pt, I$_2$(s); I$^-$	−0.5355	I$^-$ = $\frac{1}{2}$I$_2$ + e
Pt; quinhydrone(s), H$^+$	−0.6996	$\frac{1}{2}$C$_6$H$_6$O$_2$ = $\frac{1}{2}$C$_6$H$_4$O$_2$ + H$^+$ + e
Pt; Fe^{++}, Fe^{+++}	−0.771	Fe^{++} = Fe^{+++} + e
Hg; Hg$_2$$^{++}$	−0.789	Hg = $\frac{1}{2}$Hg$_2$$^{++}$ + e
Ag; Ag$^+$	−0.7991	Ag = Ag$^+$ + e
Pt; Hg$_2$$^{++}$, Hg^{++}	−0.920	$\frac{1}{2}$Hg$_2$$^{++}$ = Hg^{++} + e
Pt, Br$_2$(l); Br$^-$	−1.0652	Br$^-$ = $\frac{1}{2}$Br$_2$(l) + e
Pt; Tl$^+$, Tl^{+++}	−1.250	$\frac{1}{2}$Tl$^+$ = $\frac{1}{2}$Tl^{+++} + e
Pt, Cl$_2$(g); Cl$^-$	−1.3595	Cl$^-$ = $\frac{1}{2}$Cl$_2$(g) + e
Pb, PbO$_2$; Pb^{++}	−1.455	$\frac{1}{2}$Pb^{++} + H$_2$O = $\frac{1}{2}$PbO$_2$ + 2H$^+$ + e
Pt; Ce^{+++}, Ce^{++++}	−1.61	Ce^{+++} = Ce^{++++} + e
Pt; Co^{++}, Co^{+++}	−1.82	Co^{++} = Co^{+++} + e

[1] These oxidation potentials have been corrected to agree with those given by Latimer in *The Oxidation States of the Elements and Their Potentials in Aqueous Solutions*, Prentice-Hall, New York, 1952.

[2] Hg; Hg$_2$Cl$_2$(s), KCl (1 molar).

The relative oxidation potential of the electrode is a quantitative measure of the tendency to oxidize through the loss of electrons. We do not know what the absolute potentials are, and so we must take some arbitrary standard and measure the relative oxidation potential with respect to this standard. The *standard hydrogen electrode* with pure hydrogen at 1 atm pressure, surrounded by hydrogen ions at unit activity, is taken as the standard and *assigned a potential of 0.0000 volt.* The corresponding electrode reaction is $\frac{1}{2}H_2 = H^+ + e$. Electrodes that lose electrons more easily than this hydrogen electrode are given positive ($+$) oxidation potentials as shown in the table of oxidation potentials (Table I), and those that lose electrons with greater difficulty are given negative ($-$) potentials.

The oxidation potential depends not only on the chemical change at the electrode but also on the concentration of the surrounding ions and on the temperature. In Table I all the oxidation potentials refer to conditions where the temperature is $25°$ and the activity of the ions is unity. The electrodes are solids, liquids, or gases at 1 atm pressure. To emphasize the fact that the ions are at unit activity (designated as $a = 1$) the corresponding relative oxidation potentials are given the symbol $E°$. A solution of unit activity has an actual concentration somewhat different from 1 mole per liter. The experimental methods by which these activities are determined will be described in a later section on page 444.

Qualitatively it may be stated that *the reduced form of any element or ion at unit activity will reduce the oxidized form of any element or ion at unit activity which lies below it* in the table of $E°$ values.

The lower the position of an electrode in this table, the lower is its tendency to release electrons.

The magnitude of the oxidation potential is a measure of the ease with which the element or ion will lose its electrons; thus, in Table I, since $E°$ for Zn; Zn^{++} is 0.763, and $E°$ for Pt; Fe^{++}, Fe^{+++} is -0.771, the reduced form of the Zn; Zn^{++} pair, which is zinc, will reduce the oxidized form of the Fe^{++}, Fe^{+++} ion pair, which is ferric ion, and produce ferrous ion. The zinc loses its electrons more easily than does ferrous ion, and so the ferric ions acquire electrons from the zinc. The zinc is oxidized to zinc ions, and the ferric ions are reduced to ferrous ions. The reaction is

$$\tfrac{1}{2}Zn + Fe^{+++} = \tfrac{1}{2}Zn^{++} + Fe^{++}$$

The tables of oxidation potentials are useful not only for qualitative predictions but also for quantitative calculations of the equilibrium in the cell reaction. To carry out these calculations without ambiguity, further conventions are necessary.

Conventions for Half-Cell Potentials and Electrode Reactions.
Every electrochemical cell can be split up into two electrodes, an anode
at which oxidation occurs and a cathode at which reduction occurs.
Likewise, every chemical reaction occurring in an electrochemical cell
can be split up into two reactions—an oxidation reaction which liberates
electrons, e, and a reduction reaction which consumes electrons. Thus
the reaction

$$Zn + Cu^{++} = Zn^{++} + Cu$$

may be divided into

$$Zn = Zn^{++} + 2e \quad \text{(oxidation at the anode)}$$

and

$$Cu^{++} + 2e = Cu \quad \text{(reduction at the cathode)}$$

The definitions of anode and cathode used here apply equally well to
electrolytic cells, described in the preceding chapter, where current is
supplied from an outside source and electrons, withdrawn from the anode, are fed into the cathode. Thus in the galvanic cell the reaction
$Zn = Zn^{++} + 2e$ is oxidation which occurs at the anode; and in an
electrolytic cell which deposits zinc the reaction $Zn^{++} + 2e = Zn$ is
reduction, and it occurs at the cathode.

The zinc-copper cell with ions at unit activity is a typical electrochemical cell which is written

$$Zn; Zn^{++}(a = 1) \, \| \, Cu^{++}(a = 1); Cu$$

$$E^{\circ}_{Zn;Zn^{++}} \qquad\qquad E^{\circ}_{Cu^{++};Cu}$$

Since the electrolyte is placed between the two electrodes it is clear
that in writing down the cell the electrode at the left is always
written $E^{\circ}_{electrode;electrolyte}$ and the electrode at the right is written
$E^{\circ}_{electrolyte;electrode}$.

*The electrode at the left has the same sign as that given in the table of oxi-
dation potentials* (Table I), but the electrode at the right is opposite in
sign to that of the oxidation potential, and in agreement with the sign
of the reduction potential given in Table II. Thus at the left electrode
in the example given $E^{\circ}_{Zn;Zn^{++}} = 0.763$, but, if the zinc electrode had
been placed at the right, it would be represented in the order electrolyte-
electrode and $E^{\circ}_{Zn^{++};Zn} = -0.763$. It is opposite in sign to the oxidation
potential and is called a reduction potential.

The reduction potentials given in Table II have the same numerical
values as the oxidation potentials but the opposite sign, and the order
in which the electrode-electrolyte is given and the direction of the electrode reaction are reversed. Thus lithium as an anode (oxidizing elec-

Table II. Reduction Potentials [1]

Electrode (Cathode)	$E^\circ_{\text{electrolyte;electrode}}$ (Standard hydrogen electrode = 0)	Electrode Reaction (Cathode Reaction)
Li^+; Li	−3.045	$Li^+ + e = Li$
K^+; K	−2.925	$K^+ + e = K$
Na^+; Na	−2.714	$Na^+ + e = Na$
Zn^{++}; Zn	−0.763	$\frac{1}{2}Zn^{++} + e = \frac{1}{2}Zn$
Fe^{++}; Fe	−0.440	$\frac{1}{2}Fe^{++} + e = \frac{1}{2}Fe$
Cr^{+++}, Cr^{++}; Pt	−0.41	$Cr^{+++} + e = Cr^{++}$
Cd^{++}; Cd	−0.403	$\frac{1}{2}Cd^{++} + e = \frac{1}{2}Cd$
Tl^+; Tl	−0.3363	$Tl^+ + e = Tl$
Br^-; $PbBr_2(s)$, Pb	−0.280	$\frac{1}{2}PbBr_2 + e = \frac{1}{2}Pb + Br^-$
Co^{++}; Co	−0.277	$\frac{1}{2}Co^{++} + e = \frac{1}{2}Co$
Ni^{++}; Ni	−0.250	$\frac{1}{2}Ni^{++} + e = \frac{1}{2}Ni$
I^-; $AgI(s)$, Ag	−0.151	$AgI + e = Ag + I^-$
Sn^{++}; Sn	−0.140	$\frac{1}{2}Sn^{++} + e = \frac{1}{2}Sn$
Pb^{++}; Pb	−0.126	$\frac{1}{2}Pb^{++} + e = \frac{1}{2}Pb$
D^+; D_2, Pt	−0.0034	$D^+ + e = \frac{1}{2}D_2$
H^+; H_2, Pt	0.0000	$H^+ + e = \frac{1}{2}H_2$
Ti^{++++}, Ti^{+++}; Pt	0.04	$Ti^{++++} + e = Ti^{+++}$
Br^-; $AgBr(s)$, Ag	0.095	$AgBr + e = Ag + Br^-$
Sn^{++++}, Sn^{++}; Pt	0.15	$\frac{1}{2}Sn^{++++} + e = \frac{1}{2}Sn^{++}$
Cu^{++}, Cu^+; Pt	0.153	$Cu^{++} + e = Cu^+$
Cl^-; $AgCl(s)$, Ag	0.2224	$AgCl + e = Ag + Cl^-$
Normal calomel electrode	0.2802	$\frac{1}{2}Hg_2Cl_2 + e = Hg + Cl^-$
Cu^{++}; Cu	0.337	$\frac{1}{2}Cu^{++} + e = \frac{1}{2}Cu$
I^-; $I_2(s)$, Pt	0.5355	$\frac{1}{2}I_2 + e = I^-$
H^+, quinhydrone(s); Pt	0.6996	$\frac{1}{2}C_6H_4O_2 + H^+ + e = \frac{1}{2}C_6H_6O_2$
Fe^{+++}, Fe^{++}; Pt	0.771	$Fe^{+++} + e = Fe^{++}$
Hg_2^{++}; Hg	0.789	$\frac{1}{2}Hg_2^{++} + e = Hg$
Ag^+; Ag	0.7991	$Ag^+ + e = Ag$
Hg^{++}, Hg_2^{++}; Pt	0.920	$Hg^{++} + e = \frac{1}{2}Hg_2^{++}$
Br^-; $Br_2(l)$, Pt	1.0652	$\frac{1}{2}Br_2(l) + e = Br^-$
Tl^{+++}, Tl^+; Pt	1.250	$\frac{1}{2}Tl^{+++} + e = \frac{1}{2}Tl^+$
Cl^-; $Cl_2(g)$, Pt	1.3595	$\frac{1}{2}Cl_2(g) + e = Cl^-$
Pb^{++}; PbO_2, Pb	1.455	$\frac{1}{2}PbO_2 + 2H^+ + e = \frac{1}{2}Pb^{++} + H_2O$
Ce^{++++}, Ce^{+++}; Pt	1.61	$Ce^{++++} + e = Ce^{+++}$
Co^{+++}, Co^{++}; Pt	1.82	$Co^{+++} + e = Co^{++}$

[1] See footnotes of Table I.

trode) has a potential $E^\circ_{\text{Li;Li}^+} = 3.045$ volts and the electrode reaction is written as oxidation, namely, $Li = Li^+ + e$. Lithium as a cathode has $E^\circ_{\text{Li}^+;\text{Li}} = -3.045$ volts and the electrode reaction is written as a reduction, namely, $Li^+ + e = Li$.

Oxidation and reduction potentials are equally useful, and they are not inconsistent. The International Union of Pure and Applied Chemistry meeting in Stockholm in July 1953 recommended that the term electrode potential be reserved for reduction potentials as given in Table II. In this book both oxidation and reduction potentials are given.

Conventions identifying a given cell with a cell reaction must be capable of handling both positive and negative ions in both oxidation and reduction reactions. The following rules apply:

1. *The voltage of the cell is equal to the algebraic sum of the potentials of the two electrodes.*

2. *The reaction taking place at the left electrode is arbitrarily written as if it were an oxidation reaction.*

3. *The cell reaction is the algebraic sum of the reactions taking place at the two electrodes.*

The following examples serve to illustrate these rules and the way in which a cell reaction is associated with a given cell.

$$A; A^+ \parallel B^+; B \qquad\qquad B; B^+ \parallel A^+; A$$

$$E = E_{A;A^+} + E_{B^+;B} \qquad\qquad E = E_{B;B^+} + E_{A^+;A}$$

Oxidation	$A = A^+ + e$		Oxidation	$B = B^+ + e$
Reduction	$B^+ + e = B$		Reduction	$A^+ + e = A$

Cell reaction $\quad A + B^+ = A^+ + B \qquad$ Cell reaction $\quad B + A^+ = B^+ + A$

$$A; A^+ \parallel C^-; C \qquad\qquad C; C^- \parallel D^{+++}, D^{++}; Pt$$

$$E = E_{A;A^+} + E_{C^-;C} \qquad\qquad E = E_{C;C^-} + E_{D^{+++},D^{++};Pt}$$

Oxidation	$A = A^+ + e$		Oxidation	$C^- = C + e$
Reduction	$C + e = C^-$		Reduction	$D^{+++} + e = D^{++}$

Cell reaction $\quad A + C = A^+ + C^- \qquad$ Cell reaction $\quad C^- + D^{+++} = C + D^{++}$

In setting up a cell which corresponds to a given reaction the following rule is used.

4. *The oxidation part of a cell reaction as written is arbitrarily assigned to the left electrode.*

The reaction $A + B^+ = A^+ + B$ can be split up into:

Oxidation	$A = A^+ + e$
Reduction	$B^+ + e = B$

The reaction $B + A^+ = B^+ + A$ can be split up into:

Oxidation	$B = B^+ + e$
Reduction	$A^+ + e = A$

Then placing the oxidation at the left the corresponding cell is

$$A; A^+ \parallel B^+; B$$

Then placing the oxidation at the left the corresponding cell is

$$B; B^+ \parallel A^+; A$$

The reaction $A + C = A^+ + C^-$ can be split up into:

The reaction $C^- + D^{+++} = C + D^{++}$ can be split up into:

Oxidation $A = A^+ + e$
Reduction $C + e = C^-$

Oxidation $C^- = C + e$
Reduction $D^{+++} + e = D^{++}$

Then placing the oxidation at the left the corresponding cell is

Then placing the oxidation at the left the corresponding cell is

$$A; A^+ \parallel C^-; C$$

$$C; C^- \parallel D^{+++}, D^{++}; \text{Pt}$$

It is evident that both the cell and the cell reaction can be written in two different ways, but there is a consistent relation between the two. In order to determine whether the cell reaction as written is spontaneous and which way the cell operates, it is necessary to find the values of the oxidation potentials in tables or to measure in the laboratory the voltage of the cell or the equilibrium of the chemical reaction. The following rule may then be applied.

5. *If the voltage of the cell* (that is, the algebraic sum of the potentials of the two electrodes) *has a positive value the cell reaction is spontaneous.* Conversely, if a chemical reaction is spontaneous the voltage of the corresponding cell has a positive value. These relations follow from equation 1, which states that $\Delta F = -nFE$, and from the fact that if ΔF has a negative value the reaction is spontaneous. A cell is said to have a positive voltage when the left electrode is the negative electrode (i.e., the electrons flow spontaneously from left to right outside the cell). Such an electrode is the one which is connected to the negative terminal of the potentiometer.

For example, in the cell

$$\text{Zn}; \text{Zn}^{++}(a = 1) \parallel \text{Cu}^{++}(a = 1); \text{Cu}$$

at 25° the cell voltage is

$$E^\circ = E^\circ_{\text{Zn};\text{Zn}^{++}} + E^\circ_{\text{Cu}^{++};\text{Cu}} = 0.763 + 0.337 = 1.100 \text{ volts}$$

and ΔF° for the cell reaction has a negative value because $\Delta F^\circ = -nFE^\circ = -nF(1.100) = -50,800$ cal. The cell reaction $\text{Zn} + \text{Cu}^{++} = \text{Zn}^{++} + \text{Cu}$ must therefore be spontaneous. Most students of chemistry would know that zinc will precipitate copper from solution spontaneously, but in other instances the direction of the spontaneous reaction is not known. It can be determined, however, from a table of electrode potentials.

If the cell is written

$$\text{Cu}; \text{Cu}^{++}(a = 1) \parallel \text{Zn}^{++}(a = 1); \text{Zn}$$

$$E° = E°_{\text{Cu};\text{Cu}^{++}} + E°_{\text{Zn}^{++};\text{Zn}} = -0.337 + (-0.763) = -1.100 \text{ volts}$$

and the cell reaction

$$\text{Cu} = \text{Cu}^{++} + 2e$$
$$\text{Zn}^{++} + 2e = \text{Zn}$$
$$\overline{}$$
$$\text{Cu} + \text{Zn}^{++} = \text{Cu}^{++} + \text{Zn}$$

is not spontaneous because $\Delta F° = -nFE = +50,800$ cal.

Exercise I. It is known that zinc reacts spontaneously with silver ions to produce metallic silver. Show, with the help of the rules, that the zinc is the anode which provides electrons for the reaction.

Several examples will be given now to illustrate the applications of these conventions.

Example 2. What is the cell reaction and what is the voltage at 25° of the cell

$$\text{Pb}; \text{Pb}^{++}(a = 1) \parallel \text{Ag}^{+}(a = 1); \text{Ag}$$

The cell reaction is

Left, oxidation $\frac{1}{2}\text{Pb}(s) = \frac{1}{2}\text{Pb}^{++}(a = 1) + e$ $E°_{\text{Pb};\text{Pb}^{++}} = 0.126$
Right, reduction $\text{Ag}^{+}(a = 1) + e = \text{Ag}(s)$ $E°_{\text{Ag}^{+};\text{Ag}} = 0.799$

Cell reaction $\frac{1}{2}\text{Pb}(s) + \text{Ag}^{+}(a = 1)$
                  $= \frac{1}{2}\text{Pb}^{++}(a = 1) + \text{Ag}(s)$ $E° = 0.925$

Is the cell reaction spontaneous; that is, will lead precipitate silver from a solution in which the activity of the silver ions is unity?

$$\Delta F° = -nFE° = -(1)(96,500)(0.925)/4.184 = -21,330 \text{ cal}$$

The negative value of $\Delta F°$ and the corresponding positive value of $E°$ indicates that the reaction is spontaneous.

Multiples of a cell reaction may be taken without changing the potential, but the free energy is changed owing to the factor n in the equation $\Delta F° = -nFE°$.

Thus, if the reaction given in example 2 is written

$$\text{Pb}(s) + 2\text{Ag}^{+}(a = 1) = 2\text{Ag}(s) + \text{Pb}^{++}(a = 1)$$

$E° = 0.925$ but

$$\Delta F° = -nFE° = -\frac{(2)(96,500)(0.925)}{4.184} = -42,660 \text{ cal}$$

since twice as many atoms are involved and $n = 2$ for the reaction as written.

The sign of an oxidation potential depends upon the relation of the electrode to the standard hydrogen electrode. Whether a given electrode in a cell will give off electrons or take them up depends on the relative oxidation potential of the other electrode in the cell. For example, when a cadmium electrode is connected to a copper electrode it releases electrons and acts as the anode, but when the same cadmium electrode is connected to a zinc electrode it acts as the cathode and takes up electrons from the zinc through the connecting wire.

Example 3. Write the cell reaction and calculate $E°$ at 25° for the cell

$$\text{Cd; Cd}^{++}(a = 1) \parallel \text{Cu}^{++}(a = 1); \text{Cu}$$

Oxidation at left $\quad \frac{1}{2}\text{Cd}(s) = \frac{1}{2}\text{Cd}^{++}(a = 1) + e \quad E°_{\text{Cd;Cd}^{++}} = 0.403$
Reduction at right $\quad \frac{1}{2}\text{Cu}^{++}(a = 1) + e = \frac{1}{2}\text{Cu}(s) \quad E°_{\text{Cu}^{++};\text{Cu}} = 0.337$

$$\begin{aligned} \frac{1}{2}\text{Cd}(s) + \frac{1}{2}\text{Cu}^{++}(a = 1) \\ = \frac{1}{2}\text{Cd}^{++}(a = 1) + \frac{1}{2}\text{Cu}(s) \qquad E° = 0.740 \end{aligned}$$

Since $E°$ is positive the reaction is spontaneous as written, and cadmium loses electrons and copper ions gain them.

Example 4. What is the cell reaction and the voltage of the cell

$$\text{Zn; Zn}^{++}(a = 1) \parallel \text{Cd}^{++}(a = 1); \text{Cd}$$

Oxidation at left $\quad \frac{1}{2}\text{Zn}(s) = \frac{1}{2}\text{Zn}^{++}(a = 1) + e \quad E°_{\text{Zn,Zn}^{++}} = \quad 0.763$
Reduction at right $\quad \frac{1}{2}\text{Cd}^{++}(a = 1) + e = \frac{1}{2}\text{Cd}(s) \quad E°_{\text{Cd}^{++},\text{Cd}} = -0.403$

$$\begin{aligned} \frac{1}{2}\text{Zn}(s) + \frac{1}{2}\text{Cd}^{++}(a = 1) \\ = \frac{1}{2}\text{Cd}(s) + \frac{1}{2}\text{Zn}^{++}(a = 1) \qquad E° = \quad 0.360 \end{aligned}$$

Since $E°$ is positive the reaction is spontaneous as written, and zinc loses electrons and cadmium ions gain them.

Example 5. Write the cell which corresponds to the reaction

$$\frac{1}{2}\text{Cu}(s) + \frac{1}{2}\text{Cl}_2(g, \text{ 1 atm}) = \frac{1}{2}\text{Cu}^{++}(a = 1) + \text{Cl}^-(a = 1)$$

Oxidation: $\frac{1}{2}\text{Cu}(s) = \frac{1}{2}\text{Cu}^{++} + e$
Reduction: $\frac{1}{2}\text{Cl}_2(g, \text{ 1 atm}) + e = \text{Cl}^-$

If the oxidation reaction is placed at the left and the reduction reaction at the right, the cell is written

$$\text{Cu; Cu}^{++}(a = 1) \parallel \text{Cl}^-(a = 1); \text{Cl}_2(g, \text{ 1 atm}), \text{Pt}$$

Calculate the voltage and the change in free energy of the reaction at 25°.

$$E° = E°_{\text{Cu,Cu}^{++}} + E°_{\text{Cl}^-;\text{Cl}_2,\text{Pt}} = -0.337 + (1.360) = 1.023$$

$$\Delta F° = -nFE° = -\frac{(96,500)(1.023)}{(4.1840)} = -23,590 \text{ cal}$$

Copper and chlorine will react spontaneously to give cupric ions and chloride ions.

Example 6. Will ferrous ion reduce iodine to iodide ion at 25° according to the reaction

$$Fe^{++}(a = 1) + \tfrac{1}{2}I_2(s) = Fe^{+++}(a = 1) + I^-(a = 1)$$

$$Pt; Fe^{++}(a = 1), Fe^{+++}(a = 1) \,\|\, I^-(a = 1); I_2(s), Pt$$

$$\boldsymbol{E}^\circ = \boldsymbol{E}^\circ{}_{Pt;Fe^{++},Fe^{+++}} + \boldsymbol{E}^\circ{}_{I^-;I_2,Pt} = -0.771 + (0.535) = -0.236$$

$$\Delta F^\circ = -n\boldsymbol{F}\boldsymbol{E}^\circ = -\frac{(96,500)(-0.236)}{(4.1840)} = 5445 \text{ cal}$$

The positive value of ΔF° (or negative value of $\boldsymbol{E}^\circ$) indicates that the reaction will not go spontaneously; that is, solid iodine will not react with ferrous ion at unit activity to produce ferric ion at unit activity and iodide ion at unit activity.

However, if the reaction is written in the opposite direction, $Fe^{+++} + I^- = Fe^{++} + \tfrac{1}{2}I_2(s)$, and the electrode at which the oxidation reaction $I^- = \tfrac{1}{2}I_2 + e$ occurs is placed at the left, the cell is written

$$Pt, I_2(s); I^-(a = 1) \,\|\, Fe^{++}(a = 1), Fe^{+++}(a = 1); Pt$$

Then,

$$\boldsymbol{E}^\circ = \boldsymbol{E}^\circ{}_{Pt,I_2;I^-} + \boldsymbol{E}^\circ{}_{Fe^{+++},Fe^{++};Pt} = -0.535 + (0.771) = 0.236$$

$$\Delta F^\circ = -n\boldsymbol{F}\boldsymbol{E}^\circ = -\frac{(96,500)(0.236)}{(4.1840)} = -5445 \text{ cal}$$

The negative value of ΔF° signifies that the reaction as written is spontaneous; that is, iodide ion will reduce ferric ion to ferrous ion. This reaction illustrates the fact that the atom or ion in the lowest state of oxidation (with the most electrons) will reduce the oxidized form of any atom or ion that has a position lower in the table of oxidation potentials (all ions being at unit activity).

Exercise II. Show that in measuring the voltage of the cell

$$Zn; Zn^{++}(a = 1) \,\|\, H^+(a = 1); H_2(1 \text{ atm}), Pt$$

the zinc electrode is connected to the negative terminal of the potentiometer. Even if the cell is represented by

$$Pt, H_2(1 \text{ atm}); H^+(a = 1) \,\|\, Zn^{++}(a = 1); Zn$$

the zinc electrode would still have to be connected to the negative terminal in order to measure the voltage. Since the reduction potential (electrode potential) of zinc is negative with respect to the hydrogen electrode while the oxidation potential of zinc is positive, it is seen that the advantage of reduction potentials is that the electrode with the more negative reduction potential is connected to the negative terminal of the potentiometer.

Chemical Equilibria and Cell Voltage. According to equation 1, $\Delta F = -n\boldsymbol{F}\boldsymbol{E}$, and, for the special case where the reactants and products are at unit activity,

$$\Delta F^\circ = -n\boldsymbol{F}\boldsymbol{E}^\circ \tag{2}$$

Furthermore, from page 251,

$$\Delta F^\circ = -RT \ln K \qquad (3)$$

It is possible then to calculate the equilibrium constant for any electrochemical reaction by determining from tables or from direct experiment the value of E° for the corresponding electrochemical cell.

Example 7. Calculate from electromotive-force data the equilibrium constant for the reaction between tin and lead and their ions, thus:

$$Sn + Pb^{++} = Pb + Sn^{++}$$

Splitting up the reaction into the two electrode reactions,

$$Sn = Sn^{++} + 2e \qquad \text{and} \qquad Pb^{++} + 2e = Pb$$

and putting the oxidation reaction at the left in the corresponding cell at 25°, we have

$$Sn; Sn^{++}(a = 1) \parallel Pb^{++}(a = 1); Pb$$

$$E^\circ = E^\circ_{Sn;Sn^{++}} + E^\circ_{Pb^{++};Pb} = 0.140 + (-0.126) = 0.014 \text{ volt}$$

$$\Delta F^\circ = -nFE^\circ = -(2)(96,500)(0.014)/(4.1840) = -643 \text{ cal}$$

$$\Delta F^\circ = -RT \ln K$$

$$-643 = -(1.987)(298)(2.3) \log K$$

$$K = a_{Sn^{++}}/a_{Pb^{++}} = 2.97$$

In other words, when tin is added to a solution of lead salt, a state of equilibrium is reached in which the activity of the tin ions is 2.97 times as great as that of lead ions.

In checking this equilibrium Noyes and Toabe added metallic tin to a solution of lead perchlorate at 25° and found at equilibrium 0.0716 mole of tin perchlorate and 0.0242 mole of lead perchlorate per liter. If we assume that the concentrations of tin perchlorate and lead perchlorate may be used in place of the activities,*

$$K = a_{Sn^{++}}/a_{Pb^{++}} = 0.0716/0.0242 = 2.96$$

In order to approach the equilibrium from both sides they also added lead to a solution of tin perchlorate and found at equilibrium 0.0704 mole of tin perchlorate and 0.0233 mole of lead perchlorate per liter.

$$K = a_{Sn^{++}}/a_{Pb^{++}} = 0.0704/0.0233 = 3.02$$

Carrying out a similar calculation for the addition of zinc to copper ions, we find that $E^\circ = 1.100$, $\Delta F^\circ = -50,800$ by Example 1, and $K = a_{Zn^{++}}/a_{Cu^{++}} = 10^{37}$. In other words, the removal of copper ions by zinc is practically complete.

* This assumption is not safe except in very dilute solutions. The error involved is reduced in cases of this kind where all the ions have the same valence and the correction factors tend to cancel out.

Example 8. To what extent will mercuric ion be reduced by the addition of ferrous ion at 25°? The cell is

$$\text{Pt; } Fe^{++}(a = 1), Fe^{+++}(a = 1) \parallel Hg^{++}(a = 1), Hg_2^{++}(a = 1); \text{Pt}$$

$$E° = E°_{\text{Pt;}Fe^{++},Fe^{+++}} + E°_{Hg^{++},Hg_2^{++};\text{Pt}}$$

$$= -0.771 + 0.920 = 0.149$$

The cell reaction is

$$Fe^{++} + Hg^{++} = Fe^{+++} + \tfrac{1}{2}Hg_2^{++}$$

$$\Delta F° = -nFE° = -(1)(96,500)(0.149)/(4.184)$$

$$= -3440 \text{ cal}$$

$$\Delta F° = -RT \ln K$$

$$-3440 = -(1.987)(298.1)(2.3) \log K$$

$$K = \frac{a_{Fe^{+++}} \times a_{Hg_2^{++}}^{\frac{1}{2}}}{a_{Fe^{++}} \times a_{Hg^{++}}} = \text{antilog } 2.52 = 330$$

This calculation shows that the ferrous ion reduces the mercuric ion to such an extent that, at equilibrium, the activity of the ferric ion times the square root of the activity of the mercurous ion (Hg_2^{++}) is 330 times as great as the product of the activities of the ferrous and mercuric ions.

These examples have served to illustrate the use of equation 2 for reactions in which the reactants and products are at unit activity. However, most applications are concerned with reactions in which the reactants and products are not at unit activity. As shown on page 254 the general equation for the change in free energy in a reaction

$$aA + bB = gG + hH$$

is

$$\Delta F = -RT \ln \frac{a_G{}^g a_H{}^h}{a_A{}^a a_B{}^b} + RT \ln \frac{a'_G{}^g a'_H{}^h}{a'_A{}^a a'_B{}^b}$$

$$= -RT \ln K + RT \ln Q \qquad (4)$$

where K represents the equilibrium constant involving the activities in a state of equilibrium, and Q represents the activity quotient, that is, the ratio of the activities of the products to the activities of the reactants at any specified activities a' each raised to the appropriate power.

Remembering that according to equation 1

$$\Delta F = -nFE$$

and making the substitution into equation 4, we have

$$E = (RT/nF) \ln K - (RT/nF) \ln Q \qquad (5)$$

If the reactants and products are at unit activities $E = E°$ and $\ln Q = 0$ so that

$$E° = (RT/nF) \ln K \qquad (6)$$

Substituting equation 6 into equation 5,

$$E = E° - (RT/nF) \ln Q \qquad (7)$$

When $T = 298.1$

$$E = E° - \frac{(8.314)(298.1)(2.303)}{n(96,500)} \log Q = E° - \frac{0.0591}{n} \log Q \qquad (8)$$

The more general equation 8 which shows the relation among E, $E°$, and Q will now be applied. It can be used to calculate the voltage of a cell when the ions are not at unit activity and to calculate the activity of ions from a measurement of the electromotive force of the cell.

Example 9. Calculate the potential of the following cell at 25°.

$$\text{Sn; } Sn^{++}(a = 0.6) \parallel Pb^{++}(a = 0.3); \text{ Pb}$$

This cell is similar to that shown in Example 7. The cell reaction is

$$Sn + Pb^{++} = Sn^{++} + Pb$$

$$E = E° - (RT/nF) \ln Q = E° - (RT/nF) \ln (a_{Sn^{++}}/a_{Pb^{++}})$$

$$= 0.0140 - (0.0591/2) \log (0.6/0.3)$$

$$= 0.0140 - 0.0089 = 0.0051 \text{ volt}$$

$$\Delta F = -nFE = -\frac{(2)(96,500)(0.0051)}{(4.1840)} = -235 \text{ cal}$$

The free-energy decrease ΔF for this reaction is less than $\Delta F°$ for the reaction where both reactants and products are at unit activity (Example 7), because here the specified activity of the products is greater than the specified activity of the reactants. The activities 0.3 and 0.6 are arbitrarily assigned and are not to be confused with the equilibrium concentrations.

The validity of equation 8 may be illustrated by determining the potential of the ferric–ferrous electrode using the cell

$$\text{Pt, } H_2 \text{ (1 atm); } H^+ (a = 1) \parallel Fe^{++}(a = x), Fe^{+++}(a = y); \text{ Pt}$$

The cell reaction is

$$\tfrac{1}{2}H_2 + Fe^{+++} = Fe^{++} + H^+$$

Applying equation 8

$$E = E° - \frac{RT}{nF} \ln \frac{a_{H^+} a_{Fe^{++}}}{a_{H_2}^{\frac{1}{2}} a_{Fe^{+++}}}$$

but, since $a_{H^+} = 1$ and $a_{H_2} = 1$,

$$E = E^\circ - \frac{RT}{nF} \ln \frac{a_{Fe^{++}}}{a_{Fe^{+++}}} \tag{9}$$

E° is the electromotive force of an inert electrode surrounded by equal activities of ferrous and ferric ions when measured against the standard hydrogen electrode, for, when $a_{Fe^{++}}$ and $a_{Fe^{+++}}$ are equal, the last term becomes zero.

The value of E° calculated from the electromotive force data of Peters,[*] shown in Table III, is reasonably constant even though ratios

Table III. Change of Voltage with Change in Ratio of Oxidizing to Reducing Ions

$c_{Fe^{+++}}/c_{Fe^{++}}$	0.5/99.5	2/98	10/90	30/70	50/50	80/20
$-E$	0.580	0.615	0.655	0.690	0.713	0.747
$-E^\circ$	0.712	0.712	0.710	0.711	0.713	0.712

of concentrations are used rather than ratios of activities.

The absolute values of E° are only approximate, because no attempt was made to obtain activities. The solutions were made tenth-normal with respect to hydrochloric acid to prevent hydrolysis.

Popoff and Kunz have investigated this system more fully, extrapolating to zero concentration of iron ions and zero concentration of hydrochloric acid. They obtained a series of values of E° in progressively more dilute solutions of ferrous and ferric chloride and extrapolated to infinite dilution of iron chlorides. This extrapolated value of E° in 0.1 N hydrochloric acid is -0.731, an accurate value obtained with activities instead of concentrations. There is a complication, however, in that the hydrochloric acid changes the character of the solution and affects the value of E°. A value of -0.747 for E° in pure water was obtained by determining the extrapolated value of E° in solutions of different normality with respect to hydrochloric acid and extrapolating these values to zero concentration of hydrochloric acid. The value is somewhat in doubt on account of hydrolysis. Schumb and Sweetzer [†] obtained a value of -0.783 by measuring the equilibrium between silver and ferric perchlorate. The value selected by Latimer is -0.771.

Concentration Cells. When two electrodes of the same material are immersed in solutions of their ions at the same concentration, there will be no difference of potential. If, however, the two solutions are of

[*] Peters, *Z. physik. Chem.*, *26*, 193 (1898).
[†] Schumb and Sweetzer, *J. Am. Chem. Soc.*, *57*, 871 (1935).

different concentrations, the cell will exhibit a definite electromotive force which depends on the ratio of the activities of the ions in the two solutions. Such a cell is represented by

$$M; \; M^+(a_1) \; \| \; M^+(a_2); \; M$$

Writing the cell reaction in such a way that oxidation occurs at the left and reduction at the right, we have

$$M = M^+(a_1) + e$$

$$\underline{M^+(a_2) + e = M}$$

$$M^+(a_2) = M^+(a_1) \tag{10}$$

The mathematical formulation of this cell is particularly simple because the reactants and the products are the same. Referring to the fundamental formula 8, placing the products in the numerator as usual, and considering only the activities of the M^+ ion, we find

$$E = E^\circ - (RT/nF) \ln (a_1/a_2)$$

But $E^\circ = (RT/nF) \ln K$, and for this case $K = 1$ because equilibrium is established only when $a_1 = a_2$. Then $E^\circ = 0$, and

$$E = - (RT/nF) \ln (a_1/a_2) \tag{11}$$

If, for example, the concentrations of the univalent metal ions are such that $a_1 = 0.01$ and $a_2 = 0.1$, the electromotive force is given by the relation

$$E = - \frac{(8.314)(298.1)(2.303)}{96,500} \log \frac{0.01}{0.1} = 0.0591 \text{ volt}$$

The positive value of E shows that the reaction is spontaneous; that is, there is a tendency for ions at $a_2 = 0.1$ to diffuse into the more dilute solution where $a_1 = 0.01$. The electrode, immersed in the solution of positive ions where $a_2 = 0.1$, is positive with reference to the other metal electrode, because there are more collisions of positive ions per second per square centimeter on the surface of this electrode. Inasmuch as this positive electrode is placed at the right, the electrode at the left is negative with respect to it, and the electromotive force of the cell has a positive value in agreement with convention and in agreement with the calculations with equation 11.

Example 10. If the more concentrated solution of activity 0.1 had been placed at the left instead of the right, the negative electrode would have been at the right, and, according to convention, the electromotive force of the galvanic cell would have had a negative value. This convention is in agreement with the calculations just developed.

$$E = - \frac{(8.314)(298.1)(2.303)}{96,500} \log \frac{0.1}{0.01} = -0.0591$$

The cell reaction $M^+ (a_2 = 0.01) = M^+ (a_1 = 0.1)$ is not spontaneous.

In dilute solutions, where the activities are nearly the same as the concentrations, equation 12 may be used as an approximate form of equation 11 for positive ions where c_1 is the concentration at the left electrode and c_2 is the concentration at the right.

$$E = -(RT/nF) \ln (c_1/c_2) \tag{12}$$

If the cell involves negative ions M^-, such as iodide ions, the arrangement is

$$M; M^-(a_1) \,\|\, M^-(a_2); M$$

The cell reaction is

Left electrode $\quad M^-(a_1) = M + e \quad$ (oxidation)
Right electrode $\quad M + e = M^-(a_2) \quad$ (reduction)

$$M^-(a_1) = M^-(a_2)$$

and the formula for the voltage of the concentration cell with negative ions is

$$E = - \frac{RT}{nF} \ln \frac{a_2}{a_1} \cong - \frac{RT}{nF} \ln \frac{c_2}{c_1} \tag{13}$$

In another type of concentration cell the activity of ions in solution is uniform throughout the cell, but the concentration of the material in the two electrodes is different. For example, if two hydrogen electrodes at different pressures of hydrogen are placed in a solution of hydrogen ions, the electrode which has hydrogen at the greater pressure will tend to produce more hydrogen ions and, thus, make the electrode negative with respect to the other. The electromotive force of the cell can be calculated from the partial pressures. Thus:

$$Pt, H_2(p_1); H^+; H_2(p_2), Pt$$

The cell reaction is

$$H_2(p_1) = H_2(p_2)$$

and

$$E = -(RT/nF) \ln (p_{H_2,2}/p_{H_2,1})$$

Example 11. Two hydrogen electrodes are set in a solution of hydrochloric acid at 25°. The pressure of hydrogen over one is 1 atm, and over the other it is 0.5

atm. This reduction in partial pressure of hydrogen is accomplished by mixing the hydrogen with helium or nitrogen or other inert gas. What is the electromotive force of the cell?

If the electrode at 1 atm is placed at the left $p_1 = 1$ and

$$E = -\frac{RT}{nF} \ln \frac{p_2}{p_1} = -\frac{0.0591}{2} \log \frac{0.5}{1} = 0.0089 \text{ volt}$$

Calculations with the Hydrogen Electrode. The determination of hydrogen-ion activity with the hydrogen electrode described on page 418 is merely an application of formula 11 for the electromotive force of a concentration cell, set up in principle as follows:

$$\text{Pt, H}_2(p = 1); \text{H}^+(a) \parallel \text{H}^+(a = 1); \text{H}_2(p = 1), \text{Pt}$$

One of the hydrogen electrodes, each under a hydrogen pressure of 1 atm, is placed in an acid solution in which the activity of H^+ ions is unity, and the other hydrogen electrode is placed in a solution in which it is desired to measure the activity of hydrogen ion. The two solutions are connected by a salt bridge, and the voltage of the cell is measured with a potentiometer.

The cell reaction is

Left electrode	$\frac{1}{2}\text{H}_2 = \text{H}^+(a) + e$	(oxidation)
Right electrode	$e + \text{H}^+(a = 1) = \frac{1}{2}\text{H}_2$	(reduction)

$$\text{H}^+(a = 1) = \text{H}^+(a)$$

and, applying equation 11, we have

$$E = -\frac{RT}{nF} \ln \frac{a_{\text{H}^+}}{1} = -\frac{RT}{nF} \ln a_{\text{H}^+} \qquad (14)$$

In practice it is much easier to use a normal calomel cell in place of a standard hydrogen electrode as the reference electrode. Careful measurements have shown that the normal calomel electrode with a normal KCl bridge is negative with respect to the standard hydrogen electrode by 0.2802 volt at 25°.

The formula for the hydrogen electrode at 1 atm pressure against a normal calomel electrode with a normal KCl bridge at 25° is

$$E - 0.2802 = -0.0591 \log a_{\text{H}^+} \qquad (15)$$

Although the activities of electrolytes can be determined accurately as described later, it is not possible theoretically to determine the activities of single ions accurately on account of the uncertainty in the liquid junction potential, even when rendered small by the introduction of a salt bridge of potassium chloride. However, what is measured is very close to the hydrogen-ion activity, and equation 15 is universally used. It is of great practical value even though there are some theoretical difficulties. In low concentrations of hydrogen ions below about 10^{-4} mole per liter the concentrations become nearly equal to the activities and can be so used.

The fundamental difference between hydrogen-ion activity as registered by a hydrogen electrode, and the number of milliliters of alkali which are needed to neutralize the acid, must be clearly understood. The latter corresponds to total *quantity* of acid, that is, to ionized and un-ionized acid, but the former gives the concentration, or, more accurately, the activity, of hydrogen ions in the solution.

pH. Hydrogen-ion activities are determined down to very low values, and in order to avoid the nuisance of using very small numbers it has been found convenient to adopt an exponential notation. The term *p*H first proposed in 1909 by Sorensen is widely used. It is defined as the negative exponent of 10 which gives the hydrogen-ion activity. Thus,

$$10^{-p\mathrm{H}} = a_{\mathrm{H}^+}$$

or

$$p\mathrm{H} = -\log a_{\mathrm{H}^+} = \log\,(1/a_{\mathrm{H}^+}) \tag{16}$$

Example 12. What is the activity of hydrogen ions in a solution which has a *p*H of 4?

$$a_{\mathrm{H}^+} = 10^{-p\mathrm{H}} = 10^{-4} = 0.0001$$

What is the *p*H of a solution in which the activity of H^+ is 0.0002?

$$p\mathrm{H} = \log\frac{1}{a_{\mathrm{H}^+}} = \log\frac{1}{2 \times 10^{-4}} = \log 5 \times 10^3 = 3.70 \ *$$

Equation 15 can be converted into the working equation 17, in which E is the voltage of a cell in which a hydrogen electrode at 1 atm pressure is placed in a solution, the *p*H of which is to be determined, and connected to a normal calomel electrode through a normal KCl bridge.

$$E - 0.2802 = -0.0591 \log a_{\mathrm{H}^+} = 0.0591\ p\mathrm{H}$$

or

$$p\mathrm{H} = (E - 0.2802)/0.0591 \tag{17}$$

It is shown on page 462 that the product of the activities of the hydrogen and hydroxyl ions at 25° in aqueous solution is always

$$a_{\mathrm{H}^+} \times a_{\mathrm{OH}^-} = 1 \times 10^{-14}$$

---

* The calculation may also be made as follows: $p\mathrm{H} = -\log a_{\mathrm{H}^+} = -\log\,(2 \times 10^{-4}) = -(\overline{4} + 0.30) = 3.70$. Further examples of negative logarithms of this type are given in Daniels, *Mathematical Preparation for Physical Chemistry*, McGraw-Hill Book Co., New York, 1928, page 11.

Thus, if a solution contains exactly as many hydroxyl ions as hydrogen ions, the solution is neutral, and $a_{H^+} = a_{OH^-} = 10^{-7}$. The pH of a neutral solution then is 7. Addition of an acid increases the value of a_{H^+} and gives a pH less than 7. Addition of a base reduces the value of a_{H^+} and increases the pH above 7.

Example 13. What is the activity of hydrogen ions and the pH of a solution at 25° which has an activity of hydroxyl ions a_{OH^-} of 0.001?

$$a_{H^+} = \frac{1 \times 10^{-14}}{a_{OH^-}} = \frac{1 \times 10^{-14}}{10^{-3}} = 1 \times 10^{-11}$$

$$pH = -\log a_{H^+} = -\log 10^{-11} = 11$$

Other Electrodes. The practical limitations of the hydrogen electrode in certain solutions have been discussed. A wide selection of colorimetric indicators (page 476) is available which change color over a known range of pH. They are used extensively in analytical work, but they are limited to transparent solutions, and they are less accurate indicators of pH than the electrometric methods.

The quinhydrone electrode has been used for measuring pH values, but the glass electrode, discussed next, has been perfected to such an extent that it is displacing other electrodes for the measurement of pH.

Exercise III. When an inert electrode of platinum or gold is immersed in a solution to which quinhydrone has been added the potential of this quinhydrone electrode can be used to determine the pH of the solution. Quinhydrone is a loose compound consisting of equimolecular proportions of quinone and hydroquinone. Quinone is reduced to hydroquinone ion thus

$$C_6H_4O_2 + 2e = C_6H_4O_2^=$$

and hydroquinone ion reacts reversibly with H^+ ions to give undissociated hydroquinone according to the reaction

$$C_6H_4O_2^= + 2H^+ = C_6H_4(OH)_2$$

The whole reversible reaction is

$$2H^+ + \underset{\text{Quinone}}{C_6H_4O_2} + 2e = \underset{\text{Hydroquinone}}{C_6H_4(OH)_2}$$

Show that

$$E = E^\circ - \frac{RT}{2F} \ln \frac{[\text{Hydroquinone}]}{[H^+]^2[\text{Quinone}]}$$

and that since the ratio of hydroquinone to quinone is unity when quinhydrone is added at 25°

$$E = E^\circ + 0.0591 \log a_{H^+}$$

When the quinhydrone electrode is placed in a solution in which $a_{H^+} = 1$ and connected to a reference electrode, the value of $E°$ is found by experiment to be 0.6996 volt. When a calomel electrode is used with the quinhydrone electrode the pH of the solution is calculated from the formula pH $= (0.4194 - E)/0.0591$.

The glass electrode has become the most useful electrode for determining the pH of a solution. It is not affected by oxidizing or reducing agents, is not easily poisoned, and requires very little attention. It is widely used in industry, in analytical chemistry, and in biological investigations.

A glass electrode consists of a reversible electrode such as a calomel electrode or Ag-AgCl electrode in a solution of constant pH inside a thin membrane of a special glass. The thin glass bulb of this electrode is immersed in the solution to be studied along with a reference calomel electrode, as indicated below.

Ag, AgCl; Solution of constant pH; Glass membrane;

Solution of pH to be measured $\|$ calomel electrode

It is found experimentally that the potential of such a glass electrode varies with the activity of hydrogen ions in the same way as the hydrogen electrode, that is, 0.0591 volt per pH unit at 25°. An ordinary potentiometer cannot be used to measure the voltage of such a cell because of the high resistance of the glass membrane, and so an electronic voltmeter must be used. Vacuum-tube circuits have been developed which make it possible to measure very small currents and to determine pH values to ±0.01 pH unit with easily portable apparatus. The pH meter, as it is often called, is calibrated by means of a buffer of known pH before it is used to measure the pH of an unknown solution. The theory and use of the glass electrode have been fully treated by Bates.*

Electrodes suitable for determining the activity of hydrogen ions have reached a high state of perfection; activities of copper, silver, zinc, and other ions can also be determined with a high degree of precision using metallic electrodes.

Chlorine may be used with a platinum electrode as a gas electrode for determining the activity of chloride ions in the same way that the hydrogen electrode is used for determining hydrogen ions, but only a few other gases can be used as reversible electrodes.

Junction Potentials. In addition to the potentials at the two electrodes, already discussed, there is a third potential if two different solutions are in contact with each other. If, for example, a concentrated solution of hydrochloric acid touches a dilute solution, both

* Bates, *Electrometric pH Determinations*, John Wiley & Sons, New York, 1954.

hydrogen ions and chloride ions tend to diffuse from the concentrated solution into the dilute solution. The hydrogen ion moves faster, and, thus, the dilute solution soon becomes positively charged on account of an excess of positive hydrogen ions. The more concentrated solution is left with an excess of negative chloride ions and thus acquires a negative charge. The differential diffusion is soon offset by the charges set up.

In general, it may be stated that the difference of potential set up at the junction of the two solutions is caused by the difference in the rates of migration of the two ions, *the more dilute solution acquiring a charge corresponding to that of the faster-moving ion.*

The difference in potential at the junction of two liquids must be eliminated or corrected for in accurate measurements of oxidation potentials. The most convenient way of minimizing this potential is through the use of a salt bridge of potassium chloride connecting the two solutions of different electrolytes.

Potassium chloride is used because the transference numbers of the two ions are about the same, 0.49 for K^+ and 0.51 for Cl^-. Under these conditions each ion moves with nearly the same velocity, and each has the same tendency to give its charge to the more dilute solution.

Other ions than potassium and chloride are usually present at the two ends of the bridge, and it is desirable to minimize the effect of these ions by having a large excess of the potassium chloride, which tends to swamp out the slight effects due to other ions. For this purpose saturated potassium chloride is the most effective in eliminating the junction potential, but it is troublesome to use and normal KCl (1.0 N KCl) is generally preferred. When potassium chloride cannot be used, as, for example, in a cell containing silver nitrate, a salt bridge of ammonium nitrate is substituted.

The evaluation of the junction potential constitutes one of the most difficult problems of electrochemistry. It cannot be calculated with exactness; in fact, its theoretical significance is uncertain, and yet it is useful in trying to give numerical values to the activity of single ions as distinguished from the mean activity of the electrolyte. Such numerical values of the activity of single ions probably have no theoretical significance, but they are useful in many calculations when combined with the activities of other ions.

Particularly in the electrochemistry of nonaqueous solutions, ignorance of junction potentials constitutes a serious handicap. These potentials may be quite large. Nevertheless the uncertainty need not prevent their application in an empirical way for practical measurements, particularly if the measurements involve *differences* in concentration, for then the junction potential is largely canceled out.

Activity of Electrolytes and Ions.   The activity of an electrolyte or ion, as previously explained, is used in determining true equilibrium constants.   By definition, activities are equal to concentrations in very dilute solutions, and the difference between activities and concentrations in more concentrated solutions depends on the interaction between all the ions and the solvent.

The simple equations which apply only in dilute solutions may be made applicable also to concentrated solutions by substituting activities, or effective concentrations, for analytically determined concentrations. A similar situation was met with on page 270.   The activity may be expressed as the product of concentration and an activity coefficient. Activity coefficients may be determined from a number of different types of measurements, including vapor pressure, freezing-point lowering, boiling-point elevation, osmotic pressure, distribution coefficients, equilibrium constants, solubility, and electromotive-force measurements. Methods for determining activity coefficients are described on pages 268 and 446.   All different methods for determining activity coefficients lead to the same value for a given solution.

The expression for the activity coefficient of an electrolyte depends upon the type of electrolyte.   The 1–1 electrolytes, which have a univalent cation and a univalent anion like $NaCl$ or $AgNO_3$, are the simplest for the determination of activities.

The activity of a 1–1 electrolyte is defined as the product of the ion activities; thus

$$a_{\text{solute}} = a_+ \times a_- = a_{\text{cation}} \times a_{\text{anion}} \tag{18}$$

The activity coefficients γ_+ and γ_- of the cation and anion are defined as the ratios of the activities of the ions to their molal concentrations

$$\gamma_+ = a_+/m \quad \text{and} \quad \gamma_- = a_-/m \tag{19}$$

Then

$$a_{\text{solute}} = a_+ \times a_- = m\gamma_+ \times m\gamma_- = m^2\gamma^2 \tag{20}$$

where the γ defined by this equation is the mean ionic activity coefficient for the electrolyte.   It follows from equation 20 that

$$\gamma_\pm = \sqrt{\gamma_+\gamma_-} \tag{21}$$

For other than a 1–1 electrolyte, the expressions are slightly more complicated.   Thus, for a salt of the $CaCl_2$ type,

$$a_{\text{CaCl}_2} = a_{\text{Ca}^{++}} \times a_{\text{Cl}^-}{}^2 \tag{22}$$

If the molality of $CaCl_2$ is m, the Ca^{++} concentration is m and the Cl^- concentration $2m$.   Therefore

$$\gamma_+ = a_+/m \qquad \gamma_- = a_-/2m \tag{23}$$

Also,

$$\gamma_\pm = (\gamma_+ \times \gamma_-^2)^{\frac{1}{3}} \tag{24}$$

Finally,

$$a_{CaCl_2} = (m\gamma_+)(2m\gamma_-)^2 = 4m^3\gamma_\pm^3 \tag{25}$$

The extension to other types of electrolytes is similar.

Cells without Transference.   The cells studied thus far have been cells with liquid-junction potentials, called cells *with transference.* Those that do not contain a liquid junction are called cells *without transference.*   Through the use of a potassium chloride salt bridge it is possible to reduce greatly the junction potential.   Although cells with salt bridges have great practical value, they are not and probably never will be thermodynamically exact.*   The cells without liquid junctions are free from this difficulty of the junction potential and are thermodynamically exact.

Since a cell without transference contains a solution of a single electrolyte the two electrodes must be chosen so that one is reversible to the cation of the electrolyte and the other to the anion of the electrolyte.   For example, if the electrolyte is HCl, one electrode would be the hydrogen electrode and the other a chlorine or silver chloride electrode. In the latter case the cell may be represented by

$$Pt,\ H_2(1\ atm);\ HCl(m);\ AgCl,\ Ag$$

The cell reaction is

Oxidation $\frac{1}{2}H_2(1\ atm) = H^+(a_{H^+}) + e$
Reduction $AgCl + e = Ag + Cl^-(a_{Cl^-})$

$$\frac{1}{2}H_2(1\ atm) + AgCl = H^+(a_{H^+}) + Cl^-(a_{Cl^-}) + Ag$$

The electromotive force for this cell with the hydrogen electrode at 1 atm is given by

$$E = E^\circ - \frac{RT}{nF} \ln \frac{a_{H^+} \times a_{Cl^-}}{a_{H_2}^{\frac{1}{2}}} = E^\circ - \frac{RT}{nF} \ln \gamma^2 m^2 \tag{26}$$

The activity coefficient of HCl is represented by γ, and m is the molality of the HCl solution.   The electromotive force of the cell when the activity of hydrochloric acid is unity is represented by E°.

* Guggenheim, *J. Phys. Chem., 34,* 1758 (1930).

By determining the electromotive force of this cell without transference over a range of hydrochloric acid concentrations including dilute solutions it is possible to determine both $E°$ and the activity coefficients of hydrochloric acid solutions of various molalities. Rearranging equation 26 and substituting numerical values for 25° gives

$$E + 0.1183 \log m = E° - 0.1183 \log \gamma \qquad (27)$$

Since at infinite dilution $m = 0$, $\gamma = 1$, and $\log \gamma = 0$, it can be seen that, when $E + 0.1183 \log m$ is plotted against m, the extrapolation of $E + 0.1183 \log m$ to $m = 0$ will give $E°$.

In order to make a satisfactory extrapolation, use is made of the Debye-Hückel theory (page 483) to furnish a function which will give nearly a straight line. From this theory the following expression is obtained for the activity coefficient of any 1–1 electrolyte in dilute aqueous solutions at 25°,

$$\log \gamma = -0.509\sqrt{m} + bm \qquad (28)$$

where b is an empirical constant depending partly on the radii of the ions.

Substituting in equation 27 and rearranging terms

$$E' = E + 0.1183 \log m - 0.0602\sqrt{m} = E° - (0.1183b)m \quad (29)$$

According to this equation, the left-hand side, which we will designate as E', will give a straight line when it is plotted against m, and its value at infinite dilution is $E°$. Actually, the line will be somewhat curved, since equation 28 is exact only in very dilute solutions, but the extrapolation of E' can be made without difficulty.

In Table IV are given the measured electromotive forces and values of E' at various molalities, and, in *Fig. 15-5*, E' is plotted against m. The extrapolated value is 0.2224 volt. This is the electromotive force

Table IV. Electromotive Force of Concentration Cells of HCl [1]

m	E	E'
0.003564	0.51527	0.22207
0.004488	0.50384	0.22204
0.006239	0.48747	0.22188
0.008636	0.47135	0.22162
0.011195	0.45861	0.22144
0.01710	0.43783	0.22092
0.02563	0.41824	0.22036
0.05391	0.38222	0.21820

[1] Harned and Ehlers, *J. Am. Chem. Soc.*, *54*, 1350 (1932).

of the cell when hydrochloric acid is at unit activity (that is, is in its standard state), and it is also the negative of the silver-silver chloride standard oxidation electrode potential because the standard hydrogen electrode potential is taken as 0.0000. Similar methods have been used for calculating other standard electrode potentials. Most of the data of Table I were obtained in this way.

The value of $E°$ having been determined, the activity coefficient of hydrochloric acid may be calculated from the electromotive force of the

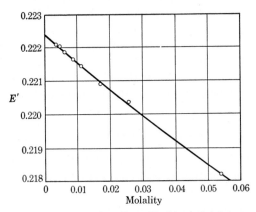

FIG. 15-5. Determination of the silver-silver chloride electrode potential by extrapolation of a function of the voltage of the cell Pt, $H_2(1 \text{ atm})$; $HCl(m)$; AgCl, Ag to infinite dilution.

cell for any concentration of HCl. For example, if the electromotive force is 0.3524 volt for $m = 0.1$, γ may be calculated from equation 27 for 0.1 m HCl (at 25°) as follows:

$$0.3524 = 0.2224 - 0.1183 \log 0.1 - 0.1183 \log \gamma$$

$$\log \gamma = (-0.3524 + 0.2224 + 0.1183)/0.1183 = -0.0989$$

$$\gamma = 0.796$$

In this general manner, the activity coefficients of the electrolytes given in Table V have been determined.

In *Fig. 15-6* the activity coefficients of these typical electrolytes are plotted against a function of the concentration, namely the square root of the ionic strength, a term which is defined on page 482. It may be noted that the activity coefficients of these electrolytes pass through a distinct minimum value but that the minima do not occur at the same concentration for each electrolyte.

Table V.   Activity Coefficients at 25°

Molality	HCl	KCl	NaCl	NaOH	H_2SO_4	$CaCl_2$	$CdSO_4$
0.005	0.930	0.927	0.928	....	0.643	0.789	.....
0.01	0.906	0.902	0.903	0.89	0.545	0.732	0.476
0.05	0.833	0.817	0.821	0.80	0.341	0.584	0.383
0.10	0.798	0.770	0.778	0.75	0.266	0.524	0.199
0.20	0.768	0.719	0.732	0.71	0.210	0.491	0.137
0.50	0.769	0.652	0.680	0.68	0.155	0.510	0.061
1.00	0.811	0.607	0.656	0.66	0.131	0.725	0.042
2.00	1.011	0.578	0.670	0.68	0.125	1.554	0.030
3.00	1.31	0.574	0.719	....	0.142	3.384	0.026
4.00	1.74	.....	0.791	....	0.172	.....	.....

Usually, the activity coefficients are less than 1, and the activities which may be regarded in an oversimplified way as effective concentration are less than the analytically determined concentrations. Interionic attraction, which tends to draw ions together and render them less

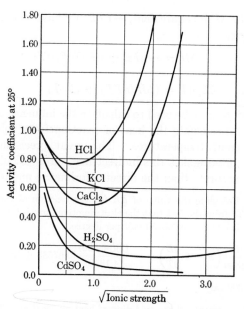

FIG. 15-6. Activity coefficients of electrolytes at various ionic strengths (p. 482).

free to move, is responsible in large part for this deviation. Sometimes, as in concentrated solutions of hydrochloric acid or calcium chloride, or in nonaqueous solutions, the activity coefficients are found to be much greater than 1. It is of doubtful value to offer a mechanism for activities, but this effective concentration, so much greater than the stoichio-metric concentration, may be attributed to a change in the solvent. The activity may be increased by removing solvent quite as well as by increasing the amount of dissolved solute. Calcium chloride, which crystallizes out with water of crystallization, may render some of the water partially inactive as a solvent and thereby make the activity in concentrated solutions greater than the analytically determined concentration.

The activity coefficients of a large number of electrolytes, both alone and mixed, in solutions of different concentrations have been determined with a high degree of accuracy.*

Influence of Temperature on Voltage. The relation between temperature, heat of reaction, and the voltage of a reversible electro-chemical cell may be obtained from the Gibbs-Helmholtz equation, derived on page 144,

$$\Delta F - \Delta H = T(\partial(\Delta F)/\partial T)_p \tag{30}$$

Substituting for ΔF its equivalent, $-nFE$, we have under conditions of constant pressure

$$\Delta H = -nFE + nFT(\partial E/\partial T) \tag{31}$$

and

$$\partial E/\partial T = (\Delta H/nFT) + (E/T) \tag{32}$$

These equations may be used to calculate the influence of temperature on voltage or to calculate the heat of reaction from voltage measure-ments at different temperatures. The great precision of electrical measurements often makes this indirect method of calculating heats of reaction more accurate than the direct calorimetric method.

Example 14. Calculate the value of ΔH for the reaction of the cadmium-silver chloride cell at 25° from the fact that the electromotive force is 0.67533 volt and the temperature coefficient is −0.000650 volt per degree.

$$\Delta H = -\frac{nF}{4.1840}\left(E - T\frac{\partial E}{\partial T}\right) = -\frac{(2)(96,500)}{(4.1840)}[0.67533 + (298.1)(0.000650)]$$

$$= -40,090 \text{ cal}$$

Calorimetric measurements of the evolution of heat give $\Delta H = -39,530$ cal.

Further examples are given in Table VI. The agreement between the calculated and the experimental values of ΔH is entirely satisfactory.

* Harned and Owen, *The Physical Chemistry of Electrolytic Solutions*, Reinhold Publishing Corp., New York, 1950; MacInnes, *The Principles of Electrochemistry*, Reinhold Publishing Corp., New York, 1939, page 167.

Table VI. Experimental Verification of the Gibbs-Helmholtz Equation

Cell	E, volts	$\partial E/\partial T$, volts/degree	ΔH (obs.) calorimeter, cal	ΔH (calc.) equation 31	ΔF, $-\dfrac{nFE}{4.1840}$
Zn, ZnCl$_2$(0.555m), AgCl, Ag(0°)	1.015	−0.000402	−52,050	−51,990	−46,830
Cd, CdCl$_2 \cdot 2\frac{1}{2}$H$_2$O (satd.), AgCl, Ag(25°)	0.67533	−0.00065	−39,530	−40,080	−31,160
Cd, CdCl$_2 \cdot 2\frac{1}{2}$H$_2$O (satd.), PbCl$_2$, Pb(25°)	0.18806	−0.00048	−14,650	−15,250	−8,670
Pb, Pb(C$_2$H$_3$O$_2$)$_2$ (0.555m), Cu(C$_2$H$_3$-O$_2$)$_2$ (satd.), Cu(0°)	0.4764	+0.000385	−17,530	−16,900	−21,990

An examination of the last two columns is interesting. When $\partial E/\partial T$ has a positive sign, as in the case of the lead-copper cell, ΔF has a larger negative value than ΔH. This means that the maximum electrical work done is greater than the heat evolved. When $\partial E/\partial T$ has a negative sign ΔF has a smaller negative value than ΔH.

It was shown on page 99 that ΔH is the heat of reaction q_p when the reaction takes place at constant temperature and pressure under conditions such that all the chemical energy is converted into heat and pressure-volume work. When the reaction takes place reversibly in an electrochemical cell, however, most of the chemical energy goes into electrical energy and only a little is available for heat effects. If the cell is operated isothermally and reversibly in a calorimeter the heat absorbed is $q_{p,\text{rev}}$. In a reversible process $\Delta S = q_{\text{rev}}/T$, and so the heat absorbed during the operation of the electrochemical cell is $T\,\Delta S$. Referring to page 142,

$$\Delta H = \Delta F + T\,\Delta S$$

It is evident then that the difference between ΔH and ΔF is due to the entropy change accompanying the reaction. It was shown in equation 31 that the difference between ΔH and ΔF is also equal to $nFT\,\partial E/\partial T$.

In the special case where there is practically no change in entropy, no heat is evolved or absorbed when the electrical cell operates reversibly. Then all the chemical energy is converted into electrical work, ΔF. Likewise in the open calorimeter where no electrical work is done all the chemical energy is converted into heat ΔH. Then $\Delta F = \Delta H$, and $\partial E/\partial T = 0$.

Potentiometric Titrations. Measurement of the potential of certain electrodes offers a convenient and accurate means for determining the end points of titrations. For example, a hydrogen electrode or a glass electrode may be used to determine the pH during the titration of an acid by a base. *Fig. 15-7* gives the electromotive force obtained with a hydrogen electrode and calomel electrode during the titration of a solution of hydrochloric acid with a solution of sodium hydroxide. The pH values on the right have been calculated with equation 17. At the beginning of the titration the pH changes slowly because a considerable amount of sodium hydroxide must be added to change the

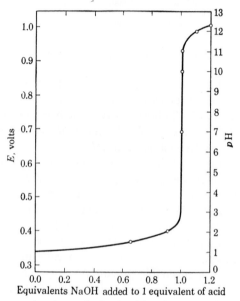

FIG. 15-7. Electromotive force obtained with a hydrogen electrode and calomel electrode in the titration of a solution of hydrochloric acid with a solution of sodium hydroxide.

hydrogen-ion concentration 10-fold. As the end point is approached the pH changes rapidly. When the solution is exactly neutral, the activities of the hydrogen ions and hydroxyl ions are the same and equal to 10^{-7} at 25°. The voltage of the hydrogen electrode against the calomel electrode, then, is

$$E = 0.0591 \log [1/(1 \times 10^{-7})] + 0.2802 = 0.6942 \text{ volt}$$

At the end point the concentration of hydrogen ions is very small, and the number of hydrogen ions in a drop of acid, or of hydroxyl ions in a drop of alkali, is large in comparison. A slight addition of either acid or alkali then makes a large change in the hydrogen-ion concentration.

Further examples of acid-base titrations are given in Figs. 16-1 and 16-2 on pages 468 and 469. When weak acids and bases are used the end point will not come at a pH of 7, because the salts produced in the neutralization are hydrolyzed and give an acid or alkaline reaction.

The end points in oxidation-reduction reactions may be determined by measuring the potential difference between a platinum wire or other inert electrode and a calomel electrode. This is illustrated in *Fig. 15-8*, which gives the results of a titration of ferrous sulfate with potassium

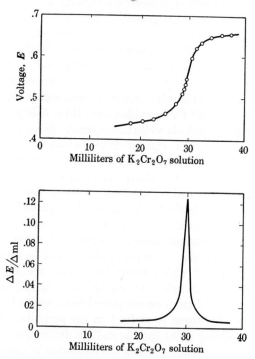

FIG. 15-8. Potentiometric titration of ferrous sulfate with potassium dichromate showing the use of a plot of $\Delta E/\Delta$ ml versus volume to obtain the end point.

dichromate. In order to locate the end point more accurately, it is helpful to plot the slope $\Delta E/\Delta V$ versus the volume V of reagent added. The maximum slope occurs at the end point of the titration. The differential graph may be obtained by drawing tangents at points on the voltage curve, or it may be obtained directly from the original data by dividing the differences in voltage by the corresponding differences in volume.

For determining end points in neutralizations it is possible to bubble oxygen or even air over a platinized platinum electrode. Since the oxygen electrode is not reversible, it is not possible to set $-nFE$ equal

to ΔF, and no theoretical significance can be attached to the absolute
voltages. But when addition of reagent leads to a rapid change in concentration of OH^- ions and of potential the end point can be identified.

In addition to neutralizations and oxidations, it is possible to obtain
end points in precipitations. The titration of iodide with silver nitrate
is a simple example. A silver wire is placed in the solution and connected to a calomel reference electrode through a galvanometer which
is set at zero by opposing a potential from a battery and adjustable
rheostat. As the silver solution is added, the galvanometer remains
near zero because the silver-ion concentration is fixed by the solubility
of silver iodide. When all the iodide is precipitated, however, the next
drop increases the silver-ion concentration enormously and the galvanometer is deflected sharply. An end point with a different electromotive force is obtained for bromides, and, thus, it is possible to determine the amounts of both chlorides and bromides in a mixture of the two.

Polarization. When a current flows between two electrodes the
nature of the electrode surfaces may be changed in such a way as to
produce new potentials. The change of voltage produced by the products of electrolysis is called polarization. Polarization may occur when
current from an outside source is passed through an electrolytic cell.
For example, when two inert platinum electrodes are in a solution of
copper chloride the cathode becomes plated with copper and chlorine
is released at the anode. A copper-chlorine cell is thus set up, the
electromotive force of which tends to oppose the applied voltage.
Polarization occurs also when an electrochemical cell operates spontaneously. If zinc and graphite are placed in an acid solution, zinc goes
into solution and hydrogen is evolved on the graphite, which polarizes
the cell. An oxidizing agent such as sodium dichromate may be added
to oxidize the hydrogen and prevent the formation of gaseous hydrogen,
which not only exerts a back electromotive force but also interposes into
the circuit a gas film of high electrical resistance.

Polarization of a cell results also from the fact that the passage of the
current changes the concentration of the ions around the electrodes and
changes the potentials. The polarization of an electrode can be determined by measuring the potential of the electrode against a reference
electrode, such as a calomel electrode, before and after the passage of
the current. Polarization does not occur when all the reactions are
rapid and the electrode is in a state of reversible equilibrium. The
existence of polarization implies that one of the reaction steps involved
is slow.

Overvoltage is a special case of polarization which depends on the
evolution of gas. It is the difference between the decomposition voltage

at which gas is evolved on an electrode and the voltage at which it is evolved under reversible conditions, as on a platinized platinum electrode. The overvoltage depends on the nature of the electrode, on the current density, and on other factors. The overvoltages for the liberation of hydrogen at a current density of 0.1 ampere per square centimeter are roughly as follows: platinized platinum 0.0; polished platinum 0.3; gold 0.6; iron 0.8; silver 0.9; nickel 1.02; zinc 1.1; lead 1.2; tin 1.2.

The decomposition potentials described on page 403 must be at least as great as the equilibrium electrode potentials of Table I plus the overvoltages. The overvoltage of lead is responsible for a higher voltage for the storage battery, and the overvoltage of zinc is responsible for the moderate resistance of zinc to corrosion.

REFERENCES

MacInnes, *The Principles of Electrochemistry*, Reinhold Publishing Corp., New York, 1939.

Glasstone, *Introduction to Electrochemistry*, D. Van Nostrand Co., New York, 1942.

Harned and Owen, *The Physical Chemistry of Electrolytic Solutions*, Reinhold Publishing Corp., New York, 1950.

Dole, *Experimental and Theoretical Electrochemistry*, McGraw-Hill Book Co., New York, 1935.

Latimer, *Oxidation States of the Elements and Their Potentials in Aqueous Solutions*, Prentice-Hall, New York, 1952.

Creighton and Koehler, *Principles and Applications of Electrochemistry*, John Wiley & Sons, New York, 1935.

Kortüm and Bockris, *Textbook of Electrochemistry*, Elsevier Publishing Co., New York, 1951.

Ricci, *Hydrogen Ion Concentration*, Princeton University Press, Princeton, N. J., 1952.

Bates, *Electrometric pH Determinations*, John Wiley & Sons, New York, 1954.

PROBLEMS

1. A small dry battery of zinc and ammonium chloride weighing 85 grams will operate continuously through a 4-ohm resistance for 450 minutes before its voltage falls below 0.75 volt. The initial voltage is 1.60, and the effective voltage over the whole life of the battery is taken to be 1.00. Theoretically, how many miles above the earth could this battery be raised by the energy delivered by this battery under these conditions? *Ans.* 5.04 miles.

2. Given the cell at 25°,

$$Pb; Pb^{++}(a = 1) \parallel Ag^{+}(a = 1); Ag$$

(a) calculate the voltage; (b) write the cell reaction; and (c) calculate the free-energy change. *Ans.* (a) 0.925 volt.

(b) $\frac{1}{2}Pb(s) + Ag^{+}(a = 1) = \frac{1}{2}Pb^{++}(a = 1) + Ag(s)$.

(c) $-21,330$ cal.

3. Given the cell at 25°,

$$Cd; \; Cd^{++}(a = 1) \;||\; I^-(a = 1); \; I_2(s), \; Pt$$

(a) write the cell reaction; (b) calculate $E°$; (c) calculate $\Delta F°$.

Ans. (a) $Cd(s) + I_2(s) = Cd^{++} (a = 1) + 2I^- (a = 1)$.
      (b) 0.939 volt.
      (c) −43,300 cal.

4. (a) Diagram the cell for the reaction

$$H_2(g, 1 \text{ atm}) + I_2(s) = 2HI(aq, a = 1)$$

(b) Calculate $E°$. (c) Calculate $\Delta F°$. (d) Calculate K. (e) What differences would there be if the reaction had been written $\frac{1}{2}H_2(g, 1 \text{ atm}) + \frac{1}{2}I_2(s) = HI(aq, a = 1)$?

Ans. (a) Pt, $H_2(g, 1 \text{ atm})$; HI(aq, a = 1); $I_2(s)$, Pt.
      (b) 0.5355 volt.
      (c) −24,650 cal.
      (d) 1.17×10^{18}.
      (e) a and b are the same; $\Delta F° = -12,330$ cal; $K = 1.08 \times 10^9$.

5. (a) Calculate the voltage of the following cell at 25°:

$$Zn; \; Zn^{++}(a = 0.0004) \;||\; Cd^{++}(a = 0.2); \; Cd$$

(b) Write the cell reaction. (c) Calculate the value of the free-energy change involved in the reaction.

Ans. (a) 0.4398 volt.
      (b) $Zn(s) + Cd^{++}(a = 0.2) = Zn^{++}(a = 0.0004) + Cd(s)$.
      (c) −20,287 cal.

6. (a) Calculate the equilibrium constant at 25° for the reaction

$$Fe^{++} + Ag^+ = Ag + Fe^{+++}$$

(b) Calculate the concentration of silver ion at equilibrium (assuming that concentrations may be substituted for activities) for an experiment in which an excess of finely divided metallic silver is added to a 0.05 M solution of ferric nitrate.

Ans. (a) 3.0.   (b) 0.0443 mole l^{-1}.

7. What is the activity of ferrous ion in a solution at 25° which originally had an activity of 0.001 of ferric ion after enough mercurous ion has been added so that the activity of mercurous ion in the solution is equal to 0.0004?   Ans. 1×10^{-3}.

8. (a) Diagram the cell for the reaction

$$\frac{1}{2}Cu(s) + \frac{1}{2}Cl_2(g, 1 \text{ atm}) = \frac{1}{2}Cu^{++}(a = 1) + Cl^- (a = 1)$$

Calculate at 25°: (b) $E°$; (c) $\Delta F°$.

Ans. (a) Cu; $CuCl_2(aq, a = 1)$; $Cl_2(1 \text{ atm})$, Pt.
      (b) 1.0225 volts.
      (c) $\Delta F° = -23,580$ cal.

9. (a) Write the cell reaction for the cell

$$Zn; \; ZnCl_2(a = 0.5); \; AgCl, \; Ag$$

(b) Calculate $E°$. (c) Calculate E for the cell as written in (a). (d) Calculate ΔF. (e) Calculate $\Delta F°$. (f) Calculate K.

Ans. (a) Zn + 2AgCl = 2Ag + ZnCl$_2$ (a = 0.5).
    (b) 0.985 volt.
    (c) 0.994 volt.
    (d) −45,860 cal.
    (e) −45,450 cal.
    (f) 2.05 × 10^{33}.

10. A cell consisting of a hydrogen electrode and normal calomel electrode connected by a normal KCl bridge has a potential of 0.664 volt at 25°. Calculate (a) the pH and (b) hydrogen-ion activity.   *Ans.* (a) 6.50. (b) 3.16 × 10^{-7}.

11. To what pH values are the following hydrogen-ion activities at 25° equal: (a) 0.3, (b) 10^{-12}? To what hydrogen-ion activities at 25° are the following pH values equivalent: (c) 10.6, (d) −1.1?

Ans. (a) 0.52. (b) 12. (c) 2.5 × 10^{-11}. (d) 12.6.

12. Calculate $E°_{Zn:Zn^{++}}$ at 25° from the following data:

Zn^{++}(aq, a = 1)	$\Delta H°_f$ = −36.43 kcal mole^{-1}	$S°$ = −25.45 cal deg^{-1} mole^{-1}
Zn(s)		$S°$ = 9.95 cal deg^{-1} mole^{-1}
H$^+$(aq, a = 1)	$\Delta H°_f$ = 0.000	$S°$ = 0.000
H$_2$(g, p = 1)		$S°$ = 31.211 cal deg^{-1} mole^{-1}

Ans. 0.763 volt.

13. Calculate the electromotive force of the cell at 25°

Ag; AgCl(s); NaCl(1 N); Hg$_2$Cl$_2$(s); Hg

from the following standard free energies of formation:

Ag$^+$	+18,488 cal mole^{-1}
AgCl(s)	−26,187
Na$^+$	−62,588
Cl$^-$	−31,367
Hg$_2$Cl$_2$	−50,274

Ans. 0.0455 volt.

14. The voltage of the cell

Pb; PbSO$_4$; Na$_2$SO$_4$·10H$_2$O(sat.); Hg$_2$SO$_4$; Hg

is 0.9647 at 25°. The temperature coefficient is 0.000174 volt per degree. Calculate (a) the heat of the reaction and (b) the free-energy change of the reaction

Pb(s) + Hg$_2$SO$_4$(s) = PbSO$_4$(s) + 2Hg(l)

Ans. (a) −42,100, (b) −44,500 cal.

15. A small, efficient battery for hearing aids is composed of zinc, potassium hydroxide, water, and mercuric oxide. (a) Write an over-all reaction for the cell in which zinc and potassium hydroxide are consumed, mercury is deposited, and potassium zincate is formed. (b) Write the reactions occurring at the electrodes.

16. Given the cell at 25°,

Pt, Cl$_2$(1 atm); Cl$^-$(a = 1) ‖ Zn^{++}(a = 1); Zn

(a) Calculate $E°$. (b) Write the cell reaction. (c) Calculate $\Delta F°$.

17. (a) Diagram the cell which corresponds to the reaction $AgCl = Cl^- + Ag^+$. Calculate at 25° (b) $E°$; (c) $\Delta F°$; (d) K.

18. Given the reaction $Fe^{++}(a = 1) + Ce^{++++}(a = 1) = Fe^{+++}(a = 1) + Ce^{+++}(a = 1)$. (a) Write the cell which corresponds to this reaction. (b) Calculate $E°$. (c) Calculate $\Delta F°$. (d) Calculate K. (e) Is the reaction spontaneous?

19. Given the cell at 25°

$$Pt, Cl_2(g); Cl^-(a = 1) \,\|\, Tl^{+++}(a = 1), Tl^+(a = 1); Pt$$

(a) Write the cell reaction. (b) Calculate $E°$. (c) Calculate $\Delta F°$. (d) Calculate the equilibrium constant for the cell reaction.

20. (a) Calculate the voltage at 25° of the cell

$$Pt; Ti^{+++}(a = 0.3), Ti^{++++}(a = 0.5) \,\|\, Ce^{+++}(a = 0.7), Ce^{++++}(a = 0.002); I\,t$$

(b) Write the cell reaction. (c) Calculate ΔF for the cell reaction as written. (d) Calculate $E°$. (e) Calculate $\Delta F°$. (f) Calculate K.

21. (a) Calculate the equilibrium constant for the reaction at 25°

$$Sn^{++++} + 2Ti^{+++} = 2Ti^{++++} + Sn^{++}$$

(b) When 0.01 mole of Sn^{++} ion is added to 1.0 mole of Ti^{++++} ion in 1000 grams of water, what will be the concentration of Ti^{+++} ions (if it is assumed for the calculation that the activities are essentially equal to the concentrations)?

22. A hydrogen electrode and a normal calomel cell give a voltage of 0.435 when placed in a certain solution at 25°. (a) What is the pH of the solution? (b) What is the value of a_{H^+}?

23. (a) What is the activity of hydrogen ions in a solution which has a pH of 8.6 at 25°? (b) Calculate the pH of a solution which has a hydrogen-ion activity of 5.1 equivalents per 1000 grams of water at 25°.

24. A hydrogen electrode and calomel cell are used to determine the pH of a solution on a mountain where the barometric pressure is 500 mm. The hydrogen is allowed to bubble out of the electrode at the atmospheric pressure prevailing there. If the pH is calculated to be 4.00, what is the correct pH of the solution?

25. The cell

$$\text{Normal calomel electrode} \,\|\, \text{solution, quinhydrone; Pt}$$

was found to have a potential of 0.212 volt for a certain solution at 25°. What is the pH of the solution?

26. The electromotive force of the cell

$$\text{Normal calomel electrode} \,\|\, \begin{pmatrix} FeCl_3(0.1\ m) \\ FeCl_2(0.1\ m) \\ HCl(0.1\ m) \end{pmatrix} ; Pt$$

is 0.446 volt at 25°. The hydrochloric acid is added to prevent hydrolysis. Assuming that the activity coefficients of the Fe^{+++} and Fe^{++} ions are 0.75 and 0.87 respectively, calculate the value of $E°$ for the ferrous-ferric electrode containing 0.1 m HCl.

27. (a) What is the activity of zinc ions in a solution which gives with a zinc electrode a voltage of -0.7500 against the standard hydrogen electrode? (b) What is the

molality of the solution if the activity coefficient for the zinc ion is 0.30 at this concentration?

28. Calculate the heat absorbed by the electrochemical cell

$$\text{Zn; Zn}^{++} \,\|\, \text{I}^-; \text{I}_2, \text{Pt}$$

when, at 25°, 0.00965 amp is drawn (nonreversibly) from the cell at a voltage of 1.5 volts, assuming that the internal resistance of the cell is negligible. The heat of formation of ZnI_2 is 49.7 kcal/mole, and its heat of solution is 11.7 kcal/mole:

$$\text{Zn} + \text{I}_2 = \text{ZnI}_2 \qquad \Delta H = 49.7 \text{ kcal/mole}$$

$$\text{ZnI}_2 = \text{Zn}^{++} + 2\text{I}^- \qquad \Delta H = 11.7 \text{ kcal/mole}$$

29. The electromotive force of the cell

$$\text{Ag, AgBr; MBr(aq. soln.); Hg}_2\text{Br}_2, \text{Hg}$$

has been determined accurately by Dakin and Ewing [*J. Am. Chem. Soc.*, *62*, 2280 (1940)], and the values of $E°_{\text{Ag,AgBr;Br}^-}$ have been determined by Owen and Foering [*J. Am. Chem. Soc.*, *58*, 1575 (1936)]. The data are as follows:

Temperature	E_{cell}	$E°_{\text{Ag,AgBr;Br}^-}$
15	0.06492	−0.07586
25	0.06804	−0.07121
35	0.07116	−0.06591

(a) Calculate $E°_{\text{Hg,Hg}_2\text{Br}_2;\text{Br}^-}$ at each temperature, and find formulas which give E_{cell} and $E°_{\text{Hg,Hg}_2\text{Br}_2;\text{Br}^-}$ a function of temperature. (b) Calculate $\Delta F°$ at 25° for the reaction $2\text{Ag} + \text{Hg}_2\text{Br}_2 = 2\text{AgBr} + 2\text{Hg}$. (c) Calculate ΔH for this reaction. (d) Calculate ΔS for this reaction. (e) Using the free energy of formation of silver bromide $\Delta F°_f = -22,935$ cal per mole, show that the free energy of formation of mercurous bromide is $-42,732$ cal mole^{-1}.

30. The cell Pt, H_2 (1 atm); HBr(m); AgBr, Ag has been studied by Harned, Keston and Donelson [*J. Am. Chem. Soc.*, *58*, 989 (1936)]. The following table gives the e.m.f.'s obtained at 25°.

m	0.01	0.02	0.05	0.10
E	0.3127	0.2786	0.2340	0.2005

Calculate (a) $E°$ and (b) the activity coefficient for a 0.10 molal solution of HBr.

---

31. (a) Design a cell in which the reaction is

$$\tfrac{1}{2}\text{Cl}_2(g, 1 \text{ atm}) + \text{Br}^-(a = 1) = \text{Cl}^-(a = 1) + \tfrac{1}{2}\text{Br}_2(l)$$

(b) Calculate the voltage at 25°, (c) calculate the free energy change of the reaction.

32. Given the cell

$$\text{Pt, Cl}_2; \text{Cl}^-(a = 1) \,\|\, \text{Zn}^{++}(a = 1); \text{Zn}$$

(a) Calculate $E°$ for the cell. (b) Write the cell reaction. (c) Calculate $\Delta F°$ for the cell reaction.

33. Given the cell at $25°$

$$\text{Pt, } X_2; \; X^-(a = 0.1) \; || \; X^-(a = 0.001); \; X_2, \text{ Pt}$$

where X is an unknown halogen. (a) Write the cell reaction. (b) Which electrode is negative? (c) What is the voltage of the cell? (d) Is the reaction spontaneous?

34. Given the cell at $25°$

$$\text{Cd; } CdCl_2(a = 1) \; || \; SnCl_2(a = 0.01); \text{ Sn}$$

(a) Write the cell reaction. Calculate (b) $E°$; (c) E; (d) ΔF; (e) $\Delta F°$; (f) K.

35. Given the cell at $25°C$

$$\text{Zn; } Zn^{++}(a = 0.001) \; || \; I^-(a = 0.1); \; I_2(s), \text{ Pt}$$

(a) Write the cell reaction. (b) Calculate the voltage of the cell as written. (c) Calculate the equilibrium constant for the reaction.

36. Develop a formula for calculating the voltage of a cell consisting of two chlorine electrodes at different pressures immersed in a solution of a chloride. Calculate the voltage if the chlorine of one electrode is at 1 atm, the other is at 0.70 atm, and the temperature is $25°$.

37. What is the pH of a solution that has an activity of hydrogen ions of (a) 1.52; (b) 4×10^{-8}? What is the value of a_{H^+} in a solution which has a pH of (c) 15.2; (d) 0.25?

38. When the pH of a solution is measured by means of a hydrogen electrode against a calomel electrode, the partial pressure of the hydrogen is usually not exactly 1 atm. At $25°$ how low can the partial pressure of the hydrogen be before a correction is necessary, if an error of 0.01 pH unit is allowable?

39. Derive expressions for the relation between the mean ionic activity coefficient and the activity of a 2-2 electrolyte and a 1-3 electrolyte.

40. A thallium amalgam of 4.93 per cent Tl in mercury and another amalgam of 10.02 per cent Tl are placed in separate legs of a glass cell and covered with a solution of thallous sulfate to form a concentration cell. The voltage of the cell is 0.029480 volt at $20°$ and 0.029971 volt at $30°$. The mercury acts only as a diluent. (a) Which is the negative electrode? (b) What is the heat of dilution per mole of thallium when mercury is added at $30°$ to change the concentration from 10.02 per cent to 4.93 per cent? (c) What is the voltage of the cell at $40°$?

41. At $25°$ for the reaction

$$2Fe^{+++} + 2Hg = 2Fe^{++} + Hg_2^{++}$$

the equilibrium constant is 0.018, and at $35°$ it is 0.054. Calculate the value of $E°$ at $45°$ for the cell which corresponds to this reaction.

42. The free energy of formation $\Delta F°_{298°K}$ of Pb^{++} is -5630 cal. The free energies of formation of the elements and of hydrogen ion at unit activity are taken as zero. Calculate the voltage of the cell at $25°$

$$\text{Pt, } H_2(1 \text{ atm}); \; H^+(a = 0.2) \; || \; Pb^{++}(a = 0.001); \text{ Pb}$$

43. E for the standard Weston cadmium cell is 1.0186 volts at $20°$ and decreases 0.0000406 volt for each degree rise in temperature above $20°$. (a) State these facts with a single mathematical equation, and calculate (b) the heat evolved or absorbed per mole of cadmium consumed, and (c) the free-energy change per mole of cadmium consumed.

44. Tartar, Newschwander, and Ness [*J. Am. Chem. Soc.*, *63*, 28 (1941)] found that the electromotive force of the cell

$$\text{Pt, H}_2; \text{H}_2\text{SO}_4(m = 1.0), \text{ZnSO}_4(m = 0.5); \text{Hg}_2\text{SO}_4; \text{Hg}$$

is 0.67281 volt at 25°. $E° = 0.61515$ volt. Calculate the activity coefficient of sulfuric acid in a solution which is 1 molal with respect to H_2SO_4 and 0.5 molal with respect to $ZnSO_4$.

45. A solution 0.5 molal with respect to H_2SO_4 and 1.5 molal with respect to zinc sulfate has a vapor pressure of 22.454 mm at 25°. For the cell

$$\text{Pt, H}_2; \text{H}_2\text{SO}_4(m = 0.5); \text{ZnSO}_4(m = 1.5); \text{Hg}_2\text{SO}_4; \text{Hg}$$

$E = 0.69021$ volt and $E° = 0.61515$ volt. For the cell

$$\text{Zn; H}_2\text{SO}_4(m = 0.5); \text{ZnSO}_4(m = 1.5); \text{Hg}_2\text{SO}_4; \text{Hg}$$

$E = 1.44561$ volts and $E° = 1.3765$ volts. The vapor pressure of pure water at 25° is 23.75 mm. Calculate (*a*) the activity of the water, (*b*) the mean activity of the sulfuric acid, and (*c*) the mean activity of the zinc sulfate.*

* Tartar, Newschwander, and Ness, *J. Am. Chem. Soc.*, *63*, 28 (1941).

16

Ionic Equilibria

The study of equilibria involving ions in solution constitutes one of the oldest branches of physical chemistry. It was shown on pages 231 and 374 that salts, acids, and bases dissociate into electrically charged ions when they are dissolved in water, but further discussion of the equilibria of ions was postponed in order to present first the concepts of chemical equilibrium, the facts of electrolytic conductance, and the significance of electromotive-force measurements.

Proton Theory of Acids. An important group of ionic equilibria is the ionizations of weak acids and bases. Certain general aspects of the behavior of acids and bases were overlooked in the early development of physical chemistry because of the importance of water and its solutions, and because of the successes of the Arrhenius theory. Thus, according to an older viewpoint, only aqueous solutions show acidic and basic properties, and the term neutralization refers to the combination of hydrogen ions and hydroxyl ions. But the formation of water is not a necessary criterion for neutralization. For example, the following reactions

$$NH_4Cl + NaNH_2 = 2NH_3 + NaCl \quad \text{(in liquid NH}_3\text{)}$$

and

$$HCl + NaC_2H_3O_2 = HC_2H_3O_2 + NaCl \quad \text{(in glacial acetic acid)}$$

give the usual neutralization curve with electrometric titration.

In 1923, under the leadership of Brönsted and Bjerrum in Denmark and Lowry in England, the proton theory of acids and bases was proposed.[*] A proton is a hydrogen atom which has lost its electron, leaving a small nucleus with a mass a little over 1 on the atomic-weight scale and with one positive charge. This tiny unit 10^{-13} cm in diameter immediately attracts solvent molecules and becomes "solvated." *Brönsted and Bjerrum defined an acid as a substance that yields protons and a*

---

[*] Hall, *J. Chem. Education*, *12*, 124 (1940). Bell, *Acids and Bases, Their Quantitative Behavior*, Methuen & Co., London, 1952.

base as a substance that accepts protons. The relative strengths of acids may be studied by determining their relative tendencies to give up protons. Thus, hydrochloric acid is classified as a strong acid in aqueous solution because it is completely ionized into H_3O^+ and chloride ions, whereas acetic acid is a weak acid. Any compound that contains hydrogen may conceivably act as an acid, but substances like methane in which the tendency to give protons is extremely small (that is, the force holding the proton is great) can hardly be classified as acids.

The strength of an acid varies with the solvent and the experimental conditions and is determined by the electronic and molecular structure of the acid. Thus, HI is intrinsically a stronger acid than HF because its internuclear distance is greater and the proton is held less firmly.

The ionization of an acid A may be represented by

$$A = H^+ + B \qquad (1)$$

where B is a *base*, defined by Brönsted as a substance which takes up protons. A and B are termed a *conjugate acid-base pair.* This view emphasizes the similarity between all such processes as the following:

Acid	=	Base	+	Proton
NH_4^+	=	NH_3	+	H^+
H_2O	=	OH^-	+	H^+
HSO_4^-	=	$SO_4^=$	+	H^+
$HPO_4^=$	=	$PO_4^{\equiv}$	+	H^+
$HFe(CN)_6^{\equiv}$	=	$Fe(CN)_6^{==}$	+	H^+
$Cr(H_2O)_6^{+++}$	=	$Cr(H_2O)_5OH^{++}$	+	H^+
$C_6H_4(NH_3)_2^{++}$	=	$H_2NC_6H_4NH_3^+$	+	H^+

As mentioned earlier, hydrogen ions do not exist free in solution, and so the solvent may be included in the reaction as follows:

$$A_1 + \text{solvent} = H^+ \cdot \text{solvent} + B_1 \qquad (2)$$

But, since

$$H^+ \cdot \text{solvent} = H^+ + \text{solvent}$$

$H^+ \cdot$ solvent may be regarded as an acid A_2 and the solvent as a base B_2. Then, rewriting equation 2, we have

$$A_1 + B_2 = A_2 + B_1 \qquad (3)$$

Hydrochloric acid in water may be taken as a specific example.

$$HCl + H_2O = H_3O^+ + Cl^-$$

The hydrated proton H_3O^+ is often called the hydronium ion. There are several types of indirect evidence that the hydrogen ion in aqueous solution can be given this formula, but presumably it is further solvated by the loose attachment of additional molecules of water. The symbol H^+ will be used to represent the hydrated hydrogen ion in the remainder of this chapter.

The extent to which an acid ionizes in different solvents depends on the base strength of the solvent, that is, the ability of the solvent to attach protons. Thus, at equal concentrations acid dissociations would be very complete in the solvent liquid ammonia and very incomplete in the solvent acetic acid. The solvent ammonia has a much greater attraction for protons than has the solvent acetic acid.

The solvation of protons leads to a leveling effect on the strength of all strong acids in a given solvent. Thus all acids which are completely dissociated in water have nearly the same acid strength in water because the actual acid is the hydrated hydrogen ion. On the other hand, various strong acids have quite different strengths in glacial acetic acid which does not solvate the hydrogen ion so strongly.

A still more general theory of acids has been proposed by G. N. Lewis,[*] who points out that substances like SO_3 and CO_2 behave as acids although they contain no hydrogen. He defines an acid as a molecule, radical, or ion which can accept an electron pair from some other atom to complete its stable quota of electrons, usually an octet. A base is a substance which can share this electron pair with an acid. In other words, an acid is an electron "acceptor," and a base is an electron "donor." This definition covers all the acids included in the proton theory of acids and many additional substances also. The fact that this concept is more general makes it less definite in describing the properties of specific acids and bases.

Ionization of Water. Water is a weak electrolyte with an ion product of 1.0×10^{-14} at $25°$, dissociating according to the reaction

$$H_2O = H^+ + OH^-$$

Rather than writing the equilibrium constant as

$$K = [H^+][OH^-]/[H_2O]$$

the concentration of water is absorbed into the ionization constant since it is very nearly constant and the *ion product* K_w is commonly used.

$$K_w = [H^+][OH^-] \tag{4}$$

* Luder, "The Electronic Theory of Acids and Bases," *Chem. Revs.*, *27*, 547 (1940); Luder and Zuffanti, *Electronic Theory of Acids and Bases*, John Wiley & Sons, New York, 1946.

The ion product of water has been carefully determined by several different methods, all of which are in excellent agreement.

Example 1. Calculate the degree of dissociation and the ion product of water at 25° from the fact that the specific conductance of the purest water has been found * to be 5.5×10^{-8} ohm^{-1} cm^{-1}. The ionic conductances at infinite dilution are $l_{H^+} = 349.8$ and $l_{OH^-} = 198$.

In pure water 18 ml contains 1 gram equivalent of H_2O. Then, the equivalent conductance Λ is given by the relation

$$\Lambda = LV = (5.5 \times 10^{-8})(18) = 9.9 \times 10^{-7}$$

$$\Lambda_0 = l_c + l_a = 349.8 + 198 = 547.8$$

$$\alpha = \frac{\Lambda}{\Lambda_0} = \frac{9.9 \times 10^{-7}}{547.8} = 1.81 \times 10^{-9}$$

The value 547.8 is the equivalent conductance of a hypothetical completely ionized water.

Since there are 1000/18 or 55.5 moles of water per liter,

$$[H^+] = [OH^-] = 55.5\alpha = (55.5)(1.81 \times 10^{-9}) = 1.00 \times 10^{-7}$$

$$K_w = [H^+][OH^-] = (1.00 \times 10^{-7})(1.00 \times 10^{-7}) = 1.00 \times 10^{-14}$$

Example 2. Calculate the ion product of water at 25° from the following data. The electromotive force of the following cell at 25° is 1.05033 volts. †

$$\text{Pt, } H_2(1 \text{ atm}); \text{ KOH}(0.01 \text{ } m), \text{ KCl}(0.01 \text{ } m); \text{ AgCl; Ag}$$

The standard electrode potential $E°$ for the cell

$$\text{Pt, } H_2; \text{ HCl}(a = 1); \text{ AgCl; Ag}$$

is 0.22239 volt at 25°.‡

$$K_w = \gamma_{H^+}c_{H^+}\gamma_{OH^-}c_{OH^-}$$

The cell reaction in both cases is $\frac{1}{2}H_2 + AgCl = H^+ + Cl^- + Ag$. Hence,

$$1.05033 = 0.22239 - (RT/nF) \ln (\gamma_{H^+}c_{H^+} \times \gamma_{Cl^-}c_{Cl^-})$$

$$= 0.22239 - \frac{RT}{nF} \ln \left[K_w \times \frac{\gamma_{Cl^-}c_{Cl^-}}{\gamma_{OH^-}c_{OH^-}} \right]$$

$$= 0.22239 - 0.05915 \log \left[K_w \times \frac{\gamma_{Cl^-} \times 0.01}{\gamma_{OH^-} \times 0.01} \right]$$

In this dilute solution, $\gamma_{Cl^-} = \gamma_{OH^-}$ very closely, although it is not accurate enough to assume that they equal unity. Hence,

$$\log K_w = (-1.05033 + 0.22239)/0.05915 = -13.997$$

$$K_w = 1.01 \times 10^{-14}$$

* Kohlrausch and Heydweiller, *Z. physik. Chem.*, *14*, 317 (1894); Jones and Bradshaw, *J. Am. Chem. Soc.*, *55*, 1800 (1933).

† Harned and Hamer, *J. Am. Chem. Soc.*, *55*, 2194 (1933).

‡Harned and Ehlers, *J. Am. Chem. Soc.*, *54*, 1350 (1932).

The ion product of water is given at various temperatures in Table I.

Table I. Ion Product of Pure Water [1]

Temperature	0°	10°	25°	40°	50°
$K_w \times 10^{14}$	0.113	0.292	1.008	2.917	5.474

[1] Harned and Hamer, *J. Am. Chem. Soc.*, *55*, 2194 (1933).

The correctness of the data of Table I can be checked further by taking the values of the ionization constant of water at two temperatures and calculating the heat of the reaction,

$$H_2O = H^+ + OH^-$$

Introducing the values for 10° and 40° into the equation

$$\Delta H = \frac{2.303R(\log K_2 - \log K_1)T_2T_1}{T_2 - T_1}$$

and solving for ΔH, we obtain 13.5 kcal mole^{-1}. This value agrees well with that found for the reverse reaction by the direct calorimetric measurement of the heat of neutralization of completely ionized acids and bases, namely, -13.8 kcal mole^{-1}.

Thus, in dilute solutions, when a strong base such as NaOH, KOH, or LiOH is neutralized with a strong acid such as HCl or HNO_3, the heat evolved is always about the same. This constancy in the heat of neutralization is easily explained by the ionization theory. Since all the reactants and all the salts are completely ionized, the sodium or potassium ions and the chloride or nitrate ions remain unchanged; and the only chemical reaction is

$$OH^- + H^+ = H_2O \qquad \Delta H = -13.8 \text{ kcal mole}^{-1}$$

It thus appears that the neutralization of a strong acid by a strong base in dilute solution consists in the combination of hydrated hydrogen and hydroxyl ions to form undissociated water. The heat of this ionic reaction is -13.8 kcal mole^{-1}. The heat of formation of water from its hydrated ions must not be confused with the heat of formation of water from its elements, or with the heat of combination of unhydrated ions.

When weak acids or bases are neutralized, not only is the heat of neutralization of H^+ and OH^- ions evolved, but, also, there is absorption of heat from the dissociation of the weak acid or base. The resulting salts are usually completely ionized. For example, the neutralization of HCN by NaOH evolves only 2.9 kcal mole^{-1}, whereas 13.8 kcal mole^{-1} would be evolved if the acid were completely ionized. The difference, 10.9 kcal mole^{-1}, represents the heat absorbed in ionizing hydrocyanic acid in water.

Ionization of Weak Acids. The ionization constants of weak acids and bases may be determined in several different ways. The most important method involves potentiometric measurements with hydrogen or glass electrodes. The conductance method has already been discussed (page 388).

The equilibrium expression for the ionization of a weak acid HA in water may be written

$$HA = H^+ + A^- \tag{5}$$

$$K_a = [H^+][A^-]/[HA] \tag{6}$$

where K_a is the ionization constant. More exactly, the ionization constant should be written in terms of activities. In the absence of information on activity coefficients, concentrations are often substituted for activities in working problems. Similarly, the pH may be considered to be equal to $-\log[H^+]$ at low concentrations of H^+, although this is an oversimplification (page 439).

Equation 6 may be used in calculating the hydrogen-ion concentration of a solution of a weak acid. In solving such a problem it is necessary to consider all the relations which must be satisfied at equilibrium. In addition to equation 6 the ion product for water must be satisfied,

$$[H^+][OH^-] = K_w \tag{7}$$

and the solution must be electrically neutral. In the present case the hydrogen-ion concentration must be equal to the sum of the concentrations of A^- and hydroxyl ions in order to maintain electrical neutrality.

$$[H^+] = [A^-] + [OH^-] \tag{8}$$

If c_a is the concentration of added weak acid

$$c_a = [HA] + [A^-] \tag{9}$$

The hydrogen-ion concentration of a solution of HA may be obtained by finding the value that satisfies equations 6, 7, and 8. Although it is possible to solve these equations simultaneously it is usually much simpler to look for satisfactory approximations, make a calculation, and test the approximation to see if it was justified. In these calculations we might expect that $[OH^-]$ would be small enough to be neglected in equation 8. When this is done substitution of equations 8 and 9 into 6 leads to

$$K_a = \frac{[H^+]^2}{c_a - [H^+]} \tag{10}$$

As a further simplification in the case of sufficiently weak acids $[H^+]$ may be neglected in the denominator, yielding

$$K_a = [H^+]^2/c_a \tag{11}$$

Example 3. Calculate the hydrogen-ion concentration and *p*H of an aqueous solution of acetic acid containing 0.1 mole per liter. Given: $K_a = 1.75 \times 10^{-5}$.

$$[H^+] = \sqrt{K_a c_a} = \sqrt{(1.75 \times 10^{-5})(0.1)}$$

$$= 1.32 \times 10^{-3} \text{ mole/l.}$$

$$pH = - \log [H^+] = 2.88$$

Thus $[H^+]$ is about 1 per cent of c_a and may be neglected in the denominator of equation 10 unless greater accuracy is required. Since, according to equation 7, $[OH^-] = (10^{-14})/(1.32 \times 10^{-3}) = 0.76 \times 10^{-11}$ mole per liter, it is seen that it was satisfactory to neglect $[OH^-]$ in equation 8 in comparison with $[A^-]$ which is equal to 1.32×10^{-3}.

The calculation of the *p*H of a solution of a weak acid containing in addition a salt of the weak acid formed with a strong base may now be considered. Such solutions are encountered in the titration of a weak acid by a strong base and are also useful as buffers (page 472). In such a solution the ionization of the weak acid is repressed by the anion of the salt, and the hydrolysis of the salt is repressed by the weak acid. Thus to a very good approximation the concentration of weak acid molecules is equal to the molar concentration of added weak acid c_a, and the concentration of anions of the weak acid is equal to the molar concentration of the added salt, which will be represented by c_s.

$$[HA] = c_a \qquad [A^-] = c_s$$

Substitution into equation 6 yields

$$K_a = [H^+]c_s/c_a \tag{12}$$

In order to make calculations of the *p*H it is convenient to write equation 12 in its logarithmic form:

$$- \log K_a = - \log [H^+] - \log (c_s/c_a) \tag{13}$$

Upon introduction of the definition of *p*H this equation becomes

$$pH = pK_a + \log (c_s/c_a) \tag{14}$$

where $pK_a = - \log K_a$. The pK_a value of a weak acid is a convenient measure of its strength. In common with the *p*H the use of negative logarithms is avoided in this way. As may be seen from equation 14, the pK_a for a weak acid is the *p*H of a solution containing equimolar quantities of salt and acid.

The acid ionization constant or pK_a depends upon the salt concentration. As long as the solution contains only the weak acid, the concentration of ions is low and the value of K_a is essentially constant. However, if the salt concentration is increased either by making a buffer mixture or by adding a neutral salt, the apparent ionization constant changes. The true thermodynamic constant is unchanged, but the ionization constant written in terms of concentrations is altered because of changes in the ionic activity coefficients. Table II shows the changes

Table II. Dissociation Constant of Acetic Acid in Potassium Chloride Solutions at 25°

Salt Molality	0	0.01	0.05	0.10	0.2
$K_a \times 10^5$	1.75	1.86	2.19	2.69	2.95
pK_a	4.76	4.73	4.66	4.57	4.53

in the ionization constant of acetic acid at 25° produced by various molalities of potassium chloride as derived from electromotive-force measurements.

Example 4. Calculate the pH at 25° of a solution containing 0.10 mole/l of sodium acetate and 0.03 mole/l of acetic acid. The value of pK_a for acetic acid in 0.1 M potassium chloride as given in Table II will give a much more accurate value than the pK_a at zero salt concentration.

$$pH = 4.57 + \log(0.10/0.030) = 5.09$$

The ionization constants and pK_a values for a number of weak acids at 25° are given in Table III. Most of these values are thermodynamic

Table III.[1] Ionization Constants of Acids in Water at 25°

Acid	K_a	pK_a
Formic	1.772×10^{-4}	3.75
Acetic	1.754×10^{-5}	4.76
Chloroacetic	1.379×10^{-3}	2.86
Propionic	1.336×10^{-5}	4.87
n-Butyric	1.515×10^{-5}	4.82
Lactic	1.374×10^{-4}	3.86
Sulfuric	$K_2 = 1.01 \times 10^{-2}$	2.00
Carbonic	$K_2 = 4.69 \times 10^{-11}$	10.33
Oxalic	$K_2 = 5.18 \times 10^{-5}$	4.29
Malonic	$K_2 = 2.014 \times 10^{-6}$	5.70
Phosphoric	$K_1 = 7.516 \times 10^{-3}$	2.12
	$K_2 = 6.226 \times 10^{-8}$	7.21
Boric	5.79×10^{-10}	9.24

[1] Harned and Owen, *The Physical Chemistry of Electrolytic Solutions*, Reinhold Publishing Corp., New York, 1950.

ionization constants, that is, values at zero electrolyte concentration, but where these have not been determined the values apply to dilute aqueous solutions.

Titration Curves of Weak Acids. The titration curve for 0.004 M acetic acid titrated with a concentrated solution of sodium hydroxide at 25° is given in *Fig. 16-1*. The pH is plotted horizontally while the number of equivalents of sodium hydroxide added to 1 equivalent of acid is plotted vertically. The pH at the midpoint of the titration is equal to the pK_a of acetic acid at this salt concentration, 4.75. The

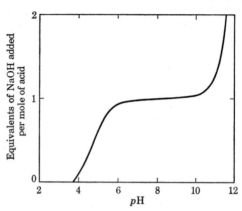

FIG. 16-1. Potentiometric titration of 0.004 M acetic acid with sodium hydroxide at 25°.

pH at any other point from about 5 to 95 per cent neutralization may be calculated with equation 14. As the end point is approached the pH changes rapidly, and the exact end point would be at the pH of a solution of sodium acetate. Since sodium acetate is slightly hydrolyzed, this pH will not be 7.0, and the method for calculating the pH of a hydrolyzed salt is discussed later (page 473).

The titration curve for 0.004 M phosphoric acid titrated with a concentrated solution of sodium hydroxide is given in *Fig. 16-2*. The three successive ionizations of phosphoric acid may be represented as

$$H_3PO_4 = H_2PO_4^- + H^+ \qquad K_1 = \frac{[H^+][H_2PO_4^-]}{[H_3PO_4]} \qquad (15)$$

$$H_2PO_4^- = HPO_4^= + H^+ \qquad K_2 = \frac{[H^+][HPO_4^=]}{[H_2PO_4^-]} \qquad (16)$$

$$HPO_4^= = PO_4^{\equiv} + H^+ \qquad K_3 = \frac{[H^+][PO_4^{\equiv}]}{[HPO_4^=]} \qquad (17)$$

For citric acid (tribasic) the values of the successive constants are enough alike so that separate steps in the titration curve are not obtained. For phosphoric acid the constants are quite different and the third ionization is so weak that it cannot be studied in dilute aqueous solutions. The first ionization of phosphoric acid is sufficiently strong so that the shape of the titration curve in the first step cannot be calculated by means of equation 14 since the assumptions are not valid.

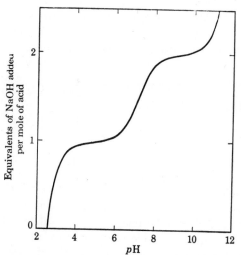

FIG. 16-2. Potentiometric titration of 0.004 M phosphoric acid with sodium hydroxide.

However, the second ionization is sufficiently weak so that the shape of the second step is in exact agreement with values calculated from equation 14. The midpoint of the second step of the titration is at pH 7.2, which is the value of pK_2.

The determination of titration curves offers one of the most convenient means for the determination of ionization constants of weak acids and bases. It is common practice to hold the salt concentration nearly constant with an added neutral salt, and then the value of K_a applies at this salt concentration. Accurate thermodynamic values may be obtained using cells without transference (page 444).

Exercise I. Sketch the titration curve for the titration of Na_2CO_3 with hydrochloric acid using $pK_1 = 6.4$ and $pK_2 = 10.3$.

Relation between Ionization Constants and Structure. From the values in Table III it may be seen that replacing one of the hydrogen atoms of acetic acid with a chlorine atom leads to an increased ionization of the carboxyl group. Apparently, the attraction of chlorine for electrons pulls the electron pair farther away from the hydrogen of the carboxyl and permits the hydrogen ion to leave with the expenditure of less energy. The substitution of more hydrogen atoms by chlorine in acetic acid further decreases the strength with which the hydrogen ion is held and gives acids with larger ionization constants. Trichloroacetic acid is so strongly ionized that its ionization constant cannot be determined with any accuracy. The substitution of $-OH$, $-CN$, or $-NO_2$ groups for hydrogen also increases the carboxyl ionization.

The influence of one atom or group on the reactivity of a near-by atom is affected by the distance and the position, as shown in the chloro-substituted benzoic acids at $25°$. In these examples the reac-

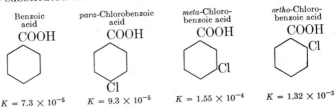

tivity of the molecule is characterized by the ease with which a hydrogen ion is released. Many other properties such as relative rates of chemical reaction with specific reactants are used to determine the influence of substituents and molecular structure on reactivity. These relations are being correlated now in terms of the electron theory of valence so that good predictions concerning acid strengths can often be made on the basis of molecular structure. The electron theory is discussed in many texts of organic chemistry.*

Ionization of Weak Bases. The dissociation of bases to give hydroxyl ions has also been the subject of extensive study. The alkali metal hydroxides are very strong bases whereas ammonia and many of the organic bases are weak.

The ionization of a weak base containing a hydroxyl group may be formulated as

$$BOH = B^+ + OH^-$$

$$K_b = [OH^-][B^+]/[BOH] \qquad (18)$$

The values of K_b for a number of weak bases are given in Table IV together with values of K_a which are defined by equations 19 and 20. A base that does not contain a hydroxyl group, aniline, for example, is

---

* Such as, for example, J. Johnson's Chapter 25 in Gilman's *Organic Chemistry*, Vol. 2, John Wiley & Sons, New York, 1943, and Remick, *Electronic Interpretations of Organic Chemistry*, John Wiley & Sons, New York, 1943.

Table IV.[1]   Ionization Constants of Bases in Water at 25°

Base	K_b	K_a	pK_a
Ammonium hydroxide	1.8×10^{-5}	5.55×10^{-10}	9.26
Aniline	3.83×10^{-10}	2.61×10^{-5}	4.58
n-Butyl amine	4.1×10^{-4}	2.4×10^{-11}	10.61
Diethyl amine	1.26×10^{-3}	7.94×10^{-12}	11.10
Ethyl amine	5.6×10^{-4}	1.78×10^{-11}	10.75
Pyridine	1.4×10^{-9}	7.1×10^{-6}	5.15
Triethyl amine	5.65×10^{-4}	1.77×10^{-11}	10.75
Urea	1.5×10^{-14}	6.7×10^{-1}	0.18

[1] Lange, *Handbook of Chemistry.*

more conveniently regarded as a substance that reacts with protons rather than as a substance that yields hydroxyl groups by dissociation. There are other advantages in formulating the ionization of a basic substance in terms of the *acid dissociation of the conjugate acid.* When this is done problems with weak bases may be handled in the same way in terms of the pH scale as for weak acids. The relation between K_b for the base and K_a for the conjugate acid may be found by dividing equation 18 into the expression for K_w.

$$K_a = K_w/K_b = [H^+][BOH]/[B^+] \tag{19}$$

which is the equilibrium constant for the ionization formulated as

$$B^+ + H_2O = H^+ + BOH$$

For a base B which does not contain a hydroxyl group, i.e., an amine

$$BH^+ = H^+ + B$$

$$K_a = [H^+][B]/[BH^+] \tag{20}$$

The values of K_a for a number of bases are also given in Table IV. The values of $pK_a = - \log K_a$ are the pH values at which the base would be half in the basic form and half in the acidic form.

If a solution contains c_b moles/l of a weak base and c_s moles/l of the salt of this weak base with a strong acid, $[BOH]$ or $[B] = c_b$ and $[B^+]$ or $[BH^+] = c_s$, equation 20 may be written

$$pH = pK_a + \log (c_b/c_s) \tag{21}$$

Example 5. Calculate the pH of a solution containing 0.10 N ammonium nitrate and 0.02 N ammonium hydroxide.

$$pH = 9.26 + \log (0.02/0.10) = 9.26 - 0.70$$
$$= 8.56$$

Glycine, $H_2N—CH_2—CO_2H$, is an example of a substance containing both a basic and an acidic group. In view of what has been said above it is convenient to consider glycine to be a dibasic acid. The two pK_a values obtained by titration are 2.3 and 9.6. Since it is to be expected from Tables III and IV that pK_a will be lower for a carboxyl group than for an amino group, $pK_a = 2.3$ must be that for the carboxyl group. In acid solution the amino group will be positively charged because of reaction with a proton, and the repulsion due to this positive charge is largely responsible for the fact that the carboxyl group of glycine is a stronger acid group than in acetic acid. The H^+ on the amino group is not removed until quite basic pH values are reached, and its pK_a is 9.6. In the pH region between these pK_a values glycine exists as a dipolar ion, $^+H_3N—CH_2—CO_2^-$, and many of its properties such as dipole moment and Raman spectrum show this interpretation to be correct.

Buffers. A buffer is a solution which contains an appreciable concentration of a weak acid or base and its salt. The addition of alkali to such a solution causes the reaction

$$OH^- + HA \rightarrow H_2O + A^-$$

while the addition of acid causes the reaction

$$H^+ + A^- \rightarrow HA$$

In either reaction the change in pH upon the addition of a small quantity of acid or base is small in comparison with that which would be observed if the acid or base were added to water. The buffering regions in Figs. 16-1 and 16-2 are those in which the slopes are the greatest. The optimum pH for a buffer is $pH = pK_a$ for the buffer weak acid or base. At 1 pH unit away from the pK_a a buffer is about 33 per cent as effective. Thus, each weak acid or base listed in Table III or IV could be used to prepare effective buffers from about 1 pH unit below its pK_a to about 1 pH unit above its pK_a.

Buffer solutions are important in analytical chemistry, in general laboratory work, and particularly in biochemistry, where it is desired to keep the number of variables to a minimum. Blood, milk, and various animal fluids are highly buffered with bicarbonate ions and carbonic acid, and with proteins. The pH of human blood in a normal person is approximately 7.4. Ordinarily variations are less than 0.1 of a pH unit, and an increase or decrease of as much as 0.4 is likely to be fatal. Different enzymes have certain pH values at which their catalytic activity is a maximum.

The type of plants growing in a certain locality is largely influenced by the pH of the soil. Forest soil with decaying leaves is likely to be acid, whereas limestone soil has a higher pH. For proper productivity of crops it is often necessary to add limestone (or sulfur, which changes to sulfuric acid) to give the proper pH to the soil.

Example 6. A buffer contains 0.04 mole of Na_2HPO_4 per liter and 0.02 mole of NaH_2PO_4 per liter. (*a*) Calculate the pH, using $pK_a = 6.84$. (*b*) One milliliter of 1 N HCl is added to a liter of the buffer. Calculate the change in pH. (*c*) Calculate the pH change to be expected if this quantity of HCl is added to 1 l of pure water.

(*a*) $$pH = 6.84 + \log (0.04/0.02) = 7.14$$

(*b*) The addition of this quantity of HCl converts 0.001 mole of Na_2HPO_4 to NaH_2PO_4.

$$pH = 6.84 + \log \frac{0.040 - 0.001}{0.020 + 0.001} = 7.11$$

$$\Delta pH = 0.03$$

(*c*) $$pH = -\log 10^{-3} = 3$$

$$\Delta pH = 7 - 3 = 4$$

Hydrolysis. It has been shown that a strong acid and a strong base react to give a salt which is completely dissociated. When such a salt is dissolved, it will dissociate to give positive and negative ions, and no change will occur in the hydrogen- and hydroxyl-ion concentrations. However, if the salt is made by neutralization of a weak acid, for example, with a strong base, the negative ions of the salt will react with the hydrogen ions of water to form the weak acid, thus upsetting the equality of free hydroxyl and hydrogen ions. The hydrolysis of sodium acetate to give an alkaline reaction is easily understood by reference to the following reactions:

$$C_2H_3O_2^- + H^+ = HC_2H_3O_2$$

$$H_2O = H^+ + OH^-$$

As the acetate ions react with the hydrogen ions to give undissociated molecules of the weak acetic acid, more and more of the water dissociates to supply hydrogen ions. Finally an equilibrium is reached at which there is a definite excess of OH^- ions over H^+ ions. Adding the above reactions yields the net reaction,

$$C_2H_3O_2^- + H_2O = HC_2H_3O_2 + OH^-$$

Ammonium chloride hydrolyzes in water to give an acid reaction because some of the hydroxyl ions from the water are removed as ammonium hydroxide, leaving an excess of hydrogen ions. Ferric chloride hydrolyzes to give an acid reaction because the hydroxyl ions are removed by the formation of ferric hydroxide, which is a very insoluble weak base.

Any method which gives the concentration of hydrogen ions in the hydrolyzed solution permits the calculation of the degree of hydrolysis x, the fraction of the salt which has reacted with water. For example, in the hydrolysis of ammonium chloride a hydrogen ion is formed for each ammonium ion which reacts with a hydroxyl ion, and so the excess concentration of hydrogen ions is equal to the number of ammonium chloride molecules which have hydrolyzed.

Example 7. When 1 mole of ammonium chloride is dissolved in 32 liters of water at 25°, a hydrogen electrode in the solution registers 0.605 volt against the normal calomel electrode. Calculate the degree of hydrolysis x.

$$pH = \frac{0.605 - 0.2802}{0.0591} = 5.48$$

$$\log [H^+] = -5.48$$

$$[H^+] = 3.3 \times 10^{-6}$$

$$x = \frac{[H^+]}{[NH_4Cl]} = \frac{3.3 \times 10^{-6}}{\frac{1}{32}} = 1.06 \times 10^{-4}$$

Exercise II. The degree of hydrolysis of a salt BA may be determined by measuring the conductance of its solution. The equivalent conductance of the unhydrolyzed salt Λ_s may be determined by measuring the conductance of the salt in the presence of one of the products of hydrolysis and deducting from it the conductance of the product added. If Λ_h is the equivalent conductance of the partially hydrolyzed salt at the same concentration, show that if the reaction is

$$BA + H_2O = HA + BOH$$

the degree of hydrolysis is given by

$$x = \frac{\Lambda_h - \Lambda_s}{\Lambda_{HA} + \Lambda_{BOH} - \Lambda_s}$$

Example 8. The equivalent conductance of a 0.0108 M solution of aniline hydrochloride is 118.6 cm^2 equiv^{-1} ohm^{-1}. When an excess of aniline is added (that is, the solution is saturated with aniline), the equivalent conductance drops to 103.6. The conductance of pure aniline in water is negligible. The equivalent conductance of hydrochloric acid at the same concentration is 411.7. Calculate the degree of hydrolysis x.

$$x = \frac{\Lambda_h - \Lambda_s}{\Lambda_{HA} + \Lambda_{BOH} - \Lambda_s} = \frac{118.6 - 103.6}{411.7 + 0 - 103.6} = 0.047$$

Calculation of Hydrolysis Constants. For a salt of a *weak acid* and a *strong base*, the hydrolysis reaction may be written

$$A^- + H_2O = OH^- + HA$$

and the equilibrium constant is given by the expression

$$K = \frac{[OH^-][HA]}{[A^-][H_2O]} \tag{22}$$

The concentration of water is regarded as constant because water is present in large excess, and the hydrolysis constant K_h is written

$$K_h = [HA][OH^-]/[A^-] \tag{23}$$

From the ion product of water

$$[OH^-] = K_w/[H^+]$$

Also, the dissociation constant of the acid K_a is

$$K_a = [H^+][A^-]/[HA]$$

Substituting these values in equation 23 gives

$$K_h = K_w/K_a \tag{24}$$

If the degree of hydrolysis of the salt is designated by x and the original concentration of the salt by c_s, then,

$$[HA] = xc_s \qquad [OH^-] = xc_s \qquad \text{and} \qquad [A^-] = (1-x)c_s$$

On substituting these values in equation 23, we have

$$K_h = K_w/K_a = c_s x^2/(1-x) \tag{25}$$

and if x, the degree of hydrolysis, is quite small,

$$x = \sqrt{K_w/K_a c_s} \tag{26}$$

Example 9. Calculate the degree of hydrolysis and pH of a 0.1 N solution of sodium acetate at 25°. The value of K_a is 2.69 × 10⁻⁵.

$$K_h = \frac{10^{-14}}{2.69 \times 10^{-5}} = \frac{0.1x^2}{1-x}$$

$$x = 6.10 \times 10^{-5}$$

$$[OH^-] = (6.10 \times 10^{-5})(0.1) = 6.10 \times 10^{-6}$$

$$[H^+] = \frac{(10^{-14})}{(6.10 \times 10^{-6})} = 1.64 \times 10^{-9}$$

$$p\text{H} = -\log[H^+] = 8.78$$

This is the pH at the equivalence point in a titration of 0.1 N acetic acid with a concentrated solution of a strong base, the point at which the number of moles of base is equal to the number of moles of acid.

A salt of a *weak base* and a strong acid hydrolyzes to give an acid reaction, according to the equation

$$B^+ + H_2O = BOH + H^+$$

and, by reasoning similar to that shown for equation 25, it is found that

$$K_h = K_w/K_b = c_s x^2/(1 - x) \tag{27}$$

Exercise III. Show that when *both acid and base* are weak and the salt hydrolyzes according to the reaction

$$H_2O + B^+ + A^- = BOH + HA$$

the hydrolysis constant is given by

$$K_h = K_w/K_b K_a$$

If the weak acid and weak base happen to have about the same ionization constant, show that the degree of hydrolysis is independent of the concentration of the salt and is given by

$$x = \sqrt{K_w/K_a K_b}$$

Indicators. Certain weak acids and bases, called indicators, change their color over a certain range of pH because the acidic and basic forms have different colors. The pH range in which the color change occurs depends upon the ionization constant of the indicator acid. In the titration of an acid with a base an indicator is chosen which has its color change in the range of the pH of the hydrolyzed salt that is formed.

The ionization of an indicator may be represented by

$$\underset{\text{(color } A)}{HIn} = \underset{\text{(color } B)}{In^-} + H^+$$

The undissociated weak acid and its ionized form have different absorption spectra because of their different molecular structure. Phenolphthalein, for example, is a weak, colorless acid which reacts with sodium hydroxide or other bases to give a salt which dissociates to give an anion which is red. Methyl orange, on the other hand, gives an acid which is pink but an anion which is orange.

The "neutral color" of an indicator is obtained when there are equal concentrations of the un-ionized acid and the anion forms giving equal quantities of the two differently colored materials. Under these conditions, since

$$[HIn] = [In^-]$$

the concentration of hydrogen ions is equal to the dissociation constant of the indicator, thus

$$[H^+] = K_{HIn}[HIn]/[In^-] = K_{HIn} \tag{28}$$

With most indicators it is difficult to detect a sharp color change over a narrow range of pH. Often it is possible to neutralize about 10 per cent of the indicator before a change in color is detectable, and the change does not appear to be complete until about 90 per cent of the indicator is neutralized. Then the visible range of color change gives values of $[HIn]/[In^-]$ from 0.9/0.1 to 0.1/0.9. This corresponds to a pH range of nearly 2.

The pH ranges in which the color changes are observed for a number of indicators are given in Table V.

Table V. Indicators

Indicator	pH Range	Indicator	pH Range
Picric acid	0.0–1.3	Bromthymol blue	6.0– 7.6
Thymol blue	1.2–2.8	Phenol red	7.2– 8.8
Bromphenol blue	3.0–4.6	Thymol blue	8.2– 9.8
Methyl orange	3.1–4.4	Phenolphthalein	8.3–10.0
Methyl red	4.4–6.0	Alizarine yellow R	10.1–12.1
Bromcresol purple	5.4–7.0	Nitramine	11.0–13.0

An indicator may be used to determine the pH of an unknown solution by comparing the color with a series of colors obtained by adding the indicator to a series of buffer solutions.

Color indicators may be used to show not only when a certain hydrogen-ion concentration is reached but also when a certain oxidation potential is reached. In the former case the color change corresponds to a definite voltage of the hydrogen electrode, whereas in the latter it corresponds to a definite voltage of an inert platinum electrode. The loss of color by the reduction of potassium permanganate is well known. The reaction takes place at a definite oxidation potential. Certain organic compounds such as diphenylbenzidine change color sharply at a given oxidation potential and pH. By having a series of these oxidation indicators and noting which one changes color when placed in a solution, the oxidation potential of the solution may be readily determined.

Products from some bacterial actions have reducing action and can be tested for by changing the color of an oxidation indicator. For example, milk that has been subjected to bacterial action will decolorize methylene blue.

Complex Ions. A number of metal ions combine with anions or neutral molecules to form ions which are referred to as complex ions. For example, CdI_2 is not completely dissociated in solution, and the species CdI^+, CdI_2, CdI_3^-, and $CdI_4^=$ are in equilibrium with Cd^{++} and

I^-. Other examples of complex ions are $Ag(CN)_2^-$, $Cu(NH_3)_4^{++}$, and $FeOH^{++}$.

The equilibria by which complex ions are formed are closely related to those already discussed in connection with acid-base equilibria and oxidation-reduction equilibria. For example, the cupric tetrammine complex may be considered to be formed by a series of equilibria.

$$Cu^{++} + NH_3 = Cu(NH_3)^{++}$$

$$Cu(NH_3)^{++} + NH_3 = Cu(NH_3)_2^{++}$$

$$Cu(NH_3)_2^{++} + NH_3 = Cu(NH_3)_3^{++}$$

$$Cu(NH_3)_3^{++} + NH_3 = Cu(NH_3)_4^{++}$$

The association constants are written as

$$K_n = \frac{[Cu(NH_3)_n^{++}]}{[Cu(NH_3)_{n-1}^{++}][NH_3]}$$

where n is the number of molecules (sometimes called ligands) associated.

Hydrogen-ion equilibria are usually studied by means of the hydrogen electrode or glass electrode, and oxidation-reduction equilibria by electromotive-force measurements. There is no universal method for studying complex-ion equilibria, but many different methods may be used. If the ligand, the substance or ion which is bound in successive steps, has acidic or basic properties, its concentration may be determined by means of a hydrogen electrode in solutions containing known total concentrations of the acidic or basic substance. For example, the concentration of free ammonia in solutions containing cupric nitrate and ammonium nitrate buffers has been determined by glass-electrode measurements,[*] and *Fig. 16-3a* gives a plot of the number of NH_3 molecules bound per copper ion for various values of $-\log [NH_3]$. Since the equilibrium constants for the binding of successive NH_3 molecules are not greatly different there are no steps in this plot. However, the values of the successive association constants may be calculated from these data; they are $K_1 = 10^{-4.15}$, $K_2 = 10^{-3.50}$, $K_3 = 10^{-2.89}$, and $K_4 = 10^{-2.13}$.

In the formation of the tetrammine mercuric ion complex, the first two ammonia molecules are bound much more strongly than the last two. In other words, the complex $Hg(NH_3)_2^{++}$ is formed at very low ammonia concentrations while $Hg(NH_3)_4^{++}$ is formed only at high ammonia concentrations as shown in Fig. 16-3b.

[*] J. Bjerrum, *Metal Ammine Formation in Aqueous Solution*, P. Haase & Son, Copenhagen, 1941.

The concentrations of colored complexes may be determined spectro-photometrically. Measurements of solubility may be used to study complex-ion equilibria in certain cases. For example, when sodium cyanide is added to silver nitrate, AgCN is precipitated, but, when an

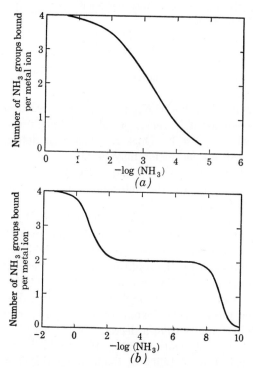

FIG. 16-3.   Formation curves for ammine complexes: (a) with Cu^{++} at 30° in 2 N NH_4NO_3; (b) with Hg^{++} at 22° in 2 N NH_4NO_3.

excess of cyanide is added, the precipitate dissolves, owing to the forma-tion of a complex ion, according to the reaction

$$AgCN + CN^- = Ag(CN)_2^-$$

Solubility of Slightly Soluble Salts.   For the solution of a slightly soluble salt A_nB_m in water which dissociates into A ions and B ions

$$A_nB_m = nA + mB$$

The equilibrium constant for this equilibrium is

$$K = a_A{}^n a_B{}^m / a_{A_nB_m} \tag{29}$$

but since $a_{A_nB_m}$ is unity if the solid A_nB_m phase is present, the *solubility product* K_{sp} may be written

$$K_{sp} = a_A{}^n a_B{}^m = (m_A{}^n m_B{}^m)(\gamma_A{}^n \gamma_B{}^m) \qquad (30)$$

By introducing the mean ionic activity coefficient $\gamma_\pm$ (page 443), this equation may be written

$$K_{sp} = (m_\pm \gamma_\pm)^{n+m} \qquad (31)$$

where $m_\pm$ is the mean ionic molality, $\sqrt[n+m]{(m_A)^n(m_B)^m}$ in the saturated solution of A_nB_m.

The thermodynamic value of K_{sp} is obtained by extrapolating values of $m_A{}^n m_B{}^m$ determined at a series of salt concentrations to zero salt concentration where $\gamma_\pm = 1$. Once K_{sp} has been determined in this way, $\gamma_\pm$ at any salt concentration may be calculated using equation 31 from the solubility measured at that salt concentration. This has been a valuable method for the determination of activity coefficients and is illustrated later in Fig. 16-4.

If $\gamma_\pm$ were simply equal to unity in electrolytic solutions, the solubility of a slightly soluble salt would not depend upon the electrolyte concentration. However, it is found that the solubility of a slightly soluble salt is *increased* by the addition of other electrolytes which do not have a common ion. For example, thallous chloride dissolves in pure water to the extent of 0.016 mole per liter, but it dissolves in 0.10-molar potassium nitrate to the extent of 0.019 mole per liter. This increase in solubility results from a decrease in the activity coefficient of thallous chloride by potassium nitrate. If the additional electrolyte is potassium chloride the solubility of thallous chloride is much reduced because of the common-ion effect, but the decrease in activity coefficient still occurs (page 447).

In making many practical calculations the activities in equation 30 are simply replaced by concentrations. In general this is satisfactory if no other electrolytes are present, since the activity coefficient is close to unity. The solubility of silver chloride in water at 25° is 1.1×10^{-5} mole per liter; since dissociation is practically complete, $[Ag^+] = [Cl^-] = 1.1 \times 10^{-5}$ and the solubility product is

$$K_{sp} = [Ag^+][Cl^-] = (1.1 \times 10^{-5})^2 = 1.2 \times 10^{-10}$$

If this ion product is exceeded in dilute aqueous solutions solid AgCl will be precipitated until the ion product is 1.2×10^{-10}. If excess chloride ions or silver ions are present the solubility of AgCl will be less than $\sqrt{K_{sp}}$.

Example 10. Calculate the solubility product of silver chromate Ag_2CrO_4 if the solubility is 8×10^{-5} mole per liter.

$$K_{sp} = [Ag^+]^2[CrO_4^=] = (0.00016)^2(0.00008) = 2 \times 10^{-12}$$

Example 11. The solubility of strontium oxalate at $20°$ is 0.00054 mole per liter. Calculate the solubility product.

$$K_{sp} = [Sr^{++}][C_2O_4^=] = (0.00054)(0.00054) = 2.9 \times 10^{-7}$$

How much strontium oxalate will be dissolved in a solution of $0.04 \ M$ sodium oxalate? Let x equal the moles of strontium oxalate which dissolve per liter.

$$K_{sp} = 2.9 \times 10^{-7} = [Sr^{++}][C_2O_4^=] = x(x + 0.04) = x^2 + 0.04x$$

$$x = 7.3 \times 10^{-6} \text{ mole}$$

(x^2 is so small in this example that it may be dropped out in solving this equation.)

A few solubility products are given in Table VI.

Table VI. Solubility Products at $25°$

AgCl	1.2×10^{-10}	$Mg(OH)_2$	$2 \ \times 10^{-11}$
AgBr	7.7×10^{-13}	CaC_2O_4	2.6×10^{-9}
AgI	0.9×10^{-16}	$CaCO_3$	9.3×10^{-8}
$SrSO_4$	2.8×10^{-7}	PbS	$1 \ \times 10^{-28}$
$BaSO_4$	1.1×10^{-10}	MnS	1.4×10^{-15}
$PbSO_4$	1.0×10^{-8}	Ag_2S	1.6×10^{-49}

Example 12. Determine the solubility of silver chloride by means of a silver electrode. The voltage E for the following cell was found to be 0.4550 volt at $25°$.

$$\text{Ag; AgCl(sat.), KCl}(0.1 \ m) \ \| \ \text{AgNO}_3(0.1 \ m); \text{Ag}$$

$$a_{Ag^+} = a_1 \qquad\qquad a_{Ag^+} = a_2$$

The activity coefficient of $0.1 \ m$ $AgNO_3$ is 0.82. Calculating the activity of silver ions in the saturated silver chloride solution at the left:

$$E = 0.4550 = -0.0591 \log \frac{a_1}{a_2} = -0.0591 \log \frac{a_1}{(0.82)(0.1)}$$

$$a_1 = 1.67 \times 10^{-9}$$

The activity coefficient of $0.1 \ m$ KCl is 0.76, and it is not appreciably changed by the very small amount of silver chloride dissolved. Then,

$$a_{Ag^+} \times a_{Cl^-} = (1.67 \times 10^{-9})(0.76 \times 0.1) = 1.27 \times 10^{-10}$$

When silver chloride is dissolved in pure water, the concentrations of silver and chloride ions are equal. Moreover, the solution is so dilute that the activities are the same as the concentrations. Then,

$$\text{Solubility} = \sqrt{[Ag^+][Cl^-]} = \sqrt{a_{Ag^+} \times a_{Cl^-}} = \sqrt{1.27 \times 10^{-10}}$$

$$= 1.13 \times 10^{-5} \text{ mole of silver chloride per 1000 g of water}$$

The Ionic Strength. Several properties of strong electrolytes have been studied in earlier chapters including the activities determined by electromotive-force measurements and the abnormal lowering of the freezing point. The total number of ions ν determines the factor by which the freezing-point depression exceeds the normal molal lowering in very dilute solution as described on p. 231. For NaCl, $\nu = 2$; for $CuSO_4$, $\nu = 2$; for $BaCl_2$, $\nu = 3$; for $K_3Fe(CN)_6$, $\nu = 4$; and so on. In more concentrated solutions the factors are smaller than these because of interionic attraction and other effects. On account of the greater attraction between ions with more than one electric charge, the salts containing high-valence ions show greater deviations from the values obtained at infinite dilution than do the univalent electrolytes.

It is useful to classify electrolytes according to the valences of the cation and anion. In the 1–1 electrolytes the positive and negative ions both have a valence of 1 as in NaCl, HNO_3, and KOH, whereas in the 2–2 electrolytes both positive and negative ions have a valence of 2 as in $ZnSO_4$ and $CuSO_4$. The first number refers to the positive ions, the second to the negative ions; thus, H_2SO_4 and K_2CO_3 are 1–2 electrolytes, $Ba(OH)_2$ and $Pb(NO_3)_2$ are 2–1, $Al(OH)_3$ is 3–1, and $Al_2(SO_4)_3$ is a 3–2 electrolyte.

When the effects of various electrolytes on the solubility of a salt, the electromotive force of an electrode, or the ionization constant of a weak electrolyte are being compared, it is found that different salts have very nearly the same effect at the same *ionic strength*. The ionic strength μ, first used by G. N. Lewis,[*] takes into account the greater effect of higher-valence ions by summing the concentrations of the ions, in gram-formula weights per liter or per 1000 g, each multiplied by the square of its valence z_i, and dividing the sum by 2. Since the divisor 2 is used the ionic strength of a 1–1 electrolyte is equal to its molarity.

$$\mu = \frac{1}{2} \sum_i c_i z_i{}^2 = \frac{1}{2} (c_1 z_1{}^2 + c_2 z_2{}^2 + \cdots + c_n z_n{}^2) \qquad (32)$$

This symbol μ must be distinguished from the same symbol μ used for chemical potential (page 150).

* Lewis and Randall, *Thermodynamics and the Free Energy of Chemical Substances*, McGraw-Hill Book Co., New York, 1923, page 373.

Example 13. Calculate the ionic strengths of the following solutions of electrolytes.

For 0.01 m NaCl, $\quad \mu = \dfrac{0.01 \times 1^2 + 0.01 \times 1^2}{2} = 0.01$

For 0.01 m CuSO$_4$, $\quad \mu = \dfrac{0.01 \times 2^2 + 0.01 \times 2^2}{2} = 0.04$

For 0.01 m H$_2$SO$_4$, $\quad \mu = \dfrac{0.02 \times 1^2 + 0.01 \times 2^2}{2} = 0.03$

It will be noted that the ionic strength for a 1–1 electrolyte is equal to its molality m while the ionic strength for a 1–2 electrolyte is 3 m and for a 2–2 electrolyte 4 m.

The theoretical justification for using the ionic strength is given by the Debye-Hückel theory, which is introduced in the next section.

The Debye-Hückel Theory.* Debye and Hückel were successful in calculating the activity coefficients of completely dissociated electrolytes in dilute solution by considering the electrical attractions and repulsions between ions. At infinite dilution the distribution of ions in an electrolytic solution can be considered to be completely random because the ions would be too far apart to exert any attraction on each other, and the activity coefficient of the electrolyte is unity. However, at higher concentrations there is a tendency for every positive ion to surround itself with negative ions and each negative ion to surround itself with positive ions. The tendency of an ion to surround itself with an "atmosphere" of oppositely charged ions is partially, but not completely, overcome by the thermal motions of the ions. The attractive or repulsive forces are governed by Coulomb's law and depend upon the magnitude of the ionic charges e_1 and e_2, the distance between ions r, and the dielectric constant D, according to the expression $e_1 e_2 / D r^2$.

Because of the attractive forces between an ion and its atmosphere, the activity coefficient of the electrolyte is reduced. We would expect that this effect would be greater for ions of high charge and greater in solvents of lower dielectric constant where the electrostatic interactions are stronger. The derivation of the Debye-Hückel equation in the Appendix (page 647) is based on the use of the Boltzmann distribution law to calculate the charge density in the ion atmosphere. For a 1–1 electrolyte, the number of positive ions dn_+ or of negative ions dn_- in a volume dV at a distance r from a particular ion will be

$$dn_+ = ne^{-e\psi/kT}\, dV$$

$$dn_- = ne^{+e\psi/kT}\, dV$$

* Debye and Hückel, *Physik. Z.*, *24*, 185, 305 (1923).

where n is the total number of positive or negative ions per cubic centimeter, k is the Boltzmann constant (R/N), e is the unit electronic charge, and ψ is the electric potential at a distance r from the central ion.

Debye and Hückel derived the following expression, which holds for strong electrolytes in dilute solution,

$$- \ln \gamma_i = \frac{e^3 z_i{}^2}{(DkT)^{3/2}} \sqrt{\frac{2\pi N\mu}{1000}} \tag{33}$$

where γ_i = activity coefficient of ion species i (page 443).

z_i = charge on ion species i.

e = charge of an electron = 4.803×10^{-10} electrostatic unit.

D = dielectric constant of the solution = 78.56 for water at 298°K.

N = Avogadro's number = 6.023×10^{23}.

k = gas constant per molecule = R/N = 1.3805×10^{-16} erg degree^{-1} molecule^{-1}.

μ = ionic strength = $\frac{1}{2}(c_1 z_1{}^2 + c_2 z_2{}^2 + c_3 z_3{}^2 + \cdots)$, the summation being taken over all the ions in the solution, where c_i is the concentration of ion species i in moles per liter.

Equation 33 shows that in dilute solution the activity coefficient of an ion depends only on its valence, the ionic strength, the dielectric constant of the medium, and the temperature. Hence, all univalent ions (both positive and negative) in the same solution will have the same activity coefficients, independent of the chemical nature of the ion.

If we introduce the mean activity coefficient $\gamma_\pm$ of the electrolyte (page 443) and put in numerical values for water at 25°, equation 33 becomes, for an electrolyte composed of just two kinds of ions,

$$- \log \gamma_\pm = 0.509 z_1 z_2 \sqrt{\mu} \tag{34}$$

The numerical constant will be different for solvents other than water and for temperatures other than 25°. In this equation z_1 and z_2 are the number of electric charges of the ions (without regard to the sign).

As a test of this equation Brönsted and LaMer * determined the solubility of three types of complex cobalt ammine salts in salt solutions of various ionic-charge types and compared the solubility with the solubility in pure water, thus obtaining values of the activity coefficients $\gamma_\pm$ of the slightly soluble salts. In *Fig. 16-4*, $- \log \gamma_\pm$ is plotted against $\sqrt{\mu}$, and the open circle on each line gives the ionic strength of the complex cobalt salt dissolved in water. The straight lines in this figure are

---

* Brönsted and LaMer, *J. Am. Chem. Soc.*, *46*, 555 (1924).

theoretical lines calculated with equation 34. The lowest line corresponds to a 1–1 cobalt compound where z_1z_2 is 1, and the slope is seen to be 0.5. The ionic strength of the solution rather than the specific nature of the added salt determines the value of $\gamma_{\pm}$. The next line corresponds to a cobalt salt of the 1–2 type where z_1z_2 has a value of 2, and

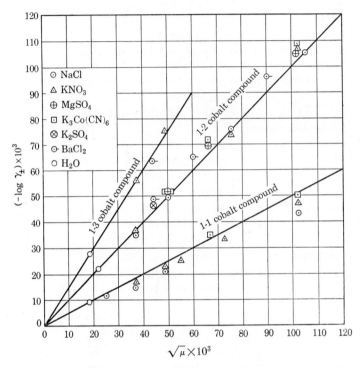

FIG. 16-4. Influence of salts of different valence type on the activity coefficients of slightly soluble cobalt ammine salts. (The various symbols indicate the salt added to increase the ionic strength.)

the slope is $2 \times 0.5 = 1$. The steepest line in Fig. 16-4 corresponds to a 1–3 compound where z_1z_2 is 3, and the slope is 1.5. Equation 34 gives a theoretical justification for the ionic strength μ which Lewis found, empirically, to be of considerable importance in the study of electrolytes. It emphasizes the fact that *in dilute solutions the activity coefficient of a given strong electrolyte is the same in all solutions of the same ionic strength, regardless of the specific electrolytes added.*

The Debye-Hückel theory has been of great value in interpreting freezing-point data, electromotive-force data, and the dependence of equilibrium constants and solubilities on salt concentration. It is a limiting law in the same sense that the ideal gas law is a limiting law at low pressures. The data of Fig. 16-4 are all for ionic strengths of less than 0.01. As the ionic strength is further increased it is found that γ deviates from that predicted with equation 34. At higher values of the ionic strength the activity coefficient usually increases with increasing salt concentration as shown in Fig. 15-6. Large deviations are encountered even at low ionic strengths if the product of the valence of the highest charged ion of the salt and the valence of the oppositely charged ion of the electrolyte medium is greater than about 4.

Attempts have been made to extend the Debye-Hückel theory to apply at higher concentrations, and forms involving semiempirical constants may be used over a wider range of ionic strengths. In concentrated electrolytic solutions there are additional effects which are difficult to interpret theoretically.

In quite concentrated solutions the nature of the solvent may be affected. There is ample evidence that many salts combine with water to form hydrates. This may be interpreted as being due to an ion-dipole attraction. Another indication that electrolytes produce a change in the properties of water is the "salting out" or decrease in solubility of nonelectrolytes produced by the addition of electrolytes. For example, the solubility of organic compounds and gases is greatly decreased when sodium chloride is added to aqueous solutions. As a practical application of this effect the extraction of solutes from water by shaking with an immiscible solvent is greatly facilitated by the addition of large quantities of electrolytes.

Another phenomenon which brings out the abnormal behavior of water in concentrated solutions is the molal depression of the freezing point. The molal depression at infinite dilution for 1–1 electrolytes is $3.7°$ and for 2–1 electrolytes is $5.56°$. When the concentration is increased, the molal depression decreases, as is to be expected from Fig. 10-4 on page 231, but, when the concentration approaches half molal, the molal depression starts to *increase;* in $MgCl_2$ and $CaCl_2$ it is larger at 1 molal than it is at infinite dilution, and in 2-molal solution it is over $9°$. The increases are but slight in electrolytes which do not form hydrates, and the large increases in $MgCl_2$ and $CaCl_2$ are probably due to the fact that these salts form hexahydrates, $CaCl_2 \cdot 6H_2O$, for example, so that at the high concentrations much of the water is tied up with the solutes, reducing the amount of normal solvent water and producing a higher *effective* concentration and, hence, an abnormally greater depression of the freezing point.

In order to avoid the changes in activity coefficients resulting from small changes of electrolyte concentration in studies of reactions in electrolytic solutions it is common practice to make such studies in the presence of an excess of electrolyte. If the concentration of the added electrolyte is much greater than that of the ions involved in the reaction, the ionic strength and the activity coefficients will be very nearly independent of the extent of reaction. Thus, although the activity coefficients cannot be calculated they are constant, and an apparent equilibrium constant or acid dissociation constant is obtained at that salt concentration.

REFERENCES

Glasstone, *Introduction to Electrochemistry*, D. Van Nostrand Co., New York, 1942.

MacInnes, *The Principles of Electrochemistry*, Reinhold Publishing Corp., New York, 1939.

Harned and Owen, *The Physical Chemistry of Electrolytic Solutions*, Reinhold Publishing Corp., New York, 1950.

Hammett, *Solutions of Electrolytes*, McGraw-Hill Book Co., New York, 1936.

Glasstone, *Textbook of Physical Chemistry*, D. Van Nostrand Co., New York, 1946.

Bell, *Acids and Bases, Their Quantitative Behavior*, Methuen & Co., London, 1952.

PROBLEMS

1. A buffer contains 0.01 mole of lactic acid and 0.05 mole of sodium lactate per liter. (a) Calculate the pH of this buffer ($pK = 3.60$). (b) Five milliliters of 0.5 N HCl is added to a liter of the buffer. Calculate the change in pH. (c) Calculate the pH change to be expected if this quantity of acid is added to 1 liter of pure water.   *Ans.* (a) 4.30. (b) 0.12. (c) 4.4.

2. Calculate the pH of (a) a 0.1 M solution of butyric acid, (b) a solution containing 0.05 M butyric acid and 0.05 M sodium butyrate, and (c) a 0.1 M solution of pure sodium butyrate. Using these data, sketch the titration curve for 0.1 M butyric acid which is titrated with a strong base so concentrated that the volume of the solution may be considered to remain constant. ($K_a = 1.48 \times 10^{-5}$; $K_w = 10^{-14}$ at 25°.)   *Ans.* (a) 2.91. (b) 4.83. (c) 8.91.

3. At 40° the ionization constant of ammonium hydroxide is 2.0×10^{-5}. (a) What is the OH$^-$ ion activity in 0.1 M NH$_4$OH? (b) What is the OH$^-$ ion activity of a solution 0.1 M with respect to ammonium hydroxide which is also 0.1 M with respect to ammonium chloride, if the latter is assumed to be completely ionized?
Ans. (a) 1.4×10^{-3}. (b) 2.0×10^{-5}.

4. The ionization constant of ammonium hydroxide is 1.4×10^{-5} at 0° and 2×10^{-5} at 40°. What is the average heat of ionization of ammonium hydroxide in this range of temperature?   *Ans.* 1515 cal mole^{-1}.

5. It can be shown that for an aqueous solution of a salt of a weak base and strong acid the hydrogen-ion concentration is given by

$$[H^+] = \sqrt{K_w c_s / K_b}$$

where c_s = concentration of the salt in moles per liter, K_w = ionization constant of water, K_b = ionization constant of base. Pyridinium perchlorate is such a salt. If $K_b = 1.6 \times 10^{-9}$, what is the pH of a 0.0001 molar solution? *Ans.* $pH = 4.60$.

6. The acid dissociation of the amino acid glycine may be formulated as

$$^+H_3NCH_2CO_2H = {}^+H_3NCH_2CO_2^- + H^+ \qquad pK_1 = 2.3$$

$$^+H_3NCH_2CO_2^- = H_2NCH_2CO_2^- + H^+ \qquad pK_2 = 9.6$$

Calculate the pH at which the concentration of the positively charged ion is equal to that of the negatively charged ion (i.e., the isoelectric point).

Ans. 6.0.

7. The solubility product of silver bromide at 18° is 4.1×10^{-13}. Calculate: (a) The solubility of silver bromide in pure water. (b) The solubility of silver bromide in 0.1 M NaBr. *Ans.* (a) 6.40×10^{-7}, (b) 4.1×10^{-12} mole per liter.

8. At 25° the potential of the cell

$$\text{Ag, AgI; KI(1 } M) \,\|\, \text{AgNO}_3(0.001 \text{ } M); \text{Ag}$$

is 0.72 volt. In a molal solution of KI the activity coefficient of I^- ion is 0.65, and in 0.001 M AgNO$_3$ the activity coefficient of Ag$^+$ ion is 0.98. (a) What is the solubility product of AgI? (b) What is the solubility of AgI in pure water?

Ans. (a) 4.0×10^{-16}. (b) 2.0×10^{-8} M.

9. What is the ionic strength of each of the following solutions? (a) 0.1 M NaCl, (b) 0.1 M Na$_2$C$_2$O$_4$, (c) 0.1 M CuSO$_4$, (d) a solution containing 0.1 M Na$_2$HPO$_4$ and 0.1 M NaH$_2$PO$_4$. *Ans.* (a) 0.1. (b) 0.3. (c) 0.4. (d) 0.4.

---

10. What concentrations of sodium acetate and acetic acid should be used to prepare an acetate buffer of pH 5.10 and 0.1 ionic strength? (Note: Only the contribution of the salt to the ionic strength needs to be considered.) ($K_{HAc} = 2.69 \times 10^{-5}$.)

11. Calculate the number of moles per liter of Na$_2$HPO$_4$ and NaH$_2$PO$_4$ which should be used to prepare a 0.10 ionic strength buffer of pH 7.30. At this ionic strength the second pK_a of phosphoric acid may be taken as 6.84.

12. How many hydrogen ions are there in 1 ml of a 0.1 M solution of an acid which has a dissociation constant of (a) 1×10^{-3}; (b) 1×10^{-8}; (c) 6×10^{-23}?

13. Calculate the concentration of (a) CO$_3^=$, (b) HCO$_3^-$, and (c) H$_2$CO$_3$,; and (d) the pH of a solution made up by dissolving 0.006 mole Na$_2$CO$_3$ and 0.004 mole NaHCO$_3$ in 1 liter of water.

$$K_1 = [H^+][HCO_3^-]/[H_2CO_3] = 4.3 \times 10^{-7},$$

$$K_2 = [H^+][CO_3^=]/[HCO_3^-] = 4.7 \times 10^{-11}.$$

14. The electromotive force of the cell

$$\text{Pt, H}_2(1 \text{ atm}); \text{ C}_6\text{H}_5\text{NH}_2\cdot\text{HCl}(0.03125 \text{ } m) \,\|\, \text{Normal calomel electrode}$$

is 0.464 volt at 25°. Calculate the per cent hydrolysis of the aniline hydrochloride.

15. In order to determine the ionization constant of the weak monobasic acid dimethyl arsinic acid a solution was titrated with a solution of sodium hydroxide using a pH meter. After 17.3 ml of sodium hydroxide had been added the pH was 6.23. It was found that 27.6 ml was required to completely neutralize the acid solution. Calculate the pK_a value.

16. The solubility of barium sulfate at 25° is 1.05×10^{-5} mole per liter. (a) What is the solubility product? (b) How much barium sulfate would dissolve in a solution having a sulfate-ion concentration of 0.01 gram ion per liter?

17. What is the ionic strength of 0.02 M solutions of each of the following substances: (a) LiCl; (b) K_2SO_4; (c) $MgSO_4$; (d) Na_3PO_4; (e) $K_4Fe(CN)_6$?

18. The free energy of formation of AgCl(s) is $-26,187$ cal at 25°. From the standard electrode potentials calculate the solubility product of AgCl, and compare it with the experimental value of 1.2×10^{-10}.

19. (a) What is the hydrogen-ion concentration of a 0.5 M solution of NH_4Br at 25° after hydrolysis? The ionization constant of NH_4OH is 1.8×10^{-5}. (b) What is the pH?

20. For the dissociation of 5-ethyl-5-hexylbarbituric acid at 25° in aqueous solution pK_a is 7.79. What is the standard free-energy change $(\Delta F°)$ for the ionization reaction?

---

21. Five grams of lactic acid is diluted with water to 1 liter. How many gram ions of hydrogen are present in the solution at 25°? The dissociation constant of lactic acid is 1.36×10^{-4} at this temperature.

22. For benzoic acid at 25° the ionization constant is 7.3×10^{-5}. Calculate the pH of a 0.001 M solution of benzoic acid at 25°.

23. A 0.1 M solution of iodic acid HIO_3 is 72.5 per cent dissociated. Calculate the freezing point of this solution, assuming that the degree of dissociation does not change with the temperature.

24. The ionization constants at 25° for acetic acid, lactic acid, and bromoacetic acid are 1.8×10^{-5}, 1.4×10^{-4}, and 1.4×10^{-3}, respectively. (a) Calculate α for a 0.01 M solution of each of these acids by the approximate method (assuming $1 - \alpha = 1$) and (b) by the exact method (see p. 388).

25. (a) Calculate and record in tabular form the degree of hydrolysis x of a 1.0 N solution of a salt of a weak acid and a strong base if the ionization constant for the acid is 10^{-4}, 10^{-6}, and 10^{-10}. (b) Repeat the calculation of (a) for a 0.01 N solution.

26. Calculate the pH at 25° of a buffer solution containing 50 ml of 0.2 M potassium hydrogen phthalate and 45.45 ml of 0.2 M NaOH solution all diluted to 200 ml. The dissociation constant for the second hydrogen of phthalic acid at 25° is 3.1×10^{-6}.

27. The hydrolysis constant of aniline hydrochloride is 2.25×10^{-5}, and the ionization constant of aniline is 4.2×10^{-10} at 25°. Calculate the concentration of the H^+ and OH^- ions in water.

28. The specific conductance of a saturated solution of AgCl in water was found to be 2.279×10^{-6} ohm^{-1} cm^{-1}. The specific conductance of the water used was 1.16×10^{-6} ohm^{-1} cm^{-1}. Using the table of ionic conductances, page 397, calculate: (a) the solubility of AgCl in grams per liter; (b) the solubility product of AgCl.

29. A solution of sodium chloride has an ionic strength of 0.24. (a) What is its concentration? (b) What concentration of Na_2SO_4 would have the same ionic strength? (c) What concentration of $MgSO_4$?

30. What is the ionic strength of a 0.4 M solution of: (a) $MnCl_2$; (b) $MnSO_4$; (c) $AuCl_3$; (d) $Fe_2(SO_4)_3$?

31. $\qquad 2Ag + CO_3^= = Ag_2CO_3 + 2e \qquad E° = -0.50$ at 25°

$\qquad Ag^+ + \tfrac{1}{2}H_2 = H^+ + Ag \qquad E° = 0.799$ at 25°

What is the solubility of Ag_2CO_3 in moles per liter at this temperature?

32. The first ionization constant of H_2S in water is 9.1×10^{-8}; the second is 1.2×10^{-15}. The solubility of H_2S in water is 3.4 grams per liter. How many

grams of $Pb(NO_3)_2$ added to 1 liter of saturated H_2S solution will just start precipitation of PbS?

33. Show that if K_a and K_b do not differ by more than a hundredfold the H^+ concentration and the OH^- concentration will be *practically* equal in the solution of the hydrolyzed salt.

34. Calculate the free energy of neutralization of a mole of strong acid by a mole of strong base in a dilute aqueous solution at $25°$, K_w being 10^{-14}.

35. In the hydrolysis of a salt of a strong base and weak acid show that

$$[H^+] = \sqrt{K_a K_w / c_s}$$

where K_a = ionization constant of the acid, K_w = ion product of water, and c_s = concentration of salt in moles per liter. Derive the expression for the pH of such a solution. How will an increase in concentration of salt affect the pH of the solution? Test this by calculating the pH of 0.1 N and of 1 N sodium isobutyrate at $25°$ ($K_a = 0.98 \times 10^{-5}$).

36. Given an amphoteric electrolyte XOH capable of dissociating according to both of the equations

$$XOH = XO^- + H^+ \qquad XOH = X^+ + OH^-$$

If the basic dissociation constant is K_b and the acidic dissociation constant K_a, derive the expression for the hydrogen-ion concentration in a solution of this electrolyte as a function of the concentration of the un-ionized substance.

17

Colloids

Introduction. In the course of his investigations on diffusion in solutions, Thomas Graham * drew a distinction between "colloids" such as proteins, gums, and polysaccharides, and "crystalloids," which are salts and substances of lower molecular weight. It was possible to distinguish between these two classes of substances since colloids did not diffuse through membranes whereas crystalloids did, and this separation process was called *dialysis*. The classifications received their names from the fact that "colloids" (from the Greek "glue-forming") left apparently amorphous solids upon evaporation of the solvent whereas "crystalloids" left crystals. Actually many proteins form crystals although they do not diffuse through membranes. That the important distinction between crystalloids and colloids is the matter of size is emphasized by the fact that many substances exist both as colloids and crystalloids; for example, colloidal gold and gold salts.

It is arbitrary to set any exact limits to the colloidal size range, but it is usually considered to include particles or molecules with dimensions in the range 10 A to 10,000 A, or 0.001 μ to 1 μ.† The dimensions of simple molecules lie below about 10 A, while particles as large as 1 μ may be seen with a microscope with visible light. Table I gives some landmarks in the land of intermediate dimensions.

Table I. Range of Sizes

C—C bond	1.5 A
Radii of particles in gold sol	20–200 A
Radii of smallest protein molecules	
(M = molecular weight = 15,000)	20 A
γ-Globulin molecule (M = 160,000)	30 × 30 × 150 A
Tobacco mosaic virus (M = 42 × 10^6)	140 × 140 × 2500 A
Limit of resolution of visible light microscope	About 2500 A
Radii of bacterial cells	About 10,000 A

If the particles of a substance are reduced in size until the dimensions become submicroscopic and are distributed throughout a second substance, the resulting system is called a *dispersed system*. The particles

* Graham, *Trans. Roy. Soc. London, 151*, 183 (1861).
† The symbol μ refers to a micron, which is 10^{-6} meter, 10^{-4} cm, or 10^{-3} mm.

are the *dispersed phase*, and the suspending liquid, gas, or solid is called the *dispersion medium*. Many of the characteristic properties of dispersed systems are attributable to the enormous surface of the dispersed phase. If a cube of any substance 1 cm on an edge, having a total surface of 6 sq cm, is cut in half in the three directions, there will be 8 cubes having edges of 0.5 cm, and the surface will be $8 \times 6 \times 0.5^2$ or 12 sq cm. If cut into 1000 cubes 1 mm on an edge, the total surface will be 60 sq cm. If the cubes are 1 μ on an edge, the surface area will be increased to 60,000 sq cm, or 6 sq m. If the cubes are 0.001 μ on an edge, there will be 10^{21} cubes, and the area will be 6000 sq m or $1\frac{1}{2}$ acres. It is obvious that surface effects which are undetected on material having an area of 6 sq cm may become very pronounced when the material is dispersed to give a total surface of many square meters. One of the most important results of this large surface is the adsorption of ions and other materials by the particles. This adsorption may lead to the accumulation of electric charges on the particles which prevent them from collecting into large aggregates.

Many different methods have been used to classify colloids. They are referred to as *lyophobic* if there is little affinity between the dispersed phase and the medium, as in colloidal metals in water. In *lyophilic* colloids, such as gelatin or proteins in water and rubber or high polymers in organic solvents, there is a strong affinity of the dispersed phase for the medium. A colloidal solution is sometimes called a sol.

Substances that spontaneously pass into the dispersed form when placed in contact with the solvent are called *intrinsic* colloids. Such solutions (e.g., of proteins and polymers) are thermodynamically stable. The *extrinsic* or accidental colloids, which represent dispersions of ordinary insoluble materials formed by grinding or by precipitation, are thermodynamically unstable. Colloidal precipitates may be formed by adding concentrated reagents together rapidly, the opposite of the procedure for the formation of precipitates which are to be filtered for operations in analytical chemistry. Material in solution may sometimes be thrown out in the colloidal state by mixing the solution with a second solvent in which the material is less soluble. For example, sulfur dissolved in alcohol is obtained as a white milky colloidal suspension when poured into an excess of water.

Liquids or solids can be effectively dispersed in liquids by means of the *colloid mill*. Large drops or coarse particles are suspended in water or other liquid and exposed to a powerful shearing force in the mill by passing the material between two accurately machined disks which rotate in opposite directions at a very high velocity while nearly touching each other.

Much of the early research on the principles of colloid chemistry was carried out with dispersions of colloidal metals. Although these are not of much practical importance, they formed excellent systems for these early studies, and are convenient models for learning about the stability of lyophobic colloids in general. An important method for preparing colloidal metals, first used by Bredig, consists of striking an arc between two metal electrodes under a solvent like ether. This is a condensation method since the vapor of the metal is condensed to form particles of colloidal size.

It is convenient to distinguish between colloids consisting of (1) small solid particles having the same internal structure as the bulk solid phase, (2) aggregates formed from smaller molecules, and (3) molecules of sufficient size that their dimensions fall in the colloid size range. A gold sol is an example of the first type. Soaps and detergents consist of organic molecules with both hydrophobic and hydrophilic parts which aggregate to form *micelles*. In these micelles, which may contain as many as 100 molecules, the hydrophobic parts are together on the inside and the hydrophilic parts are on the outside. Proteins and high polymers are examples of the third type. These substances consist of molecules in the same sense as do substances of lower molecular weight, but an important characteristic they have in common with colloidal particles and micelles is their size.

Organic macromolecules may be prepared by condensation reactions and addition reactions. The polymerization of nylon from diamines and diacids is an example of the first type. The molecular weight of a condensation polymer increases continuously during the reaction in which water is split out. The polymerization of styrene is an example of the second type. The reaction must be initiated by a catalyst, and then chain growth proceeds by way of a very rapid free radical chain mechanism. Thus, in contrast to a condensation polymerization each molecule grows to its full size extremely rapidly, and so the molecular weight of the polymer product is independent of the extent of reaction. The two different types are indicated respectively by nylon and polystyrene.

Dialysis. This method of separating colloids from lower-molecular-weight substances was introduced by Graham.

Various natural and artificial membranes may be used for dialysis; Visking sausage casings of regenerated cellulose are widely used, or sacks of thin collodion may easily be prepared. These membranes contain small pores which provide continuous *channels* for the solution, through which dissolved molecules and ions can diffuse but the large colloid particles cannot. Dialysis may be regarded as a process of fractional diffusion of solutes and colloids; it is not to be confused with osmosis, in which nothing but solvent can pass through the semipermeable membrane. The rate of dialysis depends on many factors—the area of the dialyzer, the size of the pores, the temperature, the electric charges, and the relative concentration of solution on the two sides of the membrane.

In the process of *electrodialysis*, the dialyzing chamber is placed between two electrodes and the ions migrate from the colloidal solution to the electrode which is opposite in sign.

In the process of *ultrafiltration* the liquid medium as well as the material in true solution is removed from the colloidal material. Pressure is applied to the solution in a strong cylinder so as to force the liquid through the very small holes of a special membrane. Filter papers may be used for ultrafiltration if they are first impregnated with solutions of collodion in acetic acid. Graded filters of different effective pore size can be made by changing the concentration of the acid. Ultrafiltration is a complex process, involving electric attraction and adsorption by the filter as well as ordinary mechanical separation.

Ultrafilters are useful in removing impurities from sols, that is, colloidal suspensions, and they find extensive application in bacteriology. Bacteria can generally be removed from solutions by ultrafilters, but viruses such as those connected with the common cold pass through fine ultrafilters.

Optical Behavior of Colloidal Solutions. Faraday found that a narrow beam of light passing through a suspension of colloidal gold was plainly visible when viewed against a dark background although the sol appeared quite clear. He suspected that the light was being scattered by the small particles of gold. Tyndall noted that the scattered light was polarized and bluish in color and that the transmitted light was reddish although the incident light was white. Rayleigh, who investigated the theory of the scattering in 1899, showed that the intensity of light scattered by small isotropic particles (particles having the same properties in all directions) is inversely proportional to the fourth power of the wavelength of the light used. Thus, blue light is scattered to a greater extent than red light, and therefore the light transmitted through a suspension of particles is reddish. We are familiar with these effects in the blue sky and the red sunset.

Zsigmondy's examination of the Tyndall effect under a microscope led to the development of the ultramicroscope. In an ultramicroscope a powerful beam of light is brought to a focus within the colloidal solution and this region of the solution is viewed through a microscope with its axis at right angles to the beam of light. If the particles have sufficiently different refractive index from the medium it is possible to see spots of light even though the particles are below the resolving power of the microscope. It is not possible to discern the shape of particles with an ultramicroscope, since only spots of light are seen, but elongated particles do twinkle or scintillate when they are illuminated from one side. The ultramicroscope has been of great value in the development of colloid chemistry, since the motion of the particles may be observed and the number of particles in a given volume may be counted. For example, in a solution of colloidal gold the total amount of gold per milliliter can be determined by chemical analysis and the average weight of a particle determined from a knowledge of the number of particles per milliliter.

Example 1. In the field of an ultramicroscope, 20 particles of colloidal mercury were observed. This field, approximately 0.02 mm wide, comprised a volume of 1×10^{-12} liter, so that the concentration was 2×10^{13} particles per liter. A liter of this colloidal mercury solution was stirred rapidly with a metal stirrer until all the mercury had amalgamated with the stirrer and thus had been removed from solution. The increase in weight of the stirrer was 8 mg. Assuming that the particles of mercury were spherical and that they had a density of 13.5 g cm^{-3}, calculate the average radius of the colloidal particles.

$$0.008 = (2 \times 10^{13})(\tfrac{4}{3})(3.14)r^3(13.5)$$

$$r = 1.9 \times 10^{-6} \text{ cm or 190 A}$$

These small colloid particles can be detected with the ultramicroscope only if their refractive index differs from that of the medium in which they are suspended. With metallic colloids this difference is large, and excellent definition is obtained, making possible the detection of particles as small as 0.004 μ or 40 A in diameter.

The development of the *electron microscope* has made it possible to "see" particles or molecules throughout most of the colloidal size range. The electron microscope is based upon the fact that a beam of electrons which has been accelerated in an electrical field has properties similar to those of a beam of light, and it can be deflected in electrostatic or electromagnetic fields just as visible light is deflected by lenses. In the standard instruments the accelerating potential is about 50,000 volts, which produces a wavelength of about 0.05 A. The maximum resolving power attained in electron microscopes is about 15 A.

The specimen to be studied is placed on a very thin collodion film supported on a grid. In those parts of the specimen which are thicker or denser the electrons are scattered more, but, where it is thin, the electrons continue on their course and are focused on a fluorescent screen or photographic plate. The sample is maintained in a vacuum, and so

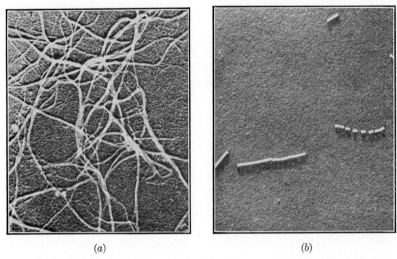

(a)   (b)

FIG. 17-1. Electron photomicrographs of (a) a fibrin clot, ×35,000; and (b) the tobacco plant mosaic virus, ×50,000. Courtesy Dr. Paul Kaesberg, University of Wisconsin.

it is not possible to study living things or solutions directly. Samples of proteins or other substances which do not scatter the electrons well may be covered with a thin film of gold or other metal which is evaporated from a filament in a vacuum. Since the atoms evaporating from the filament travel in straight lines they are not deposited in the "shadows" of tiny particles. Two electron photomicrographs obtained by shadowing with uranium are shown in *Fig. 17-1*. The molecular weight of tobacco mosaic virus obtained from measurements of the electron photomicrograph, $M = 43 \times 10^6$, is in good agreement with the values obtained by sedimentation and diffusion experiments.

Determination of Molecular Weight by Light Scattering.* Some light is scattered even by a pure liquid, because it is inhomoge-

* Bender, "The Use of Light Scattering for Determining Particle Size and Molecular Weight and Shape," *J. Chem. Education, 29,* 15 (1952).

neous on a microscopic scale. That is, the number of molecules in a very small element of volume is not constant but fluctuates because of thermal motion. The scattering by a solution is greater because of local differences due to fluctuations in concentration. The magnitude of these fluctuations is related to the osmotic work required to cause a change in concentration. Thus, Einstein was able to relate the scattering intensity of a solution to its osmotic pressure and the change in refractive index produced by the solute.

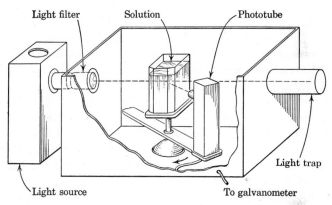

FIG. 17-2.   Apparatus for measuring light scattered by a solution.

The study of the intensity of light scattered by polymer or protein solutions offers an important method for the determination of molecular weight and shape of these large molecules.*   A measure of the light scattered by a solution is the turbidity τ, which is defined by

$$I = I_0 e^{-\tau l} \tag{1}$$

where I_0 is the incident intensity and I the intensity after passing through a length l of solution. This equation is similar to Beer's law (page 69) but is not to be confused with it. Theory shows that for a given concentration in grams per liter the turbidity is proportional to the molecular weight, whereas it will be recalled that the osmotic pressure of such a solution is inversely proportional to molecular weight. The turbidity of solutions of proteins or high polymers is so small that measurements of the decrease in intensity of the transmitted light are not practical. However, the light scattered at a particular angle may be measured accurately with a relatively simple photometer and used to calculate τ. Such an apparatus is shown in *Fig. 17-2*. Measurements

* Debye, *J. Phys. Colloid Chem.*, *51*, 18 (1947).

of the intensity of light scattered at any angle (usually 90°) may be used to obtain the molecular weight of small isotropic molecules by means of the equation

$$Hc/\tau = (1/M) + 2Bc \tag{2}$$

where M is the molecular weight, c is concentration, H is a complex constant involving a number of parameters including the refractive index increment (dn/dc) for the high-molecular-weight component in the solvent used and the wavelength of the light, and B is a constant which represents the deviation from ideality in concentrated solutions and is the same constant which would be obtained from the measurement of osmotic pressure of the same solutions as described below. Thus, Hc/τ is plotted versus c and extrapolated to $c = 0$ to obtain the value of $1/M$.

The intensity of scattered light also varies with the angle of observation. In order to obtain the molecular weights of molecules which have dimensions comparable to the wavelength of light or larger, measurements at several angles are required but information concerning the shape of the molecule is also obtained. Since the amount of light scattered is very small, special care must be taken to free the solution of dust particles which would themselves scatter considerable light.

Osmotic Pressure. The osmotic pressure is the only colligative property (page 212) which offers a practical method for the determination of molecular weights in the range above 10,000. For example, an aqueous solution containing 10 g l^{-1} of a substance of $M = 20,000$ would show a freezing-point lowering of 0.001°, a boiling-point elevation of 0.00025°, but an osmotic pressure of 128 mm of water. A slight trace of an impurity of low molecular weight might cause a freezing-point lowering or boiling-point elevation greater than this, but would pass through the membrane in an osmotic-pressure determination and not contribute to the pressure.

As discussed earlier (page 225), the van't Hoff equation represents the limit approached by real solutions at low concentrations of the solute. To extend the equation to higher concentrations it may be written

$$\pi/c = (RT/M) + Bc \tag{3}$$

in which π is osmotic pressure. In using this equation osmotic pressures are measured for a series of concentrations, and a plot of π/c versus c is extrapolated to zero concentration. Then M may be calculated from

$$\lim_{c \to 0} (\pi/c) = RT/M$$

A sample of a synthetic polymer contains molecules of a range of molecular weights, and so the molecular weight obtained from equation 3 must be an average value. In osmotic-pressure measurements, all molecules count equally, whether large or small, so that the *number average molecular weight* M_n is obtained.

$$M_n = \sum_i n_i M_i / \sum_i n_i \qquad (4)$$

Here n_i is the number of molecules of molecular weight M_i per liter. Other methods yield the *weight average molecular weight* M_w, which is defined by

$$M_w = \sum_i n_i M_i^2 / \sum_i n_i M_i \qquad (5)$$

Thus the weight average molecular weight must always be greater than the number average molecular weight, except for a sample in which all the molecules have the same weight so that $M_n = M_w$.

In solutions of proteins or other colloidal electrolytes it is necessary to distinguish between the *total osmotic pressure* which would be obtained with a membrane impermeable to both salt and protein and the *colloid osmotic pressure* which is obtained with a membrane permeable to salt ions but not to the protein. The latter type of membrane is always used when it is desired to obtain the molecular weight of the protein or other colloidal electrolyte.

In the case of colloidal electrolytes mixed with salts the measured osmotic pressure is greater than that expected for the colloidal ions alone. This is a result of the fact that, although the salt ions may pass through the membrane, they will not be distributed equally at equilibrium. This effect was discussed by Donnan and may be illustrated as follows: Let the colloidal ion which cannot pass through the membrane be represented by A^-, and let the salt be NaCl.

At equilibrium the activity of the salt must be the same on both sides of the membrane.

$$a''_{NaCl} = a'_{NaCl} = a''_{Na^+} \times a''_{Cl^-} = a'_{Na^+} \times a'_{Cl^-} \qquad (6)$$

A single prime is used to designate the pure NaCl solution at the right and a double prime to designate the solution containing the colloidal electrolyte and the salt. If it is assumed that activities may be replaced by concentrations,

$$c''_{Na^+} \times c''_{Cl^-} = c'_{Na^+} \times c'_{Cl^-} \qquad (7)$$

There is an additional condition which must be met, namely, the solutions must be electrically neutral.

$$c''_{Na^+} = c''_{Cl^-} + c''_{A^-} \qquad c'_{Na^+} = c'_{Cl^-} \qquad (8)$$

Combination of equations 7 and 8 leads to

$$(c'_{Cl^-}/c''_{Cl^-})^2 = 1 + (c''_{A^-}/c''_{Cl^-}) \qquad (9)$$

which shows how the salt will be distributed at equilibrium.

When it is desired to obtain the molecular weight of a protein from osmotic-pressure measurements it is necessary to take the Donnan equilibrium into account.* In order to minimize the Donnan effect, osmotic-pressure measurements on proteins are made in fairly concentrated salt solutions at the isoelectric point (page 516) of the protein.

The construction of a simple osmometer is illustrated in *Fig. 17-3*. The solution to be studied is placed inside the bulb attached to the capillary, and the solvent is placed outside. The osmotic pressure is calculated from the equilibrium height of the liquid in the capillary after applying a correction for capillary rise.

Example 2. The osmotic pressures of a series of solutions of a sample of polystyrene in methyl ethyl ketone are measured at 25°. When the pressure is expressed in height of the methyl ethyl ketone solution in centimeters, and concentration is expressed as g cm^{-3}, the intercept of a graph of π/c versus c is found to be 110 cm^4 g^{-1}. Calculate the number average molecular weight of this sample of polystyrene. First, it is convenient to express π/c in atm l g^{-1} by use of the densities of methyl ethyl ketone (0.80 g cm^{-3}) and mercury (13.6 g cm^{-3}).

$$\frac{(110 \text{ cm}^4 \text{ g}^{-1})(0.80 \text{ g cm}^{-3})}{(13.6 \text{ cm}^{-3})(76.0 \text{ cm Hg atm}^{-1})(1000 \text{ cm}^3 \text{ l}^{-1})} = 85 \times 10^{-6} \text{ atm l g}^{-1}$$

$$\lim_{c \to 0} (\pi/c) = RT/M$$

$$85 \times 10^{-6} \text{ atm l g}^{-1} = (0.082 \text{ l atm deg}^{-1} \text{ mole}^{-1})(298 \text{ deg})/M$$

$$M = 290,000 \text{ g mole}^{-1}$$

Brownian Motion. The English botanist Robert Brown observed the motion of pollen grains and other microscopic objects suspended in a liquid. As shown by the microscope very small particles suspended

---

* Scatchard, *J. Am. Chem. Soc.*, *68*, 2315, 2320 (1945).

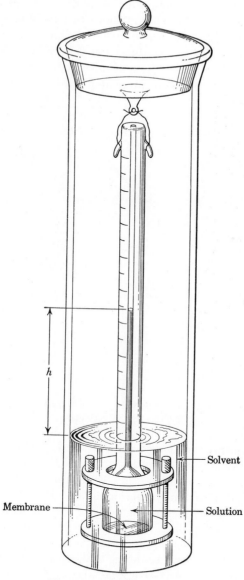

Fig. 17-3. Simple osmometer.

in a liquid are in a state of ceaseless erratic motion. In interpreting his results in 1827 Brown stated that "the movements arose neither from currents in the fluid nor from its gradual evaporation, but belonged to the particle itself." This motion, which is shown to an even greater extent by smoke particles, is due to the fact that the summated impacts of molecules on the sides of a small particle do not at every instant cancel exactly. Brownian motion constitutes a visual confirmation of the random kinetic motion which had been assumed for the molecules of a gas (or liquid or solid) at any temperature above absolute zero.

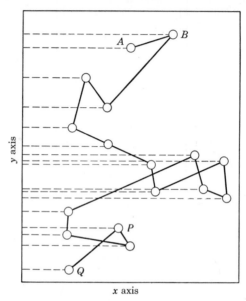

FIG. 17-4.   Movement of a colloidal particle from A to Q with intermediate positions shown every 30 seconds.

The displacements are at random, and the direction changes so fast that it is impossible to measure the velocities of the particles, but it is possible to make a quantitative study by determining the position of an individual colloid particle at regular intervals. In *Fig. 17-4* each circle represents the position of the same colloid particle at intervals of 30 seconds while it moves along a path from A to B and on to P and Q. The lengths of the dashed lines give the x coordinates of the particle. The apparent displacement Δx during a 30-second time interval is the difference between two successive x distances. For example, in going from A to B, Δx is obtained by subtracting the length of the second dashed line from that of the top one. Of course there are also displacements along the z axis, which is perpendicular to the plane of the paper.

Einstein showed that there is a relation between the Brownian displacements and the frictional coefficient of the particle. The frictional coefficient f is the force required to give the particle a velocity of 1 cm per second. This relation is

$$\frac{\overline{(\Delta x)^2}}{2\Delta t} = \frac{RT}{Nf} \tag{10}$$

where $\overline{(\Delta x)^2}$ is the mean value of the square of the displacements in the x direction, Δt is the time between observations, and R, T, and N have their usual significance. For a spherical particle in a continuous suspension medium and nonturbulent flow the frictional coefficient f is simply related to the radius r of the sphere by the equation

$$f = 6\pi\eta r \tag{11}$$

In this relation, which is due to Stokes, η is the viscosity of the solvent. Substitution of equation 11 into equation 10 yields a relation from which the radius of a spherical particle may be calculated.

$$\frac{\overline{(\Delta x)^2}}{2\Delta t} = \frac{RT}{N6\pi\eta r} \tag{12}$$

Perrin used this equation in connection with data on spherical particles of known radius r to calculate one of the early values of Avogadro's number N.

Diffusion. We are familiar with the fact that dissolved substances diffuse from a region of higher concentration to a region of lower concentration. Thus, diffusion is a spontaneous process and is accompanied by a decrease in free energy. Diffusion is closely related to Brownian motion, and indeed we may consider that the molecules or particles of a substance diffuse because of their Brownian motion.

The tendency of a substance to diffuse may be expressed as its diffusion coefficient D, which is defined by Fick's law. Fick found that for diffusion in one direction the flow J of a substance through a plane perpendicular to the direction of diffusion is directly proportional to the rate with which concentration changes with distance, dc/dx, the concentration gradient.

$$J = -D(dc/dx) \tag{13}$$

The negative sign indicates that the flow is in the direction opposite to that in which c increases. This equation is analogous to those for the flow of electric current (which is proportional to the potential gradient according to Ohm's law) and the flow of heat (which is proportional to the temperature gradient).

Diffusion coefficients may be measured by a number of different methods.* For example, the rate of diffusion from solution to solvent through a porous plate may be measured. Probably the most widely used methods are those in which a sharp boundary is formed between solution and solvent as illustrated in *Fig. 17-5a.* Initially the plot of concentration on the horizontal axis versus height in the cell on the vertical axis has the shape indicated in *b.* At a later time this bound-

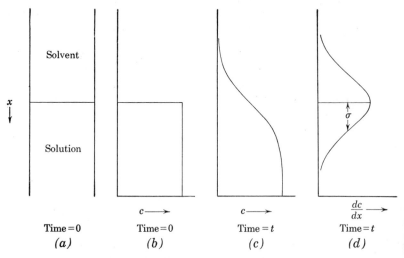

FIG. 17-5.   Diffusion of solute into solvent from an initially sharp boundary in a cell of uniform cross section.

ary will have become diffuse and the concentration will vary with height as illustrated in *c.* Instead of an abrupt change in concentration there is a more gradual one. If the solute were a colored substance, its concentration could be determined as a function of height by photographing the cell. One of the most generally useful methods for determining the diffuseness of the boundary depends upon measuring the deflection of light by the refractive-index gradient caused by the concentration gradient.† Since the bending of a light ray by the refractive-index gradient in such a boundary is proportional to the concentration gradient dc/dx, the curve obtained with such an optical system (the *schlieren* optical system) has the shape indicated in *d.* This curve has the shape of a normal probability curve if D in equation 13 is independent of concentration. The diffusion coefficient may be determined from the

* Longsworth, *Ann. N. Y. Acad. Sci.*, *46*, 209 (1945).
† Longsworth, *Ind. Eng. Chem.*, *Anal. Ed.*, *18*, 219 (1946).

shape of this curve in several ways. For example,

$$D = \sigma^2/2t \tag{14}$$

where σ is the standard deviation (half the width of the probability curve at the inflection point).

If the flow J is expressed in g cm^{-2} sec^{-1} and the concentration gradient in g cm^{-4}, it is seen that the diffusion coefficient will have the units of cm^2 sec^{-1}. The diffusion coefficient for potassium chloride in very dilute solution in water at 25° is 199×10^{-7} cm^2 sec^{-1}, and for sucrose it is 52.3×10^{-7} cm^2 sec^{-1}. These values may be compared with values for several proteins given on page 510.

The diffusion coefficient is related to the frictional coefficient f by

$$D = RT/Nf \tag{15}$$

which is derived in the Appendix on page 650. In the case of spherical particles or molecules, Stokes's law (equation 11) may be introduced.

$$D = RT/N6\pi\eta r \tag{16}$$

Thus, in the case of spherical particles the radius may be calculated from the measured diffusion coefficient. Since it is more familiar to think of size in terms of molecular weight, the relation between D and the molecular weight of the spherical particle may be derived from equation 16 by introducing

$$M\bar{v}/N = \tfrac{4}{3}\pi r^3 \tag{17}$$

where $\bar{v}$ is the partial specific volume (page 202).

$$D = \frac{RT}{N6\pi\eta} \sqrt[3]{\frac{4\pi N}{3M\bar{v}}} \tag{18}$$

Of course if the particles or molecules are not spherical, the value of the molecular weight calculated from equation 18 will not be correct, but D and a value for the sedimentation coefficient (page 509) may be combined to obtain an exact value for the molecular weight.

Example 3. Calculate the value of the diffusion coefficient at 25° of a spherical molecule with a molecular weight of 10,000 and a partial specific volume of 0.730 cm^3 g^{-1}. The viscosity of water at this temperature is 0.008937 poise.

$$D = \frac{(8.31 \times 10^7 \text{ erg deg}^{-1} \text{ mole}^{-1})(298 \text{ deg})}{(6.02 \times 10^{23})(6\pi)(0.00894)} \sqrt[3]{\frac{4\pi(6.02 \times 10^{23})}{3(10^4)(0.730)}}$$

$$= 17.1 \times 10^{-7} \text{ cm}^2 \text{ sec}^{-1}$$

Since the cube root of the molecular weight is involved, the diffusion coefficient of a molecule 1000 times as heavy ($M = 10^7$) would be 1.71×10^{-7} cm^2 sec^{-1}.

Sedimentation. The measurement of the velocity of sedimentation of particles due to the force of gravity or to a centrifugal field gives information concerning their size. If the dispersed particles are sufficiently large and dense they settle out under the action of the earth's field. The velocity with which they sediment is that velocity at which the force of gravity is exactly balanced by the frictional force of the particle moving through the suspension medium.

The radius of spherical particles may be calculated from the velocity of sedimentation if their density is known. The force causing sedimentation is equal to the effective mass of the particle times the acceleration of gravity g. Since a particle of density ρ is buoyed up by the suspension medium having a density of ρ_0, the force causing sedimentation is

$$\tfrac{4}{3}\pi r^3(\rho - \rho_0)g$$

where r is the radius of the particle. The retarding force is proportional to the velocity of sedimentation dx/dt and is $f(dx/dt)$, where f is the frictional coefficient (page 503) and is equal to $6\pi\eta r$ for a spherical particle. Since at constant velocity the retarding force is equal to the force causing sedimentation

$$\frac{dx}{dt} = \frac{2r^2(\rho - \rho_0)g}{9\eta} \tag{19}$$

This equation is useful in determining the particle size of finely divided solids.

The Ultracentrifuge. Only the largest and densest colloidal particles sediment in the earth's field, and so centrifuges have been devised to produce stronger fields. Sufficiently powerful ultracentrifuges have been built to cause even molecules as small as sucrose to sediment at measurable rates. Svedberg * was the leader in the development of ultracentrifuges, which he defined as centrifuges adapted for quantitative measurements of convection-free and vibration-free sedimentation. There are two distinct types of ultracentrifuge experiments: (1) those in which the velocity of sedimentation of a component of the solution is measured (*sedimentation velocity*) and (2) those in which the redistribution of molecules is determined at equilibrium (*sedimentation equilibrium*).

* Svedberg and Pedersen, *The Ultracentrifuge*, Oxford University Press, Oxford, 1940.

The acceleration of a centrifugal field is equal to $\omega^2 x$, where ω is the velocity of the centrifuge in radians per second (that is, 2π times the number of revolutions per second) and x is the distance from the center of rotation. Velocity ultracentrifuges in which x is about 6 cm are commonly operated at 1000 rps, and so the acceleration is

$$\omega^2 x = (2\pi\ 1000\ \text{sec}^{-1})^2\ (6\ \text{cm}) = 2.36 \times 10^8\ \text{cm sec}^{-2}$$

Since the acceleration of the earth's field is 980 cm sec^{-2}, the acceleration is 240,000 times greater than in the earth's field. With such accelerations it is possible to study the velocity of sedimentation of molecules and particles throughout the colloidal size range.

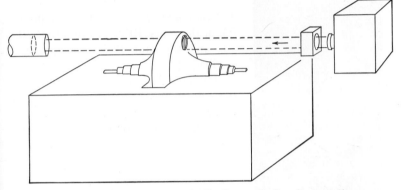

FIG. 17-6.   Rotor assembly of the Svedberg velocity ultracentrifuge.

The rotor assembly of the Svedberg oil turbine ultracentrifuge is shown in *Fig. 17-6*. The rotor of chrome-nickel steel is supported in horizontal bearings and driven by twin oil turbines on each end of the main shaft. In operation the rotor is covered and the space around it is evacuated and filled with hydrogen gas at a low pressure to avoid thermal gradients.

A solution to be studied in the velocity ultracentrifuge is placed in a cell with thick quartz windows. It has a sector shape when viewed in the direction of the axis of the centrifuge rotor since the sedimentation takes place radially. As the high-molecular-weight component throughout the solution sediments a moving boundary is formed, above which there is only solvent. The movement of such boundaries in the cell may be followed with the schlieren optical system as was mentioned in connection with diffusion (page 504).

Figure 17-7 shows the schlieren patterns for an ultracentrifuge experiment with the enzyme fumarase at 50,400 rpm. The second and third photographs were taken 35 and 70 minutes later than the top photograph. If additional components with different rates of sedimentation were present, additional peaks would be evident in the schlieren photo-graph. Thus, the ultracentrifuge is useful in analyzing complex mixtures such as plasma.

The velocity of sedimentation is expressed as the sedimentation coefficient s which is the velocity which would be observed in a unit cgs field.

$$s = \frac{dx/dt}{\omega^2 x} \tag{20}$$

The sedimentation coefficients of proteins fall in the range 10^{-13} sec to 200×10^{-13} sec, and the unit 10^{-13} sec is called a svedberg.

If a boundary is x_1 centimeters from the axis of the centrifuge at time t_1 and x_2 centimeters from the axis at time t_2 the sedimentation coefficient may be calculated from

$$s = \frac{1}{\omega^2(t_2 - t_1)} \ln \frac{x_2}{x_1} \tag{21}$$

which is obtained by integrating equation 20. In correcting sedimentation coefficients measured at one temperature to another temperature it is necessary to take into account not only the change in viscosity with temperature but also the change in the density of the solvent since there is a change in the buoyancy effect.

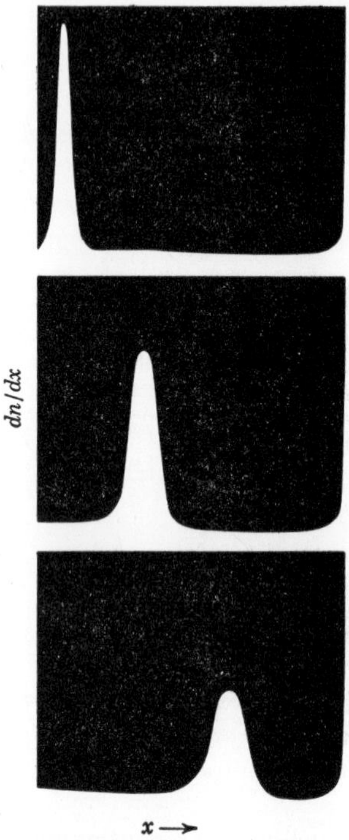

FIG. 17-7. Schlieren patterns for an ultracentrifuge experiment with fumarase at 50,400 rpm. The lower photographs were taken 35 and 70 minutes later than the top photograph. The protein is dissolved in pH 6.8 phosphate buffer.

Example 4. In the ultracentrifuge experiment illustrated in Fig. 17-7 the distance from the boundary to the axis of the ultracentrifuge was 5.949 cm in the first photograph and 6.731 cm in the last photograph. Since the speed of the rotor was 50,400 rpm, $\omega^2 = 2.82 \times 10^7$. Using equation 21,

$$s = \frac{1}{\omega^2(t_2 - t_1)} \ln \frac{x_2}{x_1} = \frac{2.303 \log (6.731/5.949)}{(2.82 \times 10^7)(60)(70)}$$

$$= 10.4 \times 10^{-13} \text{ sec}$$

This is the sedimentation coefficient at 28.2°C, the temperature of the experiment, and correction to 20° in water yields 8.90 svedbergs.

The sedimentation coefficient by itself cannot be used to determine he molecular weight of the sedimenting component unless the molecules re spherical. However, if both the sedimentation and diffusion co-fficients are measured the molecular weight may be calculated without naking any assumptions whatsoever about the shape. The equation .pon which this calculation is based may be derived by equating the orce of the centrifugal field on the particle to the frictional force, (dx/dt), where f is the frictional coefficient of the molecule and dx/dt s the speed of sedimentation. The force of the field on a particle of nass m and partial specific volume $\bar{v}$ suspended in a medium of density is

$$m(1 - \bar{v}\rho)\omega^2 x = (M/N)(1 - \bar{v}\rho)\omega^2 x \qquad (22)$$

vhere $(1 - \bar{v}\rho)$ is the buoyancy factor.

The sedimenting molecule or particle will be accelerated by the field until its velocity is such that the frictional force is equal to the force of he field

$$f\frac{dx}{dt} = \frac{M}{N}(1 - \bar{v}\rho)\omega^2 x \qquad (23)$$

or

$$\frac{dx/dt}{\omega^2 x} = s = \frac{M(1 - \bar{v}\rho)}{Nf} \qquad (24)$$

Since the velocity of sedimentation is so low that there is no appreciable orientation of the molecules, the frictional coefficient involved in sedi-mentation is taken to be the same as that involved in diffusion. Intro-duction of equation 15

$$f = RT/ND \qquad (25)$$

into equation 24 yields

$$M = \frac{RTs}{D(1 - \bar{v}\rho)} \qquad (26)$$

In order to calculate the molecular weight from measured values of s and D it is necessary to correct sedimentation and diffusion coefficients to the same temperature, usually 20°, and, if s and D depend appre-ciably upon concentration, to zero concentration. Equation 26 has probably been the most widely used in the calculation of molecular weights of proteins, and the wide range of molecular weights which can be obtained by this method is indicated by Table II.

Table II. Physical Constants at 20° in Water and Molecular Weight of Certain Proteins

	$s \times 10^{13}$, sec	$D \times 10^7$, cm^2 sec^{-1}	$\bar{v}$, cm^3 g^{-1}	M, g mole^{-1}
Beef insulin	1.7	15	0.72	12,00
Lactalbumin	1.9	10.6	0.75	17,40
Ovalbumin	3.6	7.8	0.75	44,00
Serum albumin	4.3	6.15	0.735	64,00
Serum globulin	7.1	4.0	0.75	167,00
Urease	18.6	3.4	0.73	480,00
Tobacco mosaic virus	185	0.53	0.72	40,000,00

Example 5. Using the data of Table II the molecular weight of serum albumin may be calculated as follows (the density of water at 20° is 0.9982 g cm^{-3}):

$$M = \frac{RTs}{D(1 - \bar{v}\rho)}$$

$$M = \frac{(8.31 \times 10^7 \text{ erg deg}^{-1} \text{ mole}^{-1})(293 \text{ deg})(4.3 \times 10^{-13} \text{ sec})}{(6.15 \times 10^{-7} \text{ cm}^2 \text{ sec}^{-1})[1 - (0.735 \text{ cm}^3 \text{ g}^{-1})(0.9982 \text{ g cm}^{-3})]}$$

$$= 64,000 \text{ g mole}^{-1}$$

Sedimentation Equilibrium. The earth's atmosphere is the most familiar example of sedimentation equilibrium, although, of course, it is really not completely in equilibrium or at constant temperature. The pressure, or concentration of gas molecules, drops off exponentially with altitude. This may be visualized as a result of the tendency of the molecules to sediment in the earth's field and the opposing tendency to diffuse upwards.

The effect of sedimentation equilibrium in the earth's field may be measured with gold sols, and this was actually used by Perrin in a determination of Avogadro's number.

In the case of smaller molecules it is necessary to use centrifugal fields in order to obtain an appreciable difference in concentration between the top and bottom of the cell containing the solution. This requires an ultracentrifuge such as that of Svedberg which can be run at constant speed and held at constant temperature for a period up to 2 weeks. Since this redistribution in the solution is an equilibrium phenomenon the relation between the concentrations at two levels and the molecular weight may be derived by the methods of thermodynamics. For ideal solutions the molecular weight may be calculated from

$$M = \frac{2RT \ln (c_2/c_1)}{(1 - \bar{v}\rho)\omega^2(x_2^2 - x_1^2)} \tag{27}$$

where c_1 is the concentration at distance x_1 from the axis, ω is the angular velocity of the rotor (radians per second), and ρ is the density of the solution. Optical methods are used to determine c_2 and c_1.

Although this equation applies only to a solution in which all the large molecules have the same weight, it is one of the outstanding advantages of the equilibrium centrifuge that information concerning the homogeneity of the macromolecular material may be obtained, along with various types of molecular weight averages mentioned earlier (equations 4 and 5).

Viscosity. Measurements of viscosities of high polymer solutions are particularly important since they offer one means for determining the molecular weight. The theoretical background for this method starts with Einstein's derivation, in 1906, of an equation relating the viscosity η of a dilute suspension of small rigid spheres to the volume fraction ϕ occupied by the spherical particles. According to Einstein

$$\frac{(\eta/\eta_0) - 1}{\phi} = \frac{\eta_{sp}}{\phi} = \frac{5}{2} \qquad (28)$$

where η_0 is the viscosity of the solvent. The quantity $(\eta/\eta_0) - 1$ is of frequent occurrence in viscosity studies and is known as the specific viscosity, η_{sp}. It is interesting to note that the viscosity (for the dilute suspensions covered by this equation) is independent of the size of the spheres.

Since high polymer molecules consist of chains of monomer units and are more threadlike and flexible in solution, they cannot be considered to be solid spheres. For such molecules the viscosity coefficient is greater than $\frac{5}{2}$.

Owing to the difficulty of knowing the fraction of the volume occupied by high polymer molecules in solution and to the fact that the ratio of η_{sp} to concentration is not independent of concentration, it is necessary to utilize the intrinsic viscosity $[\eta]$ defined by

$$[\eta] = \lim_{c \to 0} (\eta_{sp}/c) \qquad (29)$$

where c is the concentration of the high polymer in g/100 ml. The intrinsic viscosity is obtained by plotting the ratio of specific viscosity to concentration against concentration for a series of solutions and extrapolating to zero concentration.

The intrinsic viscosity depends upon the molecular weight of the polymer, and for a series of samples of the same polymer in a given solvent and at a constant temperature this relation is given by

$$[\eta] = KM^a \qquad (30)$$

where K and a are empirical constants. K and a may be determined by measuring the intrinsic viscosities of a series of samples of a polymer for which the molecular weights have been measured by another method, say osmotic-pressure determinations. Since the values of K and a are known for a large number of solvents and temperatures, this method for determining molecular weights is widely used because of the simple apparatus required.

Example 6. The values of K and a for polystyrene dissolved in toluene at 25° are 3.7×10^{-4} and 0.62, respectively. Calculate the molecular weight of a sample of polystyrene having an intrinsic viscosity of 0.74, using equation 30.

$$0.74 = 3.7 \times 10^{-4} M^{0.62}$$

$$M = 214,000 \text{ g mole}^{-1}$$

Concentrated solutions of polymers may have extremely high viscosities because of the intertwining of polymer molecules. Even in the absence of solvent the molecules may have considerable freedom of movement, and this is true for materials having rubberlike elasticity. In the case of long molecules in which there are many possibilities of rotations about bonds, a single molecule will not exist as an extended chain, but in a kinked and coiled-up form which is in constant thermal motion. A material consisting of such molecules may be stretched to a considerable extent by the application of a force. The stretching is resisted by the thermal motion of the molecules, and, when the force is released, the material returns to its normal length. That this is so is indicated by the fact that the tension at constant length is proportional to the absolute temperature.

At very low temperatures the energy of thermal agitation is insufficient to cause appreciable movement of the molecules, and the polymer then possesses the properties of a solid. On the other hand, as a rubberlike material is heated to higher temperatures it loses its rubberlike properties and finally becomes a viscous liquid if chemical decomposition does not occur.

Electrokinetic Phenomena. Many colloidal particles carry electric charges which are due to the adsorption of ions on the surface. In proteins there are ionizable groups such as carboxyl groups and amino groups which contribute electric charges to the molecule.

If an electric field is applied to a solution containing an electrically charged colloid the particles will move to the anode if they are negatively charged and to the cathode if they are positively charged. This motion, which is exactly like that of any ion in an electric field, is referred to as *electrophoresis.* If the particles are insoluble and form a plug or membrane the application of an electric field causes the liquid (usually water) to move through the pores. The relative motion of solvent and solid phase is the same as if the solid particles could move; that is, the solvent moves toward the cathode if the solid particles are negatively charged. In this phenomenon, which is referred to as *electroösmosis*, it may be considered that the solvent is carried along by the ions in the neighborhood of the solid surface which have a sign opposite to that of the surface.

There are two other electrokinetic phenomena which are the converses of electrophoresis and electroösmosis. These are (a) the sedimentation potential, which is produced by the sedimentation of charged particles, and (b) the streaming potential, which results from the flow of a fluid through a porous plug or membrane. Of these four effects, electrophoresis has been the most used and studied.

Electrophoresis. The mobilities of colloidal ions may be determined by the same methods used for small ions (Chapter 14). In addition, direct microscopic, or ultramicroscopic, observation may be used for the largest particles. A number of experimental difficulties impeded the application of the moving-boundary method to the study of colloids, especially proteins. One of the principal difficulties is that the passage of a current through a solution produces heat, so that the solution in the interior becomes hotter than at the walls, with the result that convection currents disrupt the boundaries. This experimental difficulty was greatly reduced by Tiselius,* who placed the moving-boundary cell in a thermostat with a temperature near the temperature of maximum density of the buffer, slightly below 4°C. When this is done, temperature gradients in the cell are accompanied by insignificant density gradients, and convective disturbances are greatly reduced.

The most widely used type of electrophoresis cell is U-shaped and is constructed in three sections which may be displaced relative to each other by sliding on greased planes. Such a cell is illustrated in *Fig. 17-8*, in which it is shown attached to electrode vessels. The bottom section and one side of the cell are filled with a protein solution; the other side and the top section of the cell, as well as the electrode vessels, are filled with buffer solution. When the center section of the cell is pushed into line with the top and bottom sections sharp boundaries are formed between the protein solution and buffer. When current is passed through the electrodes the different components of a mixture move with velocities which depend upon their electric charges and their size and shape. Silver electrodes coated with silver chloride and immersed in concentrated sodium chloride are commonly used so that no gas is formed at either electrode during the experiment.

* Tiselius, *Trans. Faraday Soc.*, *33*, 524 (1937).

Another innovation that has made electrophoresis useful and practical has been the development of schlieren optical systems (page 504). With these systems it is possible to locate moving boundaries if the substances are not colored, and an analysis of a complicated mixture may be obtained from the fact that the areas in the pattern are proportional to the changes in refractive index across the boundaries.

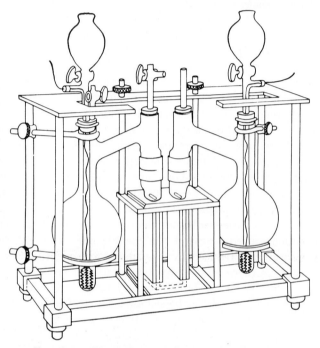

FIG. 17-8.   Electrophoretic cell and electrode vessels.

One of the most important applications of electrophoresis is in the analysis of naturally occurring mixtures of colloids, such as proteins, polysaccharides, and nucleic acids, and of the products obtained in the course of fractionations to obtain purified components. *Figure 17-9* gives an example* of an electrophoresis pattern for a mixture. In this figure the schlieren pattern is given for normal human plasma in 0.10 ionic strength sodium diethylbarbiturate buffer of *p*H 8.6 after 150 minutes at 6.0 volt cm^{-1}. The refractive-index gradient is plotted vertically versus the distance in the cell which is plotted horizontally. One pattern is obtained in the limb of the cell in which the proteins are moving

* Alberty, "Introduction to Electrophoresis," *J. Chem. Education*, *25*, 426, 619 (1948).

downwards, and the other in which the proteins are moving upwards. The positions of the initial boundaries are indicated by the rear ends of the arrows. The area under a given peak is very nearly proportional to the concentration of the protein producing that boundary. Thus the per cent of albumin, for example, may be obtained by dividing the area of the albumin peak by the total of the areas of the other protein peaks. The ϵ boundary in the descending pattern and the δ boundary in the

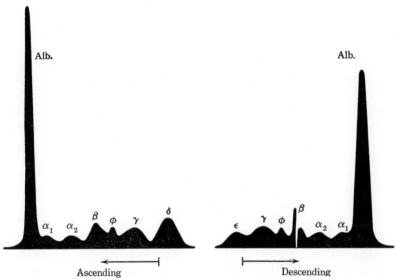

Ascending   Descending

Fig. 17-9.   Electrophoretic schlieren patterns for normal human plasma.

ascending pattern are not caused by protein components, but are related to the changes in salt concentration which occur in ordinary transference experiments near the initial boundary position.

All the components of human plasma as indicated by Fig. 17-9 have been separated by taking advantage of the differences in the solubilities of the various proteins in ethyl alcohol solutions of various pH values containing low concentrations of salts at low temperatures.* Albumin, which represents about 60% of the plasma proteins by weight, is largely responsible for the osmotic pressure of plasma since it has the lowest molecular weight of the plasma proteins (see Table II).

The mobility of a protein at a definite pH and ionic strength is a useful identifying characteristic. The way in which the mobility of a protein changes with the pH gives information as to the nature of the ionizing groups of the protein.

* Cohn et al., *J. Am. Chem. Soc.*, *68*, 459 (1946); *72*, 465 (1950).

The *isoelectric point* is the *p*H (and salt concentration) at which the mobility is zero. In solutions more acid than the isoelectric point, the mobility is positive because of the combination of hydrogen ions with the colloidal electrolyte; in solutions more alkaline than the isoelectric point, ionizable hydrogens are dissociated so that the molecule has a net negative charge due to carboxyl or other ionized acid groups. Proteins are generally least soluble at their isoelectric points.

A charged ion or surface tends to surround itself with an atmosphere of oppositely charged ions. This tendency is partially overcome by the thermal motions of the ions, and so a diffuse ion atmosphere is formed. The total potential difference between the solid phase and the liquid phase is the thermodynamic potential discussed earlier (page 411). But when a relative movement of solid and solution phase is produced by the application of an electric field, the surface of the particle carries along with it part of the charge of the atmosphere which is next to the surface. The potential difference between the particle with its adsorbed surface layer and the solution is less than the thermodynamic potential difference and is referred to as the *zeta potential*. The zeta potential may be modified by changing the nature and concentration of the electrolyte solution. Since the zeta potential is decreased by increasing electrolyte concentration the electrokinetic effects become smaller at high salt concentrations.

Precipitation of Lyophobic Colloids. The most important factors in stabilizing colloids are electric charge and hydration or solvation. Either the existence of a net electric charge which causes the particles to repel each other or a film of adsorbed solvent which prevents the particles from adhering to each other may be sufficient to keep the dispersed particles in the colloidal state. In the lyophobic colloids there is little attraction between the dispersed particles and the dispersion medium, and the stability of the colloid depends partially on the fact that the charged particles repel each other.*

The ability of dispersed particles to remain in the colloidal state is greatly affected by the concentration of ions. In the absence of ions a lyophobic colloid is not stable, and the material will coagulate. The presence of a few ions stabilizes the colloid, but, if there is an excess of electrolyte, the colloid particles will be coagulated by the ions of opposite charge. The concentrations of salts in milliequivalents per liter required to cause precipitation in 2 hours, as found by Freundlich, are recorded in Table III for a positive ferric hydroxide colloid (16 millimoles per liter) and for a negative arsenious sulfide colloid (8 millimoles

---

* Verwey and Overbeck, *Theory of the Stability of Lyophobic Colloids*, Elsevier Publishing Co., New York, 1948.

per liter). In each case, 2 ml of the electrolyte was added to 20 ml of the colloid solution.

Table III.   Precipitation of Colloids by Electrolytes

Electrolyte	Concentration of Electrolyte		Electrolyte	Concentration of Electrolyte	
	(+) Ferric Hydroxide	(−) Arsenious Sulfide		(+) Ferric Hydroxide	(−) Arsenious Sulfide
NaCl	9	51	$MgSO_4$	0.2	0.8
KCl	9	50	$AlCl_3$	...	0.1
KNO_3	12	50	$Al(NO_3)_3$	...	0.1
$Ba(NO_3)_2$	14	0.7	K_2SO_4	0.2	...
$BaCl_2$	10	0.7	$K_2Cr_2O_7$	0.2	...

Table III illustrates the general principle that positive colloids are precipitated by negative ions and negative colloids are precipitated by positive ions. It is evident that the trivalent ions are much more effective in precipitating colloids of opposite sign than are divalent ions and that the divalent ions are more effective than the univalent ions.

The action of electrolytes on lyophilic colloids is less sharply defined than their action on lyophobic colloids. Large concentrations of salts are necessary to precipitate albumins, but small amounts of the heavy metals give precipitation on account of chemical reactions.

When a lyophilic colloid is added to a solution of a lyophobic colloid, it may form a coating around the lyophobic colloid. The lyophobic colloid surrounded by the film of lyophilic colloid then behaves as a lyophilic colloid and is thus less easily precipitated by ions. Protective coatings of this kind can be illustrated by the stabilizing effect of gelatin added to lyophobic colloids such as sulfur or freshly precipitated silver bromide. They are found in organic colloids, and they play a part in the behavior of certain cements and even in the geology of certain sedimentary rocks.

Interfacial Tension.   When two partially miscible liquids are placed in contact, each dissolves to a certain extent in the other, sometimes causing marked changes in the surface tensions. The interfacial energy may be defined as the work required to increase the area of the interface by 1 sq cm. It can be measured by most of the methods already described for measuring the surface tension of pure liquids against air. The drop-weight method, in which the weight of a drop of the first liquid is determined as it rises or falls from a specially prepared tip immersed in the second liquid, may be used.

The addition of a third component may lower the surface tension considerably, but if the surface tension is increased, the effect is small. Solutes may be classified as "capillary-active" or "capillary-inactive" on the basis of their effect on the surface tension or interfacial tension. In the case of the aqueous solution–air interface, inorganic electrolytes, salts of organic acids, bases of low molecular weight, and certain non-volatile nonelectrolytes such as sugar and glycerin are *capillary-inactive*. Solutes which are *capillary-active* are organic acids, alcohols, esters, ethers, amines, ketones, etc. The effect of capillary-active substances on the surface tension of water may be very great, as illustrated in

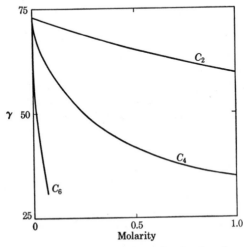

FIG. 17-10.   Influence of concentration on the surface tension of aqueous solutions of fatty acids, including acetic (C_2), butyric (C_4), and hexanoic (C_6).

Fig. 17-10.   Soaps and detergents are especially effective in lowering the surface tension or interfacial tension.

Gibbs's Equation.   According to thermodynamics, processes which are accompanied by a decrease in free energy tend to occur spontaneously. Thus the fact that organic acids can lower the surface tension of water suggests that they will spontaneously be adsorbed on the surface so that the free energy of the surface will be decreased. The thermodynamics of surface adsorption was treated by Gibbs * in 1876. He showed that

$$\Gamma_2 = -\frac{1}{RT}\frac{\partial \gamma}{\partial \ln f_2 N_2} \tag{31}$$

where Γ_2 is the excess surface concentration of the solute, γ is the surface

* *The Collected Works of J. Willard Gibbs*, Yale University Press, New Haven, Conn., reprinted in 1948.

or interfacial tension, f_2 is the activity coefficient of the solute, and N_2 its mole fraction. In dilute solutions in which concentration may be substituted for $f_2 N_2$,

$$\Gamma_2 = -\frac{c}{RT}\frac{\partial\gamma}{\partial c} \qquad (32)$$

The excess surface concentration is the difference between the total amount of a component in the actual system and that in an imaginary system in which the two phases retain the bulk composition right up to an infinitely thin surface.

If a solute causes a decrease in surface tension ($\partial\gamma/\partial c$ is negative), equation 32 shows that there will be adsorption on the surface. Thus, the surface concentration of a capillary-active solute may be much greater than the concentration in the bulk of the solution.

If a solute causes an increase in surface tension ($\partial\gamma/\partial c$ is positive), its concentration in the surface region will be less than in the bulk of the solution. Since the surface concentration of a substance which causes an increase in surface tension is therefore low, the surface tension will not be raised very much. This deduction is well confirmed by experiment. Soaps and other materials are known to reduce the surface tension of water by more than half, but no substance has yet been discovered which will raise the surface tension more than a few per cent.

Experimental tests of the Gibbs equation are difficult because the real surface layer contains such a small amount of dissolved material, but they indicate that the equation is correct. In one of the tests, froth and foam were swept out from a soap solution, and the concentration in this froth was found to be greater than that in the bulk of the solution left behind; * in another, a scoop traveling along an accurately machined track skimmed off the surface of the solution.† The most accurate work has been based upon the use of a radioisotope having a weak beta emission. From determination of beta radiation from the surface it is possible to calculate the excess surface concentration.‡

Surface Films. The calming action of oil on waves has long been known. It is due to the formation of a film on the surface which results in a lowering of the surface tension. Films formed by very slightly soluble organic acids, such as oleic and stearic acids, behave like two-dimensional solids. The movement of the film when it is pushed or blown may be made visible by dusting the surface with some inert powder.

* Nutting, Long, and Harkins, *J. Am. Chem. Soc.*, *62*, 1496 (1940).

† McBain and Wood, *Proc. Roy. Soc. London*, *A174*, 286 (1940).

‡ Niesson and Lamm, *Acta Chem. Scand.*, *6*, 1175 (1952).

Langmuir devised a method for directly measuring the pressure exerted by such films. In his apparatus a horizontal tray coated with a lacquer, which is not wet by water, is filled with clean water to a level slightly higher than the edges. Movable strips laid across the tray are used to sweep impurities off the surface, and the pressure of the film against a light floating barrier is measured by a torsion balance. A small amount of film-forming substance is added to the surface, as for example a solution of stearic acid in a volatile solvent, and the film is then pushed toward the floating barrier with one of the movable strips. With a substance like stearic acid, no pressure is detected until the film has been confined to a certain area, and then the surface pressure rises rapidly and further decreasing the area causes the film to crumple.

The reason stearic acid forms a surface film may be understood as follows: The carboxyl group, being a polar group, has a strong affinity for water, while the hydrocarbon chain does not, and as a result stearic acid is very insoluble in water. At the surface the carboxyl "heads" can be dissolved in the water phase while the hydrocarbon "tails" stick up out of the surface. If this idea is correct and the film is really *unimolecular* in thickness it should be possible to calculate the cross-sectional area of a molecule from the measured film area, the weight and molecular weight, and Avogadro's number. A few values obtained in this way are summarized in Table IV. The lengths of the molecules are

Table IV.[1] Dimensions of Molecules in Unimolecular Films

Film	Formula	Film Thickness, length of molecule	Area, sq A
Palmitic acid	$C_{15}H_{31}COOH$	24 A	21
Stearic acid	$C_{17}H_{35}COOH$	25	22
Cerotic acid	$C_{25}H_{51}COOH$	31	25
Tristearin	$(C_{18}H_{35}O_2)_3C_3H_5$	25	66
Cetyl alcohol	$C_{16}H_{33}OH$	22	21
Myricyl alcohol	$C_{30}H_{61}OH$	41	27

[1] Ketelle and Boyd, *J. Am. Chem. Soc.*, *69*, 2808 (1947).

equal to the film thickness calculated by use of the bulk density of the organic compound as illustrated in the following example.

Example 7. It is found that 0.106 mg of stearic acid covers 500 cm² of water surface. Given the molecular weight (284) and density (0.85 g cm⁻³) of stearic acid, calculate the cross-sectional area (a) per stearic acid molecule, and the thickness (t) of the film.

$$500 \text{ cm}^2 = \frac{(0.106 \times 10^{-3} \text{ g})}{(284 \text{ g mole}^{-1})} (6.02 \times 10^{23} \text{ molecules mole}^{-1})a$$

$$a = 22 \times 10^{-16} \text{ cm}^2 \text{ or } 22 \text{ A}^2 \text{ per molecule}$$

$$(500 \text{ cm}^2)t = \frac{0.106 \times 10^{-3} \text{ g}}{0.85 \text{ g cm}^{-3}}$$

$$t = 25 \times 10^{-8} \text{ cm} \quad \text{or} \quad 25 \text{ A}$$

It is seen that the cross-sectional area of an aliphatic chain is about 22 A^2. Increasing the length of the hydrocarbon chain causes a corresponding increase in the film thickness. Moreover, the length and cross section of the molecules calculated in this way are in excellent agreement with the values obtained independently by X-ray analysis of crystals and in other ways. These facts support the hypothesis that the film is exactly 1 molecule thick, and closely packed, the longer axis of the molecules being nearly at right angles to the surface of the water film. These measurements were among the first to provide direct physical evidence that the organic molecules are of the shape and size expected from theoretical organic chemistry.

Lower-molecular-weight fatty acids give films which behave more like two-dimensional gases. That is, the film occupies any given area and the pressure is inversely proportional to the area. In some cases the behavior of monolayers resembles that of a gas in the critical region, since the film pressure is independent of area over a certain region corresponding to the vapor pressure of a liquid.

Though it is convenient to talk about film pressure, these experiments may equally well be interpreted in terms of the lowering of the surface tension by the surface film. Thus, in the Langmuir surface balance it may be considered that the barrier is pulled toward the clean water surface by the surface tension of water and toward the film-covered surface by the somewhat lower surface tension on this side of the barrier. In fact the surface pressure π is exactly equal to the difference in surface tensions of the two surfaces.

$$\pi = \gamma_0 - \gamma \tag{33}$$

where γ_0 is the surface tension of pure water.

The lowering of the surface tension may be measured directly by measuring the downward pull on a thin vertical sheet of glass. This is the principle used in the Wilhelmy surface balance.

Langmuir and Blodgett have shown that unimolecular films may be transferred from the water surface to a glass or metal plate which is dipped through the surface. If the film is oriented on the plate with the hydrocarbon chains out, the coated plate cannot be wet by water. By depositing a large number of layers on a lens it is possible to reduce the surface reflection by optical interference so that more light is transmitted than by the uncoated lens. Successive films are added to the surface until the total thickness of the films is equal to a quarter wavelength of light.

Adsorption by Solids. Many practical applications are made of the adsorption of gases or of solutes from solutions upon the surface of solids. Colored material and impurities are removed from sugar and from many organic products by filtering through charcoal or other adsorbents. Obnoxious gases or valuable gases may be collected by passage through charcoal or silica gel and can be recovered later in a concentrated form by raising the temperature and desorbing the gas. Gas masks containing adsorbents are used for protection against specific poisonous gases.

Adsorption occurs on the surface of the solid and results from valence forces or other attractive forces of the atoms or molecules in the outermost layer of the solid which are not so fully utilized as in the interior of the solid. The extent of this adsorption depends greatly upon the specific nature of the adsorbing solid and the molecules being adsorbed, and it depends also on the concentration or pressure and on the temperature.

It is convenient to distinguish between *physical adsorption* and *chemisorption*. The forces causing physical adsorption are similar to those that cause the condensation of a gas to form a liquid. The heat evolved upon adsorption is small, and the adsorption is completely reversible. In chemisorption the heat evolved is considerably larger, and it may be considered that a surface compound is formed. Since this is true only a single adsorbed layer may be formed, whereas in physical adsorption the adsorbed layer may be several molecules thick.

For a given weight of adsorbent with a given surface area the amount of material adsorbed depends on the pressure (or concentration) of the material around the adsorbent. The higher the pressure or concentration, the greater the amount that can be adsorbed. When an adsorbing material is placed in contact with a gas or solution, the amount adsorbed will gradually increase, and the concentration of the surrounding molecules will decrease until the rate of desorption becomes equal to the rate of adsorption, and, thus, an equilibrium is established. If the concentration of gas or solution is increased, the weight of adsorbed substance will increase to a new equilibrium value, and, if the concentration is decreased, the adsorbent will lose adsorbed substance to its surroundings until equilibrium is again established.

The adsorption isotherm for nitrogen on finely divided potassium chloride is given in *Fig. 17-11*. The amount of gas adsorbed was determined by measuring the volume of gas taken up by the adsorbent at various pressures and at a constant temperature of 89.9°K.

Several equations have been devised to represent adsorption data. The following equation, which does not have any theoretical basis but has been found useful, is referred to as the Freundlich equation.

$$x/m = kc^n \tag{34}$$

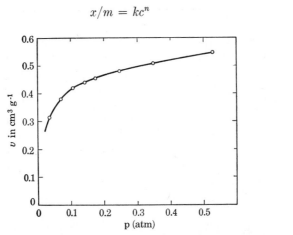

FIG. 17-11.   Adsorption of nitrogen on finely divided potassium chloride at 89.9°K. The ordinate gives the volume (at 0°C and 1 atm) adsorbed on 1 gram of salt, and the abscissa gives the pressure of nitrogen in atmospheres.   Keenan and Holmes, *J. Phys. Colloid Chem.*, **53**, 1309 (1949).

Here x is the amount adsorbed on mass m of adsorbent, and k and n are determined by experiment. The constants may be determined by plotting $\log x/m$ versus $\log c$, since

$$\log x/m = n \log c + \log k \tag{35}$$

Theory of Adsorption.   The basic theory of adsorption of gases on solids is due to Langmuir,* who considered the surface of a solid to be made up of elementary spaces each of which could adsorb one gas molecule. Furthermore, it was assumed that all the elementary spaces were identical in their affinity for a gas molecule and that the presence of a gas molecule on one space did not affect the properties of neighboring spaces. At adsorption equilibrium the rate of evaporation of the adsorbed gas is equal to the rate of condensation.

* Langmuir, *J. Am. Chem. Soc.*, **38**, 2267 (1916); **40**, 1361 (1918).

If θ is the fraction of the surface occupied by gas molecules the rate of evaporation from the surface is $r\theta$, where r is the rate of evaporation from the completely covered surface at a certain temperature. The rate of condensation of molecules on the surface is proportional to the fraction of the area that is not covered $(1 - \theta)$ and to the pressure of the gas. Thus, the rate of condensation is expressed by $k(1 - \theta)p$, where k is a constant at a given temperature and includes a factor to allow for

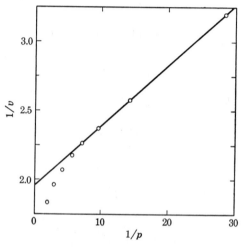

FIG. 17-12.   Plot of $1/v$ versus $1/p$ for adsorption of nitrogen on potassium chloride, using data of Fig. 17-11.

the fact that not every gas molecule which strikes an unoccupied space will stick.

At equilibrium,

$$r\theta = k(1 - \theta)p \tag{36}$$

$$\theta = \frac{kp}{r + kp} = \frac{(k/r)p}{1 + (k/r)p} \tag{37}$$

Since the volume v of gas adsorbed is proportional to θ, equation 37 may be written as

$$v = abp/(1 + ap) \tag{38}$$

where a has been substituted for k/r and b is a constant. Then v is directly proportional to p at very low pressures where $ap \ll 1$. As the pressure is increased the adsorption increases until at high pressures v approaches the value b. It is convenient to determine the constants a

and b by plotting $1/v$ versus $1/p$ since

$$1/v = (1/b) + (1/abp) \tag{39}$$

The intercept is $1/b$ and the slope $1/ab$. Such a plot is shown in *Fig. 17-12.*

Example 8. Calculate a and b from the data of Fig. 17-12. The experimental data deviate from equation 39 at higher pressures because more than a monomolecular adsorbed layer is formed. The data at low pressures may be represented by a straight line with a slope of 0.044 and an intercept of 1.95. Thus,

$$b = 1/1.95 = 0.513 \text{ cm}^3\text{g}^{-1}$$

$$a = \frac{1}{(0.044)(0.513)} = 44.3 \text{ atm}^{-1}$$

According to this calculation 0.513 cm³ of nitrogen would be sufficient to cover the surface of 1 gram of the KCl with a unimolecular layer.

Langmuir's equation represents the adsorption data very well in some cases. In others it fails at higher pressures because more than a monomolecular adsorbed layer is formed. The theory of Brunauer, Emmett, and Teller,[*] which extends Langmuir's derivation to obtain an equation for multimolecular adsorption, is based on the assumption that the same forces that produce condensation are also chiefly responsible for the binding energy of multimolecular adsorption. The heats of adsorption of gas in the second, third, $\cdots$, etc., layers are taken to be the same as the heat of liquefaction for the gas. If the adsorption takes place on a free surface, then at p°, the saturation pressure of the gas, an infinite number of layers can build up on the adsorbent. The equation is

$$\frac{p}{v(p^\circ - p)} = \frac{1}{v_m c} + \frac{(c-1)p}{v_m c p^\circ} \tag{40}$$

where v_m is the volume of gas adsorbed when the entire adsorbent surface is covered with a complete unimolecular layer. According to this equation a plot of $p/v(p^\circ - p)$ versus p/p° should give a straight line with a slope of $(c-1)/v_m c$ and an intercept of $1/v_m c$, where c is a constant at a given temperature. Such a plot of the data given in Fig. 17-11 is linear and yields a value of $v_m = 0.481$ cm³ g^{-1} for the volume of gas required to form a complete unimolecular layer.

The surface area occupied by a single molecule of adsorbate on the surface may be estimated from the density of the liquefied adsorbate. For example, the area occupied by nitrogen molecules at $-195°C$ is estimated to be 16.2 A². Thus, from the measured value of v_m the surface area of the adsorbent may be calculated. This method is widely used in the study of solid catalysts and adsorbents.

[*] Brunauer, Emmett, and Teller, *J. Am. Chem. Soc.*, *60*, 309 (1938).

Example 9. The volume of nitrogen gas v_m (measured at **760** mm and 0°C) required to cover a sample of silica gel with a monomolecular layer is 129 ml per gram of gel. Calculate the surface area of the gel if each nitrogen molecule occupies 16.2 A^2.

$$\frac{(0.129 \text{ l g}^{-1})(6.02 \times 10^{23} \text{ molecules mole}^{-1})(16.2 \text{ A}^2 \text{ molecule}^{-1})(10^{-10} \text{ m A}^{-1})^2}{(22.4 \text{ l mole}^{-1})}$$

$$= 560 \text{ m}^2 \text{ g}^{-1}$$

If a solid contains very small capillaries condensation may occur in them below the normal condensation pressure of the gas. This may lead to hysteresis effects in the adsorption isotherm; that is, the amount adsorbed at a certain pressure may be different, depending upon whether the pressure is approached from lower or higher values.

Ion Exchangers. In 1850 Way discovered that, when a solution of potassium chloride is allowed to flow through a column of soil, potassium ions but not chloride ions are adsorbed, and calcium is liberated to replace the adsorbed potassium ions. This ability of soils to bind and exchange ions is of great importance. A practical application of ion exchange is in the softening of water. The mineral zeolite is useful for this purpose. Synthetic ion-exchange resins have been introduced under names such as "Amberlite" or "Dowex." These resins may be either of the cation-exchanging or anion-exchanging type. The exchange properties may be varied by the selection of the reactants for the polymerization reaction involved in producing the resin.

A cation-exchange resin R may be considered to be a large insoluble and polyvalent anion. If it is treated with a large excess of sodium chloride it is converted to the "sodium form," NaR. The sodium ions may be displaced by calcium ions.

$$2\text{NaR} + \text{Ca}^{++} = \text{CaR}_2 + 2\text{Na}^+$$

When the resin has become saturated with calcium ions the equilibrium may be reversed and the resin regenerated by treating it with a concentrated solution of sodium chloride.

Chromatography. In 1906 Tswett discovered that, if a solution of chlorophyll from leaves is poured on the top of a column of a suitable adsorbent and a solvent is used to wash the pigments down the column, the colored band is resolved into a series of bands moving at different rates. Each component of the original mixture is represented by a band and may be obtained in a pure form by cutting the column into segments and eluting the pigment from the adsorbent. This method is widely used for separation of substances difficult to separate by other methods.*

* Cassidy, *J. Chem. Education,* **16**, 88 (1939); Strain, "Chromatographic Adsorption Analysis," Interscience Publishers, New York, 1941; Zechmeister and Cholnoky, *Principles and Practice of Chromatography,* John Wiley & Sons, New York, 1943.

Alumina, magnesia, powdered glass, charcoal, and other adsorbents may be used. Colorless materials can be separated also, if the zones separating the different materials can be brought out by fluorescence or by ultraviolet photography.

The successful separation of the rare-earth elements in a high degree of purity by fractional adsorption on organic resins is one of the striking

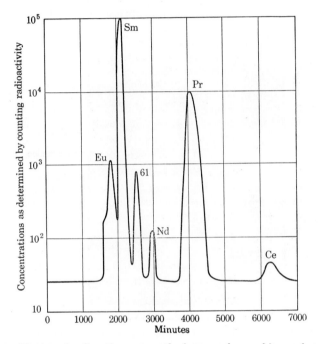

Fig. 17-13. Elution of radioactive rare earths from a column of ion-exchange resin.

developments of chromatography.* Previous to this development the separation of the rare earths was very difficult and required hundreds of tedious recrystallizations because the different elements are so similar in their chemical and physical properties. In the new process a solution of ammonium citrate at a definite pH containing several of the rare earths is run through a column packed with small pieces of these organic resins. The rare earths are adsorbed on the resin, and then they are removed by desorbing with a solution of ammonium citrate. This process of desorption is called *elution*. The equilibria and rates of adsorption and reaction with ammonium citrate are sufficiently different for the different

* "Symposium on Ion Exchange Separations," *J. Am. Chem. Soc.*, **69**, 2769–2878 (1947).

rare earths so that a slight separation is effected while traveling a short distance down the column. The separation is increased successively as the solution flows down the whole length of the column, in the same manner as gases and liquids are separated by fractionation through a long distilling column. An example of this technique * is shown in *Fig. 17-13.* It is interesting to note the good separation of element 61

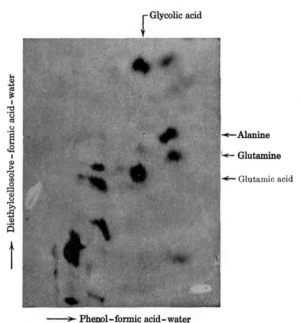

Fig. 17-14. Two-dimensional paper chromatogram of an extract of bacteria after $1\frac{1}{4}$-minute exposure to $C^{14}O_2$. The sample was placed on the paper in the lower left-hand corner and chromatographed with a solution of phenol-formic acid-water to the right, and then after drying it was chromatographed at right angles with a solution of diethylcellosolve-formic acid-water. Courtesy of Professor R. H. Burris.

produced by the fission of uranium 235 (page 629). Previous evidence for element 61 was not regarded as satisfactory.

Filter paper may be used to support an aqueous phase while an organic solvent is allowed to flow through it. The rate with which a solute is carried depends partly on its distribution coefficient between the two immiscible phases. In "two-dimensional" paper chromatography the components are first spread out along one edge of a square piece of paper with one solvent system, and then the sheet is dried and a second solvent system is used to chromatograph the components perpendicular to the original direction. *Figure 17-14* shows black spots from radioactive carbon.

* Ketelle and Boyd, *J. Am. Chem. Soc.*, *69*, 2808 (1947).

Emulsions. An *emulsion* is a system of two immiscible liquids, one of which is dispersed throughout the other in small drops. In order to prepare stable colloid emulsions, it is usually necessary to add a small amount of an *emulsifying agent,* such as a soap, which will reduce the surface tension of one of the liquids. Obviously, the introduction of a large number of small drops of another liquid within the body of a liquid increases the surface area greatly, and it is clear that the energy required for such a surface expansion will be less if the surface tension is decreased. The interfacial tension of benzene-water, which is 35 dynes per centimeter, can be reduced to 2 dynes per centimeter by the addition of sodium oleate. By such procedures it is possible to obtain emulsions which have 100 parts of oil spread out as drops through only 1 part of water. Emulsifying agents include not only soaps and detergents which reduce surface tensions but also gelatin, albumin, gum arabic, and other lyophilic colloids which tend to form protective coatings around the small drops. Sometimes unsuspected impurities act as emulsifying agents in the formation of emulsions which would not otherwise be expected.

The oil-in-water emulsion is a common type of emulsion, but it is possible also to have water-in-oil emulsions. The liquid forming the drops is called the *dispersed liquid,* and the external liquid in which the drops are dispersed is called the *dispersion medium.* In a simple test to determine which is the dispersion medium, a drop of each liquid is added to a sample of the emulsion spread out on a plate. If water mixes with the emulsion, the water is the dispersion medium; if oil mixes with it, the oil is the dispersion medium. The type of emulsion formed will depend somewhat on the relative solubilities of the emulsifying agent in the two liquids. For example, pure magnesium oleate, which is soluble in benzene but not in water, lowers the surface tension of the benzene and gives an emulsion of water dispersed in benzene.

Emulsions find many industrial applications. Mechanical homogenizers are used to mix two immiscible liquids intimately by producing very fine droplets of one in the other. For example, asphalt emulsified in water is used for building roads without the necessity of melting the asphalt. One of the most important processes in mining operations for concentrating the valuable part of ores is ore flotation. In this process the finely pulverized ore is treated with an oil emulsion and foams in such a way that the particles of valuable mineral are carried to the surface, where they are collected.

Among the household emulsions milk and salad dressing are important examples. The cleansing action of ordinary soap depends to a large extent on the production of an oil-in-water emulsion. Several drugs are prepared in the form of emulsions.

Emulsions are sometimes objectionable, as, for example, in oil wells, which give petroleum emulsified with water. Emulsions often can be broken by freezing, by filtration, by electrostatic precipitation, or by centrifuging. The centrifuge method is used extensively for the separation of cream from milk.

Gels. A given material may be produced in either the crystalline or amorphous state, depending on the conditions of its formation. Von Weimarn has shown that the degree of supersaturation, at the time of formation, and the viscosity of the medium account for the observed phenomena qualitatively at least. For example, when barium sulfate is precipitated from very dilute solutions it is possible to obtain small crystals. When the solutions are more concentrated, the state of supersaturation after mixing is greater, and the crystals become less pronounced. When the solutions contain about 1 equivalent per liter, an immediate precipitate is formed which is apparently amorphous. With still more concentrated solutions (3 to 7 equivalents per liter of barium thiocyanate and manganese sulfate), a clear jelly is produced.

A *gel* is a stiff, semirigid precipitate which retains the liquid in which it was initially dissolved. Gels may be prepared in several different ways. For example, when a 2 per cent solution of gelatin dissolved in warm water is cooled, it sets to a stiff, transparent gel. The theory of such gels has been discussed by Ferry.* Gels may be made also by precipitation, as in the case of silicic acid gel, which is produced by mixing solutions of hydrochloric acid and sodium silicate. After the combined solution stands for a while, it sets to a stiff, clear gel, the time required for setting depending on the concentrations. It is this silicic acid gel which after being dried gives silica gel with many pores and large surface areas that are effective in the adsorption of gases.

Another type of gel is produced by changing the solvent. A gel of nitrocellulose is formed, for example, when chloroform is mixed with a colloidal solution of nitrocellulose in amyl acetate. Alternatively, the nitrocellulose gel can be prepared by dissolving nitrocellulose in acetone and evaporating the solvent. The threadlike nature of the cotton can sometimes be detected even after the gel has been formed, indicating that the original character of the fibers still persists and that these fibers can retain large amounts of the liquid. Double-base "powder" used extensively as a propellent in large naval guns and in rockets is a gel composed of nitrocellulose and nitroglycerol.

On standing, gels frequently undergo an appreciable shrinkage in volume with a simultaneous extrusion of liquid. This phenomenon is

* Ferry, *Advances in Protein Chemistry*, Vol. IV, Academic Press, New York, 1948.

called *syneresis*. When placed in a dry atmosphere gels quickly dry out, and when placed in water some take up water, rapidly at first, and then more slowly. The rate depends on the difference between the weight of water which the gel holds and the maximum amount which it can hold.

The change of sol to gel is a reversible one in gelatin. The gel is readily reconverted into a sol on warming the stiff gel obtained when a moderately concentrated solution of the gelatin is cooled. In albumin and certain other lyophilic colloids, however, a chemical change accompanies the heating, and irreversible coagulation occurs, as exemplified in the boiling of an egg.

Lyotropic Series. Salts have a marked effect on the temperature of the gel-sol transformation, some tending to raise the temperature of gelation and others to lower it. The effect is not to be explained on the basis of ionic charge, and, in fact, univalent ions give widely different results. Hofmeister arranged the negative ions of sodium salts in the following order, the first having the greatest influence in lowering the temperature of gelation and the last the least influence:

$$SCN^- > I^- > Br^- > NO_3^- > ClO_3^- > Cl^- > C_2H_3O_2^- > SO_4^=$$

$$(41)$$

The same sequence of ions is maintained, not only in the gelation temperature of agar-agar and similar substances, but also in their rate of swelling, and the series finds applications in several different fields.

Industrial Colloids. Foams, which consist of air bubbles surrounded by liquid films, become troublesome in certain industrial processes of evaporation. Clouds and smokes are colloidal particles of liquids or solids dispersed in the gas phase. They tend to obscure vision and produce dirt in cities; sometimes they are responsible for large financial losses in chemical operations, and again they may constitute health hazards to animals and plants. A successful method of electrical precipitation, invented by Cottrell, is extensively used in smelting and other industries where a valuable or an objectionable dust or smoke passes out the chimney. A direct current at about 50,000 volts is passed from a central wire to the surrounding circular metal wall in the form of a corona discharge. The particles acquire electric charges by attaching ions in the discharge and are quickly drawn to the electrodes, from which they can then be scraped mechanically.

REFERENCES

Kraemer, *Colloid Science*, Interscience Publishers, New York, 1942.

Svedberg, *Colloid Chemistry*, Chemical Catalog Co., New York, 1928.

Weiser, *Colloid Chemistry*, John Wiley & Sons, New York, 1949.

Mark and Tobolsky, *Physical Chemistry of High Polymeric Substances*, 2nd ed., Interscience Publishers, New York, 1950.

Brunauer, *The Adsorption of Gases and Vapors*, Princeton University Press, Princeton, N. J., 1943.

Williams, Alberty, and Kraemer, in Taylor and Glasstone's *Treatise on Physical Chemistry*, Vol. II, D. Van Nostrand Co., New York, 1951.

Alexander and Johnson, *Colloid Science*, Vols. I and II, Oxford University Press, New York, 1949.

Flory, *Principles of Polymer Chemistry*, Cornell University Press, Ithaca, N. Y., 1953.

Kruyt, *Colloid Science*, Elsevier Publishing Co., New York, Vol. I, 1952; Vol. II, 1949.

Harkins, *The Physical Chemistry of Surface Films*, Reinhold Publishing Corp., New York, 1952.

PROBLEMS

1. A mercury sol is composed of globules having a diameter of 0.07 μ. What is the surface area of the particles formed from 1 g of mercury?

Ans. 6.33×10^4 cm^2.

2. The following osmotic pressures were measured for solutions of a sample of polyisobutylene in benzene at 25°.

c, g/100 cm^3	0.50	1.00	1.50	2.00
π, g/cm^2	0.505	1.03	1.58	2.15

The number average molecular weight may be calculated from the value of π/c extrapolated to zero concentration of the polymer. What value for M is obtained by this method? (The pressures may be converted into atmospheres by dividing by (76 cm atm^{-1}) (13.6 g cm^{-3}) = 1033 g cm^{-2} atm^{-1}.)   *Ans.* 256,000.

3. The diffusion coefficient for ovalbumin at 20° in a dilute aqueous salt solution is 7.8×10^{-7} cm^2 sec^{-1}. If the molecules are assumed to be spherical, calculate their molecular weight. Given: $\eta_{H_2O} = 0.01009$ poise at 20° and $\bar{v} = 0.75$ cm^3 g^{-1} for the protein.   *Ans.* 68,300.

4. Calculate the time necessary for a quartz particle 10 μ in diameter to sediment 50 cm in distilled water at room temperature. Density = 2.6 g cm^{-3}; $\eta = 0.0100$ poise.   *Ans.* 95.6 min.

5. Calculate the sedimentation coefficient of tobacco mosaic virus from the fact that the boundary moves with a velocity of 0.454 cm hr^{-1} in an ultracentrifuge at a speed of 10,000 rpm at a distance of 6.5 cm from the axis of the centrifuge rotor.   *Ans.* 177×10^{-13} sec.

6. The sedimentation and diffusion coefficients for hemoglobin corrected to 20° in water are 4.41×10^{-13} sec and 6.3×10^{-7} cm^2 sec^{-1}, respectively. If $\bar{v} = 0.749$ cm^3 g^{-1} and $\rho_{H_2O} = 0.998$ g cm^{-3} at this temperature, calculate the molecular weight

of the protein. If there is 1 gram atom of iron per 17,000 grams of protein, how many gram atoms of iron are there per hemoglobin molecule? *Ans.* 4.

7. The relative viscosities of a series of solutions of a sample of polystyrene in toluene were determined with an Ostwald viscometer at 25°.

Concentration, g/100 ml	0.249	0.499	0.999	1.998
η/η_0	1.355	1.782	2.879	6.090

The ratio η_{sp}/c is plotted against c and extrapolated to zero concentration to obtain the intrinsic viscosity. If the constants in equation 30 are $K = 3.7 \times 10^{-4}$ and $a = 0.62$ for this polymer, calculate the molecular weight. *Ans.* 500,000.

8. Crystallized serum albumin is dissolved in 0.1 N buffers of several different pH values for measurements of electrophoretic mobility. The distances moved by the protein boundary in the electrophoretic cell during 2 hours at a potential gradient of 6.5 volts per centimeter are given in the table.

pH	3.76	4.20	4.82	5.58
Δx, cm	0.936	0.328	0.234	0.700

Movement toward cathode	Toward anode

Plot the protein-ion mobility versus pH, and obtain the isoelectric point by interpolation. *Ans.* pH = 4.5.

9. A solution of palmitic acid ($M = 256$) in benzene contains 4.24 grams of acid per liter. When this solution is dropped on a water surface the benzene evaporates and the palmitic acid forms a continuous monomolecular film. If it is desired to cover an area of 500 cm² with a monolayer, what volume of solution should be used? The area occupied by one palmitic acid molecule may be taken to be 21 A².
Ans. 0.0239 ml.

10. The following table gives the number of milliliters (v) of nitrogen (reduced to 0°C and 1 atm) adsorbed per gram of active carbon at 0°C at a series of pressures.

p, mm	3.93	12.98	22.94	34.01	56.23
v, ml/g	0.987	3.04	5.08	7.04	10.31

Plot the data according to the Langmuir isotherm, and determine the constants.
Ans. $a = 7.1 \times 10^{-3}$ mm^{-1}, $b = 36$ ml g^{-1}.

11. In a colloidal solution of silver, it is assumed that each particle is a cube 0.04 μ on an edge. (*a*) How many colloid particles can be produced from 0.1 gram of silver? (*b*) What is the total area of the silver particles? (*c*) What is the area of a single cube of silver weighing 0.1 gram? The density of silver is 10.5 g cm^{-3}.

12. Calculate the time necessary for a spherical calcium chloride particle 40 μ in diameter to fall 1 cm in carbon tetrachloride (density = 1.595 g cm^{-3}, $\eta = 0.00975$ poise) at room temperature. The density of calcium chloride is 2.152 g cm^{-3}.

13. A solution containing 0.0015 gram of Fe_2O_3 per milliliter was diluted 1 part to 10,000. An ultramicroscopic count on the dilute solution gave an average of 4.1 particles per count in a field of view of 0.04-mm diameter and 0.04-mm depth. If it

is assumed that the density of the particles is 5.2 g cm^{-3}, and that the particles are spheres, what is the diameter of the particles?

14. Egg albumin has a molecular weight of 40,500. What is the osmotic pressure at 25° of a solution containing 5 grams per liter?

15. The sedimentation coefficient of gamma globulin at 20° is 7.1 × 10^{-13} sec. Calculate how far the protein boundary will sediment in ½ hour if the speed of the centrifuge is 60,000 rpm and the initial boundary is 6.50 cm from the axis of rotation.

16. A sample of polystyrene was dissolved in toluene, and the following flow times in an Ostwald viscometer at 25° were obtained for different concentrations:

Concentration, g/100 ml	0	0.1	0.3	0.6	0.9
Time, sec	86.0	99.5	132	194	301

The quantity $[(\eta/\eta_0) - 1]/c$ is plotted against c and extrapolated to zero concentration to obtain the intrinsic viscosity. If the constants in equation 30 are $K = 3.7 \times 10^{-4}$ and $a = 0.62$ for this polymer, calculate the molecular weight.

17. Magnesium oxide adsorbs silica from water and follows the Freundlich equation. It may be used to remove silica from boiler scale. Make a log-log plot of the following data, and calculate the constants of the Freundlich equation. Calculate the parts per million of magnesium oxide needed to reduce the residual silica to 2.9 parts per million. (1 ppm = 1 mg per 1000 g H$_2$O.)

MgO, ppm	0	75	100	200
Residual SiO$_2$, ppm	26.2	9.2	6.2	1.0
SiO$_2$ removed, ppm	0	17.0	20.0	25.2

18. The adsorption of N$_2$ on mica is as follows:

p	2.8	6.1	17.3
x/m	12	19	28.2

(p is given in dynes per square centimeter, and x/m is given in cubic millimeters of gas at 20° and 760 mm adsorbed on 24.3 grams of mica, having a surface of 5750 sq cm.) (a) Determine the constants of the Langmuir equation. (b) Calculate the value of x/m at $p = 23.8$. (The experimental value is 30.8.)

19. The diameter of the hydrogen molecule is 2.74 A. If an adsorbent has a surface of 850 sq m per ml and 95 per cent of the surface is active, how much H$_2$ (measured at standard conditions) could be adsorbed by 100 ml of the adsorbent? It may be assumed that the adsorbed molecules are arranged in cubic rather than hexagonal packing and just touch in a plane.

20. One hundred grams of oleic acid (C$_{17}$H$_{33}$COOH) is poured on the surface of a clean lake where the spreading film can be seen if the water is rippled by a gentle wind or marked with rain drops. The cross-sectional area of the molecule is about 22 A^2. What will be the maximum diameter in meters of a circular film produced in this way?

21. Human blood plasma contains approximately 40 grams of albumin ($M = 69,000$) and 20 grams of globulin ($M = 160,000$) per liter. Calculate the colloid osmotic pressure at 37°C ignoring the Donnan effect.

22. One gram of a certain activated charcoal has a surface area of 1000 sq m. If complete surface coverage is assumed, as a limiting case, how much ammonia, at standard conditions, could be adsorbed on the surface of 45 grams of activated charcoal? The diameter of the NH_3 molecule is 3×10^{-8} cm, and it is assumed that the molecules just touch each other in a plane with cubic packing.

23. If only a small amount of material q is allowed to diffuse through a porous plate from a solution of concentration c'' into a solution of concentration c', Fick's law may be written

$$D = \frac{-q}{Kt(c' - c'')}$$

where K is the cell constant which must be determined in an experiment with a substance of known diffusion coefficient. If a 0.10 N aqueous solution of KCl is allowed to diffuse into water for 12 hours and 38 minutes at 25°, it is found that 1.25×10^{-4} equivalent of salt diffuses through the porous plate. Calculate D if K has previously been found to be 1.5 cm.

24. Calculate number average and weight average molecular weights for the following mixture: 1 gram of polymer of $M = 10^4$ and 1 gram of polymer of $M = 10^6$.

25. Using Fick's first law show that for diffusion in a vertical cell of constant cross section

$$\frac{\partial c}{\partial t} = D \frac{\partial^2 c}{\partial x^2}$$

if D is a constant independent of concentration. The distance x is measured in a vertical direction.

26. Estimate the diffusion coefficient in water at 25° of a spherical molecule with a molecular weight of 10^5 and $\bar{v} = 0.73$ cm^3 g^{-1}.

27. In a centrifuge experiment with egg albumin in a buffered aqueous solution at a pH of 6, the boundary moved 6.3 mm in 105 minutes, as determined by measurement of the change in position of the refractive index gradient with time. The speed of the centrifuge was 57,000 rpm. The distance from the center of rotation was 6.43 cm. Show that the sedimentation coefficient for this material is 3.5×10^{-13} sec after multiplying by 0.81 to correct for density and viscosity.

18

Quantum Theory

The development of the theory of atomic structure began with the concept of discrete units of electric charge. The atomic nature of electricity was indicated by Faraday's experiments on the electrolysis of substances in solution, and the term "electron" for the indivisible unit of electricity was introduced by Stoney in 1891. Much of the original research on the properties of the electron was done by J. J. Thomson and others in the English laboratories during the latter part of the past century.

Conductance of Electricity through Gases. When two metal electrodes are placed in a glass vessel containing gas at atmospheric pressure, it is necessary to apply a potential of some 40,000 volts per centimeter before any appreciable amount of current will pass through the gas. Under these conditions a spark is produced. If the pressure of the gas is reduced progressively, the spark becomes more uniform and broadens out. When the pressure is decreased to about 0.5 mm, the negative electrode (cathode) appears to be surrounded by a luminous layer, and between this and the anode is a series of luminous striations separated by dark regions, the number of which depends on the pressure, the kind of gas, and the dimensions of the vessel.

The current is carried between the electrodes partly by electrons and partly by gas ions. Positive gas ions are produced when molecules have one or more of their outer electrons removed, and negative ions are produced when the electrons become attached to other molecules. Gas ions, then, are similar to electrolytic ions, which have been studied in earlier chapters, but they are not governed by the usual valence rules. Mercury atoms, for example, can exist with 0, 1, 2, 3, 4, etc., charges. Furthermore, the electrolytic ions are present before the passage of the electric current, but the gas ions are produced chiefly by the current itself, the few original electrons and ions acquiring sufficient velocity in the electric field to collide with neutral molecules, dislodging electrons from them and producing many more ions. The dark spaces in the discharge tube indicate the regions where the electrons have not yet developed sufficient kinetic energy to ionize or excite molecules. Light is produced when ions are discharged or electrons in excited atoms return to positions of lower energy. As the pressure is further reduced, the luminous columns change in appearance, and below 0.01 mm they disappear, and the glass wall opposite the cathode becomes luminescent. The color of this luminescence depends on the nature of the glass. It is produced by bombardment of the glass by negative particles or electrons driven out from the cathode.

It was found that an opaque object placed in the path of the cathode rays casts a shadow and that the rays travel in straight lines from the

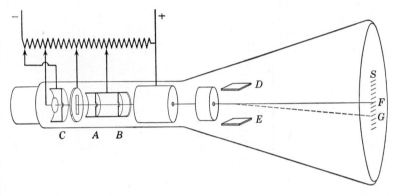

FIG. 18-1. Apparatus for measuring the ratio of mass to charge for an electron.

cathode. A small paddle wheel was made to revolve by the cathode rays, thus showing that the rays possess mechanical energy. The electrical nature of these cathode rays was demonstrated by the fact that they were deflected in an electrostatic field toward the positive electrode, thus indicating a negative charge. Again, when a magnetic field was applied, they were deflected in a direction which indicated that negative charges were moving away from the cathode.

Electrons. The experiments with cathode rays described in the preceding section were followed by quantitative measurements of the charge and mass of the electron. The apparatus used by J. J. Thomson is illustrated in *Fig. 18-1.*

In the evacuated tube electrons are emitted from the negatively charged cathode C and attracted to the positively charged anode A, which has a small hole in it. The beam of electrons passing through this hole is rendered still sharper by passing through holes in several carefully aligned plates, so that a sharply defined fluorescent spot of light F is produced on the glass scale S. A magnetic field H, not indicated in the figure, is applied, of such strength that the spot of light moves down the scale to G. The force pulling it down is equal to Hev, where e is the charge and v the velocity of the electron. There is a centrifugal force equal to mv^2/r, where r is the radius of curvature of the deflected beam and m is the mass of the electron, tending to return the electrons to a

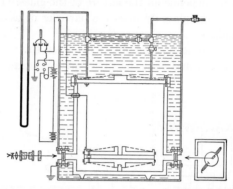

Fig. 18-2. Millikan's apparatus for measuring the charge of the electron.

straight path hitting the scale at F. The actual path of the electron beam is such that these forces are balanced.

$$Hev = mv^2/r \qquad (1)$$

Then

$$Hr = mv/e \qquad (2)$$

An electrostatic potential difference E is now applied to the electrodes D and E which is just sufficient to return the spot of light to F. Then

$$Ee = Hev \qquad (3)$$

and

$$v = E/H \qquad (4)$$

Both E and H are measured experimentally, and, thus, the velocity v can be determined. It is 6×10^9 cm per sec when the potential difference between A and C is 10,000 volts. If the value of v is substituted into equation 2, it is possible to obtain the ratio m/e. At low velocities it is 5.684×10^{-8} gram per electromagnetic unit, and at higher velocities approaching the velocity of light the mass increases and approaches infinity, as predicted by the theory of relativity (page 626).

The charge of the electron was determined in the classic oil-drop apparatus of Millikan * shown in *Fig. 18-2*. A fine mist of oil is blown

* Millikan, *Phys. Rev.*, *39*, 349 (1911); *2*, 109 (1913).

into a quiet thermostated air space between two electrodes, and the rate of fall of a single drop is observed with a microscope. The radius of the drop is determined from its rate of fall by means of Stokes's equation (page 503). When the electric field is turned on, the velocity of the drop will be increased or decreased, depending on the sign of the charge and the direction of the field, if the drop is electrically charged. If the surrounding air is ionized by an X-ray beam the oil drop will frequently pick up a gas ion and its charge, and hence the velocity in the electric field will change. The charge of the electron may be determined from the observed changes in velocity. The determination of charge may be explained most simply by considering the strength E of the field for which the velocity is zero.

$$neE = \tfrac{4}{3}\pi r^3 g(d - d_0) \tag{5}$$

where n is the number of unit electric charges of magnitude e, r is the radius of the drop, g is the acceleration of gravity, d is the density of the oil, and d_0 is the density of air. Millikan found that ne is always a multiple of 1.602×10^{-19} coulomb, or 1.602×10^{-20} electromagnetic unit, and so this is the charge of the electron. Still more accurate measurements of the charge of the electron have been made by other methods, and the value given in the Appendix is an average value.

The mass of the electron may be calculated from the values of e and m/e.

$$(5.6839 \times 10^{-8} \text{ g emu}^{-1})(1.60186 \times 10^{-20} \text{ emu}) = 9.105 \times 10^{-28} \text{ g}$$

This is the rest mass of the electron, the mass it possesses when it is moving slowly compared to the velocity of light. The ratio of the mass of an average hydrogen atom to that of an electron is

$$\frac{(1.008)}{(6.0238 \times 10^{23})(9.105 \times 10^{-28})} = 1838$$

Although the mass of an electron may be determined it should be remembered that a beam of electrons has wave properties like light. For example, electrons may be diffracted by molecules (page 77).

By experiments to be described in the next chapter Rutherford was able to show that an atom consists of a small positively charged nucleus surrounded by electrons. The number of positive charges on the nucleus was shown to be equal to the atomic number, and the number of electrons surrounding the nucleus in the neutral atom is also equal to the atomic number. The difficulty with this theory of the atom was that according to classical physics the moving electron would radiate. As a result of this loss of energy the electron would spiral into the nucleus.

The explanation of the failure of the orbital electrons to fall into the nucleus was made possible only by the introduction of a completely new idea, the quantum theory. In 1900 Planck was led to his hypothesis that radiation is discontinuous by a consideration of radiation by heated objects, and so some of the facts of radiation will be considered briefly.

Emission and Absorption of Radiation. When light strikes a substance, a portion of the incident radiation is transmitted, a portion is reflected, and a portion is absorbed. These three possibilities are illustrated by the passage of visible light through glass, the reflection from silvered glass, and the absorption by smoked glass.

It has been established by Kirchhoff that the ability of a given substance to emit radiation when heated is proportional to its ability to absorb radiation. The fraction of the radiant energy which is absorbed is called the absorptivity and represented by A. If two surfaces with emissive powers E_1 and E_2 and absorptivities A_1 and A_2 are in equilibrium in an isothermal enclosure

$$E_2/E_1 = A_2/A_1 \qquad (6)$$

A surface whose absorptivity $A = 1$ is called a *black body* or perfect radiator, and it is seen from equation 6 that, if $A_2 = 1$, E_2 has the maximum possible value since A_1 cannot be greater than unity. Thus a black body emits the maximum intensity of radiation at a given temperature.

A hollow sphere containing a single small hole acts as a perfect radiator with complete absorption and maximum emission of light. Practically all the radiation passing into the small opening is absorbed by multiple reflections inside the enclosure. An electrically heated furnace with a small opening serves as a convenient black body.

Kirchhoff's law may be illustrated with a spot of colored glass melted onto a colorless glass tube. The spot appears dark on account of the absorption of light, but when the tube is heated the spot appears brighter than the rest of the tube because, according to equation 6, the emission E is directly proportional to the absorptivity A. When the tube is placed inside a heated furnace with a small opening, however, the spot disappears because the temperature has become uniform throughout and light is reflected back and forth so as to make the absorption of light complete within the enclosure.

According to the Stefan-Boltzmann law, the total radiation E emitted by a perfect radiator is proportional to the fourth power of the absolute temperature. Thus,

$$E = \sigma T^4 \qquad (7)$$

where σ is constant, having the value 5.69×10^{-5} erg cm^{-2} sec^{-1} deg^{-4}. This law, discovered experimentally by Stefan and derived theoretically later by Boltzmann, has been abundantly verified.

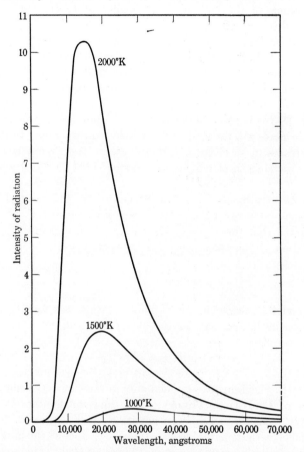

FIG. 18-3. Emission of radiation from a black body at different temperatures. The area under a curve, divided by 10,000, between specified wavelengths gives the energy in calories per second radiated from 1 cm^2 of a perfect radiator.

The average radiation from the summer sun on the surface of the earth has been found to be approximately 1.2 cal per min per sq cm in temperate zones. It has been estimated that the temperature of the surface of the sun is about 6200°K, the center of course being very much hotter.

Total radiation includes radiation of all wavelengths, visible, infrared, and ultraviolet. The intensity of the radiation from a perfect radiator varies greatly with the wavelength as shown in *Fig. 18-3*. Measure-

ments of this type may be made by spreading out with a suitable prism
the total radiation from a perfect radiator. A thermopile is then moved
along in different parts of the spectrum, and with suitable corrections
the deflections of the galvanometer connected to the thermopile are
proportional to the intensity of radiation.

When an ordinary solid is heated, similar curves are obtained except
that they fall below the curves shown in Fig. 18-3 for a perfect radiator.
The emissivity varies with the wavelength and with the nature of the
solid and its surface, but it is never greater than that for a perfect
radiator.

In Fig. 18-3 it is to be noted that, as the temperature of the perfect
radiator is increased, the area under a curve corresponding to total radiation increases in accordance with the Stefan-Boltzmann law. Moreover, the wavelength of maximum emission shifts to the shorter wavelengths.

Attempts were made to calculate theoretically the spectral distribution of black-body radiation on the basis of classical physics. In 1896
Wien showed that theoretically the energy E_λ in ergs cm^{-2} sec^{-1} of a
small portion of the spectrum lying between λ and $\lambda + d\lambda$ should be
given by

$$E_\lambda = (C_1/\lambda^5)e^{-C_2/\lambda T} \tag{8}$$

where C_1 and C_2 are constants. This equation was found to hold at
short wavelengths but not for the longer wavelengths. On the other
hand, the equation

$$E_\lambda = C_3 T/\lambda^4 \tag{9}$$

derived by Rayleigh in 1900 applied only in the long-wavelength region.

Origin of Quantum Theory. Realizing the limitations of these
formulas, Planck derived a better equation which expressed the experimental facts with remarkable exactness over the whole range of the
spectrum. In deriving this equation Planck was led to the bold conclusion that radiation is emitted and absorbed discontinuously in integral
multiples of a fundamental unit which he called a quantum ϵ, and that
the energy of a quantum is proportional to the frequency of the light.
These suggestions led to the *quantum theory*.

The development of the quantum theory is one of the important mile-
stones in science. As in many other important advances, the exact experimental facts came first, then an empirical mathematical equation to
express the facts, and, finally, a working hypothesis to explain the terms
in the equation. Then, on the basis of this hypothesis, predictions were
made and new experiments planned which led to rapid progress in many

different fields of science. General confirmation of the hypothesis soon gave it the rank of a theory.

Planck's formula * is

$$E_\lambda = \frac{2\pi c^2 h}{\lambda^5 (e^{ch/k\lambda T} - 1)} \tag{10}$$

where E_λ is the rate of emission of radiation of wavelength λ, c is the velocity of light, k is the gas constant per molecule (R/N) called the Boltzmann constant, and h is a constant now known as Planck's constant. This constant has turned out to be a very important universal constant.

Formula 10 can be integrated to give the Stefan-Boltzmann law; it approaches the Rayleigh law, equation 9, for large values of λ, and it approaches Wien's distribution law, equation 8, as λ approaches zero. Planck's radiation formula then is in remarkable agreement with the various facts of radiation, and it gives experimental values with excellent precision. In spite of these successes, the formula would probably have failed to obtain general acceptance, on account of the radically new assumption concerning quanta, except for the fact that almost at once it became extremely useful in new and unrelated fields. It has revolutionized the study of spectroscopy. Critical potentials, photoelectric effects, and specific heats have all been interpreted quantitatively with the help of the quantum theory. The study of photochemistry and chemical kinetics and the calculation of equilibrium constants have been stimulated by applications of quantum mechanics.

There seems, then, to be adequate experimental justification in many fields for the quantum theory, according to which radiation is composed of units called photons or quanta, and the energy of each quantum ϵ is given by the fundamental equation

$$\epsilon = h\nu \tag{11}$$

where Planck's constant h has the value 6.624×10^{-27} erg sec and ν is the frequency of the radiation in reciprocal seconds.

The Photoelectric Effect. One of the first applications of the quantum hypothesis was in the explanation of the photoelectric effect by Einstein in 1905. The photoelectric effect is the ejection of electrons from a metal surface by light. This interesting effect has been utilized in the photoelectric cell, which is an extremely sensitive instru-

* This formula is discussed fully in Taylor and Glasstone, *Treatise on Physical Chemistry*, D. Van Nostrand Co., New York, 1942, pages 189–196.

ment for the detection and measurement of radiation. A diagram of such a cell is shown in *Fig. 18-4*.

A receiver K is coated with a thin film of potassium or other metal in a highly evacuated tube. A wire W placed in the tube is connected

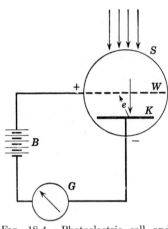

with the receiver through a battery B and a sensitive galvanometer or electrometer G. The high vacuum of the tube serves as a complete insulator between W and K, but, when the receiver is exposed to light from the source S, electrons are ejected from the receiver and attracted to the positively charged wire, thus completing the circuit. The current registered by the galvanometer is directly proportional to the number of electrons ejected per second, and this, in turn, is proportional to the number of photons striking the receiver, that is, to the intensity of the light.

FIG. 18-4. Photoelectric cell and circuit.

Although the electron current or the number of electrons per second depends on the intensity of light, that is, the number of photons (quanta) striking the surface per second, the velocity or energy of the electrons driven out depends on the frequency of the light, according to the relation

$$\tfrac{1}{2}mv^2 = h\nu - h\nu_0 = Ee/300 \tag{12}$$

where m is the mass of the electron, v its velocity, ν is the frequency of the incident light, and ν_0 is a constant sometimes called the photoelectric threshold. The kinetic energy $\tfrac{1}{2}mv^2$ of the escaping electron is equal to $h\nu$, the energy of the incident radiation, minus $h\nu_0$, the energy required to bring the electron out to the surface of the metal.

The voltage E is the potential difference necessary to retard the velocity of the electron to zero and prevent its escape. The factor 300 is required to convert ordinary volts into electrostatic units.

When the minimum voltage E required to prevent the production of an electron current is plotted against the frequency ν of the incident light, a straight line is obtained having a slope equal to $300h/e$. This relation has been accurately checked with many different metals. The experimental determination of the slope offers one means of evaluating Planck's constant h (in terms of h/e).

The current from a photoelectric cell can be amplified readily, with the aid of ordinary electron tubes, to operate a relay, and the photoelectric cell has found many important applications in automatic controls, safety devices, and laboratory appliances, as well as in television and motion pictures. In a photomultiplier tube the electrons released by the light impinge under high voltage on a second photosensitive surface and there release additional electrons which in turn are multiplied on a third photosensitive surface, etc. In this way just a few quanta can liberate many electrons and so give a large current to be measured.

Spectrum of Atomic Hydrogen. In contrast to the continuous

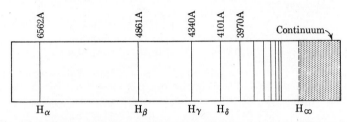

FIG. 18-5. Balmer series of lines in the spectrum of atomic hydrogen. At shorter wavelengths than the series limit (H_∞) there is continuous emission.

radiation of a heated solid it is found that the emission spectrum of a hot gas contains discrete lines. If the gas contains molecules there are families of closely spaced lines or bands. The spectrum of a gas may also be studied by passing the continuous radiation from a solid through the gas. Light of certain wavelengths is absorbed so that dark lines appear on the continuous background in the spectrograph. Although a number of relations between the wavelengths of the various spectral lines had been found empirically these relations remained unexplained until Bohr in 1913 proposed a theory based upon the quantum hypothesis of Planck.

The simplest spectrum is that of atomic hydrogen, for which a small region is illustrated in *Fig. 18-5*. In 1885 Balmer discovered that the wavelengths λ (or wave numbers $\bar{\nu}$ *) of the lines in the visible region could be expressed by a simple relation which may be written as

$$\frac{1}{\lambda} = \bar{\nu} = R\left(\frac{1}{2^2} - \frac{1}{n_2{}^2}\right) \tag{13}$$

where n_2 is an integer greater than 2 and R is the Rydberg constant, 109,677.58 cm^{-1}. The value of R may be determined very accurately

* $\bar{\nu}$ = wave number = $1/\lambda_{cm}$, and $\lambda_{cm} = 10^{-8} \times$ wavelength in angstroms.

because of the high accuracy with which the wavelengths of spectral lines can be measured.

The agreement between the wavelengths of the lines of the Balmer series and the values calculated by equation 13 is indicated by the data of Table I. It will be noticed in equation 13 that n_2 cannot be less than 2,

Table I.   Balmer Lines in the Atomic Hydrogen Spectrum

n_2	λ_{vacuo}, calculated by equation 13	λ_{air}, calculated[1]	λ_{air}, experimental
3	6564.70	6562.89	6562.8
4	4862.74	4861.38	4861.4
5	4341.73	4340.51	4340.5
6	4102.93	4101.78	4101.8

[1] $\lambda_{air} = \lambda_{vacuo}/n$, where n is the refractive index of air. Values for n are given in the *International Critical Tables*, McGraw-Hill Book Co., New York, 1930, Vol. VII, page 5.

for then $\bar{\nu}$ would be a meaningless negative number, and it cannot be 2, for then $\bar{\nu}$ becomes zero. As n_2 becomes larger than 2, the corresponding value of $\bar{\nu}$ becomes larger, but, when n_2 is already large, further increases cause $\bar{\nu}$ to increase only very slightly, and, as n_2 approaches infinity, $\bar{\nu}$ approaches $\frac{1}{4}R$ as a limit. As indicated in Fig. 18-5 there is continuous radiation at wavelengths shorter than this series limit.

The success of the Balmer formula led to further exploration, and other series of lines were discovered in the atomic hydrogen spectrum which could be represented by the equation

$$\bar{\nu} = R\left(\frac{1}{n_1{}^2} - \frac{1}{n_2{}^2}\right) \tag{14}$$

where n_1 is also an integer. The series for which $n_1 = 1$ (Lyman series) is in the ultraviolet; the series for which $n_1 = 3$ (Paschen series), 4 (Brackett series), or 5 (Pfund series) are in the infrared region. It is important to note that every line in a given series can be represented as a difference of two terms, $R/n_1{}^2$ and $R/n_2{}^2$. The spectra of other elements are more complicated, but series are found which can be represented as a difference of two terms. The significance of this observation was made apparent by the Bohr theory.

Bohr's Theory of Atomic Hydrogen.   In 1913 Bohr * was able to derive a theoretical equation for the hydrogen spectrum which agreed

* Bohr, *Phil. Mag.*, *26*, 1, 476, 857 (1913).

with the experimental observations. Bohr assumed that the electron in the neighborhood of a hydrogen nucleus is restricted to move along one of a discrete set of allowed orbits. He assumed that the electron would not radiate while it followed one orbit, and so the energy of the atom would remain constant and the electron could be considered to exist in an energy level of energy E. When the electron jumped from one energy level E_2 to one of lower energy E_1, radiation would be emitted with an amount of energy equal to the difference in the energies corresponding to the two levels.

$$E_2 - E_1 = \epsilon = h\nu \qquad (15)$$

Bohr assumed that the electrons revolve around the nucleus in circular orbits and that the centrifugal force is equal to the force of electrostatic attraction. In accordance with the new ideas he assumed further that the motion of the electron was *quantized* and that instead of an infinite number of possible orbits only those occur for which the angular momentum mvr of an electron in its orbit is an integral multiple of $h/2\pi$.

$$mvr = nh/2\pi \qquad (16)$$

where n is an integer 1, 2, 3, 4, etc., referred to as a *quantum number*, m and v are the mass and velocity of the electron, and r is the radius of the orbit. By a simple application of mechanics and electrodynamics, given in the Appendix on page 651, he showed that the energy E_n in a particular orbit n is

$$E_n = \frac{-m(Ze)^2 e^2 4\pi^2}{2n^2 h^2} \qquad (17)$$

where Z is the atomic number (page 555), e is the charge of the electron, and h is Planck's constant. Then, according to equation 15, the energy of a quantum of light emitted on changing from one orbit to another is given by the formula

$$\epsilon = h\nu = E_2 - E_1 = \frac{2\pi^2 m e^4 Z^2}{h^2} \left(\frac{1}{n_1{}^2} - \frac{1}{n_2{}^2} \right) \qquad (18)$$

By comparison with equation 14 it can be seen that according to the Bohr theory the Rydberg constant R should be given by

$$R = 2\pi^2 m e^4 / h^3 c \qquad (19)$$

in which c is the velocity of light, 2.9979×10^{10} cm sec^{-1}. The value of R calculated from the various physical constants involved in this expression is in excellent agreement with the value obtained directly from spectroscopic measurements.

The electronic energy levels in the hydrogen atom as calculated from equation 17 of the Bohr theory are summarized in *Fig. 18-6*. The Lyman series of lines is produced by electrons jumping from orbits with quantum number 2, 3, 4 ⋯ into the lowest permitted orbit $n_1 = 1$. The Balmer series of lines is produced by electrons falling from larger orbits into the second orbit ($n_1 = 2$), etc. The energies of the various orbits

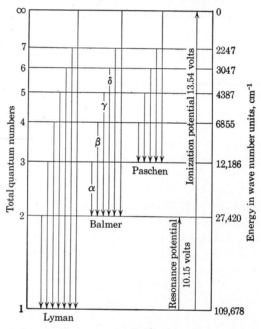

FIG. 18-6. Electronic energy levels in the hydrogen atom as calculated from the Bohr theory.

may be expressed in several ways. The energies in wave numbers given at the right in Fig. 18-6 are the wave numbers for radiation produced when an electron falls from an infinite distance into a given orbit. The wave number $\tilde{\nu}$ of any line in the spectrum may be obtained by subtracting the values at the right for the two energy levels involved. Thus the second line in the Balmer series is due to an electron falling from the fourth orbit into the second, and its wave number is 27,420 − 6,855 = 20,565 cm⁻¹.

The continuous emission beyond the convergence limit of the lines shown in Fig. 18-5 is always present, and it is particularly significant. In the region where sharp lines are obtained definite quantum restrictions are involved, but, when the electron is driven out to an indefinitely great distance, the electron can take with it unquantized kinetic energy which can vary continuously in magnitude and, thus, give a continuous range of frequencies. The convergence limit in the spectral series corresponds then to complete separation of the electron, that is, to ionization.

In this discussion the emission of light has been emphasized, but the absorption mechanism is the same except that the electrons are driven out to levels of higher energy by the absorption of quanta of energy, whereas in emission they fall back to levels of lower energy.

A helium atom which has lost one of its two electrons would be expected to have a spectrum very similar to that of a hydrogen atom. Since the atomic number of helium is 2 the frequencies or wave numbers are four times as great as for hydrogen. The spectra for Li^{+2} and Be^{+3} are also similar to that for hydrogen because there is a single orbital electron.

Actually, the spectral lines for atomic hydrogen are close doublets, and to account for this Sommerfeld introduced elliptical orbits and applied a relativity correction since the electronic mass varies with speed.

Critical Potentials. The energy levels in atoms may also be studied by bombarding atoms with electrons of known energy and determining the energy required to drive electrons in the atoms to higher energy levels. Electrons for this purpose may be accelerated by applying a potential between a grid and the hot filament which emits electrons. If the accelerated electrons have insufficient kinetic energy to cause a shift from one energy level to another in the atoms they strike, the collisions are said to be elastic. As the accelerating potential is increased, the electrons finally have sufficient energy to cause a definite displacement of electrons from one energy level to the next higher level. When the displaced electron in the atom then drops back to the lower level radiation is emitted. As the accelerating voltage is increased, new spectral lines are brought in.

An *ionization potential* is the voltage which gives to a free electron just sufficient energy to ionize the atom or molecule, that is, to drive an electron completely out, leaving a positive ion but without imparting any kinetic energy to the electron. *Resonance potentials* are potentials which cause the emission of light when the free electrons are stopped by collision.

An obvious and simple relation between the electric energy, the kinetic energy, and the radiation energy is involved in these quantum changes, as given by the following equation:

$$Ee/300 = \tfrac{1}{2}mv^2 = h\nu \tag{20}$$

where e is the charge of the electron in electrostatic units (4.80×10^{-10}), m its mass, v its velocity, and E the potential drop in volts through which the electron falls.

Referring to page 546,

$$\frac{Ee}{300} = h\nu = hc\bar{\nu} = hcR \left(\frac{1}{n_1{}^2} - \frac{1}{n_2{}^2} \right) \tag{21}$$

or

$$E = \frac{300Rhc}{e} \left(\frac{1}{n_1{}^2} - \frac{1}{n_2{}^2} \right) \tag{22}$$

where n_1 and n_2 are the quantum numbers 1, 2, 3, 4, 5, etc.

This equation is used in Table II to show the numerical relation

Table II. Spectral Lines and Critical Potentials in the Lyman Series

Quantum Number, n_2	Wave-length, λ_{obs}, A	Wave Number, cm^{-1}	Volts, E_{calc}	Volts, E_{obs}
2	1215	82,258	10.154	10.15
3	1026	97,491	12.034	12.05
4	973	102,823	12.692	12.70
5	950	105,291		
6	938	106,631	13.161	13.17
7	931	107,440	13.262	13.27
∞	912	109,678	13.539	13.54

between spectral lines and critical potentials in the Lyman series of *atomic* hydrogen, where $n_1 = 1$. The constant $300Rhc/e$ has the value of 13.539 volts.

The agreement between the calculated and observed voltages is excellent, again strengthening the underlying quantum theory on which the calculations are based.

Electron velocities and even spectral quantities are often expressed in terms of volts, calculated with the help of equation 22. The term volt when applied to energy quantities really means electron volt per electron.

Wave Mechanics. In spite of its great successes the Bohr theory was unable to explain certain phenomena, and it was felt that the definite orbits were introduced in a rather arbitrary way and means were sought for making quantum mechanics a logical whole. This search for an improved theory led to the development of *wave mechanics*. This provided a theoretical basis for the interpretation of the intensities of spectral lines as well as their positions and for the interpretation of collision phenomena. The logical basis of this new mechanics is the *uncertainty* *principle* of Heisenberg.* According to this principle, it will never be possible to know with exactness *both* the position *and* the momentum of an electron or other small particle. It is not a matter of physical imperfections in the measuring apparatus but a fundamental limit of nature, according to which the error in measuring position multiplied by the error in measuring momentum is approximately of the order of Planck's constant *h*. The position of an electron or atom may be known with exactness, but then its velocity is unknown; and in the same way the momentum can be known only at the sacrifice of information regarding the position.

If it were possible to construct a microscope using rays with very short wavelength for the purpose of determining the position and velocity of an electron, it would be found that a single photon of light would impart a portion of its energy to the electron, which would then have a different velocity. This phenomenon in which the energy of a photon is reduced and that of an electron is increased is known as the Compton effect. Compton † bombarded carbon and other light elements with short X rays and found, with the help of a crystal lattice and spectrometer, that part of the scattered radiation had a longer wavelength than the incident radiation.

The Heisenberg uncertainty principle may be expressed mathematically by

$$\Delta p \cdot \Delta x \sim h \tag{23}$$

$$\Delta E \cdot \Delta t \sim h \tag{24}$$

where Δp is the uncertainty in the momentum, Δx is the uncertainty in position, ΔE is the uncertainty in the energy, and Δt is the uncertainty in time that a particle is in a given energy state.

The principle is of no importance in ordinary work, because the particles involved are so large that the uncertainty is utterly negligible. It does have an important bearing on philosophy, ‡ however, for heretofore it had been supposed that no *theoretical* limit was imposed on the precision of scientific measurements, and we cannot expect to determine exactly the position of an electron in a Bohr orbit at a certain time. Because of the uncertainty principle the future arrangement in an atomic system cannot be predicted with certainty as was assumed in classical mechanics. Instead, only the probability that an electron will be at a given point at a given time may be predicted.

* Heisenberg, *Z. Physik, 43*, 172 (1927).

† Compton, *Phys. Rev., 21*, 483 (1923).

‡ Bridgman, *The Logic of Modern Physics*, The Macmillan Co., New York, 1927.

Heisenberg and Born devised a theory based on matrix algebra; De Broglie and Schrödinger developed a theory based on differential equations applied to waves; and Dirac embraced both in general terms with a new system of mathematics. All three treatments are aspects of the same underlying principle, and the restrictions of the quantum theory come out automatically as mathematical necessities.

The Schrödinger wave equation for a single particle is

$$\frac{\partial^2 \psi}{\partial x^2} + \frac{\partial^2 \psi}{\partial y^2} + \frac{\partial^2 \psi}{\partial z^2} + \frac{8\pi^2 m}{h^2}(E - V)\psi = 0 \qquad (25)$$

where m is the mass of the particle, V is its potential energy in a field of force, and E is its total energy, a constant. The quantity ψ is called the "wave function." Where ψ^2 is large, there is a large concentration of electrons; in general, ψ^2 determines the probability of an electron's being in a specified region. When sufficient information is available, ψ can be determined by solving the differential equation 25. The wave function is always continuous, single-valued, and finite; and zero at infinite distance. Solutions which meet these requirements are possible only when E is given certain characteristic values, *eigenvalues*, and the corresponding solutions of ψ are called *eigenfunctions*.

These characteristic values give the stationary states of the Bohr atomic model, and, thus, the quantized energy levels come automatically from the Schrödinger wave equation. According to quantum mechanics the electrons are not confined to circular or elliptical orbits, although they are confined to certain energy levels. Quantum mechanics is much superior to the older theories because, in addition to accomplishing all that they accomplished, it solves more complicated problems and often gives better agreement with experiment.

Quantum Numbers. The spectrum of atomic hydrogen can be interpreted nicely by the simple Bohr formula, making use of two numbers. Other spectra are much more complicated, and more quantum numbers are needed in specifying the spectral lines. It is found that many spectral lines have fine structure. With sufficient dispersion in a spectrograph they are seen to give doublets, triplets, and so on. Furthermore, some of the lines are affected by a strong electrostatic field, giving the *Stark effect*, and by a magnetic field, giving the *Zeeman effect*. In the more complex spectra some of the lines can be grouped together in overlapping series, depending on their behavior and general appearance. Thus, one series of lines is characterized by having particularly sharp lines and another by having diffuse lines. Several characteristic types of spectra have come to be recognized by spectroscopists, such as the principal (p), sharp (s), diffuse (d), and fundamental (f), although these symbols have lost much of their original meaning.

All these variations can be handled by using four quantum numbers. These numbers and their symbols which describe the state of an electron in an atom are as follows:

n = principal quantum number (or total quantum number).

When n =   1   2   3   4   5,
the corresponding symbols are K L M N O.*

l = orbital quantum number. l can have any integer value, except that it must be one or more units less than the principal quantum number; that is, it can never be greater than ($n - 1$).

When l =   0   1   2   3,
the corresponding symbols are s p d f.

m_l = magnetic quantum number. m_l depends on l and may have any integral value between $+l$ and $-l$, including zero. Therefore, $2l + 1$ values of m_l are possible.

m_s = electron spin quantum number. Two values of m_s are possible, corresponding to two possible orientations of the spin vector s.†
The quantum numbers can vary only by integers, and m_s can have only the values $+\frac{1}{2}$ and $-\frac{1}{2}$.

Only those combinations of numbers are allowed which are in agreement with the restrictions just given. For example, if $n = 3$, l can be only 2, 1, or 0; and m_l can be ± 2, ± 1, or 0; and m_s can be only $+\frac{1}{2}$ or $-\frac{1}{2}$. All the various combinations of the four quantum numbers permitted by the restrictions just given are recorded in Table III for values of the principal quantum number of 1, 2, 3, and 4.

The total number of permissible combinations of the four quantum numbers is given in the last column of Table III. The recognition of these four quantum numbers has been a great aid in understanding many physical and chemical phenomena, particularly through the application of the restriction to be described in the following section.

The further application of these quantum numbers to describe complicated spectra is beyond the scope of this book. It may be stated, however, that the capital letters S, P, D, and F are used to designate

* These letters refer to the shells of orbital electrons, K referring to the first electron shell, L to the second, M to the third, etc.

† The spin quantum number s, used as a subscript, is not to be confused with the orbital quantum number s.

Table III. Possible Conditions of Electronic Quantum Numbers

Principal n	Group	Orbital l	Subgroup	Magnetic m_l	Spin m_s	Total Number of Different Combinations
1	K	0	s	0	$+\frac{1}{2} -\frac{1}{2}$	2
2	L	0	s	0	$+\frac{1}{2} -\frac{1}{2}$	2 ⎫ 8
2	L	1	p	+1 0 −1	$+\frac{1}{2} -\frac{1}{2}$	6 ⎭
3	M	0	s	0	$+\frac{1}{2} -\frac{1}{2}$	2 ⎫
3	M	1	p	+1 0 −1	$+\frac{1}{2} -\frac{1}{2}$	6 ⎬ 18
3	M	2	d	+2 +1 0 −1 −2	$+\frac{1}{2} -\frac{1}{2}$	10 ⎭
4	N	0	s	0	$+\frac{1}{2} -\frac{1}{2}$	2 ⎫
4	N	1	p	+1 0 −1	$+\frac{1}{2} -\frac{1}{2}$	6 ⎪
4	N	2	d	+2 +1 0 −1 −2	$+\frac{1}{2} -\frac{1}{2}$	10 ⎬ 32
4	N	3	f	+3 +2 +1 0 −1 −2 −3	$+\frac{1}{2} -\frac{1}{2}$	14 ⎭

electronic energy levels of atoms and that superscripts and subscripts such as $^2D_{3/2}$ are used to describe sublevels.

Pauli's Exclusion Principle. According to Pauli, *two electrons in a single atom can never have all four quantum numbers the same.* This principle is a great help in explaining the spectral lines and the number of elements in the different groups of the periodic table. Referring to the last column in Table III, it may be seen that 2 different combinations of quantum numbers are possible for an s electron, 6 for a p electron, 10 for a d electron, and so on. Now, by the Pauli principle, there can be only one kind of atom for each given combination of electronic quantum numbers. The sequence 2, 8, 18, 32, given in the last column of Table III, is thus the sequence in the number of elements found in the successive groups of the periodic table.

Periodic Table. In 1869 Mendeleef arranged the elements in order of increasing atomic weight and utilized the periodicity which he observed in predicting the properties of elements that appeared to be missing. Actually the elements should be arranged in order of increasing atomic number as shown by Moseley.

Moseley placed different elements as targets in an X-ray tube and determined the wavelength of the X rays, using a crystal as a reflection grating (page 41). As the atomic weight of the element increased, the wavelength of the X rays decreased. The X-ray spectrum was quite simple, involving two lines, close together. In the heavier elements a second series of characteristic X-ray lines was found, and these too became displaced in the direction of shorter wavelengths as the atomic weight increased. In the heaviest elements a third series of X-ray lines was found. These three series are known as the K, L, and M series, respectively, and the doublets are designated as alpha and beta lines. When Moseley plotted the square root of the frequencies of the X-ray lines against the atomic number Z of the elements, he found that approximately straight lines were produced, as shown in *Fig. 18-7*.

Expressed mathematically,

$$\sqrt{\nu} = aZ - b \tag{26}$$

where a and b are constants.

This *atomic number* Z is a fundamental characteristic of an atom. It is equal to the positive charge of the nucleus of the atom, which in turn is the same as the number of electrons surrounding the nucleus in the uncharged atom.

The arrangement of elements according to their atomic numbers straightened out certain anomalies in the periodic table. Potassium follows argon, nickel follows cobalt, and iodine follows tellurium, in spite of the fact that classification by atomic weights puts them in the reverse order. The existence of nuclei with different weights but the same atomic number explains why this order is reversed and shows that the atomic number is a more fundamental property than the atomic weight. When Moseley prepared his table of atomic numbers in 1914, there were six gaps corresponding to six missing elements, but all of these have since been filled. Before the discovery of Moseley's relation there was doubt concerning the number of rare-earth elements because the chemistry of these elements is so much alike. By referring to the graph of Fig. 18-7 it was found that, to make the line continuous, there should be fourteen rare-earth elements, and also a homolog of zirconium between barium and tantalum. Thirteen of these positions could be filled from rare-earth metals then known, and the homolog of zirconium was found later by Coster and Hevesy and called hafnium.

A modern form of the periodic arrangement of elements is given in Table IV, in which the atomic number appears over the symbol for the element. The numbers below the symbols are the atomic weights on the chemical scale for naturally occurring elements or the mass number (page 608) in parentheses for a known isotope for the synthetic elements. The periodic table is of great value in correlating chemical and physical properties.

The nature of the periods in the periodic table is readily explained in terms of Pauli's exclusion principle and the four quantum numbers n, l, m_l, and m_s. The number of orbital electrons in an atom of an element

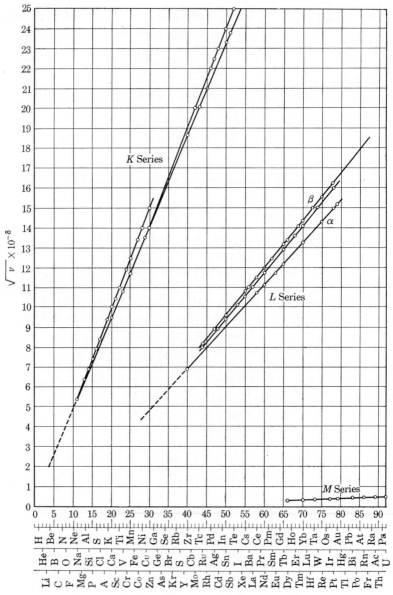

FIG. 18-7. Relation of atomic numbers of the elements to the frequencies of the X rays emitted.

Table IV. Periodic Table of the Elements

IA	IIA	IIIB	IVB	VB	VIB	VIIB	VIII	VIII	VIII	IB	IIB	IIIA	IVA	VA	VIA	VIIA	
1 H 1.0080																	2 He 4.003
3 Li 6.940	4 Be 9.013											5 B 10.82	6 C 12.010	7 N 14.008	8 O 16.0000	9 F 19.00	10 Ne 20.183
11 Na 22.997	12 Mg 24.32											13 Al 26.98	14 Si 28.09	15 P 30.975	16 S 32.066	17 Cl 35.457	18 A 39.944
19 K 39.100	20 Ca 40.08	21 Sc 44.96	22 Ti 47.90	23 V 50.95	24 Cr 52.01	25 Mn 54.93	26 Fe 55.85	27 Co 58.94	28 Ni 58.69	29 Cu 63.54	30 Zn 65.38	31 Ga 69.72	32 Ge 72.60	33 As 74.91	34 Se 78.96	35 Br 79.916	36 Kr 83.8
37 Rb 85.48	38 Sr 87.63	39 Y 88.92	40 Zr 91.22	41 Nb 92.91	42 Mo 95.95	43 Tc (99)	44 Ru 101.7	45 Rh 102.91	46 Pd 106.7	47 Ag 107.880	48 Cd 112.41	49 In 114.76	50 Sn 118.70	51 Sb 121.76	52 Te 127.61	53 I 126.91	54 Xe 131.3
55 Cs 132.91	56 Ba 137.36	57–71 Rare Earths	72 Hf 178.6	73 Ta 180.88	74 W 183.92	75 Re 186.31	76 Os 190.2	77 Ir 193.1	78 Pt 195.23	79 Au 197.2	80 Hg 200.61	81 Tl 204.39	82 Pb 207.21	83 Bi 209.00	84 Po (210)	85 At (210)	86 Rn 222
87 Fr (223)	88 Ra 226.05	89– Actinides															

Rare earths (Lanthanide series)

57 La 138.92	58 Ce 140.13	59 Pr 140.92	60 Nd 144.27	61 Pm (145)	62 Sm 150.43	63 Eu 152.0	64 Gd 156.9	65 Tb 159.2	66 Dy 162.46	67 Ho 164.94	68 Er 167.2	69 Tm 169.4	70 Yb 173.04	71 Lu 174.99

Actinide series

89 Ac (227)	90 Th 232.12	91 Pa 231	92 U 238.07	93 Np (237)	94 Pu (242)	95 Am (243)	96 Cm (245)	97 Bk (249)	98 Cf (249)	99 E (253)	100 Fm (254)	101 Mv (256)

is equal to the atomic number. The lowest energy level is referred to as the 1s level since the principal quantum number $n = 1$ and the orbital quantum number $l = 0$ (for which the corresponding symbol is s). The single electron of the hydrogen atom therefore goes into the 1s level. The 2 electrons of helium may both go into this level if they have opposite spins ($m_s = +\frac{1}{2}$ and $-\frac{1}{2}$). No more electrons are allowed in the first (or K) shell, and since considerable energy is required to remove an electron from this completed shell helium is a very inert substance.

Lithium has 3 electrons, 2 of which may go into the 1s level and the third into the 2s level ($n = 2$, $l = 0$). Since this 2s electron is much farther from the nucleus and is partially shielded from the $+3$ charge of the nucleus by the 2 inner electrons the outer electron is easily removed, producing an ion with the electronic structure of helium. In going from lithium to neon the L shell is filled with electrons, producing a total of 8 elements (see Table III) ending with neon, which has a stable structure. The next element, sodium, has one 3s electron ($n = 3$, $l = 0$). This electron is shielded from the $+11$ nuclear charge by 10 inner electrons so that it is loosely bound.

The electron configurations of atoms in their normal states are given in Table V. It may be seen that the shells continue to be filled in an orderly fashion until potassium (atomic number 19) is reached. The outer electron of potassium goes into the 4s level rather than the 3d level because the electron distribution for these levels is such that the 4s actually has a lower energy. In the transition elements which follow calcium (Sc, atomic number 21 to Zn, atomic number 30) the 3d shell is being filled while the number of electrons in the outer orbit is either 1 or 2.

The 14 rare earths (Ce to Lu) owe their similar properties to the fact that the 4f level is being completed while the outer level consists of two 6s electrons. At various times it has been suggested that at least some of the elements in the last period of the periodic table might form the beginning of a new series analogous to the rare earths. After a study of the properties of the new transuranium elements Seaborg * suggested that the closely related properties of the actinide elements may be interpreted by assuming that these elements possess an incomplete shell of 5f electrons.

Molecular Spectra. The absorption spectra of molecules are much more complicated than those of atoms because there are rotational and vibrational energy levels as well as electronic energy levels. In contrast to our experience with larger objects the rotational or vibrational energy of a molecule may be changed only by the gain or loss of discrete quanta of energy. Since only small quanta of energy are required to change

* Seaborg, *Chem. Engr. News, 23,* 2190 (1945).

Table V. Electron Configurations of Atoms in Their Normal States

Atomic Number	Element	K	L		M			N				O				P			Q
		1s	2s	2p	3s	3p	3d	4s	4p	4d	4f	5s	5p	5d	5f	6s	6p	6d	7s
1	H	1																	
2	He	2																	
3	Li	2	1																
4	Be	2	2																
5	B	2	2	1															
6	C	2	2	2															
7	N	2	2	3															
8	O	2	2	4															
9	F	2	2	5															
10	Ne	2	2	6															
11	Na	10 Neon core			1														
12	Mg				2														
13	Al				2	1													
14	Si				2	2													
15	P				2	3													
16	S				2	4													
17	Cl				2	5													
18	A				2	6													
19	K	18 Argon core						1											
20	Ca							2											
21	Sc						1	2											
22	Ti						2	2											
23	V						3	2											
24	Cr						5	1											
25	Mn						5	2											
26	Fe						6	2											
27	Co						7	2											
28	Ni						8	2											
29	Cu						10	1											
30	Zn						10	2											
31	Ga						10	2	1										
32	Ge						10	2	2										
33	As						10	2	3										
34	Se						10	2	4										
35	Br						10	2	5										
36	Kr						10	2	6										
37	Rb	36 Krypton core										1							
38	Sr											2							
39	Y									1		2							
40	Zr									2		2							
41	Cb									4		1							
42	Mo									5		1							
43	Tc									5		2							
44	Ru									7		1							
45	Rh									8		1							
46	Pd									10									
47	Ag									10		1							
48	Cd									10		2							
49	In									10		2	1						
50	Sn									10		2	2						

Table V. Electron Configurations of Atoms in Their Normal States (Continued)

Atomic Number	Element	K	L		M			N				O				P			Q
		1s	2s	2p	3s	3p	3d	4s	4p	4d	4f	5s	5p	5d	5f	6s	6p	6d	7s
51	Sb				36					10		2	3						
52	Te				36					10		2	4						
53	I			Krypton core						10		2	5						
54	Xe									10		2	6						
55	Cs															1			
56	Ba															2			
57	La													1		2			
58	Ce										1			1		2			
59	Pr										2			1		2			
60	Nd										4					2			
61	Pm										5					2			
62	Sm										6					2			
63	Eu										7					2			
64	Gd										7			1		2			
65	Tb										8			1		2			
66	Dy										10					2			
67	Ho										11					2			
68	Er										12					2			
69	Tm										13					2			
70	Yb				54						14					2			
71	Lu			Xenon core							14			1		2			
72	Hf										14			2		2			
73	Ta										14			3		2			
74	W										14			4		2			
75	Re										14			5		2			
76	Os										14			6		2			
77	Ir										14			9					
78	Pt										14			9		1			
79	Au										14			10		1			
80	Hg										14			10		2			
81	Tl										14			10		2	1		
82	Pb										14			10		2	2		
83	Bi										14			10		2	3		
84	Po										14			10		2	4		
85	At										14			10		2	5		
86	Rn										14			10		2	6		
87	Fr																		1
88	Ra																		2
89	Ac																	1	2
90	Th																	2	2
91	Pa				86										2			1	2
92	U			Radon core										3			1	2
93	Np														5				2
94	Pu														6				2
95	Am														7				2
96	Cm														7			1	2

from one rotational energy level to another these changes may be studied by themselves in the far infrared and microwave regions of the spectrum ($\lambda > 20\mu$). Larger quanta are required in general to change vibrational levels, and these changes produce absorption in the near infrared region. However, for each vibrational level there are a number of rotational levels, and so bands of closely spaced lines are obtained in the spectrum.

Still higher energies are required to shift electrons from one electronic energy level to another, and absorption due to these changes occurs in the visible and ultraviolet regions of the spectrum. Since for each electronic level there are a number of vibrational states and for each of the vibrational states there are several rotational states, the electronic spectra may be extremely complicated and in many cases continuous without any well-defined lines. Studies of the spectra of molecules have been of value in determining bond distances, dissociation energies, and strengths of bonds as well as being useful in an empirical way for identification and analysis. The determination of vibration frequencies makes it possible to calculate thermodynamic properties by use of statistical mechanics (page 567).

Rotational Spectra. It is a result of quantum mechanics that the energy E of rotational energy levels for a rigid diatomic molecule is given by

$$E = h^2 J(J + 1)/8\pi^2 I \tag{27}$$

where J is the rotational quantum number and may have values of 0, 1, 2, 3, etc. The moment of inertia, I, of the molecule is given in terms of the masses of the two atoms, m_1 and m_2, and the distance r_0 between the two nuclei by

$$I = \left(\frac{m_1 m_2}{m_1 + m_2}\right) r_0{}^2 \tag{28}$$

Since it has been shown that transitions occur only between adjacent rotational levels (that is, $\Delta J = 1$) the absorption spectra due to pure rotation consists of equally spaced lines. The rotational lines in the infrared absorption spectrum for HCl are shown in *Fig. 18-8*. The bands recur at definite intervals (1.75 and 3.5 μ in HCl), and the distance between maxima permits a calculation of the distance r_0 between atomic nuclei in the molecule. Only molecules having permanent dipole moments show pure rotational spectra. It can be shown that the molecule will absorb frequencies of $\nu_v \pm \nu_r$, where ν_v is the frequency of vibration and ν_r is the frequency of rotation. When $\nu_r = 0$, the absorption is slight. A series of absorption lines is obtained by adding terms with quantum numbers of rotation 1, 2, 3, 4, etc., and a second series of lines

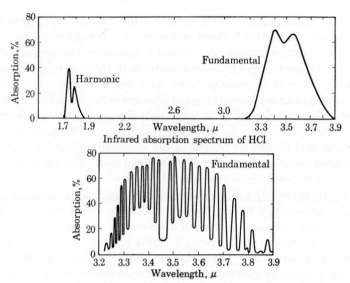

FIG. 18-8. Infrared spectrum of HCl showing rotational structure in fundamental band.

is obtained by subtracting them. These two branches have maxima as indicated in Fig. 18-8. From the absorption frequencies corresponding to changes in rotational levels the moment of inertia of the molecule may be calculated and, from it, the bond distance by means of equation 28.

Vibration-Rotation Spectra. Actually the nuclei in a diatomic molecule are not a fixed distance apart but oscillate about a mean distance r_0. If the nuclei are closer together than r_0 there is repulsion; if they are further apart than r_0, there is attraction. If sufficient energy is put in the molecule to overcome this attraction the two atoms may be dissociated. These facts may be represented by means of a potential-energy curve such as that shown in *Fig. 18-9*.

A useful equation which gives the potential energy V of a diatomic molecule as a function of internuclear distance r was developed by Morse.*

$$V = D'[e^{-2a(r-r_0)} - 2e^{-a(r-r_0)}] \qquad (29)$$

where D' is the energy of dissociation plus the zero-point energy (see below).

The magnitudes of D' and r_0 are indicated in the figure. The constant a involves the fundamental vibration frequency and can be calcu-

* A discussion of this formula and others for calculating energies of diatomic molecules is given by Hirschfelder and Hulburt, *J. Chem. Phys.*, **9**, 61 (1941).

lated from the atomic masses and infrared absorption measurements or Raman spectra. For the Morse curve in Fig. 18-9, $r_0 = 1.41\ A$, $a = 1.82$, and $D' = 90.0$ kcal.

As a first approximation the vibration of the molecule may be considered to be a simple harmonic motion. This is a good approximation only for small vibrations since the potential-energy curve becomes increasingly asymmetrical at higher potential energies. It is a result of

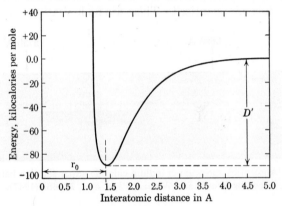

FIG. 18-9. Potential energy of an HBr molecule as a function of internuclear distance.

quantum mechanics that the energies of the vibrational levels are given by

$$E = (v + \tfrac{1}{2})h\nu \tag{30}$$

where the vibrational quantum number v may have values of 0, 1, 2, 3, etc. This equation shows that in the lowest vibrational level ($v = 0$) the molecule still has an energy of $\frac{1}{2}h\nu$, the so-called zero-point energy. The molecule would still possess this vibrational energy at absolute zero.

Electronic Spectra. The electronic energy levels in molecules differ sufficiently in energy so that the electronic spectra are found in the visible and ultraviolet regions rather than in the infrared region. The changes from one electronic energy level to another are accompanied by vibrational and rotational changes so that band spectra are obtained. *Figure 18-10* shows the band spectrum for indium chloride vapor as determined by Froslie and Winans using a 21-ft grating spectrograph. The original spectrogram shows a system of nearly equally spaced bands with alternate bands showing rotational structure and the others showing no rotational structure.

Sometimes a spectrum has a number of discrete lines adjacent to a region of continuous absorption with a definite line of demarcation between the two. From the wavelength of this edge of the continuous spectrum it is possible to calculate the energy of dissociation of the molecule. Absorption spectra are discontinuous when the molecules are excited, because the absorption is governed by quantum restrictions. However, when a molecule is dissociated, giving normal atoms, excited atoms, or ions, the fragments are given a certain amount of kinetic energy which is not quantized. There are no limitations on the amount

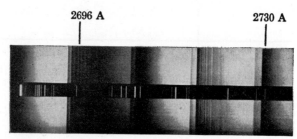

2696 A   2730 A

FIG. 18-10.   Absorption spectrum of indium chloride vapor showing bands, as determined by Froslie and Winans, *Phys. Rev.*, *72*, 481 (1947).

of energy that can then be utilized, and radiation of all wavelengths in the region is absorbed.

Accordingly, when the energy becomes great enough (the wavelengths are short enough) to cause dissociation, the absorption becomes continuous. Just as the short-wavelength limit of continuous emission in Fig. 18-5 permitted calculation of the energy of ionization of atoms, so also the short-wavelength limit of continuous absorption in band spectra permits a calculation of the energy of dissociation of the molecule. These calculations may be illustrated by chlorine, which dissociates into one normal atom and one excited atom. The continuous absorption, beginning at the convergence of the discrete lines, occurs at 4785 A, which is equivalent to 59,400 cal mole^{-1}. The extra energy of excitation of the atom corresponds to 2500 cal as determined spectroscopically. The difference, 56,900 cal, is the energy required to disrupt the molecule into normal atoms, whereas direct thermal measurements give 57,000 cal.

Raman Spectra.   When a beam of light passes through a homogeneous medium some of the photons are scattered at various angles without change in frequency. This scattering is known as Rayleigh scattering and has been discussed earlier. In 1928 Raman discovered experimentally that there was also present in the scattered light weak radiation of discrete frequencies not present in the incident light. This light of altered frequency may be considered to result from inelastic collisions of photons with molecules of the medium. Part of the energy of the photon goes to displacing the atoms in the molecule, so that after the collision the scattered radiation has a slightly different frequency from that of the incident radiation and the molecule is shifted from one energy level E to another E'.

$$h\nu + E = h\nu' + E' \tag{31}$$

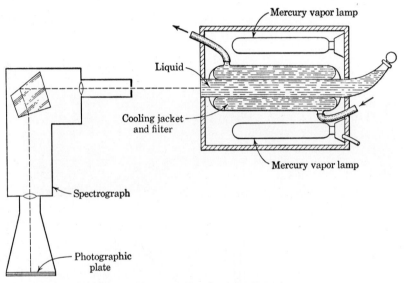

FIG. 18-11. Apparatus for obtaining Raman spectra.

Generally, the scattered light has a lower frequency (Stokes line) because energy is lost to the molecule, but when the photon interacts with a molecule in an excited state the molecule may give energy to the photon so that a line of higher frequency (anti-Stokes line) is found in the Raman spectrum. There will be both Stokes and anti-Stokes lines for any permitted transition, but the anti-Stokes lines are weaker because of the relatively small number of molecules in excited energy states.

The difference in frequency between a Raman line and the incident radiation is a measure of the difference in energy between energy levels in the molecule and is independent of the frequency of the incident light. The difference in energy levels may be calculated from the Raman shift $(\nu - \nu')$ by

$$E' - E = h(\nu - \nu') \tag{32}$$

The shifts observed are generally of the order of 100 to 4000 wave numbers and correspond to changes in vibrational energy levels.

Although the Raman lines may correspond to infrared lines, sometimes they correspond to transitions which are not directly allowed according to the restrictions of the quantum theory, that is, to frequencies which do not occur in the ordinary absorption spectrum. Valuable information concerning the nature of the spectrum can thus be obtained by combining data from both the Raman and the absorption spectra.

The experimental arrangement for determining Raman spectra is indicated in *Fig. 18-11.*

An internal source of light is provided by a bank of mercury-vapor lamps. Liquid is circulated through a jacket around the Raman tube

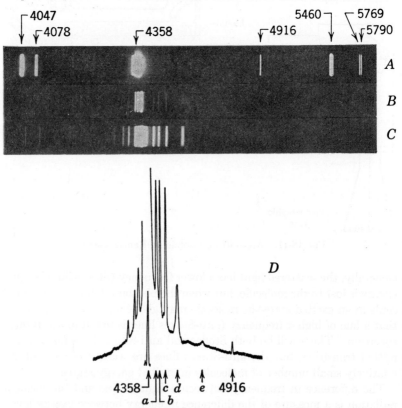

Fig. 18-12. Raman spectrum of carbon tetrachloride. *A.* Mercury arc. Wavelengths are given in angstroms. *B.* Raman spectrum of CCl$_4$ with filter that transmits 4358 A. *C.* Same as *B* with longer exposure (3 minutes). *D.* Photoelectric recording of Raman spectrum of CCl$_4$. $a = 4399$; $b = 4418$; $c = 4446$; $d = 4507$ and 4513; $e = 4670$ A. Courtesy of Professor Paul Bender, University of Wisconsin.

to remove heat produced by the lamps, and a colored substance may be dissolved in the liquid to filter out unwanted wavelengths. Since the Raman lines are faint a fairly long exposure may be required.

In *Fig. 18-12* is shown a Raman spectrum of carbon tetrachloride. The uppermost spectrum at A gives the standard spectrum of the mercury arc. At B a short exposure brings out three Raman lines clearly visible in the original spectrum plate. In a longer exposure at C there are four Raman lines on the long-wavelength side (Stokes lines) and three weaker anti-Stokes lines on the short-wavelength side. The mercury lines other than 4358 A have been filtered out except for two persistent lines showing at the left in the long exposure. At D is shown a photoelectric record of the Raman spectrum.* The prominent mercury line at 4358 A is so intense that the amplifier had to be made less sensitive to give a good record, as shown in the lower peak.

Raman spectra have been measured for a great many organic and inorganic compounds, and complete reviews are available.† They are helpful in interpreting molecular structure and are useful in analytical problems.

Statistical Mechanics.‡ If the energy levels of a single atom or molecule are known from spectroscopic studies it is possible to calculate by the methods of statistical mechanics the properties of a collection of a large number of molecules. Thus, it is possible to calculate the thermodynamic properties of an ideal gas. For complicated molecules these calculations may be difficult, but for simple molecules the resulting expressions are quite simple and give the thermodynamic properties in terms of the molecular weight and quantities which may be measured spectroscopically. Because of the high precision of spectroscopic measurements the quantities calculated in this manner are frequently more accurate than direct calorimetric measurements.

Using statistical methods for an ideal gas the thermodynamic properties may be written in terms of the partition function. The *partition function Q* is defined as

$$Q = \sum_i g_i e^{-\epsilon_i/kT} \tag{33}$$

* Chien and Bender, *J. Chem. Phys.*, **15**, 376 (1947).

† Hibben, *The Raman Effect and Its Chemical Effects*, Reinhold Publishing Corp., New York, 1939; Glockler, "The Raman Effect," *Revs. Mod. Phys.*, **15**, 112–171 (1943); Fenske, Braun, Wiegand, Quiggle, McCormick, and Rank, "Raman Spectra of Hydrocarbons," *Anal. Chem.*, **19**, 700–766 (1947).

‡ Mayer and Mayer, *Statistical Mechanics*, John Wiley & Sons, New York, 1940; Fowler and Guggenheim, *Statistical Thermodynamics*, Cambridge University Press, Cambridge, 1939; Dole, *Introduction to Statistical Thermodynamics*, Prentice-Hall, New York, 1954.

The ϵ_i is the energy of the molecule of perfect gas in the ith level. The degeneracy or statistical weight of an energy level is represented by g_i. It can be shown that in terms of this partition function the enthalpy of a perfect gas above that at absolute zero is given by

$$(H° - H_0°) = RT^2 \left(\frac{\partial \ln Q}{\partial T}\right) + RT \qquad (34)$$

where $H_0°$ is the enthalpy at absolute zero. It can be shown also that the free-energy function $(F° - H_0°)/T$ (page 265) is given in terms of the partition function by

$$-(F° - H_0°)/T = R \ln (Q/N) \qquad (35)$$

where N is Avogadro's number. All the other thermodynamic properties may be calculated from these quantities.

To a rather high degree of approximation it is possible to consider that molecular motions are independent of one another. Thus, the total energy of a molecule may be represented by

$$\epsilon = \epsilon_{tr} + \epsilon_{rot} + \epsilon_{vib} \qquad (36)$$

where these components are the translational, rotational, and vibrational energies, respectively. From the exponential nature of the partition function, it follows that we may write Q as a product of corresponding component partition functions:

$$Q = Q_{tr} \times Q_{rot} \times Q_{vib} \qquad (37)$$

The thermodynamic functions themselves involve the logarithm of the partition function and may, therefore, be broken up into sums; for example, the enthalpy may be written

$$(H° - H_0°) = (H° - H_0°)_{tr} + (H° - H_0°)_{rot} + (H° - H_0°)_{vib} \qquad (38)$$

For an ideal gas of molecular weight M

$$(H° - H_0°)_{tr} = \tfrac{5}{2}RT \qquad (39)$$

as shown on page 106, and

$$-\left(\frac{F° - H_0°}{T}\right)_{tr} = R\left[\frac{3}{2}\ln M + \frac{5}{2}\ln T - \ln p\right] - 7.282 \qquad (40)$$

represent the contributions due to translational motion. For monatomic gases these are the main contributions, unless there are low-energy electronic states, to the enthalpy and free-energy functions. For poly-atomic molecules equation 40 gives the primary contribution to the free-energy function.

For diatomic molecules with moment of inertia I (page 75 and 561) the rotational contributions to the enthalpy and free-energy function are

$$(H° - H_0°)_{rot} = RT \tag{41}$$

$$-\left(\frac{F° - H_0°}{T}\right)_{rot} = R \ln \frac{T}{\sigma\theta_{rot}} \tag{42}$$

where the symmetry number, σ, is 2 if the two atoms in the molecule are identical and is 1 if they are different. The quantity θ_{rot} is given by

$$\theta_{rot} = \frac{39.598 \times 10^{-40}}{I} = \frac{23.85}{M_1 M_2 r^2/(M_1 + M_2)} \tag{43}$$

where I is the moment of inertia in g cm^2, M_1 and M_2 are ordinary atomic weights, and r is the equilibrium separation of the atoms in angstroms.

The vibrational contributions to the enthalpy and free-energy function are given by

$$(H° - H_0°)_{vib} = R\theta_{vib}[e^{\theta_{vib}/T} - 1]^{-1} \tag{44}$$

$$-\left(\frac{F° - H_0°}{T}\right)_{vib} = -R \ln (1 - e^{-\theta_{vib}/T}) \tag{45}$$

where θ_{vib} may be calculated from the vibrational frequency $\tilde{\nu}$ in wave numbers as determined from spectroscopic measurements.

$$\theta_{vib} = 1.439\tilde{\nu} \tag{46}$$

There is another contribution to the free-energy function for molecules which have a degenerate electronic ground state.

In polyatomic molecules there are vibrational contributions from each of the modes of motion. In addition, in nonlinear molecules the rotational contributions depend upon the three principal moments of inertia. There may also be contributions due to internal rotations * which complicate the calculation of the rotational contributions.

Example 1. Calculate the entropy, enthalpy, and free-energy function of neon at 25° and 1 atm. Since neon is a monatomic gas there are no rotational or vibrational

* Pitzer, *Chem. Revs.*, 27, 39 (1940).

contributions, and so

$$(H° - H_0°)_{tr} = \tfrac{5}{2}RT = 1480 \text{ cal mole}^{-1}$$

$$-\left(\frac{F° - H_0°}{T}\right)_{tr} = (1.987)(2.303)\left[\frac{3}{2}\log 20.183 + \frac{5}{2}\log 298.1\right] - 7.282$$

$$= 29.9 \text{ cal mole}^{-1} \text{ deg}^{-1}$$

$$S° = \left(\frac{H° - H_0°}{T}\right) - \left(\frac{F° - H_0°}{T}\right)$$

$$= \frac{1480}{298.1} + 29.9$$

$$= 34.9 \text{ cal deg}^{-1} \text{ mole}^{-1}$$

Example 2. Calculate the entropy, enthalpy, and free-energy function for nitrogen gas at 25° and 1 atm pressure, assuming that it is an ideal gas. The equilibrium separation of the atoms is 1.094 A, and the vibrational wave number is 2330.7 cm^{-1}. The enthalpy at 25° relative to that at absolute zero is calculated as follows:

$$(H° - H_0°)_{tr} = \tfrac{5}{2}RT = 1480 \text{ cal mole}^{-1}$$

$$(H° - H_0°)_{rot} = RT = 591 \text{ cal mole}^{-1}$$

$$(H° - H_0°)_{vib} = R\theta_{vib}[e^{\theta_{vib}/T} - 1]^{-1} = \frac{(1.987)(3352)}{(67,507)}$$

$$= 0.099$$

where

$$\theta_{vib} = (1.439)(2330.7) = 3352 \text{ deg}$$

$$(H° - H_0°) = 1480 + 591 + 0.099 = 2071 \text{ cal mole}^{-1}$$

The value of the free-energy function at 25° is calculated as follows:

$$-\left(\frac{F° - H_0°}{T}\right)_{tr} = (1.987)(2.303)\left[\frac{3}{2}\log 28.016 + \frac{5}{2}\log 298.1\right] - 7.282$$

$$= 30.9 \text{ cal deg}^{-1} \text{ mole}^{-1}$$

$$-\left(\frac{F° - H_0°}{T}\right)_{rot} = (1.987)(2.303)\log\frac{(298.1)}{(2)(2.85)} = 7.86 \text{ cal deg}^{-1} \text{ mole}^{-1}$$

since

$$\theta_{rot} = \frac{(23.85)(28.016)}{(14.008)^2(1.094)^2} = 2.85 \text{ deg}$$

$$-\left(\frac{F° - H_0°}{T}\right)_{vib} = -(1.987)(2.303)\log\left(1 - e^{-(3352)/(298)}\right)$$

$$= 6 \times 10^{-5} \text{ cal deg}^{-1} \text{ mole}^{-1}$$

Thus

$$-\left(\frac{F^\circ - H_0{}^\circ}{T}\right) = 30.9 + 7.86 = 38.8 \text{ cal deg}^{-1} \text{ mole}^{-1}$$

$$S^\circ = \left(\frac{H^\circ - H_0{}^\circ}{T}\right) - \left(\frac{F^\circ - H_0{}^\circ}{T}\right) = \frac{2071}{298} + 38.8$$

$$= 45.8 \text{ cal deg}^{-1} \text{ mole}^{-1}$$

REFERENCES

Herzberg, *Atomic Spectra and Atomic Structure*, Prentice-Hall, New York, 1937.
Taylor and Glasstone, *Treatise on Physical Chemistry*, D. Van Nostrand Co., New York, 1942, Chapter II.
Pauling and Wilson, *Introduction to Quantum Mechanics*, McGraw-Hill Book Co., New York, 1935.
Richtmyer and Kennard, *Introduction to Modern Physics*, McGraw-Hill Book Co., New York, 1947.
Pitzer, *Quantum Chemistry*, Prentice-Hall, New York, 1953.
Gaydon, *Dissociation Energies and Spectra of Diatomic Molecules*, Chapman & Hall, London, 1953.
Herzberg, *Molecular Spectra and Molecular Structure*, D. Van Nostrand Co., New York, 1950.
Herzberg, *Infrared and Raman Spectra of Polyatomic Molecules*, D. Van Nostrand Co., New York, 1945.
Wheland, *The Theory of Resonance and Its Application to Organic Chemistry*, John Wiley & Sons, New York, 1955.
Pauling, *The Nature of the Chemical Bond*, Cornell University Press, Ithaca, 1940.
Rice and Teller, *The Structure of Matter*, John Wiley & Co., New York, 1949.

PROBLEMS

1. A hollow box with an opening of 1 sq cm area is heated electrically. (*a*) What is the total energy emitted per second at 800°K? (*b*) How much energy is emitted per second if the temperature is 1600°K? (*c*) How long would it take the radiant energy emitted at this temperature, 1600°K, to melt 1000 grams of ice?

Ans. (*a*) 2.33×10^7 ergs cm^{-2} sec^{-1}.
(*b*) 3.74×10^8 ergs cm^{-2} sec^{-1}.
(*c*) 8950 sec.

2. Calculate the velocity of an electron which has been accelerated by a potential difference of 1.00 volt. The mass of an electron at rest is 9.105×10^{-28} gram.
Ans. 5.94×10^7 cm sec^{-1}.

3. Electrons are accelerated by 100,000 volts in an X-ray tube. To what wave length in angstroms does this energy correspond, when converted into radiation?
Ans. 0.124 A.

4. The first ionization potential for Li is 5.39 volts (Li $\rightarrow$ Li$^+$ + e). The second ionization potential is 75.62 volts (Li$^+$ $\rightarrow$ Li^{++} + e). Calculate the wavelengths for the convergence limits indicated by these potentials. *Ans.* 2300, 164 A.

5. Calculate the wavelengths (in microns) of the first three lines of the Paschen series for atomic hydrogen. *Ans.* 1.88, 1.28, 1.09 μ.

6. Calculate the Raman frequencies of CCl_4 (expressed in wave numbers) using the wavelengths of the Raman lines ($a - e$) given in Fig. 18-12. Also calculate the wavelengths (expressed in microns) in the infrared at which absorption might be expected. In order to calculate the Raman frequencies accurately with a slide rule the equation must be rearranged as follows:

$$\bar{\nu}_{Raman} = \frac{\nu_{incid} - \nu_{scatt}}{c} = \left(\frac{1}{\lambda_{incid}} - \frac{1}{\lambda_{scatt}} \right)$$

$$= \frac{(\lambda_{scatt} - \lambda_{incid})}{\lambda_{incid} \lambda_{scatt}}$$

Ans.	$\bar{\nu}_{Raman}$	λ, microns
	213	47.0
	312	32.0
	454	22.0
	757	13.2
	1530	6.53

7. Calculate the entropy of argon at (a) 25°C and (b) 727°C and 1 atm pressure.
Ans. (a) 37.13, (b) 43.07 cal deg^{-1} mole^{-1}.

8. Calculate the value of (a) the free-energy function and (b) the entropy for chlorine gas at 25°C and 1 atm. The equilibrium separation of the atoms is 1.983 A, and the vibrational wave number is 556.9 cm^{-1}.
Ans. (a) 46.4, (b) 53.7 cal deg^{-1} mole^{-1}.

9. From the fact that the internuclear distance is 1.414 A in HBr, calculate (a) the moment of inertia of the molecule and (b) the change in frequency in wave numbers which corresponds to a transition between $J = 0$ and $J = 1$.
Ans. (a) 3.30 × 10^{-40} g cm^2. (b) 17.0 cm^{-1}.

10. If 10,000 cal are lost per minute by radiation from the door of an electrically heated furnace at 900°, how many more watts of electricity must be applied to offset the losses due to radiation if the furnace is heated to 1100°?

11. An experiment on the emission of photoelectrons from a sodium surface by light of different wavelengths gave the values below for the potentials at which the photoelectric current was reduced to zero. Plot voltage against frequency, and

λ, A	E, volts
5461	−2.045
4339	−1.488
4047	−1.295
3651	−0.914
3125	−0.382
2535	+0.52

determine Planck's constant from the slope of the line.

---

12. Absorption by the fundamental vibration of the hydrochloric acid molecule occurs at 3.46 μ. (a) What is the frequency of light of this wavelength? (b) What

is the energy of one quantum of light of this wavelength? (c) What is the energy of one quantum in terms of electron volts?

13. What is the wavelength of light emitted when electrons are stopped after falling through a potential of (a) 400 volts? (b) 3 volts?

14. Calculate (a) the wavelength of the first two lines of the Lyman series; (b) the wavelength of the fourth line of the Paschen series for atomic hydrogen.

15. By means of the quantum numbers and Pauli's exclusion principle calculate the number of electrons in the L and M orbits (n = 2 and 3, respectively). Explain the usual valences of the first 9 elements in the periodic table in terms of their electronic structure.

16. Calculate (a) the entropy and (b) the free-energy function for hydrochloric acid gas at 25°C and 1 atm pressure. The values obtained may be checked by reference to Table II on page 141 and Table V on page 267. The equilibrium separation of atoms is 1.272 A, and the vibrational frequency is 2885.7 wave numbers.

17. From the fact that the internuclear distance is 1.272 A in HCl calculate (a) the moment of inertia of the molecule and (b) the change in wave numbers which corresponds to a transition between $J = 1$ and $J = 2$.

18. Plot the potential-energy curve for Br_2 according to the Morse function, using $D' = 45.7$ kcal, $a = 1.98$ and $r_0 = 2.28$ A.

---

19. Calculate the value of the Rydberg constant R and the constant $300Rhc/e$ for hydrogen, and compare it with the experimentally determined value.

20. There is a Brackett series in the hydrogen spectrum where $n_1 = 4$. Calculate the wavelengths, in angstroms, of the first two lines of this series.

21. Prepare a rough calibration chart for the spectrograph used in obtaining Fig. 18-12. Plot wavelengths of the mercury lines given in spectrum A against a linear scale starting at 4047 A.

22. An electric heater of 10 sq cm is heated to 800°. How many calories of radiant heat is emitted per minute, if a perfect radiator is assumed?

23. Calculate the frequency and the wavelength of the sixth line in the Balmer series of hydrogen for which the electron falls from the eighth quantum level to the second.

24. Calculate the frequency and the wavelength in angstroms for the line in the Paschen series of the hydrogen spectrum which is due to a transition from the sixth quantum level to the third.

25. The vibrational frequency V of a simple harmonic oscillator is given by $V = (1/2\pi) \sqrt{f/\mu}$, where f is the force of restitution on the vibrating particles and μ is the reduced mass of the system. For a "dumbbell-shaped" diatomic molecule $1/\mu = (1/m_1) + (1/m_2)$, where m_1 and m_2 are the masses of the individual atoms. The fundamental frequency of the HCl^{35} molecule occurs at 3.46 μ. What would be the separation in angstroms between the fundamental vibrations for HCl^{35} and HCl^{37} if the forces of restitution are assumed the same in both cases? Between DCl^{35} and DCl^{37}? (The fundamental frequency of DCl^{35} is at 4.8 μ.)

19

Photochemistry

Collisions between Molecules and Photons. Photochemistry comprises the study of chemical reactions produced directly or indirectly by means of radiation. Typical photochemical reactions include dissociations such as

$$2HBr \rightarrow H_2 + Br_2$$

rearrangements such as

$$\text{Fumaric acid} \rightarrow \text{Maleic acid}$$

addition reactions such as

$$Br_2 + (C_6H_5)_2C{=}C(C_6H_5)_2 \rightarrow (C_6H_5)_2CBr{-}CBr(C_6H_5)_2$$

polymerizations such as

$$C_2H_2 \rightarrow (1/n)(C_2H_2)_n$$

chain reactions such as

$$nH_2 + nCl_2 \rightarrow 2nHCl$$

photocatalytic reactions such as

$$CO_2 + H_2O + \text{Chlorophyll} \rightarrow (1/n)(H_2CO)_n + O_2 + \text{Chlorophyll}$$

and many others.

It was shown on page 349 that molecular collision is the cause of ordinary chemical reactions. Only those molecules which contain an abnormal amount of energy can effect chemical reaction, and only a few molecules can obtain this energy from collision if the activation energy is large and the temperature is low. Reactions of this type are necessarily slow.

It is possible, however, to activate molecules with an external source of energy, as, for example, by introducing a beam of light having the proper frequency to be absorbed and a sufficient quantity of energy in each photon to effect the reaction. The dependence of the photochemical reaction on energy from an outside source, unconnected with molecular collision in the reacting system, is indicated in *Fig. 19-1*. The full line represents the distribution of energy among a group of molecules due to random collisions from heat, similar to that shown in Fig. 13-6 on page 344. The number of molecules with high energy (at the right) sufficient for chemical reaction is small. The dotted line represents the situation when a large number of energy-rich molecules are produced by introducing a beam of light of the proper frequency. It is clear that the intensity of light introduced from an outside source does not depend on the temperature of the reaction vessel. Accordingly, the primary process of photoactivation has a very low temperature coefficient in contradistinction to the large temperature coefficient of thermal reactions. If the over-all photochemical reaction has a large temperature coefficient, it may be concluded that an ordinary thermal reaction rather than the photoactivation process is the rate-determining step.

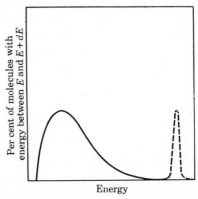

FIG. 19-1.   Distribution of energy among molecules with photochemical activation of molecules at high energies produced by radiation from an outside source.

A *photon* of radiation is a primary unit of radiation. It possesses one quantum of energy. Frequently, the term quantum is used interchangeably with the term photon.

When a photon of radiation comes close to a molecule, the photon may be completely absorbed or it may be absorbed and a photon of different energy emitted (page 565). If there is no simple electronic, atomic, or molecular change that can use the exact amount of energy contained in the photon of radiation, there may be no interaction and no chemical or physical change. However, if there is within the molecule some change which is not forbidden by quantum restrictions and which corresponds to the energy of the photon, the photon is "absorbed." After a molecule has received this energy, it may give it up on collision with other molecules, thus increasing their kinetic energy. The total effect is thus a conversion of radiant energy into thermal energy and the raising of the temperature. This is the most common effect of the absorption of radiation.

The energy of a quantum may be transformed in several different ways summarized as follows:

1. *Heat.* The temperature of the absorbing system is raised.

2. *Dissociation.* The molecule undergoes a chemical breakdown into smaller parts.

3. *Excited molecule.* The molecule retains its energy until it can be used chemically (a) by combination with some other molecule or (b) by transferring its energy to another molecule which in turn utilizes the energy to produce chemical change or to increase the translational energy of still other molecules.

4. *Dissociation and excitation.* One of the fragments produced in a photodissociation is excited.

5. *Ionization.* An electron is driven out of the molecule, leaving a positively charged ion.

6. *Fluorescence.* The excited molecule immediately reradiates part of the energy at a different wavelength, as the electron returns to a lower energy level. If there is a time lag in this reradiation, the phenomenon is known as phosphorescence.

7. *Physical interaction.* The quantum of radiation is not absorbed and re-emitted, but rather it imparts some of its energy (a) to an electron as observed in the Compton effect or (b) to atomic or molecular vibrations or rotations as observed in the Raman effect.

Types of Spectra. The absorption spectrum of a substance gives valuable information concerning the initial step, or the primary process, involved in any possible photochemical reaction. A molecule may be excited in several different ways, depending on the frequency of radiation absorbed. The changes produced by radiation in the different parts of the spectrum and the energies involved are indicated in *Fig. 19-2.*

In the upper half of the figure are given the general types of spectra together with the wavelength regions and the energy of the radiation in calories per mole. In the lower part is given a crude representation of what happens when the radiation is absorbed. The black dots represent electrons, and the larger circles represent atoms in the molecule. The same general considerations apply to polyatomic as well as to diatomic molecules. All the intramolecular changes involve definite energy increments which are governed by the quantum theory.

Absorption in the far infrared causes the molecule to rotate as indicated by the curved arrow at the right. Rotational energies of molecules are of the order of 1000 calories per mole. This is the only change which can be produced with energies of this magnitude, and so there are definite lines corresponding to changes from one energy level to another.

Absorption in the near infrared displaces atoms from their normal positions and causes them to oscillate back and forth or to move sidewise with a swinging motion within the molecule. These vibration processes involve energies of the order of about 1000 to 40,000 calories per mole. The rotations, involving small energies, are superimposed on the atomic displacements, giving rise to absorption bands. The intramolecular changes can be combined and can give harmonics absorbing approximately two or three or more times as much energy as the energy of the fundamental absorption band and causing absorption bands at roughly one-half and one-third the wavelength. Thus if there is absorption at $h\nu$ there may be absorption also at approximately $2h\nu$,

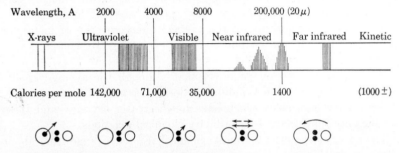

FIG. 19-2. Schematic representation of different types of spectra showing wavelength ranges and energy ranges in which they occur, and the corresponding electronic, vibrational, and rotational motions.

$3h\nu, 4h\nu$, etc. The probability of absorbing energy corresponding to two or three or more quanta is less than the probability of absorbing one, and so the fundamental band (the one-quantum operation) is the most prominent, and the absorption becomes progressively less intense at the higher harmonics. In Fig. 19-2 this decrease in intensity at the shorter wavelengths is represented diagrammatically by reducing the height of the bands.

In the visible and ultraviolet region of the spectrum the absorption causes displacements of outer electrons in the molecule. The only difference between the ultraviolet and visible spectra is that greater energies and larger displacements are involved in the ultraviolet absorption, 35,000 to 71,000 calories per mole being involved in the visible region and 71,000 to several hundred thousand in the ultraviolet. The calculation of radiation energy in calories per mole is given on page 582.

Sometimes the energy of the ultraviolet is sufficient not only to displace the electron within the molecule but also to drive it entirely out of the molecule, thus producing ionization. In the visible and ultraviolet regions of the spectrum series of bands may be obtained by combining the energies of the three quantum-restricted operations—electron displacement, atomic vibrations, and molecular rotation.

In the X-ray region of very short wavelengths (about 1 A), the electrons deep inside the atom nearest the nucleus are displaced. Energies of millions of calories per mole are required for these displacements.

If the energies of radiation or of suitable projectiles, such as alpha particles, are increased to a still greater order of magnitude (around 10^{10} calories per mole), it is then possible to affect the nucleus of atoms and produce the transmutation of elements.

The various absorption spectra produced by the displacements indicated in Fig. 19-2 are usually the same as the emission spectra produced when the electrons return to their normal positions, or the molecule goes from a higher rotational or vibrational energy level to a lower one.

The order of magnitude of the average kinetic energy of molecular translation $(3/2)RT$, a few hundred calories, is given for comparison at the extreme right of Fig. 19-2.

It was emphasized on page 344 that although the average kinetic energy may be only a few hundred calories per mole there are, nevertheless, a few molecules which have much greater energies, and these are the ones that account for ordinary chemical reactions.

The energies required for most chemical reactions range from about 10,000 to 100,000 calories per mole. It is evident then that the longer infrared radiation is powerless to produce chemical reaction and that X rays contain so much energy that they are more likely to accomplish chemical reactions through secondary effects. Direct photochemical reactions are then confined mostly to visible and ultraviolet light, and the X rays and high-energy particles produce chemical effects by secondary electrons emitted with high velocities.

Photoexcitation of Molecules. In simple molecules the absorption of light can lead to chemical rupture only of the bonds which do the absorbing because there are no other bonds. In complicated molecules, however, the energy absorbed by one atom pair or group may surge around to other atom pairs and cause reaction to take place in a different part of the molecule. For example, acetone like most molecules which contain a carbonyl group $>C=O$ absorbs ultraviolet light at about 3100 A. The $C=O$ bond, however, is very strong and it does not break to give atomic oxygen. Rather, the absorption energy leads to the cleavage of an adjacent C—C bond

$$\begin{array}{c} CH_3 \\ \diagdown \\ C=O + h\nu \rightarrow \dot{C}H_3 + CH_3\dot{C}=O \\ \diagup \\ CH_3 \end{array}$$

giving a methyl radical and an acetyl radical.

Sometimes the excited or energy-rich molecule dissociates immediately, within about 10^{-13} sec, or the time required for an atomic oscillation of the type which is associated with infrared absorption. No mechanism is available for splitting atom pairs in less than the time required for one normal vibration period. Again the absorbed energy may transform the molecule into an excited molecule which can exist for a considerable length of time before it returns to the normal form. Some of the possible types of photoexcitation are indicated in *Fig. 19-3*, where

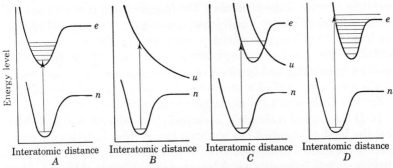

FIG. 19-3. Types of photoexcitation. *A*. Excitation to stable molecule. No dissociation. Discontinuous spectrum. *B*. Excitation to unstable molecule. Immediate dissociation. Continuous spectrum. *C*. Excitation to stable molecule which shifts to unstable molecule. Predissociation spectrum. *D*. Excitation to a stable molecule, but to an energy level above the dissociation energy. Continuous spectrum.

the Franck-Condon-Morse curves are shown with energy levels plotted as a function of the distance between atoms in an atom pair. In each diagram the potential-energy curve for the normal unexcited molecule is indicated by n. A photon of light is absorbed, and the molecule becomes excited and raised to a higher energy level as indicated by e.

In the situation indicated in *A* the excited molecule retains this energy and remains stable until it loses its energy gradually by a series of molecular collisons. Only certain quantities of energy can be stored in this excited molecule as governed by the quantum-number restrictions. Accordingly there are discrete spectral lines, and the spectrum is discontinuous.

In the situation shown at *B* the normal molecule is excited to an unstable molecule which does not have any minimum energy level of stability. The curve showing this instability is shown at u. As soon as the photon raises the molecule to this state of instability the valence bond ruptures immediately and the molecule breaks up into its atoms or groups of atoms. The fragments are thrown out with varying degrees of kinetic energy, and since kinetic energy is not quantized many different amounts of energy are utilized. The spectrum is continuous, without discrete lines.

As shown at C the normal molecule n may be raised to a higher energy state e, which is stable, but in this state there is an opportunity to shift over to an unstable state u. At certain low excitation levels the molecule cannot shift over to the unstable state, and the spectrum is discontinuous with discrete lines. At higher energies of excitation after one or more oscillations there is a chance of instability along the line u with a resulting rupture of the molecule. The fragments are then sent out with increased kinetic energy which is not quantized. The spectral lines are no longer sharp because indefinite amounts of kinetic energy can be added to the quantized energy levels. This type of spectrum which shows a broadening and fuzziness of the spectral lines in certain regions of the spectrum is called a predissociation spectrum, and the excitation followed a little later by dissociation is called predissociation.

In D the normal molecule n is excited to a stable excited molecule e, but the photon absorbed has so much energy that it raises the energy level of the excited molecule above the level of stability and the molecule dissociates into fragments which have varying amounts of kinetic energy. The spectrum then is continuous as in B.

Laws of Photochemistry. *Only that radiation which is absorbed can produce chemical change.* As Grotthus pointed out in 1818, there cannot be photochemical reaction unless the radiation is absorbed. However, it does not follow that absorbed radiation must produce chemical reaction—more often it is converted into heat.

Einstein's law of photochemistry is important in the theoretical interpretation of photochemical reactions. According to this law, *in the primary photochemical process each molecule is activated by the absorption of one photon.*

In this simple primary process, then, we should find that the number of molecules activated is exactly equivalent to the number of photons or quanta absorbed, and for a gram molecule of 6.02×10^{23} molecules there should be 6.02×10^{23} quanta absorbed. This "gram molecule" of quanta has been called the "einstein," just as a gram equivalent of electrons (6.02×10^{23} electrons or 96,500 coulombs) is called the faraday.

It must be strongly emphasized that the Einstein law is usually masked by secondary reactions and complicating circumstances which prevent a simple 1-to-1 relationship between the number of photons absorbed and the number of molecules of *final* products in the reaction. Most investigators are inclined to accept the law as applicable to the primary process and to look for the complicating circumstances which are peculiar to each particular reaction. Sometimes the activation process is followed by a simple stoichiometric reaction which gives some simple number, such as two molecules per quantum, or by a series of repeated reactions giving rise to a chain reaction. On the other hand, the activated molecules may be partially deactivated by collisions, by fluorescence, or by internal rearrangements. Again, dissociated fragments resulting from the excitation may recombine so as to give low apparent yields.

The quantum yield Φ is given by the expression

$$\Phi = \frac{\text{Number of molecules reacting chemically}}{\text{Number of quanta absorbed}} \qquad (1)$$

It provides a very convenient and significant means for describing the experimental facts and offers valuable information for drawing conclusions regarding the mechanism of the reaction.

It will be remembered that the energy in one quantum of radiation is given by the fundamental quantum relation

$$\epsilon = h\nu \qquad (2)$$

The energy per *einstein*, that is, per mole of photons, is obtained by multiplying this equation by the Avogadro number N:

$$N\epsilon = Nh\nu = (6.02 \times 10^{23})(6.62 \times 10^{-27})\nu \qquad (3)$$

The frequency of radiation ν is related to the wavelength λ and the velocity of light c (3×10^{10} cm sec^{-1}) by the relation

$$\nu = c/\lambda \qquad (4)$$

An energy unit which is used a great deal in photochemistry and nuclear chemistry is the electron volt (ev), which is the energy acquired by an electron in falling through a potential difference of 1 volt. Since the charge of the electron is 1.602×10^{-19} coulomb this energy is 1.602×10^{-19} volt coulomb or joule. The energy of Avogadro's number of electrons each accelerated by a potential of a volt is

1 electron volt

$$= \frac{(1.602 \times 10^{-19} \text{ joule electron}^{-1})(6.023 \times 10^{23} \text{ electrons mole}^{-1})}{(4.184 \text{ joule cal}^{-1})}$$

$$= 23{,}060 \text{ cal mole}^{-1}$$

This is a useful conversion factor.

Example 1. (a) Calculate the frequency of ultraviolet light having a wavelength of 3000 A.

$$\nu = \frac{c}{\lambda} = \frac{3.00 \times 10^{10} \text{ cm sec}^{-1}}{3000 \times 10^{-8} \text{ cm}} = 1 \times 10^{15} \text{ sec}^{-1}$$

(b) Calculate the wavelength in centimeters and the wave number $\tilde{\nu}$ of light which has a wavelength of 3000 A.

$$3000 \text{ A} = 3000 \times 10^{-8} \text{ cm} = 3.00 \times 10^{-5} \text{ cm}$$

$$\tilde{\nu} = \frac{1}{\lambda} = \frac{1}{3.00 \times 10^{-5} \text{ cm}} = 33,333 \text{ cm}^{-1}$$

(c) Calculate the energy in ergs per quantum and calories per "mole" or per einstein in radiation of this frequency:

$$h\nu = (6.62 \times 10^{-27} \text{ erg sec})(10^{15} \text{ sec}^{-1}) = 6.62 \times 10^{-12} \text{ erg}$$

$$Nh\nu = (6.02 \times 10^{23} \text{ molecules mole}^{-1})(6.62 \times 10^{-12} \text{ erg molecule}^{-1})$$

$$= 3.98 \times 10^{12} \text{ ergs mole}^{-1}$$

$$Nh\nu = \frac{3.98 \times 10^{12} \text{ ergs mole}^{-1}}{(4.184 \text{ joules cal}^{-1})(10^7 \text{ ergs joule}^{-1})} = 95,300 \text{ cal mole}^{-1}$$

(d) Calculate the energy in electron volts per molecule which corresponds to a wavelength of 3000 A. Since 23,060 cal mole^{-1} corresponds to 1 electron volt, 95,300 cal mole^{-1} corresponds to

$$\frac{(95,300 \text{ cal mole}^{-1})}{(23,060 \text{ cal mole}^{-1} \text{ ev}^{-1})} = 4.13 \text{ electron volts}$$

The energy associated with quanta of typical wavelengths is given in Table I.

Table I. Energy of Different Radiations

Wave-length, cm	Wave Number, $\tilde{\nu}$	Wave-length, A	Frequency, ν	Description	Energy of 1 Quantum $h\nu$, ergs	Energy of 1 Einstein, cal per mole	Electron Volts
10^{-2}	10^2	1,000,000	3×10^{12}	Far infrared	1.99×10^{-14}	286	0.01
10^{-3}	10^3	100,000	3×10^{13}	Infrared	1.99×10^{-13}	2,860	0.12
10^{-4}	10^4	10,000	3×10^{14}	Near infrared	1.99×10^{-12}	28,600	1.24
8.0×10^{-5}	1.25×10^4	8,000	3.75×10^{14}	Edge of visible	2.48×10^{-12}	35,700	1.55
7.0×10^{-5}	1.43×10^4	7,000	4.29×10^{14}	Red	2.84×10^{-12}	40,900	1.77
6.0×10^{-5}	1.67×10^4	6,000	5.00×10^{14}	Yellow	3.31×10^{-12}	47,600	2.07
5.0×10^{-5}	2×10^4	5,000	6.00×10^{14}	Blue	3.95×10^{-12}	56,900	2.48
4.0×10^{-5}	2.50×10^4	4,000	7.5×10^{14}	Edge of visible	4.97×10^{-12}	71,500	3.10
3×10^{-5}	3.33×10^4	3,000	1×10^{15}	Ultraviolet	6.62×10^{-12}	95,300	4.13
2×10^{-5}	5.00×10^4	2,000	1.5×10^{15}	Ultraviolet	9.93×10^{-12}	143,000	6.20
1×10^{-5}	1×10^5	1,000	3×10^{15}	Ultraviolet	1.99×10^{-11}	286,000	12.4
1×10^{-8}	1×10^8	1	3×10^{18}	X rays	1.99×10^{-8}	2.86×10^8	12,400
1×10^{-9}	1×10^9	0.1	3×10^{19}	γ rays	1.99×10^{-7}	2.86×10^9	124,000
1×10^{-10}	1×10^{10}	0.01	3×10^{20}	γ rays	1.99×10^{-6}	2.86×10^{10}	1.24×10^6
1×10^{-11}	1×10^{11}	0.001	3×10^{21}		1.99×10^{-5}	2.86×10^{11}	12.4×10^6

Experimental Procedure.* In quantitative photochemical investigations it is usually important to use monochromatic light of measured
intensity.

The intensity of radiation is measured by allowing the light to fall on
a thin, blackened metal strip attached to one junction of a thermopile.
The other end of the thermocouple of unlike metals, such as copper and
constantan (Cu-Ni alloy), is protected from radiation. As the radiation
is converted into heat the temperature of the receiver rises and causes
a deflection of the galvanometer, attached to the thermopile, which depends on the difference in temperature of the two junctions. The galvanometer readings may be converted into ergs of radiation per second
per square millimeter striking the thermopile, by calibrating with a
standard carbon-filament lamp from the National Bureau of Standards.

The light can be restricted to a narrow range of wavelengths with the
help of properly chosen filters which absorb the undesired wavelengths.
Optical filters transmit light within certain ranges of wavelength. They
are made of gelatin, of colored glass, or of transparent plates with metal
films of suitable thickness to give absorption by interference. The separation of light radiations may be effected still better by refraction
through a prism in a monochromator; the best results are obtained with
a source of light like a mercury-vapor lamp which gives a discontinuous
spectrum. Under these conditions a single spectral line may be isolated
for the photochemical reaction. The intensity obtainable with a monochromator is very low, and it is helpful to use capillary arcs or other
very intense sources of light and to employ prisms and lenses of large
dimensions in order to obtain sufficient intensity for investigating photochemical reactions. The reacting system is placed in glass or quartz
vessels provided with clear polished windows, and the light is usually
passed through the cell onto the thermopile. The actual energy absorbed in the reacting system is measured by subtracting these thermopile readings from those obtained when the cell is empty or filled with a
transparent solvent. It is still better to use two identical cells, one to
contain the chemically reacting material and one to act as a blank for
obtaining the light intensity.

Failure to control the wavelength and intensity may lead to erroneous
conclusions. For example, when a certain reaction mixture is exposed to
sunlight through a red filter, the reaction may proceed faster than when
a blue filter is used. But red light is present in sunlight in much greater

* Noyes and Leighton, *The Photochemistry of Gases*, Reinhold Publishing Corp.,
New York, 1941, Chapter II; Daniels, Mathews, Williams, and Staff, *Experimental
Physical Chemistry*, McGraw-Hill Book Co., New York, 1949; Daniels, *J. Phys.
Chem.*, *42*, **701** (1938).

intensity than blue, and we cannot conclude that the greater effect is due to the color; it may be due to the greater intensity. In a properly executed experiment the intensities of the two lights are adjusted until both give the same intensity as measured with a thermopile. As another example may be cited the action of the mercury-vapor lamp in producing ozone from oxygen. Ozone is synthesized by the short ultraviolet and decomposed by longer ultraviolet (2800 A). The actual yield of ozone depends then on the ratio of the intensities in these two regions, and this ratio depends on accidental conditions such as the age and the rate of cooling of the lamp. Significant measurements under such uncontrolled conditions cannot be expected.

In quantitative work where a knowledge of the reaction mechanism and rate is needed, it is not sufficient merely to place the reaction cell in front of a source of light. The reaction may slow down as the material is consumed not only on account of the decreased reaction rate due to a decrease in concentration but also on account of the lessened absorption of light. The number of calories of radiation or, better, the number of photons actually absorbed is the significant thing.

The amount of light absorbed in a given reaction cell will depend on the time of exposure, the concentration of the absorbing material, the thickness of the cell, and the intensity of the incident light. Instead of specifying all the variables it is much simpler to express the facts in terms of the number of molecules reacting per photon of radiation actually absorbed, that is, in terms of the quantum yield Φ.

Because the intensity of available monochromatic radiation is so low, it has been common practice to restrict quantitative photochemical studies to those reactions for which microanalytical methods are available or for which they can be developed.

The intensity of light available for photochemical reactions is measured most accurately with a thermopile, but with limitations it may sometimes be measured with a photoelectric cell or by the amount of photochemical reaction produced in an *actinometer*. It is necessary to calibrate these measuring devices against a thermopile. The blackened receivers of a thermopile are equally responsive to all wavelengths, whereas photoelectric cells and actinometers do not necessarily give equal response for the same energy input at different wavelengths.

The uranyl oxalate actinometer, studied with great accuracy by Leighton and Forbes,* is the best for most purposes. Although the quantum efficiency changes slightly with the wavelength, it may be taken that, in a solution 0.01 M in UO_2SO_4 and 0.05 M in $H_2C_2O_4$, 0.57 molecule of the oxalic acid is decomposed for each quantum of light ab-

* Leighton and Forbes, *J. Am. Chem. Soc.*, *52*, 3139 (1930).

sorbed between the wavelengths 2540 and 4350 A. In other words, each mole of oxalic acid decomposed is equivalent to 1.75 einsteins, or to 166,000 calories, if an average wavelength of 3000 A is assumed. The uranyl ion undergoes no chemical change.

For measuring very low light intensities photoelectric cells and Geiger-Müller counters (page 604) are useful, but in photochemical work it is usually the sensitivity of the chemical tests rather than the sensitivity of the radiation measurement which limits the accuracy.

Photochemical Kinetics. The kinetics of photochemical reactions is more complicated than the kinetics of thermal reactions because more variables are involved. The intensity of light and the size and shape of the vessel may affect the rate of the reaction. A photochemical reaction may be accompanied by a thermal reaction, identical with the photochemical reaction, or opposite to it, or entirely different in character. A photochemical reaction may produce a catalyst which then causes a thermal reaction to proceed at a measurable rate. Sometimes an *induction period* is necessary while a sufficient quantity of catalyst is being accumulated to make the reaction proceed with a measurable velocity. Again, a thermal reaction once started may continue after the illumination is stopped, giving an *aftereffect*. The energy available in a photochemical reaction is much greater than in the thermal reaction, and this fact often changes the nature of the reaction. For example, the thermal dissociation of hydrogen iodide at 450° is bimolecular ($2HI = H_2 + I_2$), but the photochemical reaction is unimolecular ($HI = H + I$) because sufficient energy to produce free atoms is available.

Not only second-order and first-order reactions but also zero-order reactions are found in photochemistry. A zero-order reaction is one in which the rate is entirely independent of the concentration. For example, if the concentration is high and the light intensity is weak, the light intensity may be the limiting factor in the reaction rate, and the concentration may be without influence on the rate.

If the reaction cell is short or the transmittancy of the material high, the absorption of light is slight, so that practically all parts of the reacting system have about the same illumination. Then stirring becomes unimportant. If, on the other hand, the light is largely absorbed in the first portion of the reacting system, the extent of the reaction will vary with the depth, and vigorous stirring may be necessary to give uniform and reproducible conditions.

If light causes a reaction in one direction, giving a zero-order reaction, and a thermal reaction occurs in the opposite direction with a rate proportional to the concentration of the photochemical product, a stationary state will be produced in which the two rates are exactly equal. The situation is described mathematically by the following equation:

$$dx/dt = k_{\text{photo}}I - k_{\text{thermal}}x \tag{5}$$

where I is the intensity of light, k_{photo} and k_{thermal} are the specific reaction rates of the photochemical and thermal reactions, and x is the amount of material produced by the photochemical reaction. When a steady state is reached,

$$k_{\text{photo}}I = k_{\text{thermal}}x, \quad \text{and} \quad x = k_{\text{photo}}I/k_{\text{thermal}} \tag{6}$$

The concentration of material in the steady state changes with the intensity of the light. An example of this type of reaction is the photopolymerization of anthracene dissolved in xylene. In the presence of ultraviolet light this substance forms dianthracene, which has twice the molecular weight of anthracene, but in the dark the dianthracene is depolymerized, giving the original anthracene.

The experimental determination of the quantum yield constitutes an excellent method for studying *chain reactions* (page 358). If several molecules of products are formed for each photon of light absorbed, the reaction is obviously a chain reaction in which the products of the reaction are able to activate additional molecules of reactants.

The photocombination of hydrogen and chlorine is a classical example of such a reaction, about a million molecules reacting for each quantum absorbed. Each molecule of hydrogen chloride formed undergoes further reaction with the hydrogen and chlorine atoms produced (page 358). The measurement of the number of molecules per photon gives a measure of the average number of molecules involved in the chain.

In studying the kinetics of a photochemical reaction it is desirable to give the experimental facts by measuring and recording the quantum yield. It is desirable also to determine the influence of concentration and thus establish the order of the reaction, to determine the influence of temperature and thus ascertain whether or not thermal reactions are playing an important part, and to determine the influence of light intensity. If the quantum yield changes with the light intensity (that is, the amount of the reaction is not directly proportional to the intensity of light), it may be concluded that the light intensity is not the limiting factor or that more than one reacting molecule or fragment is produced by the light, each in turn taking part in secondary reactions.

The facts of a photochemical reaction are described comprehensively by measuring the quantum yield and writing the rate equation for the photochemical reaction with the inclusion of a term I for the intensity of the light. Although these expressions may be largely empirical, they frequently reveal much concerning the true mechanism of the reaction.

Example 2. The following reactions describe the photochemical decomposition of hydrogen bromide with light of 2530 A at 25°. The primary process disrupts the molecule into atoms of hydrogen and bromine, which can then undergo further reactions. The quantum yield for the primary process is sometimes designated by ϕ; the quantum yield for the over-all reaction is designated by Φ. The intensity of light absorbed is designated by I.

(1)	$HBr + h\nu = H + Br$	Rate $= \phi I$
(2)	$H + HBr = H_2 + Br$	Rate $= k_2 c_H c_{HBr}$
(3)	$Br + Br + (M) = Br_2 + (M)$	Rate $= k_3 c_{Br}^2 c_M$
(4)	$H + Br_2 = HBr + Br$	Rate $= k_4 c_H c_{Br_2}$
(5)	$H + H + (M) = H_2 + (M)$	Rate $= k_5 c_H^2 c_M$ (negligible)

The sum of the first three reactions is

$$2HBr = H_2 + Br_2$$

Reaction 3, describing the recombination of bromine atoms, requires a collision with a wall or a third molecule M in order to dissipate the heat of combination and permit the two atoms to remain united.

Other reactions might be written on paper, such as $Br + HBr = Br_2 + H$ and $Br + H_2 = HBr + H$, but they involve breaking bonds which require so much energy for activation that they do not proceed at room temperature and may be neglected.

As the bromine accumulates, reaction 4 becomes important and reduces the quantum yield.

These facts can be summarized by the expression for the disappearance of hydrogen bromide:

$$\Phi = \phi + \phi \frac{1 - (k_4 c_{Br_2}/k_2 c_{HBr})}{1 + (k_4 c_{Br_2}/k_2 c_{HBr})}$$

When the concentration of bromine is zero at the beginning of the illumination or when mercury or other "acceptor" is added capable of removing the bromine chemically,

$$\Phi = 2\phi \cong 2$$

Photosensitization. Very often the molecules that absorb the light take part in the photochemical reaction only in an indirect manner and act merely as carriers of energy. One of the outstanding examples is mercury vapor activated by the absorption of ultraviolet light of 2536.7 A which is emitted by a mercury-vapor lamp. The energy corresponding to this radiation is very large (112,000 calories per mole), and it is more than the 102,400 calories necessary to dissociate hydrogen molecules into atoms. When mercury vapor is mixed with hydrogen and exposed to light from a mercury-vapor lamp, the chief reactions may be represented by the following equations, where Hg* represents an activated mercury atom:

$$Hg + h\nu = Hg^* \tag{7}$$

$$Hg^* + H_2 = Hg + 2H \tag{8}$$

The hydrogen is transparent to this radiation. The mercury acts as a photosensitizer, and the hydrogen atoms readily reduce metallic oxides, nitrous oxide, ethylene, carbon monoxide, and other materials. The excited mercury atoms decompose not only hydrogen but also ammonia and many different organic compounds.

The photodecomposition of oxalic acid, sensitized by uranyl ion, has already been referred to as a reproducible reaction suitable for use as an actinometer. The light is absorbed by the colored uranyl ion, and the energy is transferred to the colorless oxalic acid, which then decomposes. The uranyl ion remains unchanged and can be used over and over again indefinitely as a sensitizer. It is probable that some kind of loose chemical compound, or "complex," must be formed in order that this energy may be transferred. Supporting this view is the fact that the absorption of light is increased somewhat by adding colorless oxalic acid to a solution containing uranyl ion. This change in absorption of light on mixing is one method by which chemical interaction of solutes (or gases) can be detected. Uranyl ion and light will not bring about chemical reaction in all substances even if the energy of the light in calories per mole exceeds the activation energy of the reaction. Apparently the transfer of energy during an ordinary instantaneous collision is not often possible; some kind of "sticky" collision or a loose or temporary chemical combination is helpful in giving favorable conditions for the transfer.

Typical Reactions. A few typical photochemical reactions * are summarized in Table II.

Reaction 1 is one of the most exact photochemical reactions, and it has the same value of Φ from 2800 to 3000 A, at low pressures and high pressures, in the liquid state or in solution in hexane. The primary process $HI + h\nu = H + I$ is followed by the thermal reactions $H + HI = H_2 + I$ and $I + I = I_2$, thus giving two molecules of HI decomposed for each photon absorbed. Reaction 2 has a quantum yield of unity. Reaction 3 has a quantum yield of unity initially, but the reverse thermal reaction reduces it as the product accumulates. In reaction 4 at 3660 A the photoprocess is completely efficient ($\Phi = 2$) if correction is made for internal screening by the accompanying N_2O_4, which absorbs some light at 3660 A. The reactions are $NO_2 + h\nu = NO_2^*$, $NO_2^* + NO_2 = 2NO + O_2$, where the asterisk indicates an activated molecule. At longer wavelengths the spectrum is of a different type, and at 4350 A no reaction occurs when the radiation is absorbed.

Reaction 5 likewise shows a greater photochemical efficiency at the shorter wavelengths where the absorption spectrum is different. This

* Noyes and Leighton, *Photochemistry of Gases*, Reinhold Publishing Corp., New York, 1941, Appendixes, pages 415–465; Daniels, *J. Phys. Chem.*, *41*, 713 (1938).

Table II. Quantum Yields in Photochemical Reactions at Room Temperature

Reaction	Approximate Wavelength Region, angstroms	Approximate Φ
1. $2HI \rightarrow H_2 + I_2$	3000–2800	2
2. $S_2O_8^{--} + H_2O \rightarrow 2SO_4^{--} + 2H^+ + \frac{1}{2}O_2$	3000–2500	1
3. $C_{14}H_{10} \rightleftarrows \frac{1}{2}(C_{14}H_{10})_2$	<3600	1–0
4. $2NO_2 \rightarrow 2NO + O_2$	4350	0
	3660	2
5. $CH_3CHO \rightarrow CO + CH_4 (+ C_2H_6 + H_2)$	3100	0.5
	2537	1
6. $(CH_3)_2CO \rightarrow CO + C_2H_6 (+ CH_4)$	<3300	0.2
7. Crotonaldehyde	<3100	0.0
8. $NH_3 \rightarrow \frac{1}{2}N_2 + \frac{3}{2}H_2$	2100	0.2
— 9. $H_2C_2O_4 (+ UO_2^{++}) \rightarrow CO + CO_2 + H_2O (+ UO_2^{++})$	4300–2500	0.5–0.6
10. $2NO_3^- \rightarrow 2NO_2^- + O_2$	3000–2500	0.01–0.3
11. $Cl_2 + H_2 \rightarrow 2HCl$	4000	10^5
12. $Br_2 + C_6H_5CH{=}CHCOOH \rightarrow C_6H_5CHBrCHBrCOOH$	<5500	100–1
13. $C_2H_2 \rightarrow \frac{1}{n}(C_2H_2)_n$	2000	7
14. $CO + Cl_2 \rightarrow COCl_2$	4000–4360	1000

reaction is interesting because at 300° Φ has a value of more than 300, indicating that the free radicals which are first produced by the absorption of light are able to propagate a chain reaction at the higher temperatures. At room temperature the reactions involved in the chain do not go fast enough to be noticed. The products given in parentheses are present also but in small amounts.

In reaction 6 the primary reaction is probably $CH_3COCH_3 + h\nu = CH_3 + COCH_3$. The acetyl radical can then decompose into CO and CH_3, or it can react with CH_3 to give back acetone. At room temperature it forms biacetyl $(COCH_3)_2$. In crotonaldehyde, reaction 7, no photochemical decomposition is observed, probably because the molecule is so complex that the energy taken up from the light is dissipated through the vibrations of many different atom-pairs within the molecule before it can become localized for the breaking of a bond.

In the photolysis of ammonia, reaction 8, hydrogen atoms are split off, and the low yield is probably due to partial recombination of the fragments. The quantum yield varies with pressure and reaches a maximum at 80–90 mm.

Reaction 9 illustrates a photosensitized reaction. Reaction 10 is complicated and depends on the pH of the solution. It is more efficient at the shorter wavelengths. Reaction 11 is the best-known example of a chain reaction, and it is one of the longest chains. Oxygen and certain other substances act as inhibitors by combining with the chlorine or hydrogen atoms, thus stopping the propagation of the chain and reducing the quantum yield.

The addition of bromine to cinnamic acid,[*] reaction 12, is a chain reaction, the length of the chains depending on the temperature, the concentration of bromine, and the amount of dissolved oxygen. The reaction can be split up into the primary photoprocess, which is not affected by temperature, and the subsequent thermal reaction, which has a large temperature coefficient. When oxygen is removed, the breaking of chains is less frequent, and the quantum yield is of the order of hundreds and more.

The polymerization of acetylene, reaction 13, to give an insoluble substance called cuprene, is effected by short ultraviolet light with a quantum yield of about 7, showing that the primary process is followed by a short chain reaction.

Reaction 14 varies with the pressures of carbon monoxide and chlorine and, like all chain reactions, is sensitive to impurities.[†]

Luminescence. When a solid body, a bar of iron, for example, is heated to about 500°, it becomes "red hot"; when the temperature is raised still higher, it becomes "white hot," as the wavelengths of maximum intensity shift toward the shorter end of the spectrum in accordance with Wien's displacement law. It is possible, however, to produce light by other agencies than heat, and the radiation thus produced is called *luminescence* or sometimes "cold light." All emission of visible light may be attributed to the return of an outer electron to its normal position after being displaced by kinetic bombardment of atoms and molecules, or by chemical or electric or other forms of energy.

Chemiluminescence is the emission of light by certain chemical reactions. Thus Evans and Dufford [‡] have shown that the oxidation of ether solutions of magnesium p-bromophenyl bromide gives rise to marked chemiluminescence, the greenish-blue glow which accompanies the exposure of the solution to air being visible in daylight. The oxidation of decaying wood containing certain forms of bacteria, of luciferin in fireflies, and of yellow phosphorus are further examples.

[*] Bauer and Daniels, *J. Am. Chem. Soc.*, *56*, 378 (1934).

[†] Further details of facts and theories for these and other photochemical reactions may be found in Noyes and Leighton, *loc. cit.*

[‡] Evans and Dufford, *J. Am. Chem. Soc.*, *45*, 278 (1923).

Fluorescence is the emission of light by molecules or atoms which have been excited by the absorption of light, the fluorescent light having a wavelength different from that of the incident radiation. In general, the wavelength of the transformed radiation is greater than that of the incident radiation, indicating that, since the radiated light has a lesser amount of energy, the molecule has absorbed some energy. This relation, to which numerous exceptions have been found, was first enunciated by Stokes. When the incident radiation is cut off, fluorescence ceases.

Among the numerous substances known to exhibit fluorescence may be mentioned fluorite (from which the phenomenon derived its name), uranium glass, petroleum, solutions of certain organic dyestuffs, eosin, fluorescein, quinine sulfate, chlorophyll, and the vapors of sodium, mercury, iodine, and acetone. Fluorescent dyes have been developed which will emit visible light when activated with the light in the near ultraviolet or short visible range present in daylight, and this fluorescent light added to the light reflected from the colored paint or cloth gives an appearance of unusual brightness. Again a blue fluorescent dye of suitable characteristics added to a washing compound produces a blue color which combines with the brown color of the clothes to give a brilliant and attractive white.

The characteristic fluorescence of various substances when exposed to invisible ultraviolet light often provides an effective means of analysis.* Moreover, the intensity of fluorescence can be used for quantitative analysis. For example, the concentration of riboflavin in chloroform is determined by this method. The fluorescence produced by X rays falling on a film of barium platinocyanide or other material is the principle of the fluoroscope used in X-ray diagnosis.

Also many substances are known which continue to emit light for some time after the external light stimulus is removed. This phenomenon is termed *phosphorescence*. The sulfides of the alkaline earths may be mentioned as examples of such substances. A trace of one of the heavy metals greatly intensifies the light emitted by a phosphorescent substance. Usually impurities, in the form of mixed crystals, are necessary for phosphorescence. Many different colors are now available among phosphorescent and fluorescent compounds.

Bombardment by electrons produces luminescence in rarefied gases at low pressures and in certain organic and inorganic crystals. The amount of visible fluorescence produced by a given input of energy may be large. This is the basis of the development of "fluorescent" lighting. Alpha

* Radley and Grant, *Fluorescence Analysis in Ultraviolet Light*, D. Van Nostrand Co., New York, 1933.

particles from radioactive elements produce bright luminescence when they hit a screen of zinc sulfide. Luminescent paints for watch dials are made by mixing the zinc sulfide and the radioactive material together with a binder.

The effect of radiation on crystals is interesting. X rays give rise to characteristic colors when passed through alkali halides and other crystals. Sodium chloride becomes yellow and potassium chloride blue, the coloration being due to the absorption of light by electrons which have been released by X rays and trapped in negative-ion "vacancies" in the crystal lattice. When an irradiated crystal is heated the trapped electrons are released, and in returning to a lower energy level they give off light, a phenomenon known as *thermoluminescence*.

If the crystal is heated slowly a series of light emissions occur at definite temperatures. The nature of these curves, in which the intensity of light emitted is plotted against the temperature, depends on the extent of the radiation exposure, the impurities present, and other factors. Certain minerals such as limestones and fluorites exhibit thermoluminescence even without laboratory exposure to radiation, because they contain traces of uranium in parts per million which have been giving off radioactive radiations for geological ages.

Photography.* If silver chloride or bromide is mixed with gelatin and exposed very briefly to light, no change is observed; but, when it is immersed in a solution of a mild reducing agent, such, for example, as pyrogallic acid, the parts that have been exposed to light are developed; that is, they are reduced to metallic silver much more rapidly than the unexposed parts. The photographic plate consists of a large number of minute grains of crystalline silver halide; some of these grains are completely reduced by the developer to black metallic silver, and others are unaffected. Apparently, it is necessary for a quantum of energy to strike a sensitive spot in the crystal lattice in order that the silver halide may be reduced to give a nucleus of silver which then spreads, on further reduction, to include the whole grain. These sensitive spots seem to be identified with minute impurities of silver sulfide in the crystal lattice which are particularly responsive to the action of light. By increasing the number of these sensitive spots and by other means the speed of photographic films and plates has been greatly increased; that is, satisfactory photographs can be made with much weaker light than was possible heretofore.

The camera and lens focus the image of the object on the photographic plate; the brightest parts of the image have a greater concentration of

* James and Higgins, *Fundamentals of Photographic Theory*, John Wiley & Sons, New York, 1948.

photons, and, consequently, more grains are reduced to silver. The unaffected grains are dissolved out with sodium thiosulfate ("hypo"), and the plate is washed and dried. The bright parts of the image become the dark spots on the plate, and the plate is therefore called a negative.

In printing, the plate is placed over a paper coated with silver halide and exposed to the light. The dark spots of silver on the negative absorb the light, whereas the unaffected areas permit light to pass through and act on the silver halide, producing a negative of the first negative. This double reversal produces a print in which the dark and light parts agree with the dark and light parts of the original object.

The silver halides respond only to the ultraviolet and to the shorter wavelengths of the visible spectrum, but, if certain red dyes, such as dicyanin, are mixed in the emulsion, the plate becomes sensitive also to red. Such red-sensitive plates, called panchromatic plates, give much better tone values to colored objects. This phenomenon constitutes another example of photosensitization. The red light is less scattered by a hazy atmosphere than the blue, and much clearer pictures of distant objects are obtained with red-sensitive plates using a color filter which absorbs the blue. This method is used in aerial photography.

Biological Applications of Photochemistry. The most important photochemical reaction in the world is the union of carbon dioxide and water in plants through the agency of sunlight and chlorophyll. Chlorophyll which gives plants their green color, is a complex organic compound containing magnesium. It absorbs red and blue and, to a lesser extent, green light, as shown in Fig. 4-4 on page 72. The activated chlorophyll thus formed is responsible for the production from carbon dioxide and water of the starting material of all plant growth.

The important primary reaction involved in the growth of plants may be represented by the equation

$$CO_2 + H_2O + \text{Light} + \text{Chlorophyll}$$

$$\rightarrow (1/n)(CH_2O)_n + O_2 + \text{Chlorophyll} \quad (9)$$

where $(CH_2O)_n$ represents a carbohydrate such as cellulose or sugar.

When cellulose is burned the reaction is

$$(1/n)(CH_2O)_n + O_2 \rightarrow CO_2 + H_2O \qquad \Delta H = -112,000 \text{ cal per mole}$$

The endothermic formation of carbohydrates from CO_2 and H_2O must require therefore the absorption of 112,000 cal mole^{-1}, and the activation energy must be at least as great as this, as pointed out on page 351. This activation energy is equivalent to radiation of 2300 A or less. There is no radiation as short as this in the sunlight that reaches the earth's surface, and, moreover, carbon dioxide and water are both transparent down to even shorter wavelengths.

Chlorophyll, however, acts as a photosensitizer, absorbing visible light and making it available for photosynthesis in the plant. But there is something unique about the reaction. Red light will cause photosynthesis, but red light corresponds to only 40,000 calories per mole; and more than 112,000 calories are required to bring about the reaction. Obviously three or more photons must be utilized, but there is no simple way by which several low-energy photons can collide simultaneously with two molecules to effect a high-energy reaction. Apparently the reaction takes place in steps. Laboratory experiments with algae have shown that normally about eight photons are required for each carbon dioxide molecule utilized and each oxygen molecule evolved in photosynthesis.

Exercise I. Show that, in photosynthesis, if eight photons of absorbed light at 6000 A produce one molecule of a product which has a heat of combustion of 112,000 calories per mole, the efficiency of conversion of absorbed light into stored chemical energy is 30 per cent.

In these experiments the conditions for growth were optimum with favorable conditions and low light intensity. In ordinary agriculture the efficiency of plant growth is much less.

Example 3. If a good agricultural crop yields about 2 tons per acre of dry organic material per year with a heat of combustion of about 4000 calories per gram, what fraction of a year's solar energy is stored in an agricultural crop if the solar energy is about 1000 calories per minute per square foot and the sun is shining about 500 minutes per day on the average? 1 acre = 43,560 sq ft, and 1 ton = 907,000 grams.

$$\text{Solar heat} = (43,560 \text{ ft}^2 \text{ acre}^{-1})(500 \text{ min day}^{-1})(1000 \text{ cal min}^{-1} \text{ ft}^{-2}) \times$$

$$(365.25 \text{ day year}^{-1})$$

$$= 7.96 \times 10^{12} \text{ cal acre}^{-1} \text{ year}^{-1}$$

$$\text{Heat stored} = (2 \text{ ton acre}^{-1} \text{ year}^{-1})(9.07 \times 10^5 \text{ gram ton}^{-1})(4000 \text{ cal gram}^{-1})$$

$$= 7.26 \times 10^9 \text{ cal acre}^{-1} \text{ year}^{-1}$$

$$\frac{\text{Heat stored}}{\text{Solar heat}} \cong 0.001$$

This 0.001 storage of average agriculture cannot be compared with the 0.300 storage of the laboratory, because in the open field the plants grow only during a third of the year and then the absorption of light is not complete. Half of the solar energy is in the infrared, which is not absorbed by chlorophyll; the concentration of carbon dioxide in the air is 0.03 per cent instead of the 3 per cent used in the laboratory experiments; and the sunlight is much too bright for efficient photosynthesis.

Another photochemical reaction of biological importance is the production of vitamin D, which prevents rickets and brings about the normal deposition of calcium in growing bones. Steenbock found that rickets could be prevented by subjecting the food as well as the patient to ultraviolet light below 3100 A. Later the substance which is converted into vitamin D was traced to ergosterol and cholesterol.

Example 4. When ergosterol is irradiated with ultraviolet light below 3100 A, vitamin D, the antirachitic vitamin, is produced in proportion to the number of quanta absorbed. When irradiated ergosterol was included in a diet otherwise devoid of vitamin D, it was found that absorbed radiant energy of about 750 ergs was necessary to prevent rickets in a rat when fed over a period of 2 weeks. The light used had a wavelength of 2650 A.

(a) How many quanta are necessary to give 750 ergs?

$$\epsilon = h\nu = \frac{(6.62 \times 10^{-27})(3.0 \times 10^{10})}{2.65 \times 10^{-5}} = 7.5 \times 10^{-12} \text{ erg}$$

$$\text{Number of quanta} = \frac{750}{7.5 \times 10^{-12}} = 1.00 \times 10^{14}$$

(b) If we assume that the primary photoprocess is the only chemical reaction, how many molecules of vitamin D per day are necessary to prevent rickets in a rat?

$$\text{Molecules per day} = 1.00 \times 10^{14}/14 = 7.14 \times 10^{12}$$

(c) If vitamin D has a molecular weight of the same order of magnitude as ergosterol (382), how many grams of vitamin D per day are necessary to prevent rickets in a rat?

$$\text{Grams per day} = \frac{(7.14 \times 10^{12})(382)}{6.02 \times 10^{23}} = 4.53 \times 10^{-9}$$

The first measurements of this type were made before the vitamin D had been isolated. After the vitamin was isolated in nearly pure form, it was found that 5×10^{-8} gram per day was the minimum dosage required to prevent rickets in a rat. This value is in fair agreement with the quantity estimated from theoretical photochemistry at a time when the nature of the vitamin was still unknown.

Radiation Chemistry. Chemical reactions may be brought about not only by collisions and by the absorption of light but also by alpha, beta, gamma, and X rays, by rapidly moving electrons, and by high-voltage electrical discharges. The energy available in these sources exceeds greatly the activation energy of the reaction. Thus a million volt electron has an energy equivalent of

$$(10^6 \text{ volt})(23,060 \text{ cal mole}^{-1} \text{ volt}^{-1}) = 2.3 \times 10^{10} \text{ cal mole}^{-1}$$

These high-energy radiations and particles lose their energy by knocking out electrons from molecules, forming secondary electrons of high kinetic energy and leaving positive ions. Most of the chemical reaction is then brought about by the rapidly moving secondary electrons. They have sufficient energy to break molecules down into free radicals and carry on reactions which would take place thermally only at very high temperatures. Whereas most chemical reactions require less than 100,000 calories per mole or 4.3 electron volts for thermal activation, the activation by secondary electrons seems to require considerably more. When brought about by electron bombardment many chemical reactions require 30 to 35 electron volts, or about 700,000 calories per mole. Apparently a considerable amount of energy must be dissipated in ionizations and electron displacements. Many ions recombine and convert the energy of ionization into heat without producing any chemical reaction.

To simplify the recording of data it is customary in radiation chemistry to use the term G defined as follows:

$$G = \frac{\text{Number of molecules reacting}}{100 \text{ electron volts of energy introduced}}$$

High-voltage electrical discharges in gases such as used in ozonizers provide a convenient means for bringing about chemical reactions. Almost any gas or vapor is changed chemically by passing an electrical discharge through it at low pressures. The activation is produced by both electrons and gaseous ions which are accelerated to high velocities between the electrodes. Decompositions predominate, but the fact that a discharge through ethane will produce some butane and liquid hydrocarbon shows that some free radicals are produced which may combine to give products of higher molecular weight than the starting material. The recombination of ions leads to the emission of light, some of which lies in the ultraviolet. Almost all electrical discharges through organic or inorganic vapors give an intense emission band which is identified with the OH radical from the trace of water that is almost always present as an impurity.

REFERENCES

Noyes and Leighton, *The Photochemistry of Gases*, Reinhold Publishing Corp., New York, 1941.

Rollefson and Burton, *Photochemistry and the Mechanism of Reactions*, Prentice-Hall, New York, 1939.

Steacie, *Atomic and Free Radical Reactions*, Reinhold Publishing Corp., New York, 1946.

Hoellander, *Radiation Biology*, Vols. I, II, III, McGraw-Hill Book Co., New York, 1954, 1955.

National Research Council, Report of the Committee on Photochemistry, *J. Phys. Chem., 32*, 480–575 (1928); *42*, 699–854 (1938).

PROBLEMS

1. A certain photochemical reaction requires an activation energy of 30,000 cal per mole. To what values does this correspond in the following units? (a) Ergs per molecule, (b) frequency of light, (c) wave number, (d) wavelength in angstroms, (e) electron volts.

   $Ans.$ (a) 2.08×10^{-12} erg molecule^{-1}. (b) 3.14×10^{14} sec^{-1}. (c) 10,500 cm^{-1}.
   (d) 9520 A. (e) 1.30 electron volt.

2. According to the hypothesis of Franck, the molecules of the halogens dissociate into one normal atom and one excited atom. The wavelength of the convergence limit in the spectrum of iodine is 4995 A. (a) What is the energy of dissociation of iodine into one normal and one excited atom? (b) The lowest excitation energy of the iodine atom is 0.94 volt. What is the energy corresponding to this excitation? (c) Compute the heat of dissociation of the iodine molecule into two normal atoms, and compare it with the value obtained from thermochemical data, 34.5 kcal per mole. $Ans.$ (a) 57.22, (b) 21.67, (c) 35.55 kcal mole^{-1}.

3. The following calculations are made on a uranyl oxalate actinometer, on the assumption that the energy of all wavelengths between 2540 A and 4350 A is completely absorbed. The actinometer contains 20 ml of 0.05 M oxalic acid, which also is 0.01 M with respect to uranyl sulfate. After 2 hours of exposure to ultraviolet light, the solution required 34 ml of KMnO$_4$ solution to titrate the undecomposed oxalic acid. The same volume, 20 ml, of unilluminated solution required 40 ml of the KMnO$_4$ solution. If the average energy of the quanta in this range may be taken as corresponding to a wavelength of 3500 A, how many ergs were absorbed per second in this experiment? $Ans.$ 124,000 ergs.

4. A sample of gaseous acetone is irradiated with monochromatic light having a wavelength of 3130 A. Light of this wavelength decomposes the acetone according to the equation

$$(CH_3)_2CO + h\nu \rightarrow C_2H_6 + CO$$

The reaction cell used has a volume of 59 ml. The acetone vapor absorbs 91.5 per cent of the incident energy. During the experiment the following data are obtained

Temperature of reaction	= 56.7°
Initial pressure	= 766.3 mm
Final pressure	= 783.2 mm
Time of radiation	= 7 hours
Incident energy	= 48,100 ergs per second

How many molecules are decomposed per quantum of absorbed energy; that is, what is the quantum yield? $Ans.$ 0.17 molecule per quantum.

5. In the photobromination of cinnamic acid using blue light of 4358 A at 30.6° an intensity of 14,000 ergs per second produced a decrease of 0.075 millimole of Br$_2$ during an exposure of 1105 seconds. The solution absorbed 80.1 per cent of the light passing through it. The bromine which reacted produced dibromocinnamic acid. Calculate the quantum yield for the photo reaction of bromine.

   $Ans.$ 16.6 molecules of Br$_2$ per photon absorbed, or 16.6 moles einstein^{-1}.

6. A 100-ml vessel containing hydrogen and chlorine was irradiated with light of 4000 A. Measurements with a thermopile showed that 11 ergs of light energy was absorbed by the chlorine per second. During an irradiation of 1 minute the partial

pressure of chlorine, as determined by the absorption of light and the application of Beer's law, decreased from 205 to 156 mm (recalculated to 0°C). What is the quantum yield? *Ans.* 2.6×10^6 moles HCl einstein^{-1}

7. Discuss the economic possibilities of using photochemical reactions in industry for valuable products with electricity at 1 cent per kilowatt-hour. Assume that 4 per cent of the electric energy consumed by a quartz-mercury-vapor lamp goes into light, and 30 per cent of this is photochemically effective. (a) How much will it cost to produce 1 lb (453.6 grams) of an organic compound having a molecular weight of 100, if the average effective wavelength is assumed to be 4000 A and the reaction has a quantum yield of 0.8 molecule per photon? (b) How much will it cost if the reaction involves a chain reaction with a quantum yield of 100?

Ans. (a) 31.4, (b) 0.251 cents

8. (a) How many calories per mole are equivalent in energy to 2 electron volts? A lead storage battery gives about 2 volts. (b) How many calories per mole is equivalent to 100,000 volts? X rays have energies of about 100,000 volts. (c) How many calories per mole is equivalent in energy to 5 million electron volts? Some alpha particles have energies of about 5 million electron volts.

9. If a reaction responds to both red and violet light, 7000 A and 4000 A, with an equal quantum efficiency, will there be more photochemical reaction per 100 cal of light in the red or in the blue? How much more?

10. The photopolymerization of anthracene reaches a stationary state, owing to the thermal decomposition of the dianthracene. For the photoreaction the temperature coefficient r is 1.1, and for the thermal reaction r is 2.8, where r is defined as k_{t+10}/k_t. Calculate the effect of a 5° rise in temperature on the amount of dianthracene formed when the photostationary state is reached.

11. In the ethyl chlorophyllide actinometer developed by Warburg and Shocken and by Gaffron, ethyl chlorophyllide and thiourea are dissolved in pyridine and shaken vigorously in an atmosphere containing oxygen. The oxygen is taken up in the photoöxidation of thiourea activated by the ethyl chlorophyllide which has absorbed light. One photon causes the consumption of practically one molecule of oxygen. The reduction in volume of oxygen is measured with a capillary gas buret, and the same vessel and buret are used in the measurement of photosynthesis and respiration. All are measured directly in cubic millimeters of oxygen absorbed or evolved. With the actinometer an exposure of 15 minutes gave a decrease in oxygen of 81 mm^3 when exposed to red light between 6200 and 6500 A. When the vessel was filled with algae under the same conditions there was an evolution of oxygen amounting to 10.7 mm^3 in 15 minutes, after correcting for the absorption of oxygen in respiration as determined by measurements taken in the dark. (a) What is the quantum yield of photosynthesis, i.e., the number of molecules of oxygen evolved per photon absorbed? (b) How many calories of light were absorbed during the 15 minute exposure? (c) The cross section of the vessel with its flat window is 8 cm.^{2} Assuming that sunlight has about 0.4 cal per cm^2 per min of photosynthetically active light, how intense was the light of this experiment expressed in per cent of sunlight intensity?

12. Nitrogen dioxide is decomposed photochemically by light of 3660 A with a quantum yield of 2.0 molecules per photon, according to the reaction

$$2NO_2 = 2NO + O_2$$

The thermal reaction runs in the reverse direction. When an enclosed sample of nitrogen dioxide is illuminated for a long period of time, the quantum yield decreases and approaches zero. Suggest a mechanism to explain these facts, and write the chemical equations.

13. Two mechanisms have been proposed for the photochemical decomposition of NOCl:

$$A \begin{cases} NOCl + h\nu \rightarrow NO + Cl \\ Cl + NOCl \rightarrow NO + Cl_2 \end{cases} \text{ and } B \begin{cases} NOCl + h\nu \rightarrow NOCl^* \\ NOCl^* + NOCl \rightarrow 2NO + Cl_2 \end{cases}$$

(a) What quantum yield would be expected for each mechanism? (b) Given the following experimental facts, state which mechanism is probably correct: The range of wavelengths effective in decomposition lies between 3650 and 6400 A. The substance NOCl possesses well-defined absorption bands above 2500 A, with no regions of continuous absorption. The minimum dissociation energy required to give NO and Cl is 46,400 cal mole^{-1}.

14. Most chemical reactions require activation energies ranging between 10,000 and 100,000 cal per mole. What are the equivalents of 10,000 and 100,000 cal per mole in terms of (a) angstroms, (b) wave numbers, (c) electron volts?

15. The oxidation of rubrene ($C_{42}H_{28}$) is effected by oxygen at a wavelength of 4360 A with a quantum yield of 1 molecule per quantum. How many calories of this light will be required to photoöxidize 1 gram of rubrene?

16. For 900 seconds light of 4360 A was passed into a carbon tetrachloride solution containing bromine and cinnamic acid. The average energy absorbed was 19,190 ergs per second. Some of the bromine reacted to give cinnamic acid dibromide, and, in this experiment, the total bromine content decreased by 3.83×10^{19} molecules. (a) What was the quantum yield? (b) State whether or not a chain reaction was involved. (c) If a chain mechanism is involved, suggest suitable reactions which might explain the observed quantum yield.

17. Chloroform is often kept in dark bottles to prevent photoöxidation by air, giving phosgene, which is poisonous. The quantum yield of the photoöxidation has been reported to be about 100 molecules per photon with light of 4360 A. How many calories of this light will be required to oxidize 1 mg of chloroform when the chloroform containing dissolved air is placed in a transparent bottle?

18. Ammonia is decomposed by ultraviolet light of 2000 A with a quantum yield of 0.14 molecule per photon absorbed. (a) How many calories of this light would be necessary to decompose 1 gram of ammonia? (b) Offer a suggestion to explain this comparatively low quantum yield.

19. A cold high-voltage mercury lamp is to be used for a certain photochemical reaction which responds to ultraviolet light of 2537 A. The chemical analysis of the product is sensitive to only 10^{-4} mole. The lamp consumes 150 watts and converts 5 per cent of the electric energy into radiation of which 80 per cent is at 2537 A. The amount of the light which gets into the monochromator and passes out of the rear slit is only 5 per cent of the total radiation of the lamp. Fifty per cent of this 2537 A radiation from the monochromator is absorbed in the reacting system. The quantum yield is 0.4 molecule of product per quantum of light absorbed. How long an exposure must be given in this experiment if it is desired to measure the photochemical change with an accuracy of 1 per cent?

20. Calculate the maximum possible theoretical yield in tons of carbohydrate material $(H_2CO)_n$ that can be produced on an acre of land by green plants or trees during a 100-day growing season. Similar calculations apply to algae growing in a square mile of lake or ocean. Assume that the sun's radiation averages 1.0 cal per cm^2 per min for 8 hours per day and that one-half the area is covered by green leaves. Assume that one-third of the radiation lies between 4000 and 6500 A, which is the range of the light absorbed by chlorophyll and that the average wavelength is 5500 A. Assume that the leaves are thick enough to absorb practically all the light that strikes them. Assume that the quantum yield is 0.12 molecule per photon; that is, 8 photons with chlorophyll can produce 1 H_2CO unit from 1 molecule of carbon dioxide and 1 molecule of water. Criticize these several assumptions.

21. The photochemical oxidation of phosgene, sensitized by chlorine, has been studied by Rollefson and Montgomery.* The over-all reaction is

$$2COCl_2 + O_2 = 2CO_2 + 2Cl_2$$

and the rate expression which gives the effect of the several variables is

$$\frac{dc_{CO_2}}{dt} = \frac{kI_0c_{COCl_2}}{1 + k'c_{Cl_2}/c_{O_2}}$$

where I_0 is the intensity of the light. The quantum yield is about 2 molecules per quantum. Devise a series of chemical equations involving the existence of the free radicals ClO and COCl which will give a mechanism consistent with the rate expression.

* Rollefson and Montgomery, *J. Am. Chem. Soc.*, **55**, 142, 4025 (1932).

20

Nuclear Chemistry

The Discovery of Radioactivity. After Roentgen's discovery of X rays, Becquerel studied the action of a number of fluorescent substances on a covered photographic plate. He had considered the possibility that those crystals which exhibited fluorescence under the action of X rays might emit X rays when caused to fluoresce by exposure to sunlight. Among the materials with which Becquerel experimented were salts of uranium, and he found that a photographic plate brought near a fluorescent uranium salt was darkened by subsequent development, even though the photographic plate had been protected by an opaque cover. In carrying out a proper control experiment he was surprised to find that exposure to sunlight with the attendant fluorescence was not necessary for the action on the photographic plate. Thus, in 1896 Becquerel discovered a spontaneous emission of penetrating rays similar to X rays from uranium salts and other substances. The phenomenon was called radioactivity.

In a classic investigation Professor and Madame Curie carried out a systematic examination of uranium minerals and found that one of them, pitchblende, was considerably more radioactive than uranium itself. With this clue they separated from tons of pitchblende a trace of a substance which possessed great radioactivity. After extensive chemical purification and a great many recrystallizations Professor and Madame Curie discovered the element radium.

Alpha, Beta, and Gamma Rays. The radiations emitted by the radioactive elements are of three kinds. The alpha particles have a mass equal to that of the helium nucleus and are shot out with a velocity about one-tenth that of light. They have a positive charge of 2 units and are deflected slightly in an electrostatic or magnetic field. They possess great ionizing power but relatively little penetrating power— only a few centimeters in air at atmospheric pressure. The beta rays consist of negatively charged particles moving with speeds varying from nine-tenths of the speed of light to much lower velocities. Whereas the alpha particles emitted by a particular radioelement have a definite velocity, the corresponding beta-ray emission consists of a flight of particles having widely different speeds. The penetrating power of the beta rays depends upon the speed of the particles, those which move most rapidly possessing the greatest penetrating power. The ionizing action of the beta rays is weaker than that of the alpha rays per unit length of path, but the total number of ions produced by an alpha particle and a beta particle of the same energy is about the same. The beta rays are readily deflected by electrostatic or magnetic fields, and by quantitative measurements of these deflections Becquerel was able to show that beta particles are electrons.

The gamma rays consist of electromagnetic radiations like X rays. except that they come from the nucleus, whereas the X rays come from electron displacements outside the nucleus. Gamma rays cannot be deflected from a rectilinear path by either electric or magnetic fields, and the fact that they may be deflected by crystals proves that they have very short wavelengths.

Direct proof of the nature of alpha rays was obtained by an experiment in which a very thin glass bulb was filled with a radioactive substance emitting alpha rays and then enclosed in an outer glass tube with suitable windows. The outer tube was evacuated and allowed to stand. After several days the spectrum of helium was observed in the outer vessel when an electric discharge was applied. In a control experiment the inner bulb was filled with pure helium under pressure, but no trace of helium gas could be detected in the outer tube. These experiments showed that the helium as such could not go through the thin glass walls, but that the alpha particles were able to penetrate the walls and, after losing their velocities and gaining electrons, they became helium atoms.

The direct counting of alpha particles combined with a measurement of the total charge of electricity carried by a large number of alpha particles gave a value of 3.1×10^{-19} coulomb per alpha particle. Deflection in an electrostatic field was in the direction which showed that the charge was positive. Since the fundamental unit of electricity (the charge of the electron) is 1.602×10^{-19} coulomb, the alpha particle must carry 2 positive charges.

The properties of alpha, beta, and gamma rays are summarized in *Fig. 20-1*, which represents the action of a magnetic field which is perpendicular to the plane of the paper. Radioactive material is placed in a deep hole in a block of lead so that the rays emerge as a narrow vertical beam. The alpha particles are deflected to the left only slightly because of their large mass; the beta particles are deflected to a greater extent to the right. The gamma rays are unaffected by the magnetic field.

The relative penetrating power of the three rays are roughly in the order 1, 100, and 10,000 for alpha, beta, and gamma rays. The alpha rays have definite path lengths, but the gamma rays fall off exponentially in intensity.

Other types of radiations have been observed with synthetic radio-isotopes which will be discussed later. These include positrons (positive

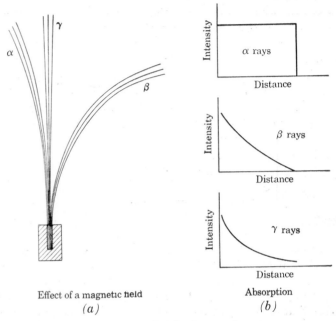

Effect of a magnetic field
(a)

Absorption
(b)

FIG. 20-1.   Properties of alpha, beta, and gamma rays.

electrons) and X rays resulting from the capture of an orbital electron by the nucleus.

Measurement of Radioactivity.   Action on a photographic plate through opaque paper constitutes one of the simplest tests for the radio-activity of a substance.   This method can be used to reveal the distri-bution of a radioactive substance within an object, such as a mineral or a leaf.

Radiation from radioactive substances may be detected by the ions produced in a gas.   A rapidly moving alpha or beta particle causes the ejection of orbital electrons from the atoms or molecules of the gas. Alpha particles produce 50,000 to 100,000 ion pairs per centimeter of air, but beta particles produce only a few hundred per centimeter. However, owing to the greater distance traversed by beta particles, approximately the same total number of ion pairs are produced by alpha and beta particles of the same energy.

An ionization chamber contains two electrodes across which a sufficient voltage is maintained by a battery so that all the ions produced by incoming radiations are drawn to the electrodes and the resulting current may be measured.

A Geiger-Müller counter consists of a cylindrical negative electrode with a central wire as the positive electrode. A sufficient voltage is

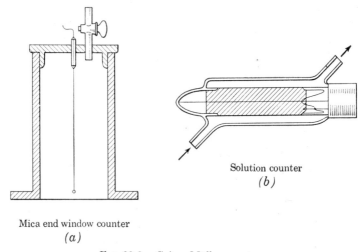

Solution counter
(b)

Mica end window counter
(a)

Fɪɢ. 20-2.   Geiger-Müller counters.

applied so that the production of a single ion pair produces an avalanche of ions and an electrical pulse is obtained. Large pulses which are easily counted by use of an appropriate circuit are obtained. In order to prevent the formation of further pulses by the positive ions of the avalanche striking the cathode and causing the ejection of electrons, a polyatomic organic gas is placed in the tube so that the discharge will be self-quenching. Such a Geiger-Müller tube contains a mixture of argon and a few per cent of, say, methane. Since organic compounds ionize more readily than argon, the argon ions initially formed transfer their charges to the organic molecules. When these organic ions reach the cathode of the Geiger-Müller tube the energy which would otherwise have caused the emission of electrons is now used to decompose the organic ions. Two types of Geiger-Müller counter tubes are illustrated in *Fig. 20-2*. In the first, the ionizing radiation enters through a thin window in the end of the tube; and in the second, ionizing radiation from a solution passes through the walls of the tube.

The Wilson cloud chamber provides an important means for studying ionizing radiations. The paths of individual particles are rendered visible in a chamber containing supersaturated water vapor. Air saturated with water vapor is cooled suddenly by an adiabatic expansion. The ions produced by an alpha, beta, or gamma ray may serve as nuclei for condensation. Thus condensation of water vapor in fine droplets occurs along the path which may be photographed with suitable illumination. The cloud tracks left by alpha, beta, and gamma particles are indicated in *Fig. 20-3*. Alpha particles travel in straight lines until near the ends of their paths, when their speeds have been greatly reduced.

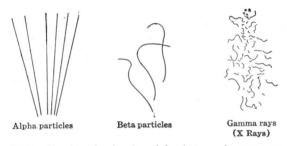

Alpha particles   Beta particles   Gamma rays
                                             (X Rays)

Fig. 20-3.   Cloud tracks showing alpha, beta, and gamma rays.

Beta rays are more easily deflected, and their paths are quite crooked. Gamma rays or X rays release a large number of secondary electrons from the molecules they strike. The energy of these secondary electrons is lower, and the paths are short and crooked. A cloud-chamber photograph of alpha-particle and proton tracks is shown in Fig. 20-10 on page 622.

Some materials such as zinc sulfide luminesce when exposed to radiation from radioactive materials. This luminescence consists of individual flashes visible with a microscope, each flash or scintillation being caused by a single particle. By means of a photomultiplier tube it is possible to count the scintillations in a crystal of anthracene, and this method is especially useful in counting gamma rays.

Avogadro's Number.   Since it has been proved that each alpha particle is transformed into a helium atom, and since we can count the alpha particles and measure the volume of helium, we have at once a direct method for determining the number of molecules in a gram molecule of helium, the *Avogadro number*.

Example 1.   Rutherford and Geiger found that radium emits 3.4×10^{10} alpha particles per gram per second.   Rutherford and Boltwood found that radium produces helium at the rate of 1.07×10^{-4} ml per gram per day, measured under standard conditions. What is the value of the Avogadro constant?

$$\frac{(22,400)}{(1.07 \times 10^{-4})} (3.4 \times 10^{10})(24)(60)(60) = 6.15 \times 10^{23}$$

The measurement of the charge of the electron gives a more accurate method for calculating Avogadro's number.

Example 2. The charge on the electron is 1.602×10^{-19} coulomb. When water is electrolyzed, each electron releases an atom of hydrogen at the cathode, and 96,496 coulombs release 1.008 grams of hydrogen ions. What is the Avogadro number?

$$\frac{96,496 \text{ coulombs equiv}^{-1}}{1.601 \times 10^{-19} \text{ coulombs electron}^{-1}} = 6.024 \times 10^{23} \text{ electrons equiv}^{-1} \text{ or g atom}^{-1}$$

After the weight of a single atom of hydrogen has been established, the weight in grams of a single atom of any other element may be determined by dividing its atomic weight by 6.02×10^{23}.

The mass of an individual electron can be determined also. On page 539 it was shown that the mass of the electron must be 1/1838 the mass of the hydrogen ion. Inasmuch as the weight of the latter is 1.0081, the weight of the electron on the physical atomic weight scale is 0.000549.

Disintegration of the Radioelements. Most of the elements with atomic numbers greater than that of lead, 82, are unstable and undergo radioactive disintegration into lighter elements. This involves changes in the nuclei of the atoms, whereas ordinary chemical reactions involve changes only in the arrangement of atoms in molecules. The nuclear changes have energies of the order of 10^9 cal per mole and more, whereas molecular changes require energies of only 10^4 to 10^5 cal per mole. The energies involved in nuclear disintegrations are so great that the slight increases in energy produced by raising the temperature are entirely negligible, and, as a result, no detectable change in the rate of radioactive disintegrations has been observed in studies extending from liquid-air temperatures to 1000°.

Again the radioactivity of an element is unaffected by chemical combination with other elements.

It will be shown presently that radioactivity is not confined to the heavy elements; in fact, radioactivity has been produced in most of the elements.

In all radioactive disintegrations the number of atoms disintegrating is proportional to the number present; and so radioactive decay always follows the first-order equation

$$-dn/dt = kn \tag{1}$$

and the number n of atoms (or gram atoms) remaining unchanged after time t is given by the expression

$$k = \frac{2.303}{t} \log \frac{n_0}{n} \tag{2}$$

where n_0 is the number at the beginning, when $t = 0$. The exponential expressions are used more commonly than the logarithmic for studying radioactivity. Thus:

$$n = n_0 e^{-kt} \tag{3}$$

When one radioactive element disintegrates, another may be formed, and the disintegration constant of the second radioelement is usually different from that of the first one. A series of consecutive first-order decompositions results which can be handled by the methods of differential equations, as illustrated on page 337. Radon is produced continuously by the disintegration of radium; and radon disintegrates into another radioelement, polonium. The rate at which radon is produced from a quantity of radium is given by the expression $k_1 n_1$, where n_1 is the number of radium atoms, and k_1 is the disintegration constant of radium or the fraction disintegrating per unit of time; the rate at which it decomposes is given by the expression $k_2 n_2$, where n_2 is the number of radon atoms and k_2 is the disintegration constant of radon. When the rate of production of a radioelement from its parent element is equal to its rate of disintegration into the next succeeding element of the series, the substance is said to be in radioactive equilibrium. Strictly speaking this is an example of a "steady state" rather than "equilibrium." In this steady state, radon is decomposing at the same rate that it is being formed, and

$$k_1 n_1 = k_2 n_2$$

Then,

$$n_1/n_2 = k_2/k_1 = t_{\frac{1}{2},1}/t_{\frac{1}{2},2} \tag{4}$$

where $t_{\frac{1}{2}}$ is the period of half-life, or $0.693/k$.

If the life of the parent element is long compared with the life of the disintegration products, and if sufficient time is allowed for equilibrium to be attained, the ratio of the quantities of successive radioelements is the same as the ratio of their half-lives. It is evident that the short-lived elements cannot accumulate in large quantities, but because of their rapid disintegration they may contribute largely to the radioactivity of the total material.

Example 3. Radium loses an alpha particle and leaves a gaseous element, radon. For the radio disintegration of radium, $t_{\frac{1}{2}} = 1590$ years, and for radon $t_{\frac{1}{2}} = 3.82$

days. How many milliliters of radon at 25° and 1 atm are in equilibrium with 1 gram of radium?

$$1 \text{ g radium} = \tfrac{1}{226} = 0.00442 \text{ g atom}$$

$$\frac{\text{gram atom}_{Ra}}{\text{gram atom}_{Rn}} = \frac{t_{1/2,Ra}}{t_{1/2,Rn}}$$

$$\frac{0.00442}{\text{gram atom}_{Rn}} = \frac{(1590)(365.25)}{3.82}$$

$$\text{gram atom}_{Rn} = 2.91 \times 10^{-8} \text{ g atom}$$

$$\text{Volume radon} = (2.91 \times 10^{-8})(0.08205)(298)(1000)/1$$

$$= 7.11 \times 10^{-4} \text{ ml}$$

When a short-lived radioelement is removed from its long-lived parent, a new supply of the daughter element is regenerated, rapidly at first and then more slowly as the rate of decay of the daughter element increases, owing to the presence of the larger quantity which has accumulated. Thus, when gaseous radon is pumped or swept out of a solution of a radium salt with a current of air, the solution loses some of the short-lived beta and gamma radioactivity but regains it as the radon and its further decay products are allowed to accumulate again. If the decay of the daughter element is given by equation 3, the number of atoms of the daughter element at time t is given by the equation

$$n = n_0(1 - e^{-kt}) \tag{5}$$

where n_0 is the number approached at long times.

The study of radioactive elements led to the realization that certain radioactive substances could not be separated by ordinary chemical procedures. Soddy pointed out that the end products of the radioactive disintegration of uranium and thorium are both lead but the atomic weight of lead produced from uranium should be 206 in comparison with 208 from thorium. Painstaking measurements of atomic weights of lead from uranium and thorium minerals confirmed this expectation. Various forms of an element having different atomic weights are called *isotopes*. The atomic weights of isotopes are nearly, but not exactly, whole numbers. The integer nearest the atomic weight of an isotope is called the *mass number* of the isotope.

The radioactive disintegration of an element may be represented by an equation which indicates the masses of the various substances as well as their chemical identity (i.e., atomic number). For example, the disintegration of radium to give radon and an alpha particle may be represented by

$$_{88}\text{Ra}^{226} \rightarrow {}_{86}\text{Rn}^{222} + {}_{2}\text{He}^{4}$$

The mass numbers indicated by superscripts must balance on the two sides of the equation. The atomic numbers indicated by subscripts must also balance. Whenever an alpha particle is emitted the mass of

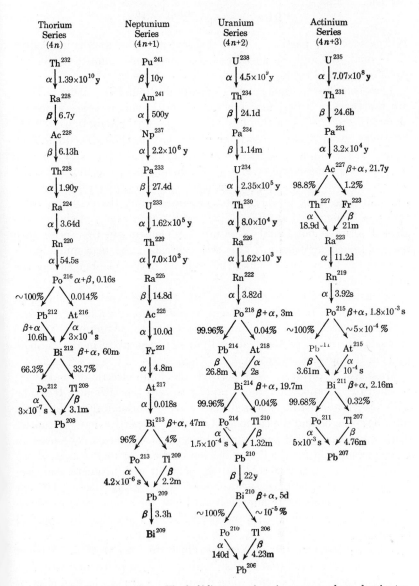

Fig. 20-4. Radioactive series. The half-lives are given in years, y; days, d; minutes, m; or seconds, s.

the nucleus is decreased by 4 units and the positive charge, or atomic number, of the nucleus, is decreased by 2 units.

Another isotope of radium, Ra^{228}, disintegrates by loss of a beta particle.

$$_{88}Ra^{228} \rightarrow {}_{89}Ac^{228} + {}_{-1}e^0$$

Whenever a beta particle is emitted the mass of the nucleus is substantially unaltered and the positive charge, or atomic number, of the nucleus is increased by 1.

Three families of radioactive elements are found in nature. These are the thorium series, uranium series, and actinium series, which are shown in *Fig. 20-4*. In this table the nature of the radiations and the half-lives are indicated. It will be noted that branching occurs in each series. For example, Po^{216} disintegrates in two ways, but with the same half-life. The mass numbers of all the members of the thorium series are multiples of 4 and may be represented by $4n$. The fact that the uranium series may be represented by $4n + 2$ and the actinium series by $4n + 3$ suggested that a $4n + 1$ series might exist. Although the $4n + 1$ series is not found in nature, the elements in this series have been obtained artificially. This series is called the neptunium series because the laboratory-produced neptunium is the member having the longest half-life.

Fajans and Soddy pointed out in 1913 that the emission of an alpha particle causes a radioactive element to shift its position in the periodic table two places in the direction of decreasing atomic numbers, and the emission of a beta particle causes it to shift one place in the periodic table in the opposite direction.

Mass Spectrometer. The positive ions in an electric discharge are repelled by the anode and move rapidly toward the cathode. If a tube with a perforated cathode is used, they will pass through the perforations into the space behind the cathode where their properties may be studied. These rays were called *positive rays* by Sir J. J. Thomson, who used an ingenious method for the determination of the individual masses of the positively charged particles by sifting them out with magnetic and electrostatic fields. The mass spectrometer for separating ions of different mass has been constantly improved until now the atomic weights of isotopes can be determined with much greater accuracy than by chemical means.

The mass spectrometer of Nier * is illustrated in *Fig. 20-5*. A beam of positive ions is produced by bombardment of gas molecules with electrons from a heated filament. The positive ions are accelerated electro-

---

* Nier, *Rev. Sci. Instruments, 11,* 212 (1940).

statically and passed through slits to form a narrow beam which passes between the poles of a powerful magnet. Since ions having different ratios of mass to charge are deflected through different angles the strengths of the magnetic and electrostatic fields may be adjusted so that only a certain isotope reaches the collector. The ion current may be measured electrically, or in mass spectrographs a photographic plate serves to record the ion beam.

If a charged particle of mass m, charge e, and velocity v (which is very much less than the velocity of light) is sent into a magnetic field of

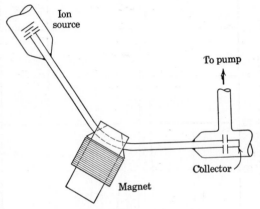

Fig. 20-5.   Mass spectrometer.

strength H in a direction at right angles to the lines of force, the radius r of the circular path followed will be that for which the force of the field and the centrifugal force are balanced (page 538).

$$r = mv/eH \qquad (6)$$

The velocity of the charged particle is related to the accelerating potential difference E by

$$\tfrac{1}{2}mv^2 = eE \qquad (7)$$

Combining equations 6 and 7 to eliminate v yields

$$m/e = r^2H^2/2E \qquad (8)$$

which is the basic equation for the mass spectrometer.

Care is necessary in the interpretation of results because the particles may have two or more charges, and there may be ionized fragments of molecules, such as CH^+, CH_2^+, and CH_3^+. The relative abundances of various isotopes may be determined by measurements of the ion current as the magnetic or electric field in the mass spectrometer is slowly changed. *Figure 20-6* shows the results obtained by Nier * for a sample of lead. The relative amounts of the various isotopes are given by the relative heights of the peaks. Less than a milligram of material is needed for an analysis, and, when the spectrometer is operating properly, analysis may be made rapidly with an error of less than 0.1 per cent in the abundance ratio. With modern apparatus atomic weights of isotopes may be determined to a few parts in 100,000.

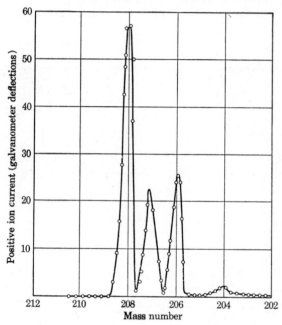

FIG. 20-6.   Isotopes of ordinary lead as determined with the mass spectrometer.

The isotopes of cadmium are shown in *Fig. 20-7* as obtained by Professor A. J. Dempster of the University of Chicago, using a sensitive mass spectrograph. The differences in the two spectra are discussed later.

Extensive use has been made of the mass spectrometer as an analytical tool for following the separation of isotopes and for studying petroleum reactions. Some of the fragments of organic vapors produced by thermal decomposition can be found with the mass spectrometer, particularly if the ionization voltage for producing the ions is below the ionization potential of the undecomposed molecules.

* Nier, *J. Am. Chem. Soc.*, *60*, 1572 (1938).

Occurrence of Isotopes. The development of the mass spectrograph as a precision instrument has led to the discovery of a large number of isotopes. The reference standard for chemical atomic weights is ordinary oxygen taken as 16, which is really a mixture of isotopes with the distribution $O^{16} = 99.758\%$, $O^{17} = 0.0373\%$, $O^{18} = 0.2039\%$. The reference standard for physical atomic weights, obtained with the mass spectrometer, is the most abundant isotope of oxygen O^{16}. It is a more definite standard than the ordinary oxygen, in which the isotope ratios may change slightly. In all chemical and physical-chemical calculations except those concerned with nuclear changes the chemical atomic weights are used.

Since the standard for the physical atomic weight scale, O^{16}, is lighter than the mixture of oxygen isotopes, 1.000000 unit on the chemical atomic weight scale is equal to 1.000272 on the physical scale.

It has been known since 1913 that the atomic weight of lead can vary, depending on the source of the material. Lead obtained, for example, from a radioactive ore rich in uranium has a higher atomic weight than

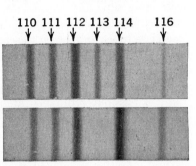

FIG. 20-7.   Isotopes of cadmium. Cd^{113} has been converted into Cd^{114} by absorbing neutrons.   From Dempster, *Phys. Rev.*, *71*, 829 (1947).

lead derived in part from the radio disintegration of thorium, because the isotopes of lead from uranium are heavier. This situation may be understood by reference to Fig. 20-4. Moreover, it has been pointed out by Urey that in the lighter elements the atomic-weight measurements have about reached the limit of useful accuracy and that, if further accuracy is obtained, it will be necessary to take account of the concentration of isotopes which inevitably accompanies the chemical and physical operations of purification and analysis.

In Table II on page 619 are listed a few elements with their exact atomic masses obtained on the basis of mass-spectrometer data together with the relative abundance of the different isotopes.

The presence of oxygen isotopes having masses of 16, 17, and 18 was discovered by a study of bands in the absorption spectrum of the sun as its light passed through the atmosphere surrounding the earth. Deuterium was discovered by the appearance of a new neighboring line in the emission spectrum after continued fractional distillation of hydrogen.

Concentration of Isotopes. The ratio of isotopes may be altered by fractional diffusion or evaporation, or by centrifuging, or, in fact, by any physical or chemical method which makes use of the difference in weights. It will be remembered that the relative velocities of gas molecules are inversely proportional to the square roots of the molecular weights. Effective concentration of small quantities of isotopes has been accomplished in the lighter elements with a battery of mercury diffusion pumps operating in series.*

One of the simplest methods for concentrating isotopes combines thermal diffusion and convection. When a vertical central wire or tube is maintained at a temperature 200 or 300° above the walls of a larger containing tube and allowed to stand, the heavier constituents of an enclosed gas concentrate at the bottom of the tube.† Bromine and air in a glass tube can be seen to separate within a few minutes. In such a tube 60 ft high filled with methane the carbon at the bottom of the tube becomes enriched with C^{13} in a few weeks from 1 per cent to several per cent, and by flowing a fresh supply of methane through slowly at the top it is possible to draw off at the bottom over 100 ml per day of the methane enriched with C^{13}.‡

Isotopes may be separated also by chemical means, although isotopes were originally thought to have identical chemical properties. The natural vibration frequency of atoms in a molecule depends to a slight extent on the mass of the atoms involved, and this vibration frequency affects the "zero-point energy," or the energy at the very bottom of the Morse curve shown in Fig. 18-9 on page 563. In other words, there is a very slight difference in the activation energies for chemical reactions of different isotopic forms of the same element. In competing reactions, then, the heavier isotope should react somewhat more slowly.§ The difference is sufficient for complete separation in the case of hydrogen, where the masses are 1 and 2, and the method can be used to obtain a concentration of isotopes of the other light elements. This slight difference in reactivity shows up also in the position of chemical equilibrium.‖ For example, the equilibrium constant for the reaction

$$N^{15}H_3(g) + N^{14}H_4^+(aq) = N^{14}H_3(g) + N^{15}H_4^+(aq)$$

is not unity; calculations show that it is 1.033. Thode and Urey¶ carried out experimental concentration of N^{15}, using this reaction, in an

---

* Hertz, Z. Physik, *79*, 108 (1932).

† Clusius and Dickel, Naturwiss., *26*, 546 (1938); *27*, 149 (1938); Brewer and Bramley, Phys. Rev., *55*, 590 (1939).

‡ Taylor and Glockler, J. Chem. Phys., *7*, 850 (1939); *8*, 843 (1940).

§ Schmitt and Daniels, J. Am. Chem. Soc., *75*, 3564 (1953).

‖ Urey and Greiff, J. Am. Chem. Soc., *57*, 321 (1935).

¶ Thode and Urey, J. Chem. Phys., *7*, 34 (1939).

effective column passing the ammonia gas up against a solution of ammonium nitrate flowing down. Concentration of N^{15} up to 72 per cent was obtained, and the experimentally determined value of K was 1.023. It is now possible to purchase ammonium nitrate containing 60 per cent of the ammonium nitrogen as N^{15}. Heavy carbon C^{13} has been prepared by a similar method, using HCN gas and KCN solution, and KCN in which 40–60% of the carbon atoms are C^{13} also may be purchased.*

An important method for the separation of isotopes involves the diffusion of a gas through a porous barrier. As shown on page 30 the rate

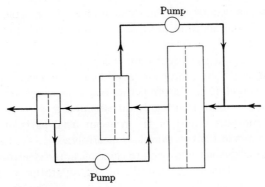

FIG. 20-8.   A cascade of gaseous diffusion units.

of diffusion is inversely proportional to the square root of the molecular weight. If diffusion is allowed to proceed for a long time the composition of the gas will become the same on both sides of the barrier, but if only half the gas is allowed to diffuse through the barrier there will be an enrichment of lighter isotopes in the gas which has passed through the barrier. During World War II a tremendous plant was built at Oak Ridge for the concentration of U^{235}, which occurs in natural uranium to the extent of 0.72 per cent. Volatile uranium hexafluoride, UF_6, was used as the process gas partly because fluorine exists in nature as a single isotope. The ratio of the square roots of the molecular weights of $U^{238}F_6$ and $U^{235}F_6$ is only 1.0043, and therefore many, many diffusion cells in cascade must be used. The principle of a cascade is illustrated in *Fig. 20-8*. Half of the gas which enters a diffusion cell is allowed to diffuse through the barrier and allowed to pass on to the next stage. The half which does not pass through the barrier is pumped back to the preceding stage. Since only half of the gas passes on to the next higher

* Eastman Kodak Co., Rochester, N. Y.

stage the area of barrier required is less in the higher stages. Experiments with UF_6 showed that about 4000 diffusion stages would be required to increase the abundance of U^{235} from its normal value to 99 per cent. Consequently, a very large plant was required for this process.

Another method for the separation of U^{235} involved the principle of the mass spectrometer. A volatile compound of uranium was ionized by means of a beam of electrons, and the positively charged ions produced in this way were accelerated and the beam passed into a strong magnetic field. Collectors were placed in positions to collect the desired isotopes.

Stable isotopes of many of the elements have been separated by the electromagnetic method and are available for research throughout the world.*

It is likely that all the slight differences in *chemical* behavior of isotopes, which make their separation possible, have not yet been explored. The kinetic method, utilizing competing reactions which are not in equilibrium, should be more thoroughly investigated.

Hydrogen contains 1 part of H^2 in about 5000 parts of H^1, and, if most of the water in a given sample is electrolyzed away, the residue of water containing the last hydrogen to come off in the electrolysis is much richer in H^2.† ‡ This is an example of the separation of isotopes by competitive reactions.

The properties of this heavy isotope of hydrogen are so different from ordinary hydrogen that a special name was assigned to it—*deuterium,* the symbol for which is D.

In the large-scale production of deuterium oxide, known as heavy water, advantage is taken of the fact that in the isotopic exchange reaction between hydrogen gas and liquid water the proportion of deuterium in the water is about three times as great as it is in the gas phase. A mixture of hydrogen gas and steam is passed upward through a tower containing a catalyst, which accelerates the exchange, with water flowing down. The water flowing out at the bottom of the tower is considerably enriched in deuterium. Hydrogen gas is obtained from the water by electrolysis, and the process is repeated by using a number of towers in cascade. Heavy water which is 99.59 per cent D_2O is available for 50 cents per gram.

The properties of water and heavy water are compared in Table I.

* They can be obtained at a nominal price from the U. S. Atomic Energy Commission at Oak Ridge, Tenn.

† Washburn and Urey, *Proc. Natl. Acad. Sci.,* 18, 496 (1932).

‡ Lewis, *J. Am. Chem. Soc.,* 55, 1297 (1933).

Table I. Properties of D_2O and H_2O

	Specific Gravity 20°	Freezing Point	Boiling Point	Heat Vaporization, cal mole^{-1}	Surface Tension 20°	Viscosity 20° $\times 10^3$	Dielectric Constant	Refractive Index, n_D^{20}	Solubility NaCl, grams per 1000 g
D_2O	1.1059	3.82°	101.42°	9960	67.8	12.6	80.5	1.32844	305
H_2O	0.9982	0.00°	100.00°	9700	72.75	10.09	82.0	1.33300	359

The Neutron. In 1932 the *neutron* was discovered by Chadwick. Previous investigators had bombarded light elements with alpha particles and obtained ionization effects at great distances. The nature of these penetrating radiations was in doubt. Chadwick bombarded beryllium with alpha particles and showed by the great penetration, by the failure to produce cloud tracks, and by the failure to be deflected in a magnetic field that the effects were produced by an uncharged particle having the mass of the hydrogen atom. The reaction is

$$_2He^4 + {_4Be^9} \rightarrow {_6C^{12}} + {_0n^1}$$

where $_0n^1$ is the neutron. Since the neutron has no charge but approximately the same mass as a hydrogen atom it is sometimes considered to be the element of atomic number zero. The existence of such a particle had been predicted by Rutherford and by Harkins.

Since they are uncharged, neutrons pass readily through matter and interact with nuclei at close distances of approach. The neutrons suffer collision with atoms and acquire velocities which can be calculated on the basis of the Maxwell-Boltzmann theory, with a distribution which depends on temperature in the same way that the distribution of molecular velocities depends on temperature. When neutrons are emitted in fission (page 629), they may have very great velocities, corresponding to millions of electron volts. Their velocities are quickly reduced to those prevailing at room temperature by collisions with surrounding atoms, the light atoms with masses not greatly different from that of the neutrons being the most effective in slowing them down. Neutrons are readily captured by hydrogen nuclei in substances like paraffin whereas they penetrate through deuterium compounds and many substances of much greater density.

Neutrons can be detected by the ionizing particles which are produced when they are absorbed by the nuclei of certain atoms, such as B^{10}. The reaction is

$$_5B^{10} + {_0n^1} \rightarrow {_3Li^7} + {_2He^4}$$

Ionization is produced by the resulting lithium nucleus and alpha particle which have a total energy of 2.5 mev. An ionization chamber can be filled with a volatile boron compound, or a solid boron compound can be used as a target in a Geiger-Müller counter. The amount of ionization measured is directly proportional to the number of neutrons absorbed by the boron target.

Nuclear Units. Rutherford found that, when alpha particles were passed through a thin sheet of metal, most of them continued their straight paths, but occasionally an alpha particle would suffer a large deflection. Remembering that these alpha particles, with a mass four times that of a hydrogen atom, are traveling with one-tenth the velocity of light, he calculated that the large deflections cannot be explained on the basis of uniform distribution of charge but must be due to a repulsion by a small charged object. He came to the conclusion that the positive charge of the atom must be centered in a nucleus occupying a very small volume.

There are now strong theoretical reasons for believing that the nucleus is made up of neutrons and protons. The number of protons in the nucleus is the atomic number, which determines the chemical properties. The sum of the protons and the neutrons gives approximately the mass of the nucleus. The mass of the atom is not exactly equal to the mass of the constituent neutrons, protons, and orbital electrons for reasons to be discussed later (page 627).

A given element may occur as several different isotopes, each having the same number of protons and, hence, the same nuclear charge and atomic number, but different numbers of neutrons and, hence, differing atomic masses. The atomic weight of the element on the chemical scale is a weighted average of the masses of all the isotopes of which the element is composed.

These fundamental relations are illustrated in Table II. Only a few of the elements are given in this table, which includes only naturally occurring isotopes.

Other Particles. In 1930 Dirac presented theoretical arguments that the positive electron, or *positron*, should exist. The positron was discovered in 1932 by Anderson, during an examination in a cloud chamber of particles emitted during the bombardment of a gas by cosmic rays. A powerful magnetic field of known strength was placed across the chamber, and cloud tracks were obtained with such a large curvature that the particle producing the track would have a mass only of 0.000549 on the atomic-weight scale, that is, the mass of an electron. But the curvature was in the wrong direction. In previous experiments, there was no way of telling in which of the two directions along the cloud track the particle was traveling. In this particular experiment the particle passed through a thin lead sheet, and a photograph was taken at right

Table II. Isotopic Weights [1]

Symbol	Number of Protons	Number of Neutrons	Abundance, per cent	Atomic Weight [2] Physical Scale	Atomic Weight [2] Chemical Scale
$_1H^1$	1	0	99.9851	1.00814 ⎱	1.008
$_1H^2$	1	1	0.0149	2.01474 ⎰	
$_2He^3$	2	1	1.3×10^{-4}	3.01698 ⎱	4.003
$_2He^4$	2	2	99.9999	4.00387 ⎰	
$_3Li^6$	3	3	7.52	6.01702 ⎱	6.940
$_3Li^7$	3	4	92.47	7.01822 ⎰	
$_6C^{12}$	6	6	98.892	12.00380 ⎱	12.011
$_6C^{13}$	6	7	1.108	13.00747 ⎰	
$_7N^{14}$	7	7	99.635	14.00752 ⎱	14.008
$_7N^{15}$	7	8	0.365	15.00486 ⎰	
$_8O^{16}$	8	8	99.758	16.00000 ⎫	16.00000
$_8O^{17}$	8	9	0.0373	17.00453 ⎬	
$_8O^{18}$	8	10	0.2039	18.00487 ⎭	
$_{17}Cl^{35}$	17	18	75.4	34.98018 ⎱	35.457
$_{17}Cl^{37}$	17	20	24.6	36.97762 ⎰	
$_{82}Pb^{204}$	82	122	1.48	204.03612 ⎫	207.21
$_{82}Pb^{206}$	82	124	23.6	206.03859 ⎬	
$_{82}Pb^{207}$	82	125	22.6	207.04034	
$_{82}Pb^{208}$	82	126	52.3	208.04140 ⎭	
$_{92}U^{234}$	92	142	0.0058	234.11379 ⎫	238.07
$_{92}U^{235}$	92	143	0.715	235.11704 ⎬	
$_{92}U^{238}$	92	146	99.28	238.12493 ⎭	

[1] Bainbridge in Segrè, *Experimental Nuclear Physics*, Vol. 1, John Wiley & Sons, New York, 1953.
[2] Since the standard of atomic mass O^{16} is lighter than the mixture of oxygen isotopes, 1.000000 unit on the chemical scale is equal to 1.000272 unit on the physical scale.

angles to the sheet. It showed the curvature of the path on one side to be greater than that on the other, and, hence, the particle was traveling through the lead in the direction pointing to the greater deflection (lower velocity). The observed curvature of the path in the magnetic field could be explained only on the assumption that the particle was charged *positively*. Certain synthetic radioactive elements emit positrons.

In 1935 Yukawa postulated the existence of a new charged particle in the development of a theory of short-range intranuclear forces. He calculated that this particle would have a mass of about 140 times that of the electron. In 1937 such particles, now called *mesons*, were detected in cloud-chamber photographs of cosmic-ray tracks. Several types of mesons which differ with respect to mass or charge have now been found.

The masses and charges of various particles are summarized in Table III.

Table III.   Fundamental Particles

Unit	Symbol	Mass [1]	Charge
Proton [2]	p	1.00759	+
Electron	e, β^-	0.000549	−
Neutron	n	1.00897	0
Positron	e^+, β^+	0.000549	+
Deuteron	d	2.01419	+
Alpha particle	α	4.00277	+2
Mesons		~0.1	±

[1] On the physical scale.
[2] The mass of the hydrogen atom is 1.00759 + 0.000549 = 1.00814.

Transmutation. It was known that the heaviest metals disintegrate spontaneously, and attempts were made to disintegrate other elements by artificial means. Alpha particles with their enormous kinetic energy were used successfully as missiles by Rutherford and Chadwick in 1921 to disintegrate nitrogen atoms. The alpha particles have a definite range in nitrogen of about 7 cm, but some flashes of light, apparently due to the impact of fast-moving particles, could be detected on a sensitive screen at much greater distances. Deflections in a magnetic field indicated that the particles that caused these scintillations were protons. It might be expected that, if an alpha particle hits a hydrogen atom squarely, the hydrogen atom with a mass one-fourth as great could travel considerably farther—up to 28 cm. As a matter of fact, in pure nitrogen, flashes were detected up to a distance of 40 cm. Such a great range was explained on the hypothesis that the nucleus of the nitrogen atom is actually altered by the collision with the alpha particle, and intranuclear energy is released which drives the proton out with great additional force. The nuclear reaction is represented by

$$_2\text{He}^4 + {}_7\text{N}^{14} \rightarrow {}_1\text{H}^1 + {}_8\text{O}^{17}$$

Several other light elements such as boron and fluorine were disintegrated in the same way.

The study of the atomic nucleus received a great impetus when projectiles other than alpha particles were used for bombardment. Protons or deuterons, traveling at enormous velocities under potentials of several million volts, are effective in disintegrating nuclei. Several different types of apparatus are used for the acceleration. In the cyclotron, developed by Lawrence at the University of California, the ions are subjected to a moderately high voltage and guided around a spiral path by a powerful magnetic field. The voltage is altered at just the right frequency so that the ions (protons, deuterons, or helium or other nuclei) are accelerated each time they make one half-circle, and the applied voltage is thus cumulative. As the projectiles attain higher and higher velocities they move in circles of increasing radius, and, when they reach the outer edge of the apparatus, they are deflected by an electric field and strike a target of the material that is to be bombarded.

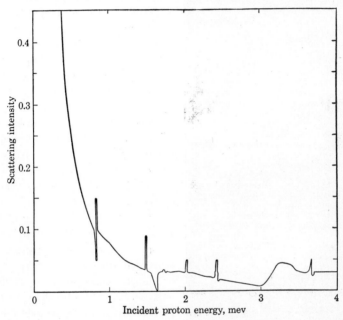

FIG. 20-9. Scattering of high-voltage protons by the nucleus of Mg^{24}, showing nuclear energy levels, as measured by L. J. Koester and Professor R. G. Herb, of the University of Wisconsin.

In the electrostatic generator, a rapidly moving belt carries electricity from charged points to a cylindrical or spherical electrode until a very high steady voltage is reached. The difficulties of insulation have been solved by placing the whole apparatus in a large steel tank containing gas at several atmospheres pressure to increase the resistance against sparking.* A series of metal hoops is arranged to give a gradual change of potential along an evacuated tube, within which the ions are accelerated. The electrostatic generator gives energies up to about 6 million volts, and it is especially useful for carrying out nuclear transformations at definite and controlled voltages. *Figure 20-9* shows the scattering of

* Herb, Parkinson, and Kerst, *Phys. Rev.*, **51**, 76 (1937).

protons by Mg^{24}. The scattering at the lowest energies corresponds to that expected for a simple electrostatic repulsion as first calculated by Rutherford for alpha particles. By analyzing the scattering curve at higher energies the nuclear energy levels may be determined.

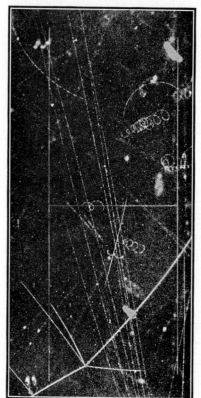

Fig. 20-10. Cloud-track photograph at a cosmic-ray shower in a magnetic field, showing a nuclear disintegration with heavily ionizing tracks produced by protons and alpha particles. Courtesy of Professor R. W. Thompson.

The energy levels in the nucleus have very high energies, and in order to study them and the reactions produced by high-energy particles, more and more powerful accelerators have been built. The 184-inch (diameter of magnet pole pieces) cyclotron at the University of California accelerates deuterons up to an energy of 200 mev or alpha particles to 400 mev. In more recent accelerators designed to reach energies in the billion electron volt (bev) range the accelerating chamber has a radius of about 50 feet. The bevatron at the University of California which was designed to accelerate protons to an energy of 6.25 bev started in operation in 1954.

The transmutation of elements can be brought about as just explained by giving enormous velocity to charged particles such as protons, deuterons, and helium ions so that they can penetrate the surrounding layers of electrons and reach the nucleus of the atom.

The nucleus can be reached, however, much more easily by neutrons, because they do not have an electric charge. The shells of electrons, then, do not constitute a strong barrier against these neutral neutrons. Accordingly the neutrons attach quite readily to atomic nuclei of many isotopes of the elements and bring about a variety of transmutations.

Fermi, in Italy in 1935, exposed most of the elements in the periodic table to neutrons and obtained a large number of new isotopes.

Neutrons for these transmutations can be produced by mixing radium compounds with beryllium compounds or by bombarding beryllium or lithium targets with a beam of fast deuterons from a cyclotron or an electrostatic generator. These sources of neutrons give only small amounts of new isotopes, but, with the vast new sources of neutrons from nuclear chain-reacting piles described on page 630, the way has been opened for the production of much larger quantities of transmuted elements and isotopes.

Gamma rays of very high energies liberated from certain nuclear reactions are able to bring about nuclear reactions similar to photochemical reactions. Cosmic rays coming from interstellar space are also able to effect nuclear transmutations. Such a transmutation is shown in *Fig. 20-10* with cloud tracks of condensed water from supersaturated vapor as photographed by Professor R. W. Thompson of the Department of Physics of Indiana University.

The concentration of radioactive elements may be facilitated if the nuclear reaction produces also a chemical reaction which permits a separation from the original material, as was pointed out first by Szilard and Chalmers. For example, when a bottle of ethyl bromide is exposed to neutrons, the bromine atoms which are rendered radioactive are broken away from their organic linkages and can be extracted with water containing a little alkali. In this way the ratio of radioactive to normal bromide is greatly increased in the aqueous solution.

Nuclear Reactions. In 1932, Irene Curie, daughter of the discoverers of radium, with her husband, F. Joliot, discovered that ordinary light elements can be made radioactive. They bombarded boron and aluminum and other light elements with alpha particles and obtained an emission of positrons which continued after the excitation by the alpha particles had ceased.

With magnesium the reaction is

$$_{12}Mg^{24} + {}_2He^4 \rightarrow {}_{14}Si^{27} + {}_0n^1$$

The silicon produced from the magnesium is radioactive with a half-life of 4 seconds and gives off positrons, leaving a stable isotope of aluminum according to the reaction

$$_{14}Si^{27} \rightarrow {}_{13}Al^{27} + \beta^+$$

Most artificial radioelements emit electrons (β^-) or positrons (β^+), but other types of decay also occur. In some cases a given isotope may undergo disintegration by one or two or even three different processes.

The beta particles emitted from the nucleus exhibit a continuous distribution of energy. According to the neutrino theory of beta decay the electron which is emitted is produced by the conversion of a neutron into a proton, an electron, and a neutrino, a small particle with no charge. The electron and neutrino are emitted together, and the available energy is divided between them in such a way that the electrons show a wide range of energies.

The emission of beta particles is frequently accompanied by the emission of gamma rays. The nature of the nuclear change may be represented by diagrams such as *Fig. 20-11.*

Nuclei which have the same number of neutrons and protons but different energies are called *nuclear isomers.* Of the nuclear isomers of

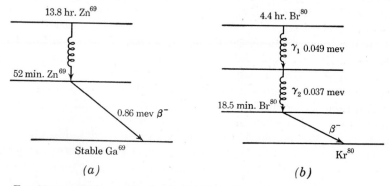

13.8 hr. Zn^{69}

52 min. Zn^{69}

0.86 mev β^-

Stable Ga^{69}

(a)

4.4 hr. Br^{80}

γ_1 0.049 mev

γ_2 0.037 mev

18.5 min. Br^{80}

β^-

Kr^{80}

(b)

Fig. 20-11. Nuclear energy levels as indicated by radioactive disintegration.

Zn^{69} the one with the higher energy decays to the ground state with a half-life of 13.8 hours, and a gamma ray is emitted. This process is called an *isomeric transition.* As a further example, the bromine isotope $_{35}Br^{80}$ characterized by a half-life of 4.4 hours emits gamma radiation without loss of either mass or charge, the isomeric transition resulting in the isotope having a half-life of 18.5 minutes. The gamma ray from the nucleus may transfer its energy to one of the electrons in an inner orbit, causing the electron to be ejected from the atom. When another electron falls into this vacant orbit an X ray is emitted.

The lower-energy isomer of Zn^{69} decays to Ga^{69} by emission of a beta particle. Two gamma rays are emitted by Br^{80}. The gamma-ray frequency provides information concerning nuclear energy levels just as the ultraviolet, visible, and infrared spectra provide information concerning the energy levels in atoms and molecules. Nuclear data of this type and other information have been tabulated by the Bureau of Standards.*

* Nuclear Data, *Circular of the National Bureau of Standards* 499, U. S. Government Printing Office, Washington, D. C., 1950.

Some disintegrations involve the process known as *K-electron capture*, in which an external electron from the shell nearest the nucleus, the K shell, enters the nucleus, causing the atomic number to decrease by 1 unit. The filling of the vacancy in the K shell by other electrons causes the emission of X rays from the atom.

Sometimes associated with gamma radiation are so-called *conversion electrons*. The nucleus interacts with an inner electron and expels it with high speed instead of emitting a gamma ray. Such a process leaves the atom in an excited state of high-energy content, which often results in chemical reactivity. In such cases as $_{35}Br^{80}$, where the product is radioactive, its chemical properties may be studied by following its radioactivity.

The processes by which radioelements are produced fall into a few general types. The reaction

$$_{12}Mg^{24} + {}_2\alpha^4 \rightarrow {}_{14}Si^{27} + {}_0n^1$$

is an example of the type reaction

$$_Z X^M + {}_2\alpha^4 \rightarrow {}_{Z+2}Y^{M+3} + {}_0n^1$$

A simplified notation for the same reaction is

$$Mg^{24}(\alpha, n)Si^{27}$$

where the first symbol in the parentheses is the bombarding particle, and the second is the emitted particle. A few examples of nuclear reac-

Table IV. Typical Nuclear Reactions

General Reactions	Example	Notation
$_Z X^M + {}_0n^1 \rightarrow {}_Z Y^{M+1} + {}_0\gamma^0$	$_{25}Mn^{55} + {}_0n^1 \rightarrow {}_{25}Mn^{56} + {}_0\gamma^0$	$Mn^{55}(n, \gamma)Mn^{56}$
$_Z X^M + {}_1p^1 \rightarrow {}_{Z+1}Y^M + {}_0n^1$	$_3Li^7 + {}_1p^1 \rightarrow {}_4Be^7 + {}_0n^1$	$Li^7(p, n)Be^7$
$_Z X^M + {}_2\alpha^4 \rightarrow {}_{Z+1}Y^{M+3} + {}_1p^1$	$_{20}Ca^{43} + {}_2\alpha^4 \rightarrow {}_{21}Sc^{46} + {}_1p^1$	$Ca^{43}(\alpha, p)Sc^{46}$
$_Z X^M + {}_1d^2 \rightarrow {}_{Z+1}Y^M + {}_2{}_0n^1$	$_{52}Te^{130} + {}_1d^2 \rightarrow {}_{53}I^{130} + {}_2{}_0n^1$	$Te^{130}(d, 2n)I^{130}$
$_Z X^M + {}_0n^1 \rightarrow {}_{Z-2}Y^{M-3} + {}_2\alpha^4$	$_{27}Co^{59} + {}_0n^1 \rightarrow {}_{25}Mn^{56} + {}_2\alpha^4$	$Co^{59}(n, \alpha)Mn^{56}$

tions are given in Table IV, and a summary of the principal types is given in Table V.

Table V. Principal Nuclear Reactions

Neutron Reactions	Deuteron Reactions	Proton Reactions	Alpha Reactions	Photonuclear Reactions
n, γ	d, p	p, n	α, n	γ, n
$n, 2n$	d, n	p, γ	α, p	
n, p	d, α	p, α		
n, α	$d, 2n$			

A good demonstration of a nuclear reaction produced by neutrons was shown in Fig. 20-7, obtained by Professor A. J. Dempster, of the University of Chicago. The upper mass spectrogram of cadmium shows isotopes 110, 111, 112, 113, 114 and 116. The lower spectrogram was obtained from surface scrapings of cadmium that had been exposed to neutron irradiation for a long time in an atomic pile, page 630. The neutron reaction is

$$_{48}Cd^{113} + {_0}n^1 \rightarrow {_{48}}Cd^{114}$$

The concentration of Cd^{113} in the mixture of cadmium isotopes has been reduced from 12.3 to 1.6 per cent, and that of Cd^{114} has been increased from 28 to 39 per cent. Within the accuracy of the measurements the gain of cadmium 114 is practically equal to the loss of cadmium 113, whereas there has been very little change in the concentrations of the other isotopes. Cadmium 113 has a very great absorption for neutrons, so great, in fact, that cadmium is used in various experiments where it is desired to screen out neutrons having low velocities.

The Einstein Equation—The Packing Fraction. In experiments such as shown in Fig. 18-1 at ordinary voltages the velocity of the electron is less than 10^9 cm per sec, and the value of e/m is independent of the velocity. As the velocity is increased, however, and approaches the velocity of light, the value of m increases in accordance with the theory of relativity. The actual mass m of a particle is related to the "rest mass" m_0 and the velocity v by the equation

$$m = \frac{m_0}{\sqrt{1 - (v/c)^2}}$$

where c is the velocity of light.

Differentiating this equation and applying the relations that force is the rate of change of momentum, and that kinetic energy is force acting through a distance, we can show that

$$dE = c^2 dm$$

Einstein in 1906 proposed this epoch-making theory according to which

$$E = c^2 m \qquad (9)$$

and pointed out that the annihilation of 1 gram of matter will produce $(2.9978 \times 10^{10})^2$ or 8.9868×10^{20} ergs of energy.

In the nuclear reaction

$$2_1H^1 \quad + \quad 2_0n^1 \quad \rightarrow \; _2He^4$$

$$2 \times 1.00759 + 2 \times 1.00897 \rightarrow 4.00277$$

there is an actual loss of mass of $(4.00277 - 4.03312) = -0.03035$. If the Einstein equation is applied, the formation of a mole of alpha particles or helium nuclei from neutrons and protons evolves $0.03035 \times 8.9868 \times 10^{20}$ ergs or 6.5×10^{11} cal. This nuclear energy is many orders of magnitude greater than the chemical energy produced by changes of atoms to give different molecules.

The *packing fraction* is defined as the difference between the actual mass of the isotope and the nearest whole number, divided by this whole number. Thus, the mass of one of the chlorine isotopes is 34.980, and the packing fraction is $(34.980 - 35.000)/35.000 = -0.00057$. Packing fractions are usually expressed in parts per 10,000, and so the packing fraction of $_{17}Cl^{35}$ is written -5.7. Since oxygen is taken as the standard, elements with positive packing fractions are less stable than oxygen; those with negative packing fractions are more stable. The elements in the middle range of the periodic table seem to be the most stable, the light elements and the heavy elements possessing positive packing fractions.

With the development of the theory that the nucleus contains neutrons and protons it is now possible to calculate the mass which would be converted into energy if the isotope were formed from protons, neutrons, and electrons. If the atomic number is represented by Z, and the mass number by A, then the nucleus contains Z protons and $(A - Z)$ neutrons, and there are Z orbital electrons. If the actual isotopic weight is M, the mass defect is

$$\text{Mass defect} = Zm_H + (A - Z)m_n - M \qquad (10)$$

where m_H is the mass of a hydrogen atom (that is, one proton plus one electron) and m_n is the mass of one neutron. This quantity of mass would be converted into energy if the particular isotope was formed directly from protons, neutrons, and electrons. The binding energy corresponding to this quantity of mass may be calculated using equation 9.

$$\text{Binding energy in mev} = 931[Zm_H + (A - Z)m_n - M]$$

Exercise I. Calculate the value of the coefficient in the preceding equation from the fact that $c = 3 \times 10^{10}$ cm sec^{-1}, and one mev is equivalent to 1.602×10^{-6} ergs.

This is the energy which would be required to break up the atom into its constituent particles which are referred to as nucleons.

Example 4. Calculate the mass defect and the binding energy for $_6C^{12}$, which has an isotopic weight on the physical scale of 12.0038. The mass of a hydrogen atom is 1.00814, and that of a neutron is 1.00897 on this scale.

$$\text{Mass defect} = [(6)(1.00814) + (6)(1.00897) - 12.0038]$$

$$= 0.0990 \text{ atomic mass units}$$

$$\text{Binding energy} = (931)(0.0990) = 92.3 \text{ mev}$$

This value divided by the number of protons and neutrons gives the binding energy per nuclear particle or nucleon, which is $92.3/12 = 7.69$ mev.

The binding energy per nucleon for stable isotopes is plotted versus mass number in *Fig. 20-12*. With the exception of He^4, C^{12}, and O^{16},

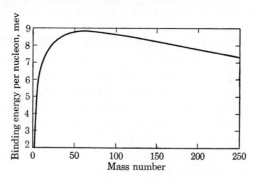

FIG. 20-12.   Nuclear binding energy.

the values are quite close to a smooth curve. This figure shows that energy will be released if heavy elements are broken down to give elements in the region of the maximum in the binding-energy curve. This plot explains why energy is released in the splitting of uranium. It can also be seen that energy will be liberated when lighter elements to the left of the maximum are combined to form heavier elements. Such reactions are the source of energy radiated by the sun and the hydrogen bomb.

Example 5. Calculate the energy for the fission of uranium 235 into approximate halves, using data from Fig. 20-12. The binding energy per nucleon is about 7.5 mev for U^{235} and about 8.4 mev for elements of half this mass number. Thus

$$92p + 143n \rightarrow U^{235} + (235)(7.5) \text{ mev}$$

$$92p + 143n \rightarrow \text{Fission products} + (235)(8.4) \text{ mev}$$

Subtracting the first equation from the second,

$$U^{235} \rightarrow \text{Fission products} + (235)(8.4 - 7.5) \text{ or } \sim 200 \text{ mev}$$

Nuclear Fission. In 1939 Hahn and Strassman exposed uranium to neutrons and obtained unexpected products which were identified as barium and other elements of the middle of the periodic table. Meitner interpreted this nuclear reaction as a complete breakdown of the uranium atom into two elements of approximately half the atomic weight of uranium. This new phenomenon was called fission and led immediately to a large number of confirmatory experiments in many different laboratories throughout the world. It was soon found that it is the isotope of uranium U^{235} that undergoes fission when it absorbs neutrons. The equation for this fission process is

$$n + U^{235} \rightarrow \text{Fission products} + \begin{array}{l} \nearrow \, n \\ \searrow \, n \end{array}$$

$$n + U^{235} \rightarrow \text{Kr} + \text{Ba} + \begin{array}{l} \nearrow \\ \searrow \end{array} \qquad \text{etc.}$$

$$n + U^{235} \rightarrow \text{Fission products} + \begin{array}{l} \nearrow \, n \\ \searrow \, n \end{array}$$

In this nuclear reaction Kr and Ba are representative of a large number of possible middleweight elements, and the number of neutrons produced is sometimes 2 and sometimes 3 with an average value of 2.5.

There are two remarkable things about nuclear fission. First, it is chain-reacting, so that the neutrons from the fission of the first atom cause other uranium atoms to undergo fission and produce more neutrons in an expanding process. Second, the sum of all the masses of the elements and the neutrons produced in fission is slightly less than the sum of the masses of the original U^{235} plus the original neutron. It was evident at once that here might be a source of atomic energy on a large scale, because, once the reaction was started with a neutron, the process might be self-sustaining, and the loss of mass in the reaction would lead, of necessity, to the evolution of enormous quantities of energy. Previous considerations for producing useful atomic energy would have required the expenditure of large quantities of energy in a cyclotron or other device to sustain the nuclear reaction. Fission, however, might be a process which would run spontaneously without the investment of large amounts of energy.

On December 2, 1942, the first test of this idea was carried out by Fermi, Szilard, Wigner, and others under the administration of A. H. Compton, at the University of Chicago. The experiment, pictured in

Fig. 20-13, was successful in proving that it is possible to obtain a controlled, self-sustaining chain reaction. It was necessary to obtain uranium in a high state of purity and to imbed it in graphite of high purity. The graphite acted as a moderator to slow down the neutrons to such a velocity that they would be more easily captured by the surrounding uranium. This self-sustaining nuclear reactor was called a "pile." Instead of the graphite moderator, light elements like deuterium and beryllium can be used as they do not absorb neutrons.

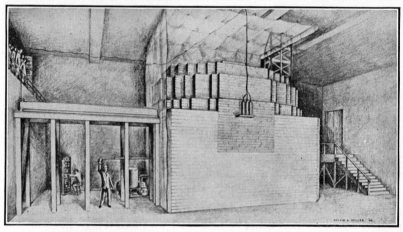

Fig. 20-13.   First nuclear chain-reacting pile.

These reactors supply not only large quantities of heat but also an excess of neutrons which can be used for the transmutation of elements.

When neutrons are absorbed by uranium 238, the following nuclear reactions take place:

$$_{92}U^{238} + {_0}n^1 \rightarrow {_{92}}U^{239} \qquad _{92}U^{239} \rightarrow {_{93}}Np^{239} + \beta^-$$

$$_{93}Np^{239} \rightarrow {_{94}}Pu^{239} + \beta^-$$

Plutonium 239 undergoes fission in the same manner as uranium 235. Uranium 233, which also undergoes fission, can be produced from nuclear reactions starting with the action of neutrons on thorium.

The rate at which this fission process takes place in a pile can be controlled easily with the help of rods of cadmium- or boron-containing material or other material which has great absorption for neutrons. When the rods are inserted into the pile, the chain reaction cannot continue, because the neutrons are absorbed by the rods. By pulling out the rods the absorption of the neutrons in the pile is decreased, so that by proper mechanical regulation the pile may be made to develop heat at any rate desired, limited only by the rate at which heat can be removed from the pile. The accumulation of too much heat will endanger the materials of which the pile is constructed. Several nuclear reactors are now in operation at comparatively low temperatures. Nuclear reactors operating at much higher temperatures, however, utilize the heat removed for the operation of heat engines or turbines which generate electricity.

In the future it is expected that many power plants will be operated by atomic fuel, but the large capital investment for the fissionable material and the pile, together with the special difficulties due to radioactivity, makes it appear that electricity generated by atomic power will not be immediately cheaper than the electricity generated by the burning of coal. There are certain considerations, however, which are of special interest. If 1 gram of uranium 235 undergoes complete fission, the loss in mass will result in the evolution of 2×10^{10} cal; in contrast, in chemical reactions, the combustion of 1 gram of carbon evolves 7,827 cal of heat. One pound of uranium 235 will generate as much heat on fission as is generated by the burning of 1500 tons of coal, equivalent to 11 million kilowatt-hours of heat or, at present turbine efficiencies, to about 3 million kilowatt-hours of electricity. Accordingly, atomic fuel may be essentially regarded as weightless fuel and may well find its first practical applications in isolated regions where coal and other fuels are not now available and transportation is difficult.

A certain critical amount of U^{235} or other fissionable material is necessary before the pile can be self-sustaining. With lesser amounts a sufficiently large number of neutrons escape from the pile so that the nuclear chain is no longer self-propagating. This critical size involves an investment of such a large amount of material and the nuclear reactor requires such a heavy protecting shield that small units for the production of power or heat will not be practical. It is expected that ships will be operated by atomic fuel but that automobiles cannot be. An atomic power submarine is now in operation. Worldwide regulation of atomic energy is necessary because it can be used equally well for military purposes or for the generation of industrial electricity.

The abundances of isotopes of various mass numbers among the fission products of U^{235} are given in *Fig. 20-14.** Since the percentages vary over such a wide range it is convenient to use a semi-logarithmic plot. It can be seen that the most probable type of fission, representing approximately 6 per cent of the total, gives products with mass numbers

* "Plutonium Project," *J. Am. Chem. Soc.*, *68*, 2411 (1946).

of 95 and 139. The probability that the uranium nucleus will be split into equal halves is very small.

When U^{235} undergoes fission, all the elements between zinc with an atomic number of 30 and gadolinium with an atomic number of 64 are

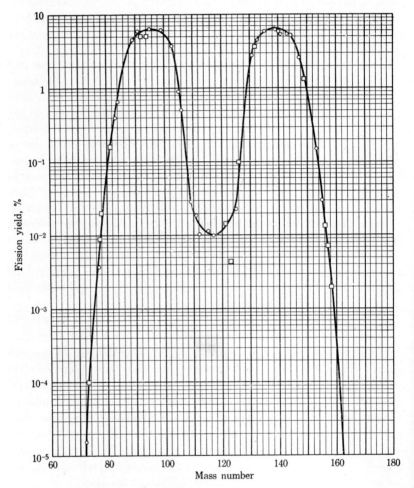

FIG. 20-14.   Distribution of fission products. ○ certain mass assignment. □ uncertain mass assignment.

produced, including about 300 isotopes, most of which are radioactive with half-lives ranging from fractions of a second to many years. Since uranium has a higher ratio of neutrons to protons than do stable forms of the elements produced as fission products, the fission products are unstable. Thus the fission products emit neutrons and beta particles and are converted into more stable forms. The emission of beta particles increases the stability since it increases the number of protons in the nucleus.

The energy evolved in the fission of U^{235} is of the order of 200 million electron volts. The cyclotron at California with 200 million electron volts has been able to cause the fission of many heavy elements such as lead. The pattern of distribution of the lighter elements produced differs from that shown in Fig. 20-14 in that the base is broader and the peaks are lower. These disintegrations produced with the common heavy elements are not chain-reacting and will not continue to produce energy when the exciting energy is removed.

The reactors supply large quantities of neutrons which can be utilized for experimental studies and for the production of many useful isotopes, as, for example, radioactive carbon C^{14} from nitrogen. A few of these radioisotopes are indicated in Table VI along with the reaction by

Table VI. Radioisotopes Produced by Irradiation with Neutrons [1]

Isotope	Reaction	Radiation	Half-Life [2]
Ba^{131}	$Ba^{130}(n, \gamma)Ba^{131}$	γ	12.0 d
Br^{82}	$Br^{81}(n, \gamma)Br^{82}$	β, γ	35.5 h
C^{14}	$N^{14}(n, p)C^{14}$	β (0.15 mev)	5720 y
H^3	$Li^6(n, \alpha)H^3$	β (0.0189 mev)	12.5 y
I^{131}	$Te^{130}(n, \gamma)Te^{131}$ $\rightarrow \beta + I^{131}$	β, γ	8 d
Fe^{59}	$Fe^{58}(n, \gamma)Fe^{59}$	β, γ	46.3 d
P^{32}	$S^{32}(n, p)P^{32}$	β (1.7 mev)	14.3 d
Na^{24}	$Na^{23}(n, \gamma)Na^{24}$	β, γ	14.9 h
S^{35}	$Cl^{35}(n, p)S^{35}$	β (0.16 mev)	87.1 d

[1] Catalog of isotopes procurable from the Atomic Energy Commission at the Oak Ridge National Laboratory.
[2] h, hour; d, day; y, year.

which they are formed and their radiation and half-life. The quantity of radioisotope which must be present to supply 3.7×10^{10} disintegrations per second is termed a *curie*. Thus a microcurie of radon, or C^{14} or Na^{24} will each give 37,000 disintegrations per second, although the number of atoms in a curie will be very different for these elements.

The number of isotopes now known is so great that it is not possible to give a complete table here. Various types of charts have been developed for listing all the known isotopes in a logical fashion. In one type the isotopes are plotted on a graph of number of protons vertically versus number of neutrons horizontally. Other types are also useful.*

The nuclear reactions by which elements 95–98 are formed are

$$_{94}\text{Pu}^{239}(n, \gamma)_{94}\text{Pu}^{240}(n, \gamma)_{94}\text{Pu}^{241} \xrightarrow{\beta^-(10\ y)} {}_{95}\text{Am}^{241}$$

$$_{95}\text{Am}^{241}(n, \gamma)_{95}\text{Am}^{242} \xrightarrow{\beta^-(17\ h)} {}_{96}\text{Cm}^{242}$$

$$_{95}\text{Am}^{241}(\alpha,2n)_{97}\text{Bk}^{243}$$

$$_{96}\text{Cm}^{242}(\alpha,\ 2n)_{98}\text{Cf}^{244}$$

Beams of neutrons from the pile are of value for certain physical measurements. They can, for example, be used like beams of electrons or X rays in the study of crystal and molecular structure.

Biological Effects of Radioactivity. Serious damage can be done to living tissue by excessive exposure to radioactivity. The exact nature of these reactions is not fully understood, but the ionizing radiations may produce hydrogen peroxide and other chemical substances which then react chemically with the material of the cells. As a rough approximation, the effect of X rays, gamma rays, beta rays, alpha particles, and neutrons is proportional to the amount of ionization which these various agents can produce. The biological effect can be thus correlated with the intensity of radiation of the various types as measured by physical instruments, such as photographic plates, ionization chambers, and Geiger-Müller counters.

Fortunately, these instruments are so sensitive to radioactivity that they give an adequate measure of the radiation at most levels long before any biological damage can be expected. As a matter of fact, the limitation of the Geiger-Müller counters is usually the background of ionization produced by cosmic rays, and all living matter is and always has been exposed to these cosmic rays. Considerable study has been devoted to establishing a safe limit for exposure to X rays and radioactivity. Overexposure to radioactivity may cause severe burns which heal very slowly. Even though no immediate effect appears, difficulties may appear years later. In the more severe cases the concentration of red blood cells is reduced through destructive action on material in the bone marrow; so counting red blood corpuscles is a standard procedure in checking for overexposure to radioactivity. Exposure to neutrons leads to effects quite similar to the exposure to gamma rays or beta or alpha particles, because the neutrons are absorbed by the nuclei of so-

* Sullivan, *Trilinear Chart of Nuclear Species,* John Wiley & Sons, New York, 1949.

dium and other elements in the living body with the production of radioactive isotopes.

Those who work with radioactive materials must guard themselves against damage from exposure to radioactivity. The gamma rays are stopped by shields of sheet lead or by walls of interlocking bricks of lead. Concrete is also used. For gamma rays the stopping power of the shield material depends on the thickness and density of the material. Sometimes gloves containing lead are used to protect the hands. Neutrons are stopped by paraffin or other hydrogen-containing material and by cadmium sheets or boron-containing material. Alpha particles are stopped by thin walls of glass or any type of shield. Beta rays require somewhat thicker glass. It is necessary to guard against dust particles of radioactive material, because tiny particles of material which are radioactive must be kept out of the lungs, the stomach, and the blood stream.

These hazards call for special shielding, ventilation, and waste disposal, and frequently lead to the requirement of remote control for laboratory experiments, but the techniques have been fully worked out, and there need be no danger if the precautions are followed and there is adequate monitoring of the laboratory with instruments suitable for detecting radioactivity.

The *roentgen* is the unit of radiation used for X rays or gamma rays; it is defined in terms of the ionization produced in gases. One roentgen will produce 1 *electrostatic* unit of charge per cubic centimeter of air at standard conditions. It produces 2.083×10^9 pairs of gaseous ions in air per cubic centimeter under standard conditions and generates 83.3 ergs per gram of air. The intensity of gamma radiation (or X rays) obviously is decreased as one moves away from the source or interposes shields. For a typical gamma radiation the passage through 1 cm of lead will reduce the intensity by half. For laboratory work the exposure of the body to 0.30 roentgen per week is regarded as the maximum dosage which should be permitted.

Uses of Isotopes. Many uses had been developed for the naturally occurring radioactive elements (from lead to uranium in the periodic table), but the new artificially produced radioactivity has greatly increased the interest in this work because radioactive forms of almost any element can now be obtained.

The medical uses of radioactivity are well known. Although serious burns can be produced by radium, it is possible under properly controlled conditions to destroy early cancerous tissue and other abnormal growths without serious injury to the normal flesh. For such purposes radon is used, sealed off in small glass tubes. Radioactive cobalt produced by neutrons from a nuclear pile has also found use in this field. Other radioactive elements may find therapeutic uses. Radioactive iodine is concentrated in the thyroid gland and is being used successfully in the cure of certain types of goiter.

Several applications of radioactivity have been made to geology.* † One of the earliest was the determination of the age of the earth. The rates of radioactive disintegration are well established, and the age of a given uranium or other radioactive mineral is obtained by simply dividing the amount of disintegration product by the rate at which the product is generated. If the life of the parent element is very long, the calculations are simplified. The amount of lead found in a uranium mineral is a measure of the amount of uranium which has undergone radioactive disintegration, provided that no lead has been brought from other places and none has been leached out. A determination of the atomic weight or a measurement of the relative distribution of isotopes can be used to correct for any ordinary lead present which did not come from the uranium or thorium in the sample of mineral. The accumulation of helium from alpha particles is used also for dating minerals. The earth must be at least as old as the oldest mineral which is found, and several have been established to be about a billion years old. ‡

Example 6. A sample of pitchblende was found to contain 51.16 per cent uranium and 2.492 per cent lead, giving a lead-uranium ratio of 0.0487. An atomic-weight determination showed that, whereas most of the lead came from uranium and had an atomic weight of 206, some ordinary lead was present, requiring a correction of Pb^{206}/U^{238} to 0.0453. The disintegration constant for uranium is 1.52×10^{-10} year^{-1}. How old must this mineral have been in order to accumulate this much lead?

The mole ratio of Pb^{206}/U^{238} is 0.0453 (238/206) = 0.0523. Therefore, 0.0523 g atom of Pb^{206} has been formed from 1.0523 g atom of U^{238}.

$$- dn/dt = kn$$

$$0.0523/dt = (1.52 \times 10^{-10})(1.0523)$$

$$dt = 326 \text{ million years}$$

This is an approximate calculation assuming that for this problem 326 million years are infinitesimal! The exact calculation is

$$1.52 \times 10^{-10} = \frac{2.303}{t} \log \frac{1.0523}{1.0523 - 0.0523}$$

$$t = 335 \text{ million years}$$

The use of radioactive isotopes offers a solution for certain analytical problems. The test for radioactivity is so much more sensitive than

* Goodman, "Geological Applications of Nuclear Physics," *J. Applied Phys.*, *13*, 276 (1942).

† Faul, *Nuclear Geology*, John Wiley & Sons, New York, 1954.

‡ Linnenbom, "Radioactivity and the Age of the Earth," *J. Chem. Ed.*, *32*, 58 (1955).

other physical or chemical tests that the minutest amount of material can be detected. The solubility of a difficultly soluble lead salt may be determined by placing a trace of radio lead in a saturated solution and allowing the radio lead to distribute itself between the solution and the solid. The distribution ratio can be easily and accurately determined by measuring the intensity of radioactivity. Again, it is possible with radio indicators to determine the actual number of atoms of lead or other elements exposed in a crystal, and, accordingly, the absolute surface can be calculated.

The use of isotopes as tracers is furnishing an important means for studying the mechanisms of biological processes and chemical reactions.* For example, radioactive iodine and bromine have been used to follow the course of the halogen in organic reactions, and radioactive manganese has been used to show that there is no interchange of manganese between the ions of different valence, as, for example, between MnO_4^- and Mn^{++}, but that there is a rapid exchange between manganous ion and manganic oxalate ion.

By feeding radioactive phosphorus to a colony of rats and determining the radioactivity of the bone ash at frequent intervals, Hevesy found that a given atom of phosphorus remains in the bones only about a month, a fact which proved the hypothesis that the bones of a living animal are in a state of dynamic equilibrium with their surroundings. Radioactive phosphorus has been used also to determine the time required for inorganic phosphorus in the food to be converted into organic phosphorus material in the blood of rats.

Radioactive carbon C^{14} with a half-life of 5720 years is being widely used as a tracer in many biochemical, chemical, and industrial laboratories. One of the most important uses of radioactive carbon is in the study of photosynthesis, the process by which carbon dioxide and water are combined in the growing plants through the agency of sunlight. A method is now available for studying the first products.

In the formation of an isotope by an (n, γ) reaction the emission of the gamma ray causes the nucleus to recoil with an energy depending on the frequency of the gamma ray and the weight of the nucleus. The recoil energy is often great enough to break a chemical bond. Thus when an aqueous solution of $NaClO_3$ is exposed to neutrons the reaction $Cl^{37}(n, \gamma)Cl^{38}$ takes place. Most of the Cl^{38} atoms formed are detached from the chlorate ion and pass into solution as chloride ions. The term "hot-atom chemistry" refers to the study of the chemical reactions produced by recoil energy.

* *Isotopic Tracers in Biology and Medicine*, University of Wisconsin Press, Madison, 1948; Shoenheimer, *Dynamic State of Body Constituents*, Harvard University Press, Cambridge, Mass., 1942.

The stable isotopes as well as the radioactive isotopes are finding extensive use as tracers.

Deuterium, heavy carbon, and heavy oxygen have been used effectively as tracer elements in physical-chemical and biochemical investigations. The positions in a molecule or an organism taken by these tagged atoms can be ascertained with the help of a mass spectrometer which gives the ratio of the heavy isotope to the common isotope. For example, previously unavailable information has been found with the help of N^{15}, concerning the biochemical behavior of certain amino acids and proteins.

Many uses have been developed for deuterium, but, thus far, they have been restricted to the laboratory. Its use as an ionized particle in nuclear disintegrations has been stressed. By substituting deuterium for hydrogen large band shifts are produced, and it is thus possible to connect spectral bands with definite bonds in the molecule. A large variety of new organic compounds has been synthesized in which deuterium takes the place of hydrogen. In one of the first tracer experiments ordinary sugar was dissolved in heavy water and the water distilled off. The density of this water was less than before, showing that some of the deuterium of the water had exchanged with hydrogen of the sugar. Quantitative measurements showed that half the hydrogen atoms of the sugar had exchanged with deuterium. It is known from the structure of sugar that half the hydrogens are attached to carbon and half to oxygen. It is concluded that those hydrogen atoms attached to oxygen ionize and mix with the deuterium ions of the water, but that the hydrogen atoms attached directly to carbon do not ionize and are unable to leave the sugar molecule.

By determination of the radioactivity of carbon Libby * has shown that it is possible to establish accurately the date at which a plant or animal died. This method is based upon the fact that long-lived C^{14} is formed in the upper atmosphere by the $N^{14}(n, p)C^{14}$ reaction between nitrogen and neutrons produced by cosmic rays. Since the radiocarbon is converted into carbon dioxide and mixed through the atmosphere it is taken up by growing plants and it also becomes a part of the bodies of animals since they eat plants. It is found that samples of new wood uniformly give 12.5 counts per minute per gram of carbon due to their content of C^{14}. When the tree is cut down the incorporation of C^{14} ceases and the C^{14} present decays with a half-life of 5720 years. This makes it possible to determine the age of various carbon products in the range of about 1000 to 30,000 years by determination of their radioactivity due to C^{14}. The determination of tritium in water similarly

* Libby, *Science, 109*, 227 (1949).

gives a means for dating water samples over a period of about 3 to 60 years.

Gold has been transmuted into Hg^{198} through long exposure to neutrons in nuclear reactors by the reaction

$$_{79}Au^{197} + _{0}n^{1} \rightarrow {}_{79}Au^{198} \rightarrow {}_{80}Hg^{198} + \beta^{-}$$

The platinum-iridium bar at Paris has been accepted as the world's standard unit of length, but it is not sufficiently precise for some purposes; therefore, the red spectroscopic line of cadmium has been widely used. The green mercury line would be a better standard, because the heavier metal leads to a lower temperature of excitation with a line about half as wide as the cadmium line. But, ordinary mercury cannot be used because it contains seven isotopes each with a slightly different spectral line. However, 60 mg of mercury transmuted from gold has been distilled out and, being free from other isotopes, gives a very convenient narrow line at 5461 A which can perhaps be determined with an accuracy of 1 part in a billion and will probably become the primary standard of length.

REFERENCES

Taylor and Glasstone, *Treatise on Physical Chemistry*, D. Van Nostrand Co., New York, 1942, Chapter I.

Hoag and Korff, *Electron and Nuclear Physics*, D. Van Nostrand Co., New York, 1948.

Bethe, *Elementary Nuclear Theory*, John Wiley & Sons, New York, 1948.

Pollard and Davidson, *Applied Nuclear Physics*, John Wiley & Sons, New York, 1951.

Gamow, *Structure of Atomic Nuclei and Nuclear Structure*, Oxford University Press, New York, 1937.

Lapp and Andrews, *Nuclear Radiation Physics*, Prentice-Hall, New York, 1948.

Glasstone, *Sourcebook on Atomic Energy*, D. Van Nostrand Co., New York, 1950.

Whitehouse and Putnam, *Radioactive Isotopes*, Oxford Press, London, 1953.

Calvin, Heidelberger, Reid, Tolbert, and Yankwich, *Isotopic Carbon*, John Wiley & Sons, New York, 1949.

Friedlander and Kennedy, *Introduction to Radiochemistry*, John Wiley & Sons, New York, 1949.

Williams, *Principles of Nuclear Chemistry*, D. Van Nostrand Co., New York, 1950.

Wahl and Bonner, *Radioactivity Applied to Chemistry*, John Wiley & Sons, New York, 1951.

PROBLEMS

1. The following measurements of the radioactivity of a sample of Ag^{111} were obtained with a Geiger-Müller counter.

Time, days	0	5	10	15	20
Counts per minute	2157	1373	850	557	359

Calculate graphically the half-life which best fits these data, if the background counting rate is 25 counts per minute. *Ans.* 7.5 days.

2. Calculate the weight of Pb^{210} in equilibrium with 1 gram of Bi^{210} in the uranium series. *Ans.* 1606 g.

3. How many grams of Ra^{226} will be required to give as much radioactivity for luminous paint as 1 gram of Po^{210}? These isotopes are found in the uranium series. *Ans.* 4.5 kg.

4. In A.D. 1960, 1 kg of purified uranium is sealed in a vault as an indicator of time. If a chemist of the future finds 1 mg of lead, what year A.D. will it be? *Ans.* A.D. 9460

5. Actinium emanation comes in the group of rare gases, having zero valence. It loses an alpha particle, the product loses another alpha particle, and then the new radioelement loses a beta particle. (*a*) To what group in the periodic table does this radioelement belong? (*b*) With what element are its physical and chemical properties identical? *Ans.* (*a*) Fifth group. (*b*) Bismuth.

6. What is the weight of a curie of (*a*) C^{14} ($t_{1/2} = 5720$ y) and (*b*) Na^{24} ($t_{1/2} = 14.8$ h)? *Ans.* (*a*) 0.224, (*b*) 1.14×10^{-7} g.

7. Radioactive carbon is obtained from the Atomic Energy Commission at Oak Ridge as barium carbonate. (*a*) If the carbon contains 3 atomic per cent radio carbon 14, 1 atomic per cent carbon 13, and 96 atomic per cent carbon 12, how many grams of the barium carbonate does it take to give 1 millicurie? (*b*) The radioactivity can be measured with sufficient accuracy for a given experiment if there are 100 disintegrations per minute, using the equivalent of 50 ml of carbon dioxide gas measured at standard conditions. How much can this material be diluted; that is, how many grams of ordinary carbon can be added to 1 gram of carbon from the sample of radioactive barium carbonate, if the same accuracy of counting is to be maintained, that is, 100 counts per minute in a 50 ml sample of gas at 25°? *Ans.* (*a*) 0.105 g. (*b*) 8.5×10^7.

8. In the reaction

$$_1H^1 + {_3Li^7} \rightarrow 2{_2He^4}$$

the range of the alpha particles in air (8.3 cm) shows that their energy is 8.6 mev. Calculate the energy of the alpha particles expected from the mass change in the reaction. *Ans.* 8.7 mev per alpha particle.

9. The mass spectrum of a mixture of carbon dioxide and methane gave lines which corresponded to the following ratios of mass to number of charges:

$$6, \quad 8, \quad 12, \quad 13, \quad 14, \quad 15, \quad 16, \quad 28, \quad 32, \quad 44$$

Suggest positive ions which may be responsible for each of these lines.

Ans.	6	8	12	13	14	15	16	28	32	44
	C^{++}	O_2^{++++}	C^+	CH^+	CO^{++}	CH_3^+	O_2^{++}	CO^+	O_2^+	CO_2^+
		O^{++}			CH_2^+		CH_4^+			
		CH_4^{++}								

10. One gram of uranium 235 evolves about 20 billion calories when it undergoes fission. (*a*) Compare this heat of fission with the heat evolved in the combustion of 1 gram of carbon. Carbon has the highest heat of combustion per gram of any organic material. (*b*) How many tons (2000 lb) of coke will it take to give as much heat on oxidation as 1 lb (454 grams) of uranium 235 evolves on fission? (Coke is

assumed to be pure graphite.) (c) If it is assumed that one-fourth of the heat of fission is converted into electricity with standard steam boilers, turbines, and dynamos, how many kilowatts of electricity can be generated by the consumption of 1 lb of uranium 235 per day?

Ans. (a) 2.55×10^6 times greater. (b) 1272 tons. (c) 110,000 kw.

11. Thorium B is an isotope of lead and thus has nearly identical chemical and physical properties. A given quantity of thorium B was mixed with a lead salt containing 10 mg of lead, taken into solution, and precipitated as the chromate. Ten milliliters of the supernatant liquid, when evaporated, gave a residue which was 1/24,000 as active as the original quantity of thorium B. What is the solubility of lead chromate in moles per liter? Ans. 2×10^{-7} mole per liter.

---

12. A sample of radioactive manganese was measured in a counting chamber with the following results:

Time, hours	0	0.28	0.75	2.13	7.13	10.03	12.82	17.45	∞
Counts per minute	20,862	19,197	17,129	11,602	3,159	1,451	690	246	27

The continuing value of 27 counts per minute is due to background and to long-lived impurities in the manganese. What is the half-life of this radioactive manganese?

13. (a) Radon is removed from a sample of radium with which it was in equilibrium and is allowed to decay. Starting with 100 units of radon, how many will be left after 2, 4, 8, and 16 days? (b) The sample of radium immediately starts regenerating radon. How many units of radon will be in equilibrium with the radium after 2, 4, 8, and 16 days? (c) Plot the data of (a) and (b) against time, and draw two curves through the points.

14. Radioactive carbon C^{14} with a half-life of 5720 years is formed in the upper atmosphere by the following reaction of neutrons produced by cosmic rays.

$$_0n^1 + {_7}N^{14} \rightarrow {_1}H^1 + {_6}C^{14}$$

This radioactive carbon has been distributed over the earth wherever carbon compounds occur as $C^{14}O_2$ in air and $NaHC^{14}O_3$ in the sea. As a consequence, growing plants incorporate C^{14}, but once they are dead this process stops and the radioactive carbon decays with the above half-life. A sample of new wood has a radioactivity of 15.3 counts per minute when determined in a special way. If a sample of wood from an old Egyptian mummy case gives 9.4 counts per minute for the same weight of wood under the same conditions, how old is the wood?

15. Pa^{234} in equilibrium with 1 gram of U^{238} gives off 740,000 particles per minute. Calculate the half-life of U^{238}.

16. (a) Some beta particles have an initial velocity of 0.3 the velocity of light. What voltage would have to be applied to electrons in order for them to be equivalent to beta rays? (b) To how many beta particles per second would an electron current of 2 milliamperes correspond? (c) To how many grams of Pb^{214}, which has a half-life of 26.8 m, would this be equivalent?

17. (a) How many grams are there in a millicurie of $_{53}I^{131}$ which has a half-life of 8.0 days? (b) After 30 days, how many disintegrations will there be in a sample of $_{53}I^{131}$ which originally weighed 1 milligram?

18. The beryllium isotope with a mass of 7.01916 emits gamma rays of 0.48 million electron volts. (a) What is the product of this radioactive decay, and (b) what is its mass?

19. Calculate the heat energy in calories evolved in the following nuclear reactions:

(a)
$$_1H^1 + {}_1H^2 \rightarrow {}_2He^3 + \gamma$$

(b)
$$_2He^4 + {}_7N^{14} \rightarrow {}_1H^1 + {}_8O^{17}$$

20. An element gives off beta rays at 1.5 million electron volts. How much less per gram atom will the new element, which is formed by the radioactive decay, weigh?

21. State what isotopic element is produced when the following emit β^-:

$$_1H^3 \qquad {}_{11}Na^{24} \qquad {}_{35}Br^{82} \qquad {}_{47}Ag^{108}$$

22. (a) How many grams of uranium 235 must be consumed per day in driving a large ship at 20 miles per hour with 100,000 kilowatts of power, if it is assumed that 25 per cent of the heat of fission can be converted into useful work through boilers, turbines, and dynamos? (b) How many kilograms of uranium 235 would be consumed in traveling 20,000 miles?

---

23. A sample of radioactive sodium, with a half-life of 53,300 seconds, is injected into an animal. How many days will it take for the radioactivity to fall to one-tenth of its original intensity?

24. (a) After how many years will 1 gram of Po^{210} decay to such a point that it is equivalent in radioactivity to 1 gram of Ra^{226}? (b) After 10 years what will be the relative intensities of radioactivity of equal weights of Ra^{226} and Po^{210}?

25. The weight of lead in a sample of uraninite from the Black Hills of South Dakota was found to be 22.8 per cent of the weight of the uranium. Calculate from this fact a minimum age for the earth.

26. If the products of a transmutation weigh 0.001 gram more per gram atom than the reactants, what is the minimum energy which must be supplied to effect the transmutation: (a) expressed in kilogram-calories per gram atom; (b) expressed in voltage?

27. A hospital maintained a solution containing 0.200 gram of radium as a source of radon for therapeutic purposes. The radon was pumped off under reduced pressure once a week. (a) How many grams of radon were obtained each week? (b) What volume would it occupy at 25° and 740 mm pressure?

28. (a) How many grams of radioactive bromine 82 with a half-life of 34.0 hours is required in order to give a millicurie? (b) How many days can one wait before the millicurie of bromine becomes worthless for an experiment which requires 100 disintegrations per minute for counting?

29. How many disintegrations per second are produced in a microgram of P^{32} ($t_{1/2} = 14.3$ d)? What weight of KH_2PO_4 containing a mole fraction of 10^{-9} of $KH_2P^{32}O_4$ would be needed in an experiment requiring a sample in which there are 2000 disintegrations per second?

30. How large would a proton current have to be in amperes in a high-voltage transmutation apparatus in order to correspond to 1 microcurie?

31. Balance the following nuclear reactions:

(a)
$$_7N^{14} + _0n^1 \rightarrow _6C^{14} + ?$$

(b)
$$_{15}P^{31} + _0n^1 \rightarrow _{15}P^{30} + ?$$

(c)
$$_9F^{19} + _1H^1 \rightarrow _8O^{16} + ?$$

(d)
$$_1H^2 + \gamma \rightarrow _1H^1 + ?$$

(e)
$$_8O^{16} + _1H^2 \rightarrow _7N^{14} + ?$$

32. Radioactive phosphorus P^{30} can be prepared with the five different agencies, α, n, p, d, and γ rays. State what elements you would use for each process. Write the nuclear reaction in each case.

33. The slow neutron flux in a certain nuclear chain-reacting pile is 10^{12} neutrons per cm^2 per sec, and a 1-gram sample of $MnSO_4$ is exposed to this flux in order to prepare radioactive manganese according to the reaction

$$_{25}Mn^{55} + _0n^1 \rightarrow _{25}Mn^{56}$$

The $_{25}Mn^{56}$ decays by K capture with a half-life of 2.59 hours. The $MnSO_4$ is placed in the pile for 1 hour. Assuming that the only radioactivity formed in the sample is due to $_{25}Mn^{56}$ and taking the cross section for its formation as 12.8×10^{-24} cm^2, calculate the activity present in the sample expressed in disintegrations per minute 4 hours after removal from the pile. Cross section is defined as fraction of neutrons per square centimeter absorbed by an atom.

This appendix includes the derivations of several equations which are mentioned in the text but not derived there.   It contains also advanced material such as the Debye-Hückel theory.

$$C_p - C_v = R$$

(Page 105)

The method of partial differentiation may be illustrated in the following proof that

$$C_p - C_v = R \tag{1}$$

This equation was developed in a different way on page 105.   The molar heat capacity at constant pressure C_p is defined as the rate of change of enthalpy with temperature at constant pressure.   The molar heat capacity at constant volume C_v is defined as the rate of change of internal energy E with temperature at constant volume.

$$C_p = \left(\frac{\partial H}{\partial T}\right)_p \quad \text{and} \quad C_v = \left(\frac{\partial E}{\partial T}\right)_v \tag{2}$$

Therefore,

$$
\begin{aligned}
C_p - C_v &= \left(\frac{\partial H}{\partial T}\right)_p - \left(\frac{\partial E}{\partial T}\right)_v \\
&= \left[\frac{\partial(E + pv)}{\partial T}\right]_p - \left(\frac{\partial E}{\partial T}\right)_v \\
&= \left(\frac{\partial E}{\partial T}\right)_p + p\left(\frac{\partial v}{\partial T}\right)_p - \left(\frac{\partial E}{\partial T}\right)_v
\end{aligned} \tag{3}
$$

But, since E is a single-valued function of the variables T and v, it follows that

$$dE = \left(\frac{\partial E}{\partial T}\right)_v dT + \left(\frac{\partial E}{\partial v}\right)_T dv \tag{4}$$

and differentiating with respect to T at constant pressure gives

$$\left(\frac{\partial E}{\partial T}\right)_p = \left(\frac{\partial E}{\partial T}\right)_v + \left(\frac{\partial E}{\partial v}\right)_T\left(\frac{\partial v}{\partial T}\right)_p \tag{5}$$

Substituting in equation 3, we obtain

$$C_p - C_v = \left(\frac{\partial E}{\partial T}\right)_v + \left(\frac{\partial E}{\partial v}\right)_T\left(\frac{\partial v}{\partial T}\right)_p + p\left(\frac{\partial v}{\partial T}\right)_p - \left(\frac{\partial E}{\partial T}\right)_v \tag{6}$$

But for an ideal gas $(\partial E/\partial v)_T = 0$ (page 101). Hence equation 6 becomes

$$C_p - C_v = p\left(\frac{\partial v}{\partial T}\right)_p \tag{7}$$

and, since $v = RT/p$, we may replace $(\partial v/\partial T)_p$ by R/p, and equation 7 then simplifies to

$$C_p - C_v = R \tag{8}$$

The Maxwell Distribution Law

(Page 344)

The mathematical statement * of the distribution of velocities is

$$\frac{dn}{n} = 4\pi\left(\frac{M}{2\pi RT}\right)^{3/2} e^{-(Mv^2/2RT)} v^2\, dv \tag{1}$$

where M is the molecular weight, v is the probable velocity of the molecule, and dn/n is the fraction of the molecules having velocities between v and $v + dv$, n being the total number of molecules, which is a constant.

Introducing E, the energy expressed in calories per mole, we find

$$E = \tfrac{1}{2}Mv^2$$

$$dE = Mv\, dv$$

$$\frac{dn}{n} = \frac{2}{\sqrt{\pi}}\left(\frac{1}{RT}\right)^{3/2} e^{-E/RT} E^{1/2}\, dE \tag{2}$$

This gives the fraction of the molecules having energies between E and $E + dE$.

Of particular interest in physical chemistry is the number of molecules $\dfrac{n'_E}{n}$ having energies greater than some fixed value E per mole.

Integration between E and infinity gives n_E'/n, the fraction of molecules which have energies greater than E.

$$\frac{n'_E}{n} = \int_E^\infty \frac{2}{\sqrt{\pi}}\left(\frac{1}{RT}\right)^{3/2} e^{-E/RT} E^{1/2}\, dE \tag{3}$$

$$= \frac{2}{\sqrt{\pi}}\left(\frac{E}{RT}\right)^{1/2} e^{-E/RT}\left\{1 + \frac{RT}{2E} - \left(\frac{RT}{2E}\right)^2 + \cdots\right\}$$

In practical applications E is large compared to RT, and so the only term of importance in the brackets is the first, or

$$\frac{n_E'}{n} = \frac{2}{\sqrt{\pi}}\left(\frac{E}{RT}\right)^{1/2} e^{-E/RT} \tag{4}$$

* A derivation is given in Glasstone, *Textbook of Physical Chemistry*, D. Van Nostrand Co., New York, 1946, page 267.

The Rate Equation

(Page 352)

Eyring's equation for the activated complex is

$$k = (RT/Nh)e^{\Delta S_a/R}e^{-\Delta H_a/RT} \tag{1}$$

The concentration of the activated molecules is given in terms of an equilibrium constant K_a and the concentration of the reacting molecules, thus:

$$c_{\text{activated molecules}} = K_a c_{\text{reactants}} \sqrt{\frac{2\pi MRT}{N^2 h^2}}\, l$$

$$= e^{-\Delta F_a/RT}\left(\sqrt{\frac{2\pi MRT}{N^2 h^2}}\, l\right) c_{\text{reactants}} \tag{2}$$

where the term under the square-root sign allows for the fact that, in addition to the three translational degrees of freedom, there is an extra degree of freedom along which the activated molecule is decomposing. N is the Avogadro number, h is Planck's constant, and l is a measure of the width of the activated state on the energy surface. The activated molecules are moving along the top of the energy barrier with a velocity $\sqrt{RT/2\pi M}$ so that the length of time spent in the activated state is $l/\sqrt{RT/2\pi M}$. Then the rate of the reaction is given by the expression

$$\text{Rate} = \frac{\text{Number of molecules in activated state}}{\text{Average time spent in activated state}} = \frac{e^{-\Delta F_a/RT}\left(\sqrt{\frac{2\pi MRT}{N^2 h^2}}\, l\right) c_{\text{reactants}}}{l/\sqrt{\frac{2\pi M}{RT}}} \tag{3}$$

and

$$\text{Rate} = (RT/Nh)e^{-\Delta F_a/RT} c_{\text{reactants}} \tag{4}$$

$$k = \kappa(RT/Nh)e^{\Delta S_a/R}e^{-\Delta H_a/RT} \tag{5}$$

The term κ is included to allow for the probability that a molecule once fully activated will give the products of the reaction. Ordinarily, it is assumed that this probability is practically unity.

Debye-Hückel Theory

(Page 483)

The density of charge ρ in the vicinity of an ion is

$$\rho = \frac{(dn_+ - dn_-)\epsilon}{dV} = n\epsilon(e^{-\epsilon\psi/kT} - e^{\epsilon\psi/kT}) \tag{1}$$

where n is the total number of positive and negative ions per cubic centimeter, ϵ is the electronic charge, k is the Boltzmann constant, and ψ is the electric potential at a distance r from a particular ion. Expanding the exponential terms into a series and neglecting higher terms, we have, as a close approximation for small potentials,

$$\rho = -2n\epsilon^2\psi/kT \tag{2}$$

The Poisson equation, derived from Coulomb's law, also relates ψ and ρ. Since ψ depends only on r, the equation is

$$\frac{d^2\psi}{dr^2} + \frac{2}{r}\frac{d\psi}{dr} = \frac{-4\pi\rho}{D} \tag{3}$$

In this equation D is the dielectric constant of the medium. Substituting equation 2 into equation 3, we have

$$\frac{d^2\psi}{dr^2} + \frac{2}{r}\frac{d\psi}{dr} = \frac{8\pi n\epsilon^2\psi}{DkT} = \kappa^2\psi \tag{4}$$

where

$$\kappa^2 = 8\pi n\epsilon^2/DkT \tag{5}$$

It can be verified that a solution of equation 4 is given by

$$\psi = A\frac{e^{-\kappa r}}{r} + B\frac{e^{\kappa r}}{r} \tag{6}$$

and, since there are two independent arbitrary constants A and B, this must be a general solution. The potential must approach zero as the distance r from the selected ion becomes very large, and so B must be zero; otherwise the term $e^{\kappa r}/r$ will make ψ very large at large values of r.

A can be evaluated by making use of the fact that the total charge surrounding the ion (which we will assume to be positive) must be $-\epsilon$, since the solution as a whole is neutral. Comparison of equations 3 and 4 shows that

$$\rho = -D\kappa^2\psi/4\pi = -D\kappa^2 A e^{-\kappa r}/4\pi r \tag{7}$$

Hence, integrating (by parts) from the closest distance of approach of the ions, which we will call a, gives

$$-\epsilon = \int_a^\infty 4\pi r^2 \rho \, dr$$

$$= -\int_a^\infty rD\kappa^2 A e^{-\kappa r} \, dr$$

$$= -DAe^{-\kappa a}(1 + \kappa a) \tag{8}$$

Therefore

$$A = \frac{\epsilon e^{\kappa a}}{D(1 + \kappa a)} \tag{9}$$

and

$$\psi = \frac{\epsilon e^{\kappa(a-r)}}{D(1 + \kappa a)r} \tag{10}$$

The potential at the ion is the value of ψ at $r = a$,

$$\psi = \frac{\epsilon}{D(1 + \kappa a)a} \tag{11}$$

In calculating the activity coefficients and other properties of the solution, Debye attributed all the deviation from the behavior of ideal solutions to the electric charges on the ions.   Consider the following imaginary process:[*]

1. Gradually discharge an ion in an extremely dilute solution of the electrolyte.
2. Transfer the discharged ion to a more concentrated solution.
3. Gradually charge the ion again.

The changes in free energy in steps 1 and 3 are equal to the electric work done on the system, and the free-energy change in step 2 is the same as for ideal solutions.

$$\Delta F_1 = \int_{q=\epsilon}^{q=0} \psi \, dq = \int_{q=\epsilon}^{q=0} \frac{q}{D(1 + \kappa a)a} \, dq$$

$$= - \frac{\epsilon^2}{2Da} \; (\kappa \cong 0 \text{ here})$$

$$\Delta F_2 = \frac{RT}{N} \ln \frac{c}{c_0} = kT \ln \frac{c}{c_0}$$

where c and c_0 are the concentrations of the final and initial solutions, respectively, and q is electric charge.

$$\Delta F_3 = \int_{q=0}^{q=\epsilon} \frac{q}{D(1 + \kappa a)a} \, dq = \frac{\epsilon^2}{2D(1 + \kappa a)a}$$

$$= \frac{\epsilon^2}{2Da} - \frac{\epsilon^2 \kappa}{2D(1 + \kappa a)}$$

Therefore,

$$\Delta F = \Delta F_1 + \Delta F_2 + \Delta F_3 = kT \ln \frac{c}{c_0} - \frac{\epsilon^2 \kappa}{2D(1 + \kappa a)} \tag{12}$$

The free-energy change is also given by the equation

$$\Delta F = \frac{RT}{N} \ln \frac{\gamma c}{c_0} = kT \ln \frac{c}{c_0} + kT \ln \gamma \tag{13}$$

where γ is the activity coefficient of the ion in the final solution. $\gamma = 1$ in the initial solution.

Comparing equations 12 and 13, we see that

$$kT \ln \gamma = - \frac{\epsilon^2 \kappa}{2D(1 + \kappa a)} \tag{14}$$

If we use equation 5 and $n = c/1000N$, where c is the concentration in moles per liter and N is the Avogadro number, equation 14 may be written

$$\log \gamma = - \frac{\epsilon^2 \sqrt{\dfrac{8\pi c \epsilon^2}{1000NDkT}}}{2.303 \times 2DkT \left(1 + a \sqrt{\dfrac{8\pi c \epsilon^2}{1000NDkT}}\right)} \tag{15}$$

[*] Guntelberg, Z. physik. Chem., *123*, 199 (1926).

If c is small, equation 15 becomes

$$\log \gamma = -A\sqrt{c} \tag{16}$$

where

$$A = \frac{\epsilon^3 (2\pi)^{\frac{1}{2}}}{2.303 (DkT)^{\frac{3}{2}} (1000N)^{\frac{1}{2}}} \tag{17}$$

This equation was derived for a 1–1 electrolyte. The expression for the activity coefficient of other types of electrolytes in solutions containing different electrolytes (page 444) can be derived in a similar manner.

For water at 25°, $A = 0.509$.

Relation between the Diffusion Coefficient and Frictional Coefficient

(Page 505)

If a system is not in equilibrium it will move toward equilibrium and the negative gradient of the chemical potential may be considered the driving force of diffusion just as the negative gradient of the total potential is the driving force in a gravitational or electrical field.

Let us consider diffusion in a rectangular cell in which there is no convection and there is flow due to diffusion only in the x direction. Here the force F per mole of substance is

$$F = -\frac{d\mu}{dx} = -\frac{d\mu}{dc}\frac{dc}{dx} = -\frac{RT}{c}\frac{dc}{dx} \tag{1}$$

for an ideal solution, since $\mu = \mu_0 + RT \ln c$.

Now according to hydrodynamics the velocity of a particle in a continuous medium is directly proportional to the applied force, and, by definition, the frictional coefficient f is the force required to give the particle unit velocity.

$$F/N = fv \tag{2}$$

where f is the molecular frictional coefficient and v is the velocity. Therefore,

$$v = \frac{F}{Nf} = \frac{-RT}{Nfc}\frac{dc}{dx} \tag{3}$$

Fick's first law is

$$J = vc = -D\frac{dc}{dx} \tag{4}$$

Substituting equation 3 for v yields

$$J = -\frac{RT}{Nf}\frac{dc}{dx} = -D\frac{dc}{dx} \tag{5}$$

Therefore,

$$D = RT/Nf \tag{6}$$

which is a relation first obtained by Einstein.

Bohr's Formula for the Energy of an Electron in a Circular Orbit

(Page 547)

$$E_n = -2\pi^2 m(Ze)^2 e^2 / n^2 h^2$$

It is assumed that a negative electron moves in a circular orbit around a central nucleus which has a positive charge Ze, where Z is the atomic number and e is the unit electric charge, that is, the charge of an electron or proton.

The centrifugal force of the electron moving in its orbit is mv^2/r, where m is the mass of the electron, v is the velocity, and r is the radius of the orbit, that is, the distance between the electron and the nucleus.

The electric force of attraction is $(Ze)e/r^2$, as given by Coulomb's law.

In the stable orbit the centrifugal force must be equal and opposite to the electric force in order to maintain equilibrium. Then,

$$mv^2/r = Ze^2/r^2 \tag{1}$$

The total energy E is equal to the sum of the kinetic energy E_k and the potential energy E_p.

$$E_k = \frac{1}{2} mv^2 = \frac{1}{2} \frac{Ze^2}{r} \tag{2}$$

and

$$E_p = \int_\infty^r \frac{Ze^2}{r^2} dr = -\frac{Ze^2}{r} \tag{3}$$

Then,

$$E = E_k + E_p = \frac{1}{2} \frac{Ze^2}{r} - \frac{Ze^2}{r} = -\frac{Ze^2}{2r} \tag{4}$$

The energy has a negative sign because the reference state with zero energy is taken as that state in which the electron is at infinite distance from the nucleus, and the lower limit of integration is taken as $r = \infty$.

These considerations apply to any coulombic field and can be applied to elliptical orbits as well as to circular orbits.

The angular momentum p of the moving electron is given by the expression

$$p = mvr \tag{5}$$

Then substituting equations 5 and 1 into equation 4 yields

$$E = -\frac{Ze^2}{2r} = -\frac{Ze^2 mv}{2p} = -\frac{Ze^2}{2p} \frac{Ze^2}{rv} = -\frac{Ze^2}{2p} \frac{Ze^2 m}{p} = -\frac{mZ^2 e^4}{2p^2} \tag{6}$$

If this formula were strictly correct, E would change continuously over a wide range, and a continuous spectrum containing all wavelengths would be produced. To account for the discontinuous spectrum which is actually produced, Bohr assumed that the angular momentum of the electron in its orbit must be an integral multiple of $h/2\pi$, where h is Planck's universal constant. In other words, he assumed that the only values of p which are permitted by the restrictions of the quantum theory are those which meet the requirement of the equation,

$$2\pi p = nh \qquad \text{or} \qquad p = nh/2\pi \tag{7}$$

where n is an integer 1, 2, 3, 4, etc.

Substituting into equation 6 gives

$$E_n = -\frac{mZ^2 e^4 (2\pi)^2}{2(nh)^2} = -\frac{2\pi^2 mZ^2 e^4}{n^2 h^2} \tag{8}$$

Symbols Used for the More Common Abbreviations

A	work content	a	activity
A	angstrom unit	c	concentration
C	molar heat capacity	d	density
E	internal energy	e	electron; electronic charge
$\boldsymbol{E}$	voltage	h	Planck's constant
emf	electromotive force	k	specific reaction rate; gas constant
F	free energy		per molecule
ΔF	change in free energy	m	molality
ΔF°	change in free energy (standard	n	number of moles; refractive index
	state)	p	pressure
$\boldsymbol{F}$	faraday (96,500 coulombs equiv^{-1})	pH	measure of hydrogen-ion activity;
H	enthalpy		$-\log a_{\mathrm{H}}{}^{+}$
I	intensity of light	q	heat absorbed
K	equilibrium constant; absolute	t	centigrade temperature; time
	temperature scale	v	volume
K_b	boiling-point constant	w	work done
K_f	freezing-point constant	α	angle of optical rotation
L	specific conductance	γ	activity coefficient; surface tension
M	molecular weight; molarity	ϵ	quantum; dielectric constant
N	Avogadro number; mole fraction	η	viscosity
π	osmotic pressure	Λ	equivalent conductance
R	gas constant	λ	wavelength of radiation
$\boldsymbol{R}$	Rydberg constant	μ	micron; dipole moment; chemical
S	entropy		potential; ionic strength
T	absolute temperature	ν	frequency of radiation
V	volume of 1 mole of gas	$\bar{\nu}$	wave number
$\overline{V}$	partial molal volume	Φ	quantum yield

Mathematical Formulas *

CALCULUS

Δ = small finite increment; d = differential; dy/dx = derivative = limit of $\Delta y/\Delta x$ as Δx approaches zero

$y = x^n$; $dy/dx = nx^{n-1}$

$y = f_1(x) + f_2(x)$; $dy/dx = \dfrac{df_1(x)}{dx} + \dfrac{df_2(x)}{dx}$

$y = k$; $dy/dx = 0$

$y = kf(x)$; $dy/dx = k\dfrac{df(x)}{dx}$

$y = uv$; $dy/dx = u\,dv/dx + v\,du/dx$

$y = u/v$; $dy/dx = \dfrac{v\,du/dx - u\,dv/dx}{v^2}$

* An elementary treatment of the mathematics needed for the study of physical chemistry is given by Daniels, *Mathematical Preparation for Physical Chemistry*, McGraw-Hill Book Co., New York, 1928.

$y = e^x; \; dy/dx = e^x$

$y = \log_e x; \; dy/dx = 1/x$

$y = \log x; \; dy/dx = 0.4343/x$

$y = \log_a x; \; dy/dx = \dfrac{\log_a e}{x}$

$y = a^x; \; dy/dx = a^x \log_e a$

$y = f_2[f_1(x)]; \; dy/dx = \dfrac{df_2[f_1(x)]}{d[f_1(x)]} \times \dfrac{d[f_1(x)]}{dx}$

For a maximum or minimum or point of horizontal inflection, $dy/dx = 0$.
For a differential, $dy = (dy/dx)\,dx$.
For partial differentiation where $u = f(x, y, z)$, and $\partial x = $ partial differential

$$du = \left(\frac{\partial u}{\partial x}\right)_{y,z} dx + \left(\frac{\partial u}{\partial y}\right)_{x,z} dy + \left(\frac{\partial u}{\partial z}\right)_{x,y} dz$$

$$\int dx = x + C$$

$$\int x^n \, dx = x^{n+1}/(n+1) + C$$

$$\int x^{-1} \, dx = \log_e x + C$$

$$\int k f(x) \, dx = k \int f(x) \, dx$$

$$\int f_1(x) + f_2(x) + f_3(x)]\, dx = \int f_1(x)\, dx + \int f_2(x)\, dx + \int f_3(x)\, dx$$

$$\int [k + f(x)] \, dx = \int k \, dx + \int f(x) \, dx = kx + \int f(x) \, dx + C$$

$$\int e^x \, dx = e^x + C$$

$$\int a^x \, dx = \frac{a^x}{\log_e a} + C$$

$$\int \log_e x \, dx = x(\log_e x - 1) + C$$

$$\int \log_e x \, dx = 0.4343x(\log_e x - 1) + C$$

$$\int \log_a x \, dx = (\log_a e)(x)(\log_e x - 1) + C$$

Integrating between limits gives $\displaystyle \int_a^b x \, dx = \left[\frac{x^2}{2}\right]_a^b = \frac{b^2}{2} - \frac{a^2}{2}$

Power-Series Expansions

The region of convergence for the series is indicated in parentheses.

$$(1 \pm x)^n = 1 \pm nx + \frac{n(n-1)x^2}{2!} \pm \frac{n(n-1)(n-2)x^3}{3!} + \cdots \qquad (x^2 < 1)$$

For example,

$$(1 + x)^{-1} = 1 - x + x^2 - x^3 + \cdots \qquad (x^2 < 1)$$

$$(1 + x)^{\frac{1}{2}} = 1 + \frac{x}{2} - \frac{x^2}{8} + \frac{x^3}{16} + \cdots \qquad (x^2 < 1)$$

$$e^x = 1 + x + \frac{x^2}{2!} + \frac{x^3}{3!} + \cdots$$

$$\ln(1 + x) = x - \tfrac{1}{2}x^2 + \tfrac{1}{3}x^3 - \tfrac{1}{4}x^4 + \cdots \qquad (-1 < x < 1)$$

TRIGONOMETRY

sine = ordinate/hypotenuse
cosine = abscissa/hypotenuse
tangent = ordinate/abscissa
$1° = 0.0175$ radian
$\sin^2 x + \cos^2 x = 1$
$y = \sin x;\ dy/dx = \cos x$
$y = \cos x;\ dy/dx = -\sin x$
$y = \tan x;\ dy/dx = \sec^2 x$

$$\int \sin x\, dx = -\cos x + C$$

$$\int \cos x\, dx = \sin x + C$$

MISCELLANEOUS

If $ax^2 + bx + c = 0$, $\qquad x = \dfrac{-b \pm \sqrt{b^2 - 4ac}}{2a}$

1 inch = 2.54 cm   1 pound = 453.6 g   1 gallon (U.S.) = 3.785 l

log means $\log_{10}$;   ln means $\log_e$

Greek Alphabet

A	α	Alpha	N	ν	Nu
B	β	Beta	Ξ	ξ	Xi
Γ	γ	Gamma	O	o	Omicron
Δ	δ	Delta	Π	π	Pi
E	ϵ	Epsilon	P	ρ	Rho
Z	ζ	Zeta	Σ	σ	Sigma
H	η	Eta	T	τ	Tau
Θ	θ	Theta	Υ	υ	Upsilon
I	ι	Iota	Φ	ϕ	Phi
K	κ	Kappa	X	χ	Chi
Λ	λ	Lambda	Ψ	ψ	Psi
M	μ	Mu	Ω	ω	Omega

Physical-Chemical Constants

The following tables give the recommended values of the fundamental constants for physical chemistry as of July 1, 1951.* They are based upon the reanalysis and re-evaluation of experimental values by DuMond and Cohen.†

Table I. Values of the Basic Constants

Velocity of light	c	2.997902×10^{10} cm sec^{-1}
Planck constant	h	6.6238×10^{-27} erg sec molecule^{-1}
Avogadro constant	N	6.0238×10^{23} molecules mole^{-1}
Faraday constant	F	96,493 coulombs equivalent^{-1}
		23,062 cal (volt equiv)$^{-1}$
Absolute temperature of the "ice" point, 0°C	$T_{0°C}$	273.16°K.
Pressure-volume product for 1 mole of a gas at 0° and zero pressure	$(pV)_{T_{0°}}^{p=0}$	22,414.6 cm^3 atm mole^{-1}
		22.4140 liter atm mole^{-1}
		2271.16 joules mole^{-1}

Table II. Values of the Derived Constants

Electronic charge	$e = \dfrac{F}{N}$	1.60186×10^{-19} coulomb
		1.60186×10^{-20} emu
		4.8022×10^{-10} esu
Gas constant	$R = \dfrac{(pV)_{T_{0°}}^{p=0}}{T_{0°}}$	1.9872 cal deg^{-1} mole^{-1}
		82.057 cm^3 atm deg^{-1} mole^{-1}
		0.082054 l atm deg^{-1} mole^{-1}
		8.3144 joules deg^{-1} mole^{-1}
Boltzmann constant	$k = R/N$	1.38026×10^{-16} erg deg^{-1} molecule^{-1}

Table III. Values of the Defined Constants

Standard gravity	980.665 cm sec^{-2}
Standard atmosphere	1,013,250 dynes cm^{-2}
Standard millimeter of mercury pressure	$\frac{1}{760}$ atm
Calorie (thermochemical)	4.1840 joules
	4.18331 international joules
	41.2929 cm^3 atm
	0.0412917 l atm

* Rossini, Gucker, Johnston, Pauling, and Vinal, *J. Am. Chem. Soc.*, *74*, 2699 (1952).

† DuMond and Cohen, *Phys. Rev.*, *82*, 555 (1951).

Table IV.   Values of Certain Auxiliary Relations

1 second (mean solar) = 1.00273791 sidereal seconds
1 joule = 0.999835 international joule
1 ohm = 0.999505 international ohm
1 ampere = 1.000165 international amperes
1 volt = 0.999670 international volt
1 coulomb = 1.000165 international coulombs
1 watt = 0.999835 international watt
1 liter = 1,000.028 cm^3

International Atomic Weights

1954

Journal of the American Chemical Society

	Symbol	Atomic Number	Atomic Weight [a]		Symbol	Atomic Number	Atomic Weight [a]
Actinium	Ac	89	227	Molybdenum	Mo	42	95.95
Aluminum	Al	13	26.98	Neodymium	Nd	60	144.27
Americium	Am	95	[243]	Neptunium	Np	93	[237]
Antimony	Sb	51	121.76	Neon	Ne	10	20.183
Argon	A	18	39.944	Nickel	Ni	28	58.69
Arsenic	As	33	74.91	Niobium			
Astatine	At	85	[210]	(Columbium)	Nb	41	92.91
Barium	Ba	56	137.36	Nitrogen	N	7	14.008
Berkelium	Bk	97	[245]	Osmium	Os	76	190.2
Beryllium	Be	4	9.013	Oxygen	O	8	16
Bismuth	Bi	83	209.00	Palladium	Pd	46	106.7
Boron	B	5	10.82	Phosphorus	P	15	30.975
Bromine	Br	35	79.916	Platinum	Pt	78	195.23
Cadmium	Cd	48	112.41	Plutonium	Pu	94	[242]
Calcium	Ca	20	40.08	Polonium	Po	84	210
Californium	Cf	98	[248]	Potassium	K	19	39.100
Carbon	C	6	12.011	Praseodymium	Pr	59	140.92
Cerium	Ce	58	140.13	Promethium	Pm	61	[145]
Cesium	Cs	55	132.91	Protactinium	Pa	91	231
Chlorine	Cl	17	35.457	Radium	Ra	88	226.05
Chromium	Cr	24	52.01	Radon	Rn	86	222
Cobalt	Co	27	58.94	Rhenium	Re	75	186.31
Columbium				Rhodium	Rh	45	102.91
(see Niobium)				Rubidium	Rb	37	85.48
Copper	Cu	29	63.54	Ruthenium	Ru	44	101.1
Curium	Cm	96	[245]	Samarium	Sm	62	150.43
Dysprosium	Dy	66	162.46	Scandium	Sc	21	44.96
Erbium	Er	68	167.2	Selenium	Se	34	78.96
Europium	Eu	63	152.0	Silicon	Si	14	28.09
Fluorine	F	9	19.00	Silver	Ag	47	107.880
Francium	Fr	87	[223]	Sodium	Na	11	22.991
Gadolinium	Gd	64	156.9	Strontium	Sr	38	87.63
Gallium	Ga	31	69.72	Sulfur	S	16	32.066 [b]
Germanium	Ge	32	72.60	Tantalum	Ta	73	180.95
Gold	Au	79	197.0	Technetium	Tc	43	[99]
Hafnium	Hf	72	178.6	Tellurium	Te	52	127.61
Helium	He	2	4.003	Terbium	Tb	65	158.93
Holmium	Ho	67	164.94	Thallium	Tl	81	204.39
Hydrogen	H	1	1.0080	Thorium	Th	90	232.05
Indium	In	49	114.76	Thulium	Tm	69	168.94
Iodine	I	53	126.91	Tin	Sn	50	118.70
Iridium	Ir	77	192.2	Titanium	Ti	22	47.90
Iron	Fe	26	55.85	Tungsten	W	74	183.92
Krypton	Kr	36	83.80	Uranium	U	92	238.07
Lanthanum	La	57	138.92	Vanadium	V	23	50.95
Lead	Pb	82	207.21	Xenon	Xe	54	131.3
Lithium	Li	3	6.940	Ytterbium	Yb	70	173.04
Lutetium	Lu	71	174.99	Yttrium	Y	39	88.92
Magnesium	Mg	12	24.32	Zinc	Zn	30	65.38
Manganese	Mn	25	54.94	Zirconium	Zr	40	91.22
Mercury	Hg	80	200.61				

[a] A value given in brackets denotes the mass number of the isotope of longest known half-life.

[b] Because of natural variations in relative abundance of the sulfur isotopes, its atomic weight has a range of ±0.003.

Author Index

Subject Index